This Book is Dedicated to the Memory
of the Author's Teacher

JOHN WARREN, M.D.

Late Professor of Anatomy, Harvard Medical School
Fifth in a distinguished succession.

His unerring craftsmanship in
resolving the gross fabric of man's body,
Genius as a lecturer in the great tradition,
Edwardian presence born of inherited gentility,
Served through four decades
to inspire the sentient student.

PREFACE

For the first edition of the ATLAS OF HUMAN ANATOMY it was the author's purpose to offer pictorial records of gross structure based upon new dissections prepared in serial progression, and upon variable morphological features presented statistically.

In carrying out this undertaking the drawings were accurately prepared by the artists; they were neither warped to conform to preconceived, stereotyped concepts of human morphology, nor simplified to serve as conventionalized chartings for a laboratory excursion. So-called anomalies have been minimized; instead, unemphasized as individual aberrances, they find their place as predictable elements in a natural occurrence of variations.

The student's attachment to the concept of an archetypal plan in the fabric of the human body is perennial and persistent. Frequently he is annoyed by departure from the standard type of vascular branching, of visceral position or muscular form described and figured in his atlas, laboratory guide and textbook (no matter whether the latter be encyclopedic or abbreviated). In order to insure a rational approach to the study of gross anatomy it is essential that the dissector become promptly aware of nonconformity as a salient feature of every bodily system. This may best be accomplished by pictorial means, with the support of ample statistical data. It is self-evident, of course, that such information, helpful in the training of the first-year student, will become an indispensable part of his knowledge as a doctor.

To include the additional records with earlier accumulations, plates from articles used in the first edition were redrawn, and notations on the incidence of variations were computed on the basis of final totals. In most instances it has been possible to present the essential information in a single plate of figures for each of some thirty anatomical parts. As a result, although the number of original observations reaches a total of approximately twenty five thousand, the space required to present this new information is a small part of the entire volume. These instructional plates on the range of variation cover the several bodily systems. They are purposefully most extensive for the blood vessels, the muscles and nerves, and the abdominal viscera, since departures from the anatomic norm are most frequent in these systems and because foreknowledge of their occurrence is a vital possession in practice.

For the vascular system, patterns are presented for the following: neck (subclavian); thorax (aortic arch, bronchial, esophageal and mammary arteries and azygos veins); abdomen and pelvis (celiac, mesenteric, phrenic, renal, obturator and internal iliac arteries and lumbar veins); and for the lower member (vessels related to the saphenous hiatus). Variations are illustrated for the musculature of the chest and the anterior abdominal wall, of the arm (biceps branchii), forearm and hand (palmaris longus, abductor pollicis longus) and the leg (plantaris). Types of nerve-muscle relationships are presented for median nerve with the pronator teres muscle and the ischiadic nerve with the piriformis muscle. In the field of visceral anatomy comparable figures are presented for the cecum and vermiform appendix, gall-bladder, kidneys, and sigmoid colon.

Early in the author's career, in the course of teaching at graduate and post-graduate levels, it became evident that no distinction could be drawn between the subject-matter of a course for first-year students and the material in the field of applied anatomy needed by graduates and postgraduates. Therefore, the ATLAS OF HUMAN ANATOMY was designed to be continuously useful to the reader from his days as a novice through those in which his responsibilities as a doctor require a reference book based upon unbiased portrayal of human structure.

Nowadays, when the specialized textbooks of embryology, histology, and neuroanatomy outnumber, in each category, the encyclopedic treatises on gross anatomy, there would seem to be no plausible excuse for burdening an atlas with illustrations or descriptive matter for which the student finds little or no immediate use in the dissection laboratory. Therefore, with rare, and perhaps defensible, exceptions, the author has limited the contents of this volume to those features of human anatomy which are demonstrable in regular study of the cadaver.

The author has depended continuously upon suggestions from students in all of the curricular grades. Sophomores serving as prosectors, juniors and seniors acting as assistants, and graduates in medicine awaiting residency appointments have aided in the preparation of dissections and in selecting features that warranted special emphasis. Their efforts frequently led them into programs of graduate study, in which colleagues in surgery, medicine, and in several specialties offered guidance. Publications resulting from these efforts ofttimes contained illustrations that proved serviceable in the ATLAS. Many of the studies have appeared in journals of the preclinical and clinical services, references to which appear under Acknowledgements. Thanks are due to Doctors Lindsay E. Beaton, Arthur F. Reimann, J. Watson Miller, Sherman S. Coleman and John Budinger for preparing the dissections of the skeletal musculature, the vessels and nerves of the extremities and the pelvis, and the abdominal and thoracic viscera. To these associates, past and present, the author is deeply indebted; their scholarship, ability and zeal have shortened his work; and association with them has converted an otherwise overwhelming task into a manageable and inspiring endeavor.

More than one hundred and fifty new illustrations have been provided for the present edition—mostly from dissections carried out in the author's laboratory. These drawings were executed by Mary Dixon Elder, Lucille Cassell Innes, Jean McConnell, and Angela Bartenbach Mailer. Part of the labelling was done by Rosamond Howland and Jane Gordon.

Through the generosity of Mr. Ralph T. Esterquest, Librarian of the Schools of Medicine and Public Health, Harvard University Medical School, and of Dr. Don Fawcett, Chairman of the Department of Anatomy at that institution, the author has been permitted to republish copies of drawings by the late Hamlet Aitken for Dr. John Warren's *Handbook of Anatomy*. This courtesy is deeply appreciated. The reappearance of these fine drawings bring sentimental pleasure to the author, since he witnessed their preparation and took part in the task of labelling them.

In many and diverse ways, the writer has been aided by his former colleagues, the members of the Department of Anatomy at Northwestern University Medical School. Their advice was frequently sought and cheerfully tendered. Special thanks are due to Dr. Harold A. Davenport for preparing the Index to the present edition. Again, keeping in mind the student's dissection-room requirements, the indexing has been made selective by directing primary attention to illustrations which most effectively portray the structure sought.

Once more, through the kind offices of Dr. Loyal Davis, Chairman of the Department of Surgery, it is possible to republish numerous figures which have appeared in *Surgery, Gynecology and Obstetrics.*

In the preparation of this book, the author has been consistently aided and encouraged by the Medical School through the Dean, Richard H. Young.

It has been very pleasant and altogether satisfactory to continue a long-term association with the publisher, the W. B. Saunders Company. Beginning with the contribution of a single chapter in an edited work, collaborative effort has expanded to include new chapters in other volumes, a textbook of surgical anatomy, and the current product. Inspiration has been derived from their high sense of ethics in the business of providing guidance in the Aesculapian training of the student and the doctor. Tribute is paid to the dignity and service of their craft by the use of the ancient printers' emblematic devices which appear on several pages of this volume.

Iowa City, Iowa   Barry J. Anson

TERMINOLOGY

Up to the close of the nineteenth century a great deal of confusion existed among different countries, and even in parts of the same country, in the use of anatomic names. At last, in 1895, a system of names was adopted by the German Anatomical Society at an international meeting of anatomists held at Basle; this system became known as the Basle Nomina Anatomica (BNA). The names in the BNA are in Latin, which was regarded as best suited for world-wide usage. Although many of the names were translated into the language of the country where the revised terminology was used, nevertheless, it was widely accepted and constituted the basis of a unified system of terminology.

Although a definite and notable advance in anatomic terminology, the BNA contained some errors and inconsistencies, and further revisions have been made, notably, the British Revision (BR) in 1933, revisions of the Nomenklatur-Kommission (NK), and the Jena Nomina Anatomica (JNA or INA). The goal of establishing an up-to-date unified terminology was not attained until 1955, when the present Nomina Anatomica (NA or NAP) was adopted by the Sixth International Congress of Anatomists in Paris. A revised edition of the NA terminology appeared in 1961, made by the International Anatomical Nomenclature Committee, appointed by the Fifth International Congress of Anatomists held at Oxford in 1950.

The NA is based on the BNA. A few new names have been added, but these pertain chiefly to the lungs, the central nervous system, and to some minor structures of other parts of the body.

Wherever practicable, the NA terminology is used in this *Atlas*. However, in the selection of terms for a textbook, a dissection-guide or an atlas in gross anatomy, an author must recognize that the history of anatomical terminology is one of instability; it was revolutionary at Basle in 1895, temperate at the Paris conclave in 1955, evolutionary in the sixty years separating these dates. Even at the present rate of sober, undramatic revision, a few terms have become "old" when a book leaves the press. Despite this circumstance, all first-year students of anatomy who use the text and illustrations in books of an earlier vintage will encounter both the old and the new terms. Moreover, his clinical teachers and associates will find little reason to abandon the BNA or other antecedent system which happened to be their pedagogic heritage.

Therefore, the author must regard current usage as possessing both a past and a future. The gap between the contemporary and the recent past has been bridged by including new terms in revised labelling, wherever practicable, and by supplying equivalent names (NA) in the legends for the illustrations.

In most instances the change involves the part of the term which indicates form, position, relation or direction; of these the following (italicized) will serve as examples:

BNA	NA
Ampulla membranacea superior	Ampulla membranacea *anterior*
A. digitales volares communes	A. digitales *palmares* communes
A. mammaria interna	A. *thoracica* interna
Auricula cordis	Auricula *atrii*
Facies parietalis	Facies *externa*
Facies volaris (ulnae)	Facies *anterior*
Fascia lumbodorsalis	Fascia *thoracolumbalis*
Linea semicircularis	Linea *arcuata*
M. flexor digitorum sublimis	M. flexor digitorum *superficialis*
M. iliocostalis dorsi	M. iliocostalis *thoracis*
Mm. oculi	Mm. *bulbi*
N. interosseus dorsalis	N. interosseus *posterior*
Vv. radiales	Vv. *comitantes a. radialis*

The following represent substitution of a new name for an old one:

BNA	NA
Appendix ventriculi laryngis	Sacculus laryngis
A. appendicularis	A. appendicis vermiformis
A. auditiva interna	A. labyrinthi
A. buccinatoria	A. buccalis
A. haemorrhoidalis inferior	A. rectalis inferior
A. hypogastrica	A. iliaca interna
A. anonyma	Truncus brachiocephalicus
Epistropheus	Axis
Extremitas (corporis)	Membrum
Fossa ovalis	Hiatus saphenus
Gi. submaxillaris	Gi. submandibularis
Incisura umbilicalis	Incisura lig. teretis
Inscriptio tendinae	Intersectio tendinae
Linea poplitea	Linea m. solei
Lymphoglandula	Nodus lymphaticus
Membrana vestibularis	Paries vestibularis ductus cochlearis
M. caninus	M. levator anguli oris
N. acusticus	N. stato-acusticus (N. octavus)
Os multangulum majus	Os trapezium
Os multangulum minus	Os trapezoideum
Plexus spermaticus	Plexus testicularis
Plexus sympathetici	Plexus autonomici
Processus vermiformis	Appendix vermiformis
Sinus pleurae	Recessus pleuralis
Vertex vesicae	Apex vesicae

Infrequently, names have been mercifully shortened; in this category belong such rarities as *fascia masseterica* (for *fascia parotideomasseterica*) and *palma manus* (replacing *regio volaris manus*).

In several instances adjectives have been elevated to the status of nouns; thus, *intestinum jejunum* becomes *jejunum*, and *intestinum rectum* is changed to *rectum*.

In a few cases the alteration merely involves spelling. Two examples will suffice to illustrate this type of minor change:

BNA	NA
Annulus femoralis	*Anulus* femoralis
Antibrachium	*Antebrachium*

ACKNOWLEDGEMENT TO JOURNALS

The following is a list of journal articles, published by the author in coauthorship with his colleagues and graduate students, from which illustrations in the *Atlas* were derived. In most instances the figures were engraved from the original drawings; in other cases, new drawings were prepared or the earlier plates were altered to include augmented data.

AMERICAN JOURNAL OF ANATOMY

J. W. Pick, B. J. Anson and F. L. Ashley: The origin of the obturator artery. A study of 640 body-halves. *70*:317–343, 1942.

AMERICAN JOURNAL OF ROENTGENOLOGY AND RADIUM THERAPY

B. J. Anson and H. V. Smith: The accessory pulmonary lobe of the azygos vein. An anatomical report of three cases. *35*:630–634, 1936.

AMERICAN JOURNAL OF PHYSICAL ANTHROPOLOGY

F. L. Ashley and B. J. Anson: The hypogastric artery in American Whites and Negroes. *28*:381–395, 1941.

ANATOMICAL RECORD

B. J. Anson and C. B. McVay: The anatomy of the inguinal and hypogastric regions of the abdominal wall. *70*:211–225, 1938.

B. J. Anson and C. B. McVay: The fossa ovalis and related blood vessels. *72*:399–404, 1938.

B. J. Anson, L. E. Beaton and C. B. McVay: The pyramidalis muscle. *72*:405–411, 1938.

C. B. McVay and B. J. Anson: Aponeurotic and fascial continuities in the abdomen, pelvis and thigh. *76*:213–231, 1940.

C. B. McVay and B. J. Anson: Composition of the rectus sheath. *77*:213–225, 1940.

B. J. Anson and F. L. Ashley: The midpalmar compartment, associated spaces and limiting layers. *78*:389–407, 1940.

A. F. Reimann and B. J. Anson: Vertebral level of termination of the spinal cord with report of a case of sacral cord. *88*:127–138, 1944.

A. F. Reimann, E. H. Daseler, B. J. Anson and L. E. Beaton: The palmaris longus muscle and tendon. A study of 1600 extremities. *89*:495–505, 1944.

J. Dykes and B. J. Anson: The accessory tendon of the flexor pollicis longus muscle. *90*:83–87, 1944.

R. R. Wright, B. J. Anson and H. C. Cleveland: The vestigial valves and the interatrial foramen of the adult human heart. *100*:331–355, 1948.

JOURNAL OF BONE AND JOINT SURGERY

L. E. Beaton and B. J. Anson: The sciatic nerve and the piriformis muscle: their interrelation a possible cause of coccygodynia. *20*:686–688, 1938.

E. H. Daseler and B. J. Anson: The plantaris muscle. An anatomical study of 750 specimens. *25*:822–827, 1943.

QUARTERLY BULLETIN OF NORTHWESTERN UNIVERSITY MEDICAL SCHOOL

B. J. Anson and F. L. Ashley: The anatomy of the region of inguinal hernia. I. The parietal coverings of the round ligament of the uterus. *15*:32–38, 1941.

F. L. Ashley and B. J. Anson: The anatomy of the region of inguinal hernia. II. The parietal coverings and related structures in indirect inguinal hernia in the male. *15*:114–121, 1941.

F. L. Ashley, B. J. Anson and L. E. Beaton: The anatomy of the region of inguinal hernia. III. The parietal coverings and related structures of direct (diverticular) inguinal hernia in the male. *15*:192–204, 1941.

E. H. Morgan and B. J. Anson: The anatomy of the region of inguinal hernia. IV. The internal surfaces of the parietal layers. *16*:20–37, 1942.

L. E. Beaton and B. J. Anson: The arterial supply of the small intestine. *16*:114–122, 1942.

B. J. Anson, E. H. Morgan and C. B. McVay: The anatomy of the region of the inguinal hernia. V. The fundamental structure of the inguinal and scrotal layers, as demonstrated in cases of indirect inguinal hernia. *16*:128–141, 1942.

B. W. Carr, W. E. Bishop and B. J. Anson: Mammary arteries. *16*:150–154, 1942.

W. E. Bishop, B. W. Carr, B. J. Anson and F. L. Ashley: The parietal intermuscular plexus of the thoracic nerves. *17*:209–216, 1943.

E. W. Cauldwell, B. J. Anson and R. R. Wright: The extensor indicis proprius muscle. A study of 263 consecutive specimens. *17*:267–279, 1943.

H. E. Greig, B. J. Anson and S. S. Coleman: The inferior phrenic artery. Types of origin in 850 body-halves and diaphragmatic relationship. *25*:345–350, 1951.

R. W. Jamieson and B. J. Anson: The relation of the median nerve to the heads of origin of the pronator teres muscle. A study of 300 specimens. *26*:34–35, 1952.

R. W. Jamieson, D. B. Smith and B. J. Anson: The cervical sympathetic ganglia. An anatomical study of 100 cervicothoracic dissections. *26*:219–227, 1952.

H. W. Greig, B. J. Anson and J. M. Budinger: Variations in the form and attachments of the biceps brachii muscle. *26*:241–244, 1952.

S. S. Coleman, D. K. McAfee and B. J. Anson: The insertion of the abductor pollicis longus muscle. An anatomical study of 175 specimens. *27*:117–122, 1953.

B. J. Anson, R. W. Jamieson, V. J. O'Connor, Jr., and L. E. Beaton: The pectoral muscles. An anatomical study of 400 body-halves. *27*:211–218, 1953.

H. W. Greig, B. J. Anson, D. K. McAfee and L. E. Kurth: The ductus arteriosus and its ligamentous remnant in the adult. An anatomical study of 150 specimens. *28*:66–75, 1954.

R. H. Bell, B. I. Knapp, B. J. Anson and S. J. Larson: Form, size, blood-supply and relations of the adult thymus. *28:*156–164, 1954.

B. J. Anson: Anatomical considerations in surgery of the gall bladder. *30:*250–259, 1956.

J. K. Liechty, T. W. Shields and B. J. Anson: Variations pertaining to the aortic arches and their branches. With comments on surgically important types. *31:*136–143, 1957.

SURGERY, GYNECOLOGY AND OBSTETRICS

B. J. Anson: The anomalous right subclavian artery. Its practical significance; with a report of three cases. *62:*708–711, 1936.

A. H. Curtis, B. J. Anson and C. B. McVay: The anatomy of the pelvic and urogenital diaphragms, in relation to urethrocele and cystocele. *68:*161–166, 1939.

B. J. Anson and R. R. Wright: Blood supply of the mammary gland. Surgical considerations by J. A. Wolfer. *69:*468–473, 1939.

A. H. Curtis, B. J. Anson and L. E. Beaton: The anatomy of the subperitoneal tissues and ligamentous structures in relation to surgery of the female pelvic viscera. *70:*643–656, 1940.

W. K. Jennings, B. J. Anson and R. R. Wright: A new method of repair for indirect inguinal hernia considered in reference to parietal anatomy. *74:*697–707, 1942.

A. H. Curtis, B. J. Anson and F. L. Ashley: Further studies in gynecological anatomy and related clinical problems. *74:*708–727, 1942.

A. H. Curtis, B. J. Anson, F. L. Ashley and T. Jones: The blood vessels of the female pelvis in relation to gynecological surgery. *75:*421–423, 1942.

A. H. Curtis, B. J. Anson, F. L. Ashley and T. Jones: The anatomy of the pelvic autonomic nerves in relation to gynecology. *75:*743–750, 1942.

B. J. Anson, R. R. Wright, F. L. Ashley and J. Dykes: The fascia of the dorsum of the hand. *81:*327, 331, 1945.

F. L. Ashley and B. J. Anson: The pelvic autonomic nerves in the male. *82:*598–608, 1946.

E. J. Cummins, B. J. Anson, B. W. Carr and R. R. Wright: The structure of the calcaneal tendon (of Achilles) in relation to orthopedic surgery. With additional observations on the plantaris muscle. *83:*107–116, 1946.

E. H. Daseler, B. J. Anson, W. C. Hambley and A. F. Reimann: The cystic artery and constituents of the hepatic pedicle. A study of 500 specimens. *85:*47–63, 1947.

E. W. Cauldwell, R. G. Siekert, R. E. Liniger and B. J. Anson: The bronchial arteries. An anatomic study of 150 human cadavers. *86:*395–412, 1948.

B. J. Anson, E. H. Morgan and C. B. McVay. The anatomy of the hernial regions. I. Inguinal hernia. *89:*417–423, 1949.

B. J. Anson, A. F. Reimann and L. L. Swigart: The anatomy of hernial regions. II. Femoral hernia. *89:*752–763, 1949.

B. J. Anson, L. J. McCormack and H. C. Cleveland: The anatomy of the hernial regions. III. Obturator hernia and general considerations. *90:*31–38, 1950.

L. L. Swigart, R. G. Siekert, W. C. Hambley and B. J. Anson: The esophageal arteries; an anatomic study of 150 specimens. *90:*234–243, 1950.

L. J. McCormack, E. W. Cauldwell and B. J. Anson: Brachial and antebrachial arterial patterns. A study of 750 extremities. *96:*43–54, 1953.

B. J. Anson and L. E. Kurth: Common variations in the renal blood supply. *100:*156–162, 1955.

R. A. Davis, B. J. Anson, J. M. Budinger and L. E. Kurth: Surgical anatomy of the facial nerve and parotid gland based upon a study of 350 cervicofacial halves. *102:*384–412, 1956.

R. A. Davis, F. J. Milloy, Jr., and B. J. Anson: Lumbar, renal and associated parietal and visceral veins based upon a study of 100 specimens. *107*:1–22, 1958.

E. H. Daseler and B. J. Anson: Surgical anatomy of the subclavian artery and its branches. *108*:149–174, 1959.

B. J. Anson, E. H. Daseler and C. B. McVay: Surgical anatomy of the inguinal region based upon a study of 500 body-halves. *111*:707–725, 1960.

B. J. Anson and E. H. Daseler: Common variations in renal anatomy affecting blood supply, form and topography. *112*:439–449, 1961.

S. S. Coleman and B. J. Anson: Arterial patterns in the hand based upon a study of 650 specimens. *113*:409–424, 1961.

F. J. Milloy and B. J. Anson: Variations in the inferior caval veins and in their renal and lumbar communications. *115*:131–142, 1962.

A. Falla, F. W. Preston and B. J. Anson: Classification and calibration of the azygos venous system in 100 specimens. In press.

CONTENTS

I.   TOPOGRAPHY   1–9

II.   THE HEAD   11–96

III.   THE NECK   97–135

IV.   THE UPPER MEMBER   137–220

V.   THE BACK AND THORAX   221–309

VI.   THE ABDOMEN   311–429

VII.   THE PELVIS AND PERINEUM   431–515

VIII. THE LOWER MEMBER   517–618

INDEX   619

Section One

TOPOGRAPHY

PRIMARY DIVISIONS OF THE BODY.. 3–4

PLANES OF ORIENTATION... 5

REGIONS OF BODY; ANTERIOR... 6

REGIONS, CONTINUED; POSTERIOR... 7

REGIONS, CONTINUED; HEAD, NECK.. 8

REGIONS, CONCLUDED; PERINEUM.. 9

PRIMARY DIVISIONS OF THE BODY

For purposes of convenience in description, the human body is divided into the following portions: *head*, *neck*, *trunk*, and superior and inferior *members*. The head includes the *cranium* and the *face*. The neck is the part between the head and trunk. The trunk includes the *thorax*, *abdomen*, and *pelvis*. The superior member includes the *shoulder*, *arm*, *forearm*, and *hand;* the inferior member consists of the *hip*, *thigh*, *leg*, and *foot*. Each of these primary divisions has a number of subdivisions.

REGIONS AND SURFACE AREAS

THE HEAD (page 8)

The cranial portion contains the brain; the facial portion: the eyes, nose, mouth, and jaws. The *cranium* includes the crown, back of the head, frontal region, temples, and ears. The forehead is a part of the sinciput, and the external part of the ear is called the *auricle*.

The *face* includes the regions of the eyes, nose, mouth, cheeks, and lower jaw. The upper jaw is not a separate entity among the classic areas because it contributes to parts of both the nose and the mouth.

THE NECK (page 8)

The neck has numerous superficial regions, most of which are named for their relation to subjacent structures. The term *nucha*, or nuchal region, is used to indicate the *back of the neck* only. Seven cervical vertebrae constitute the skeletal component of the neck.

THE TRUNK (pages 6, 7, 9)

The Thorax (page 6)

The *thorax* consists of a wall that encloses a potential space, the *thoracic cavity*, and the *contents* of this cavity. Skeletal components of the wall are the sternum, 12 pairs of ribs, and 12 thoracic vertebrae. The *breast* is the common term for the anterior thoracic region, but anatomic description requires recognition of *right* and *left pectoral* regions separated by a *sternal* region. The *mammary glands* (commonly called *breasts*) are superficially located in the lower parts of the bilateral pectoral regions. A narrow triangular region, the infraclavicular, lies adjacent to each pectoral region superiorly. The thoracic cavity contains the thoracic viscera, notably the heart and lungs.

The Abdomen (page 6)

The *abdomen* is that part of the trunk situated between the thorax and the pelvis. Matching the thorax in its general anatomy, the abdomen possesses a wall, a nominal cavity, and contents (visceral, vascular, and neural). The thoracic and abdominal cavities are separated, both anatomically and functionally, by the diaphragm (diaphragm, respiratory diaphragm, thoracoabdominal diaphragm); but because this partition is dome-shaped, some of the upper abdominal viscera lie deep to the lower ribs.

This means that there is an overlap between the superficial and the deep relationships of lower thoracic viscera (lungs) and upper abdominal viscera (liver, stomach, and spleen). In a comparable manner, there is a sharing of the pelvic and the abdominal cavities by their organs. From the standpoint of skeletal structure, the pelvis is divided into an upper part, the false pelvis (pelvis major), and a lower part, the true pelvis (pelvis minor). However, the cavity of the pelvis major is generally treated as a part of the abdominal cavity because the hypogastric and inguinal regions of the abdominal wall lie superficial to it. Areas of overlap

3

between the thoracic wall and the abdominal cavity are similarly included in the *epigastric* and *hypochondriac* regions. The *umbilical* and *lumbar* regions, intermediate between the epigastric and the hypochondrias, are purely abdominal in topography.

The Back (*page 7*)

The *back* is the posterior part of the trunk. Its skeletal component is the *vertebral* (or spinal) column, except for the cervical vertebrae, which are included in the neck. Additional features are the *spinal cord*, within the *vertebral canal*, and the musculature of the back (forming the dorsal wall of body cavities). Superficial regions derive their names from deeper structures or from the positions they occupy.

The Pelvis (*page 9*)

The *pelvis* is the lowermost division of the trunk. Its skeletal framework consists of the two *hip bones*, each of which contains an ilium (os ilium), an ischium (os ischii), and a pubis; the *sacrum* (os sacrum) and the *coccyx* (os coccygis). This framework is customarily divided for descriptive purposes into two parts, with the hip bone (os coxae) included in the skeleton of the inferior member, and the sacrum and coccyx belonging to the vertebral column. Regarded in this way, the pelvis shares its bones with two other regions of the body. Its external features include the *buttocks*, the pubic eminence (mons pubis), and the *perineum* with its associated genital organs and the anus. Internally, only the lower division of the pelvic cavity, the *true pelvis*, contains pelvic organs (exceptions: the urinary bladder during distention and the uterus during pregnancy extend into the abdominal cavity).

THE SUPERIOR AND INFERIOR MEMBERS (pages 6, 7)

At the sites of their attachments to the trunk, both superior and inferior extremities have zones of transition between regions of the trunk and regions that belong to the members exclusively. Thus the *axilla* has part of its surface on the lateral wall of the thorax and part on the medial surface of the arm (brachium). The *scapular region*, although classified as a part of the back, is related to the arm because it includes muscles with humeral attachments. Similarly, the *buttock*, adjacent to bones of the pelvis, contains muscles which act upon the lower limb.

The skeletal components of the *superior member*, in addition to those of the arm, forearm, and hand, include the *scapula* and *clavicle*. Regionally, the scapula is in the back, whereas the clavicle occupies the zone that divides the neck from the thoracic region. The member proper begins at the shoulder joint (scapulohumeral articulation) and has three main parts: the *arm*, the *forearm*, and the *hand*. Although a separate region for the elbow (containing the humeroulnar and humeroradial articulations) has been recognized, the smaller region associated with the wrist (radiocarpal joint) is topographically included with regions of the hand. Part of the upper portion of the *arm* is occupied by the *deltoid region* but, except for a few minor areas, the areas of the arm and forearm are indicated by designations based upon directions—anterior, lateral, posterior, medial. In the *hand*, the anterior aspect, called the *palmar* region, contains subdivisions of the *thenar* and *hypothenar* regions, which are located proximal to the thumb and to the little finger, respectively.

In addition to the hip bone, the inferior member includes the femur, the tibia and fibula, the bones of the tarsus (ossa tarsi), the metatarsus (ossa metatarsalia), and the digits (ossa digitorum pedis). Regional designations of parts of this member that have not been named in association with the pelvis are *femoral*, *genicular* (of the knee), *crural* (of the leg), *tarsal* (of the ankle), metatarsal (of the foot), and digital (of the toes).

The region of the knee includes the knee joint (articulatio genu) and most of the popliteal region (or space), which lies behind the joint. The upper end of the popliteal space is in the lowermost part of the femoral region, and the tibiofibular articulation is located in the zone of transition between the knee and the leg. The ankle joint (articulatio talocruralis) occupies the upper part of the tarsal region; its distal boundary is marked by the tarsometatarsal articulations. Progressing distally, the metatarsal and digital regions follow. The *instep* is the arched part of the dorsum of the foot which lies anterior to the ankle joint.

Several regions mentioned in the foregoing descriptions are not indicated on the topographical diagrams, and since physical limitations do not permit all regions to be charted, some that are shown have not been described. Also, regions not mentioned in the text but labeled on the charts are obvious enough without explanatory description.

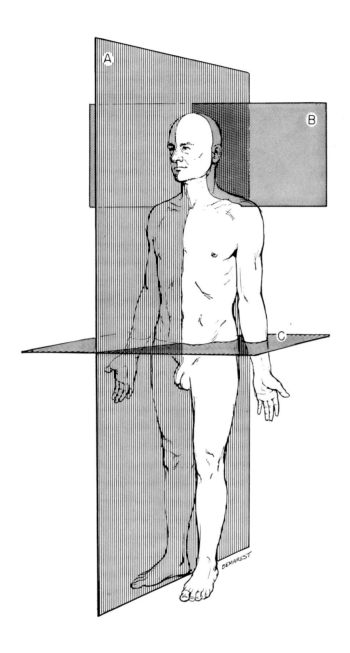

Planes of orientation.

A, Sagittal; *B*, frontal or coronal; *C*, transverse. (H. A. Davenport's section in Morris' Human Anatomy, 12th Edition. Barry J. Anson, Editor. Published by McGraw-Hill Book Co., New York.)

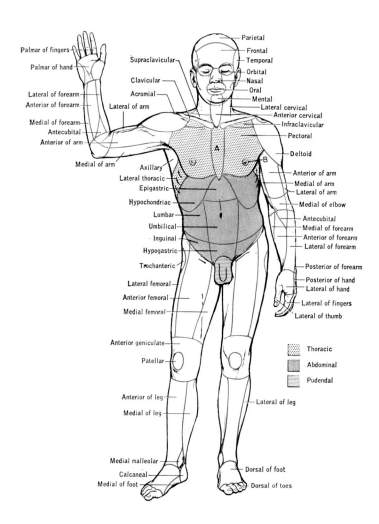

Regions seen from an anterior view.

A, Sternal; *B*, mammary. (H. A. Davenport's section in Morris' Human Anatomy, 12th Edition. Barry J. Anson, Editor. Published by McGraw-Hill Book Co., New York.)

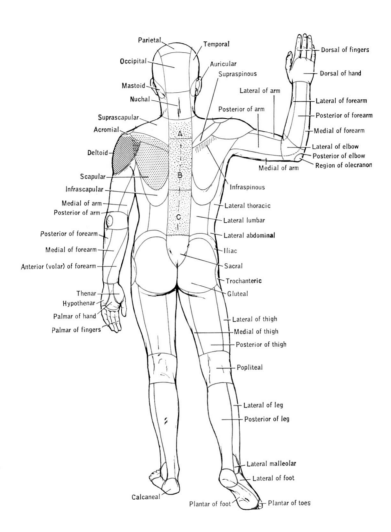

Regions seen from a posterior view.

A, *B*, and *C* comprise the middorsal region. *A*, Superior portion; *B*, interscapular (middle) portion; *C*, midlumbar (inferior) portion. (H. A. Davenport's section in Morris' Human Anatomy, 12th Edition. Barry J. Anson, Editor. Published by McGraw-Hill Book Co., New York.)

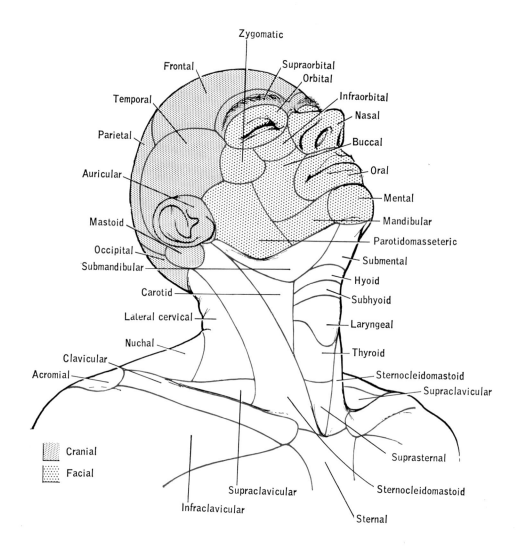

Zygomatic

Frontal

Supraorbital

Orbital

Temporal

Infraorbital

Nasal

Parietal

Buccal

Auricular

Oral

Mental

Mastoid

Mandibular

Parotidomasseteric

Occipital

Submental

Submandibular

Hyoid

Carotid

Subhyoid

Lateral cervical

Laryngeal

Nuchal

Thyroid

Clavicular

Sternocleidomastoid

Acromial

Supraclavicular

Cranial

Facial

Suprasternal

Supraclavicular

Sternocleidomastoid

Infraclavicular

Sternal

Regions of the head and neck. (H. A. Davenport's section in Morris' Human Anatomy, 12th Edition. Barry J. Anson, Editor. Published by McGraw-Hill Book Co., New York.)

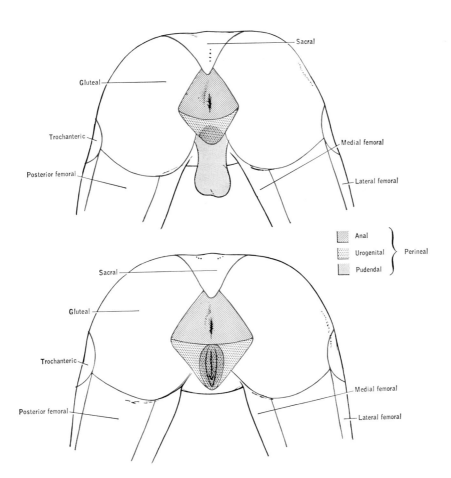

Perineal and other adjacent regions.

In the male (above), the urogenital triangle is overlapped by only a small portion of the pudendal region. In the female (below), the pudendal region lies within the urogenital triangle. (H. A. Davenport's section in Morris' Human Anatomy, 12th Edition. Barry J. Anson, Editor. Published by McGraw-Hill Book Co., New York.)

Section Two

THE HEAD

SKULL; EXTERIOR, SEVERAL VIEWS... 13–17

STYLOID PROCESS; VARIATIONS.. 18

SKULL; INTERIOR.. 19–20

SKULL; INTERIOR AND EXTERIOR.. 21

CRANIAL BONES.. 22–27
    Occipital.. 22
    Sphenoid.. 23
    Temporal.. 24
    Frontal... 25
    Parietal.. 26
    Ethmoid... 27

FACIAL BONES... 28–31
    Vomer... 28
    Maxilla; Nasal and Lacrimal... 29
    Palatine, Zygomatic... 30
    Mandible.. 31

TEETH... 32

AREAS OF MUSCULAR ATTACHMENT... 33–34
    Skull and Mandible.. 33
    Occipital Bone... 34

CRANIAL FOSSAE AND FORAMINA.. 35–36

PARANASAL SINUSES, MASTOID CELLS... 37–39

LAYERS OF THE SCALP.. 40

MUSCLES OF FACIAL EXPRESSION: THREE STAGES IN DISSECTION.................................... 41–43

MUSCLES OF MASTICATION... 44–46

VESSELS AND NERVES OF THE HEAD: THREE STAGES IN DISSECTION................................. 47–49

ORAL PHARYNX... 50

VENOUS DRAINAGE OF THE HEAD AND NECK... 51

COLLATERAL ARTERIAL CIRCULATION... 52

CEREBROSPINAL CIRCULATION; SCHEMATIC... 53

TRIGEMINAL NERVE.. 54–56

FACIAL NERVE AND PAROTID GLAND.. 57–62

NOSE; CARTILAGE, BONE, AND BLOOD VESSELS.. 63–64

EAR... 65–76

11

(Continued)

Ear (*Continued*)

Ear.. 65
Development of the Auricle... 66
Muscles of the Auricle.. 67
External Ear, Temporal Bone, and Auditory Tube......................... 68
External and Middle Ear... 69
Tympanic Cavity... 70
Bony Labyrinth.. 71
Tympanic Cavity, Opened... 72
Cochlea and Spiral Organ.. 73
Parts of the Ear; Schematic.. 74–75
Internal Acoustic Meatus.. 76

Paranasal Sinuses and Lacrimal Apparatus................................ 77

Eye and Orbit... 78–84
Eye... 78
Eyeball, Sectioned... 79–80
Conjunctiva, Fascia, and Ocular Muscles............................... 81
Orbit and Contents... 82
Orbit, Layers of Eyeball... 83
Orbit and Contents... 84

Cranial Cavity and Orbit: Three Stages in Dissection................. 85–86

Head and Neck, Hemisection... 87

Cerebral Ventricles.. 88

Brain; Entire and Hemisected.. 89–90

Cranial Bones from Within.. 91
Sulci for Arteries and Venous Sinuses................................. 91

Cranial Vessels; Schematic... 92

Meningeal and Cerebral Blood Vessels................................. 93–94

Cranial Nerves, Base of Brain.. 95–96

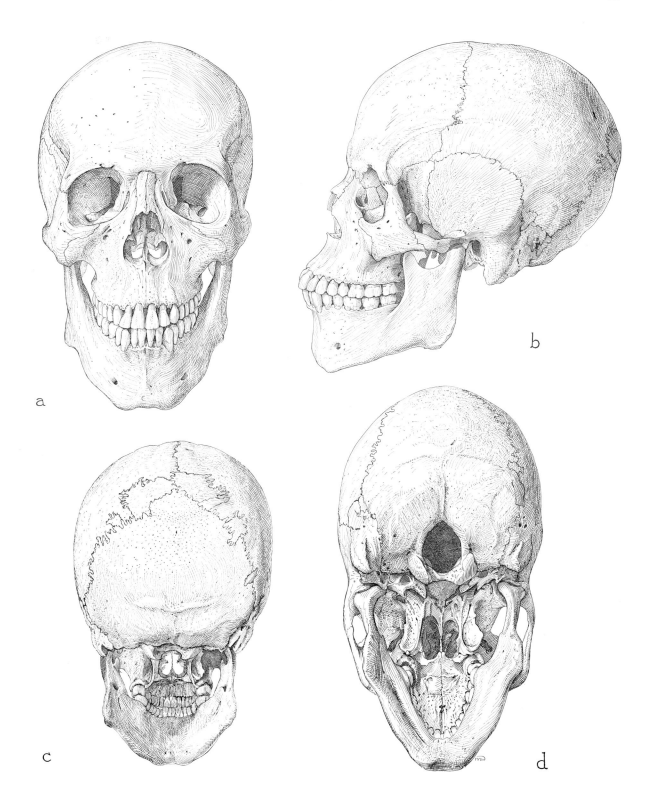

Skull of an adult male.

a, The skull, anterior aspect. *b*, Lateral view. *c*, Posterior aspect, showing wormian bones. *d*, Inferior surface.

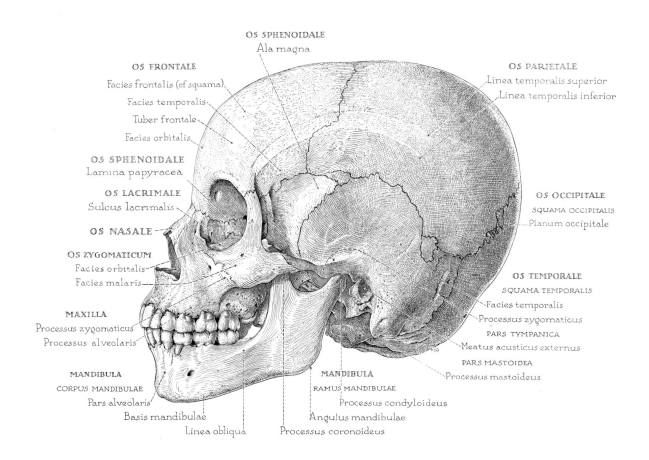

OS SPHENOIDALE
Ala magna

OS FRONTALE

Facies frontalis (of squama)

Facies temporalis

Tuber frontale

Facies orbitalis

OS SPHENOIDALE
Lamina papyracea

OS LACRIMALE
Sulcus lacrimalis

OS NASALE

OS ZYGOMATICUM
Facies orbitalis
Facies malaris

MAXILLA
Processus zygomaticus
Processus alveolaris

MANDIBULA
CORPUS MANDIBULAE
Pars alveolaris
Basis mandibulae
Linea obliqua

OS PARIETALE
Linea temporalis superior
Linea temporalis inferior

OS OCCIPITALE
SQUAMA OCCIPITALIS
Planum occipitale

OS TEMPORALE
SQUAMA TEMPORALIS
Facies temporalis
Processus zygomaticus
PARS TYMPANICA
Meatus acusticus externus
PARS MASTOIDEA
Processus mastoideus

MANDIBULA
RAMUS MANDIBULAE
Processus condyloideus
Angulus mandibulae
Processus coronoideus

Exterior of the skull; adolescent specimen.

The skull, seen from the side, showing the portions of each of the constituent bones.

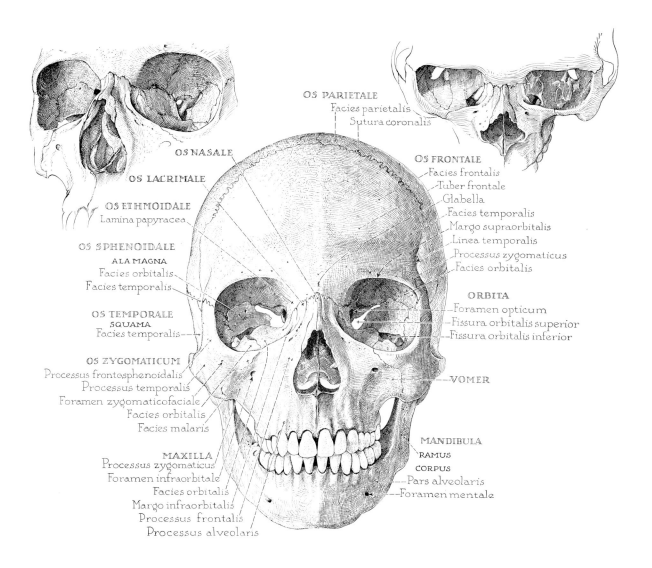

OS PARIETALE
Facies parietalis
Sutura coronalis

OS NASALE

OS LACRIMALE

OS ETHMOIDALE
Lamina papyracea

OS SPHENOIDALE
ALA MAGNA
Facies orbitalis
Facies temporalis

OS TEMPORALE
SQUAMA
Facies temporalis

OS ZYGOMATICUM
Processus frontosphenoidalis
Processus temporalis
Foramen zygomaticofaciale
Facies orbitalis
Facies malaris

MAXILLA
Processus zygomaticus
Foramen infraorbitale
Facies orbitalis
Margo infraorbitalis
Processus frontalis
Processus alveolaris

OS FRONTALE
Facies frontalis
Tuber frontale
Glabella
Facies temporalis
Margo supraorbitalis
Linea temporalis
Processus zygomaticus
Facies orbitalis

ORBITA
Foramen opticum
Fissura orbitalis superior
Fissura orbitalis inferior

VOMER

MANDIBULA
RAMUS
CORPUS
Pars alveolaris
Foramen mentale

Exterior of an adult skull.

The main figure shows the entire skull, seen from the front. The smaller figures picture the orbital region seen in anterolateral and anterosuperior views.

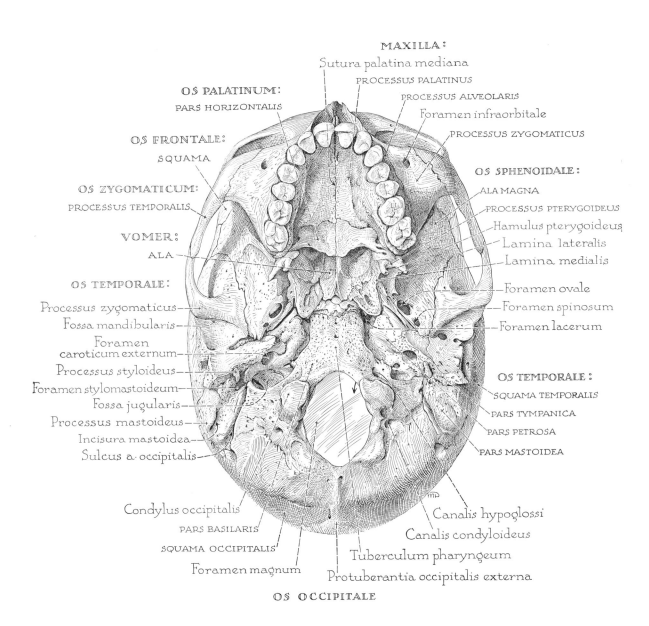

MAXILLA:
Sutura palatina mediana
PROCESSUS PALATINUS
PROCESSUS ALVEOLARIS
Foramen infraorbitale
PROCESSUS ZYGOMATICUS

OS PALATINUM:
PARS HORIZONTALIS

OS FRONTALE:
SQUAMA

OS SPHENOIDALE:
ALA MAGNA
PROCESSUS PTERYGOIDEUS
Hamulus pterygoideus
Lamina lateralis
Lamina medialis

OS ZYGOMATICUM:
PROCESSUS TEMPORALIS

VOMER:
ALA

Foramen ovale
Foramen spinosum
Foramen lacerum

OS TEMPORALE:
Processus zygomaticus
Fossa mandibularis
Foramen caroticum externum
Processus styloideus
Foramen stylomastoideum
Fossa jugularis
Processus mastoideus
Incisura mastoidea
Sulcus a. occipitalis

OS TEMPORALE:
SQUAMA TEMPORALIS
PARS TYMPANICA
PARS PETROSA
PARS MASTOIDEA

Condylus occipitalis
PARS BASILARIS
SQUAMA OCCIPITALIS
Foramen magnum

Canalis hypoglossi
Canalis condyloideus
Tuberculum pharyngeum
Protuberantia occipitalis externa

OS OCCIPITALE

Exterior of the skull; adolescent specimen.

The base of the skull. Showing the chief portions of each bone and the foramina.

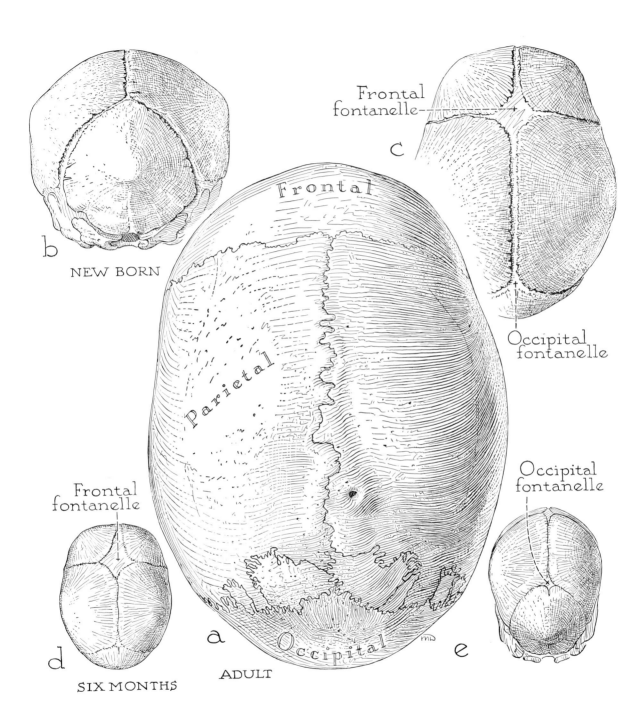

Skulls of an adult male, six-month fetus and newborn infant.
Viewed from above or from behind. Drawn to scale.

a, Adult skull, seen from above; showing wormian bones and a large, unilateral, parietal foramen (for transmission of a parietal emissary vein). *b* and *c*, Skull of the newborn, posterior and superior views, respectively; showing the fontanelles. *d* and *e*, Skull of the fetus; superior and posterior views, respectively.

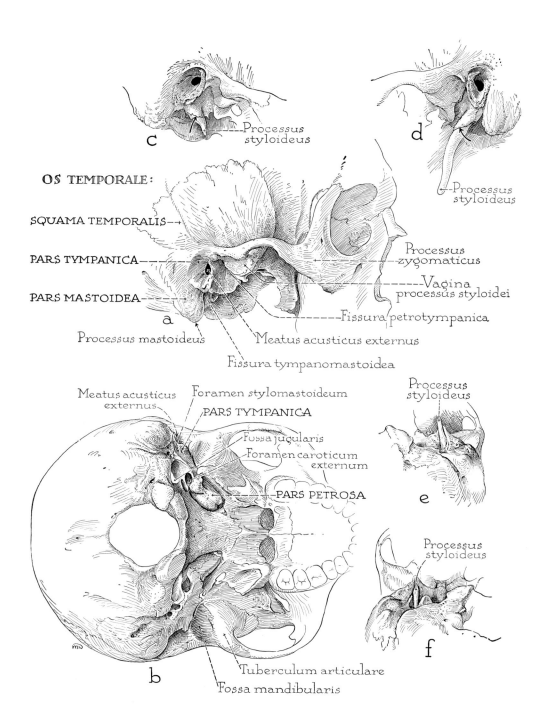

Styloid process.

Variations encountered in a study of 150 cranial halves. *a, c* and *d* are seen in lateral view; *b, e* and *f,* inferior views.

a, An example of small process concealed, in lateral view, by the *vagina processus styloidei. b,* A specimen in which a styloid process was absent. *c,* An example of a process of usual length (arrows here and in *d* indicate the margin of the sheath). *d,* An exceptionally long process. *e,* A process that projects slightly beyond the border of the sheath. *f,* A process concealed by the sheath.

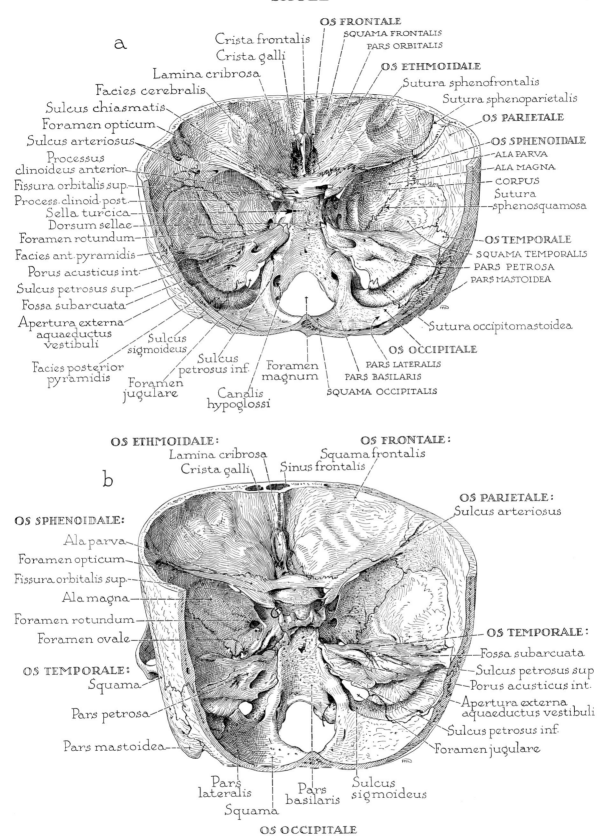

a

OS FRONTALE
SQUAMA FRONTALIS
PARS ORBITALIS

Crista frontalis
Crista galli

OS ETHMOIDALE

Lamina cribrosa

Facies cerebralis
Sulcus chiasmatis
Foramen opticum
Sulcus arteriosus
Processus clinoideus anterior
Fissura orbitalis sup.
Process. clinoid. post.
Sella turcica
Dorsum sellae
Foramen rotundum
Facies ant. pyramidis
Porus acusticus int.
Sulcus petrosus sup.
Fossa subarcuata
Apertura externa aquaeductus vestibuli
Facies posterior pyramidis

Sutura sphenofrontalis
Sutura sphenoparietalis

OS PARIETALE

OS SPHENOIDALE
ALA PARVA
ALA MAGNA
CORPUS
Sutura sphenosquamosa

OS TEMPORALE
SQUAMA TEMPORALIS
PARS PETROSA
PARS MASTOIDEA

Sutura occipitomastoidea

Sulcus sigmoideus
Sulcus petrosus inf.
Foramen jugulare
Foramen magnum
Canalis hypoglossi

OS OCCIPITALE
PARS LATERALIS
PARS BASILARIS
SQUAMA OCCIPITALIS

OS ETHMOIDALE:
Lamina cribrosa
Crista galli

OS FRONTALE:
Squama frontalis
Sinus frontalis

b

OS SPHENOIDALE:
Ala parva
Foramen opticum
Fissura orbitalis sup.
Ala magna
Foramen rotundum
Foramen ovale

OS TEMPORALE:
Squama
Pars petrosa
Pars mastoidea

OS PARIETALE:
Sulcus arteriosus

OS TEMPORALE:
Fossa subarcuata
Sulcus petrosus sup
Porus acusticus int.
Apertura externa aquaeductus vestibuli
Sulcus petrosus inf.
Foramen jugulare

Pars lateralis
Squama
Pars basilaris
Sulcus sigmoideus

OS OCCIPITALE

Interior of the cranium; two adolescent specimens. Viewed from behind.

a, Base of the skull. *b*, Posterior portion cut away. Opened ring encircles fused anterior and posterior clinoid processes.

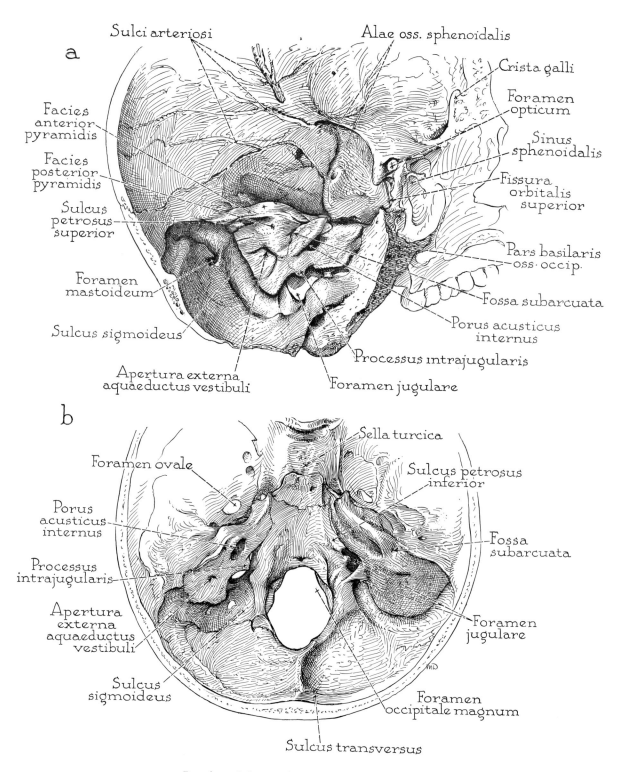

a

Sulci arteriosi

Alae oss. sphenoidalis

Crista galli

Foramen opticum

Facies anterior pyramidis

Facies posterior pyramidis

Sinus sphenoidalis

Fissura orbitalis superior

Sulcus petrosus superior

Pars basilaris oss. occip.

Foramen mastoideum

Fossa subarcuata

Porus acusticus internus

Sulcus sigmoideus

Processus intrajugularis

Apertura externa aquaeductus vestibuli

Foramen jugulare

b

Sella turcica

Foramen ovale

Sulcus petrosus inferior

Porus acusticus internus

Fossa subarcuata

Processus intrajugularis

Apertura externa aquaeductus vestibuli

Foramen jugulare

Sulcus sigmoideus

Foramen occipitale magnum

Sulcus transversus

Interior of the cranium; two adult specimens.

a, Base of the skull, from within. Parasagittal section; posterolateral view of the left side. Showing especially the petrous part, or pyramid, of the temporal bone and the related anatomy of the middle and posterior cranial fossa.

b, Base of the posterior portion of a second specimen of adult skull seen from within. Superior (cranial) view of both sides, to include the posterior cranial fossa and the adjacent part of the middle fossa.

Interior of the skull.

The inner surface of the base of the skull presents numerous irregular depressions corresponding to the convolutions of the cerebrum, and series of branching arterial and venous grooves to accommodate the meningeal vessels.

The floor of the cranial cavity presents three subdivisions termed the anterior, middle, and posterior fossae in adaptation to the contour of the base of the brain. The fossae lie at successively lower levels from before backward.

The floor of the anterior cranial fossa is formed by the orbital part of the frontal bone, the cribriform plate of the ethmoid, the lesser wings of the sphenoid, and the forepart of the body of the sphenoid. It supports the frontal lobes of the cerebrum. On the floor of the fossa are situated the following: the crista galli, the foramen cecum, the frontal crest, the cribriform plate of the ethmoid bone, and the orbital part of the frontal bone.

The floor of the middle cranial fossa, on each lateral half, is formed by the body and great wing of the sphenoid bone and the anterior surface of the petrous portion of the temporal. On the floor of each lateral part of the fossa are found conspicuous sulci for lodgement of the middle meningeal vessels, the shallow trigeminal impression on the apex of the petrous pyramid, the foramen ovale, the foramen rotundum, the superior orbital fissure, and the carotid canal. The middle portion of the middle cranial fossa is occupied mainly by the sella turcica, which includes the hypophyseal fossa. The sella is limited behind by a quadrilateral plate, the dorsum sellae, and laterally by the clinoid processes.

The floor of the posterior cranial fossa is formed by the dorsum sellae and clivus of the sphenoid, the occipital bone, the petrous and mastoid portions of the temporal bones, and the mastoid angles of the parietal bones. The fossa is bounded posteriorly and above by the transverse sulcus of the occipital bone. Inferiorly the posterior cranial fossa communicates with the vertebral canal through the foramen magnum. On the floor of the fossa are seen the internal acoustic meatus, the subarcuate fossa, the vestibular aqueduct, foramen magnum, and grooves for lodgement of the inferior petrosal, transverse, and sigmoid venous sinuses. A low ridge in the midline of the occipital squama extends from the internal occipital protuberance to the foramen magnum. To either side of the foramen are situated the hypoglossal canal, the condyloid foramen, and the jugular foramen.

Exterior of the skull.

The outer surface of the base of the skull (exclusive of the mandible) extends from the incisor teeth to the occipital protuberance, and is bounded on each side by the alveolar arch, zygomatic arch, temporal bone, and the superior nuchal line of the occipital bone.

The external surface of the cranial base is formed by the palatine processes of the maxillary and palatine bones, the vomer, the pterygoid process, the inferior surfaces of the great wings, the spinous processes and body of the sphenoid bone, and the inferior surfaces of the squamous, mastoid, and petrous portions of the temporal bones. On this undersurface of the skull the following openings and prominences are readily identifiable: incisive canals and palatine foramina; the posterior nasal spine, choanae, pterygoid canals, and hamulus; the pharyngeal tubercle; the foramen ovale, foramen spinosum, stylomastoid foramen, and foramen lacerum; the carotid canal, the depression leading to the cochlear aqueduct, the jugular foramen, the foramen magnum, and the condyloid canal; the mandibular fossa, occipital groove, the sulcus for the auditory tube, and the mastoid process.

For portrayal of the less prominent features the reader is referred to the illustrations of the separate bones of the skull (pages 22 to 31).

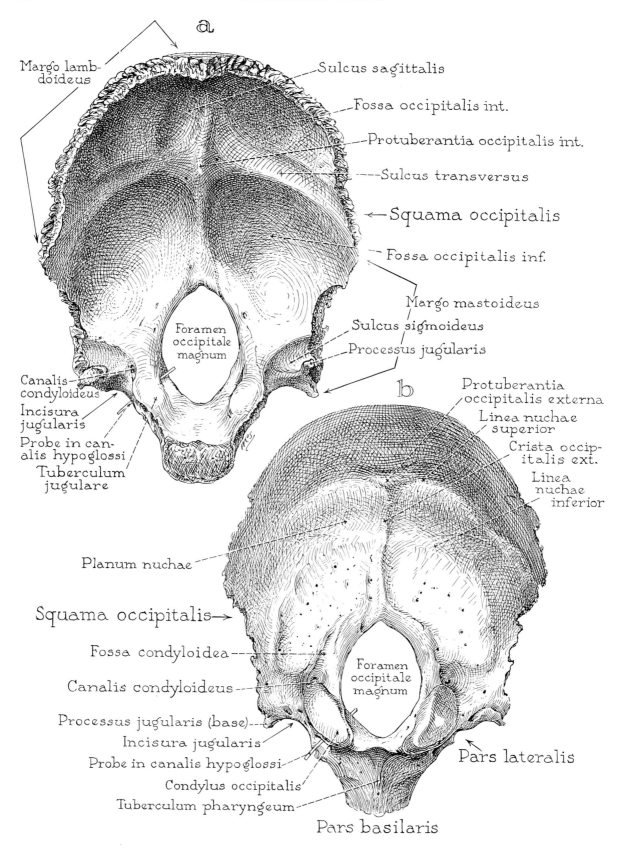

a

Margo lamb-
doideus

Sulcus sagittalis

Fossa occipitalis int.

Protuberantia occipitalis int.

Sulcus transversus

Squama occipitalis

Fossa occipitalis inf.

Margo mastoideus

Sulcus sigmoideus

Processus jugularis

Foramen
occipitale
magnum

Canalis
condyloideus

Incisura
jugularis

Probe in can-
alis hypoglossi

Tuberculum
jugulare

b

Protuberantia
occipitalis externa

Linea nuchae
superior

Crista occip-
italis ext.

Linea
nuchae
inferior

Planum nuchae

Squama occipitalis →

Fossa condyloidea

Canalis condyloideus

Processus jugularis (base)

Incisura jugularis

Probe in canalis hypoglossi

Condylus occipitalis

Tuberculum pharyngeum

Foramen
occipitale
magnum

Pars lateralis

Pars basilaris

Occipital bone.

a, The interior surface. *b*, The exterior aspect.

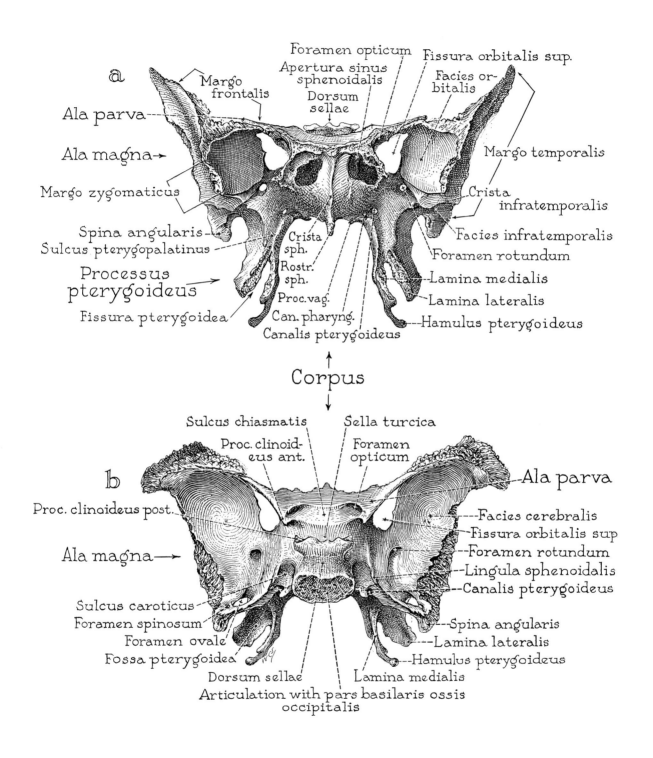

Sphenoid bone.

a, Anterior view. *b*, Posterior view.

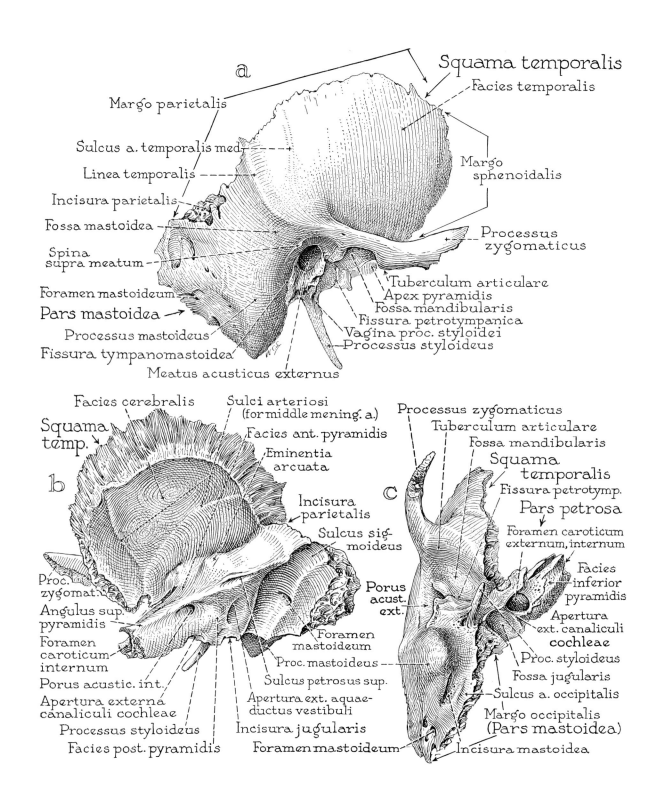

a

Margo parietalis

Sulcus a. temporalis med.

Linea temporalis

Incisura parietalis

Fossa mastoidea

Spina supra meatum

Foramen mastoideum

Pars mastoidea →

Processus mastoideus

Fissura tympanomastoidea

Meatus acusticus externus

Squama temporalis

Facies temporalis

Margo sphenoidalis

Processus zygomaticus

Tuberculum articulare

Apex pyramidis

Fossa mandibularis

Fissura petrotympanica

Vagina proc. styloidei

Processus styloideus

b

Facies cerebralis

Squama temp. ↘

Proc. zygomat.

Angulus sup. pyramidis

Foramen caroticum internum

Porus acustic. int.

Apertura externa canaliculi cochleae

Processus styloideus

Facies post. pyramidis

Sulci arteriosi (for middle mening. a.)

Facies ant. pyramidis

Eminentia arcuata

Incisura parietalis

Sulcus sigmoideus

Foramen mastoideum

Proc. mastoideus

Sulcus petrosus sup.

Apertura ext. aquae-ductus vestibuli

Incisura jugularis

Foramen mastoideum

c

Processus zygomaticus

Tuberculum articulare

Fossa mandibularis

Squama temporalis

Fissura petrotymp.

Pars petrosa

Foramen caroticum externum, internum

Porus acust. ext.

Facies inferior pyramidis

Apertura ext. canaliculi cochleae

Proc. styloideus

Fossa jugularis

Sulcus a. occipitalis

Margo occipitalis (Pars mastoidea)

Incisura mastoidea

Right temporal bone.

a, Seen from the lateral, or right external, aspect; *b*, the same bone from the medial, or internal (cerebral), aspect; *c*, the temporal bone from the inferior aspect.

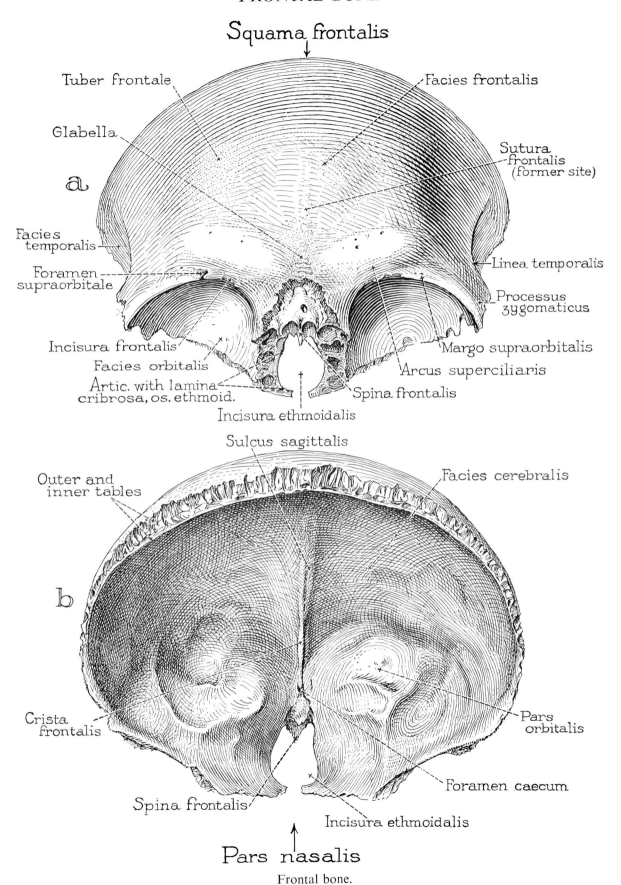

Squama frontalis

Tuber frontale

Facies frontalis

Glabella

Sutura frontalis (former site)

a

Facies temporalis

Foramen supraorbitale

Linea temporalis

Processus zygomaticus

Incisura frontalis

Facies orbitalis

Artic. with lamina cribrosa, os. ethmoid.

Margo supraorbitalis

Arcus superciliaris

Spina frontalis

Incisura ethmoidalis

Sulcus sagittalis

Outer and inner tables

Facies cerebralis

b

Crista frontalis

Pars orbitalis

Spina frontalis

Foramen caecum

Incisura ethmoidalis

Pars nasalis

Frontal bone.

a, Anterior, or external, aspect. *b*, Posterior, or internal, aspect.

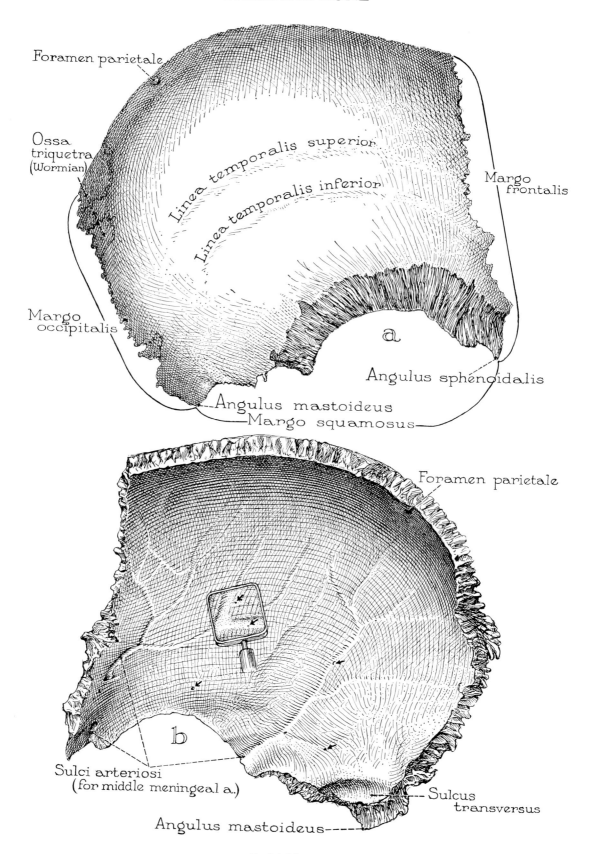

Parietal bone.

a, External surface. *b*, Internal surface; arrows indicate foramina for nutrient vessels.

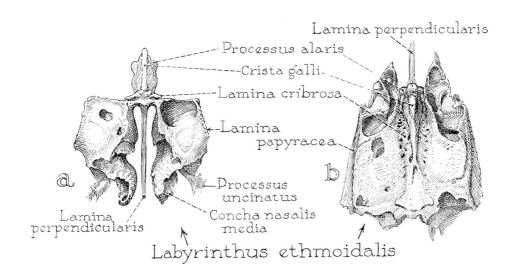

Lamina perpendicularis

Processus alaris

Crista galli

Lamina cribrosa

Lamina papyracea

Processus uncinatus

Concha nasalis media

Lamina perpendicularis

a   b

Labyrinthus ethmoidalis

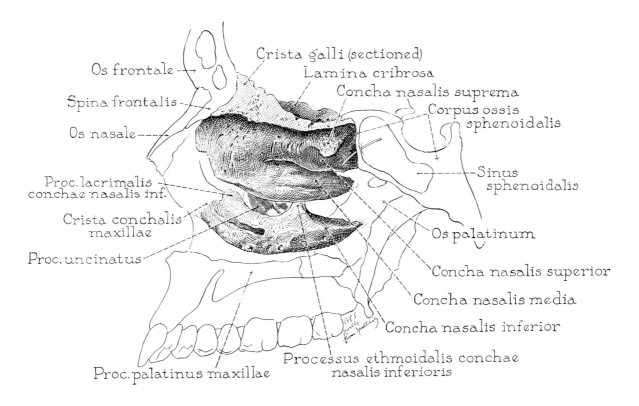

Os frontale

Spina frontalis

Os nasale

Proc. lacrimalis conchae nasalis inf.

Crista conchalis maxillae

Proc. uncinatus

Proc. palatinus maxillae

Crista galli (sectioned)

Lamina cribrosa

Concha nasalis suprema

Corpus ossis sphenoidalis

Sinus sphenoidalis

Os palatinum

Concha nasalis superior

Concha nasalis media

Concha nasalis inferior

Processus ethmoidalis conchae nasalis inferioris

Ethmoid bone.

a and *b*, The bone seen from behind and above, respectively. *c*, The labyrinthine part shown in a parasagittal section.

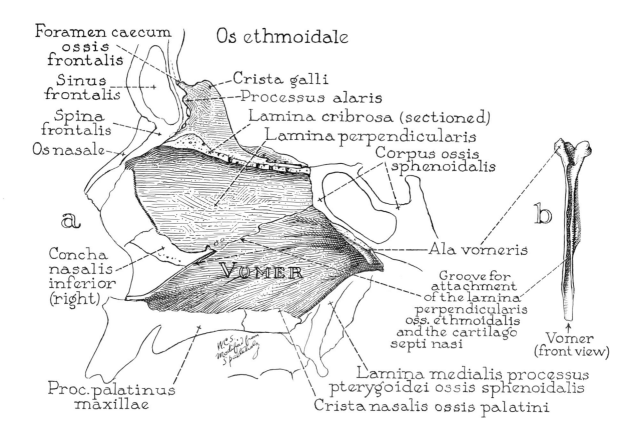

Vomer, or plowshare bone.

a, The vomer, viewed from the left side shown in relation to other bones of the skull; *b*, seen from the front.

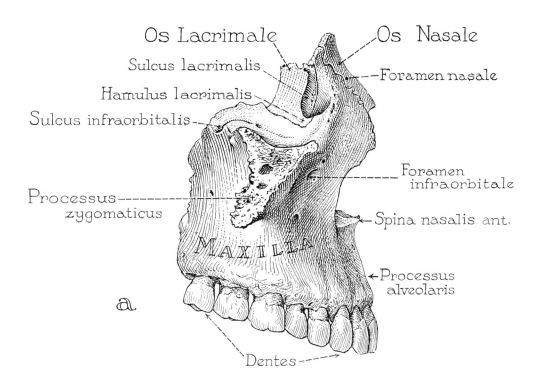

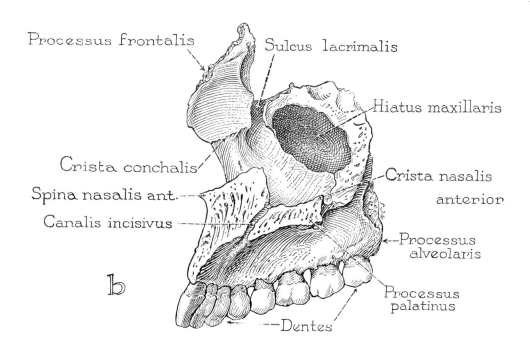

Maxilla; nasal and lacrimal bones.

a, Lateral view; *b*, medial view.

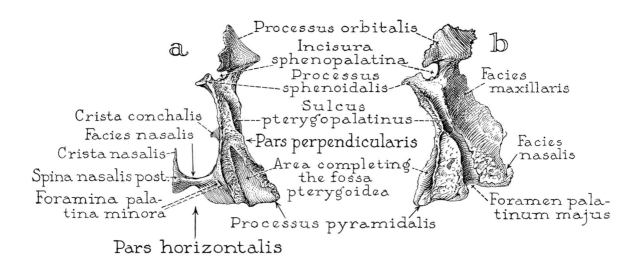

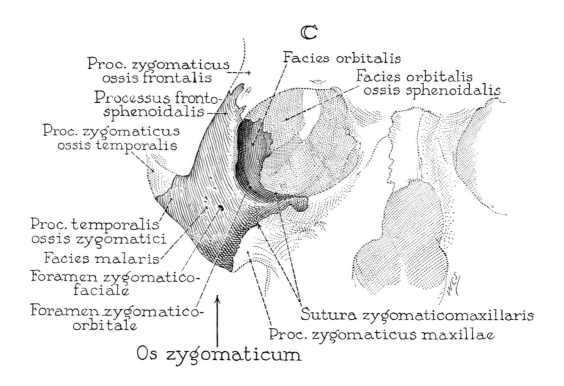

Palatine and zygomatic bones.

a and *b*, The right palatine bone, viewed from behind and from the side, respectively.
c, The right zygomatic, or yoke, bone in anterior view with related bones of the skull.

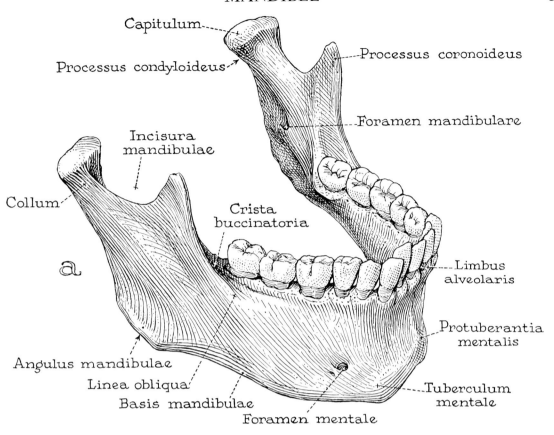

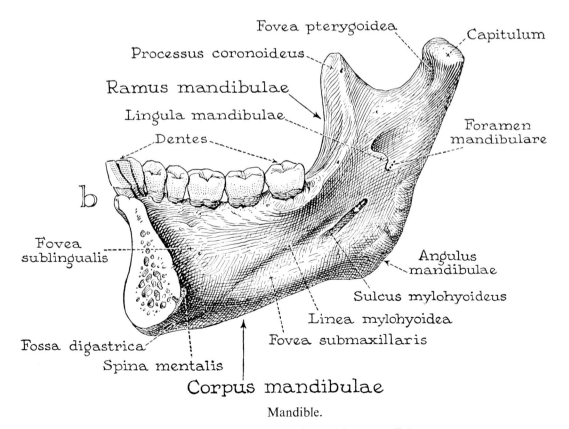

Mandible.

a, Mandible entire; *b*, the hemisected bone, medial aspect.

(Right side)

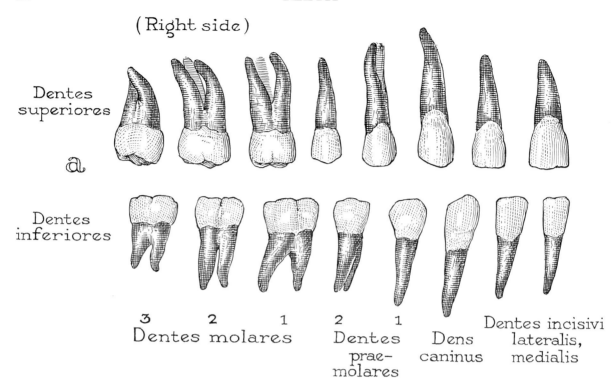

Dentes
superiores

a

Dentes
inferiores

| 3 | 2 | 1 | 2 | 1 | | |
| Dentes molares | | | Dentes prae-molares | Dens caninus | Dentes incisivi lateralis, medialis | |

(Right side)

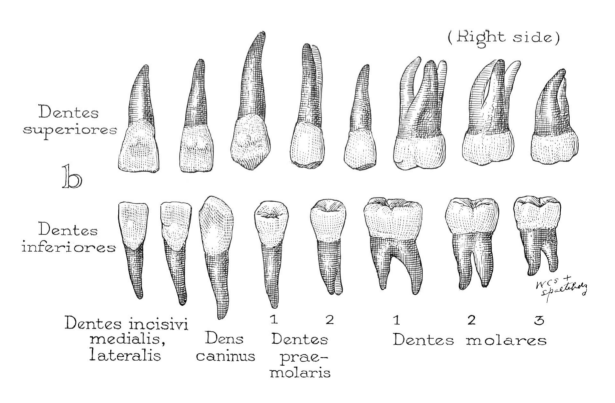

Dentes
superiores

b

Dentes
inferiores

| | | | 1 | 2 | 1 | 2 | 3 |
| Dentes incisivi medialis, lateralis | Dens caninus | Dentes prae-molaris | | Dentes molares | | | |

Teeth of the upper and lower jaws.

a, Teeth of the right half of both jaws, seen from the outer, or labial, aspect. *b*, The teeth, seen from the inner, or lingual, aspect.

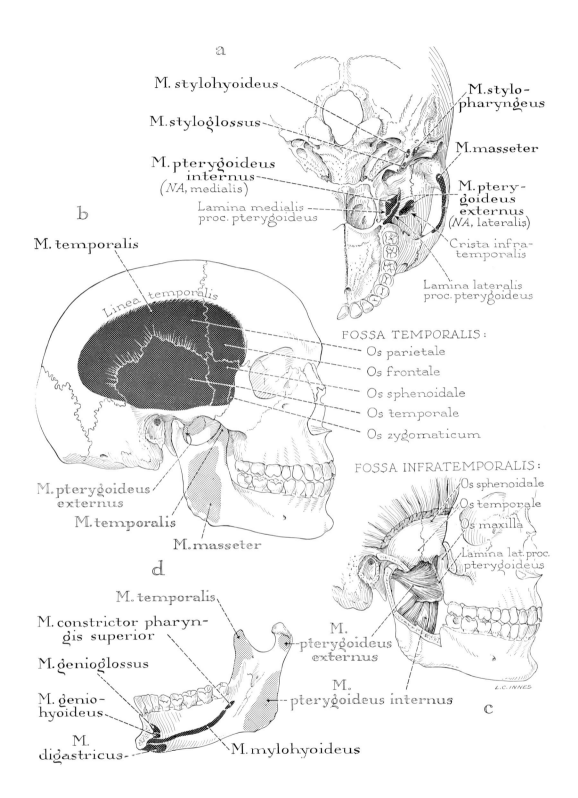

Skull and mandible, showing the areas of attachment of the muscles of mastication.

a, The skull viewed from below. *b*, The skull, in lateral view. *c*, The temporal and pterygoid muscles. *d*, The mandible; medial surface.

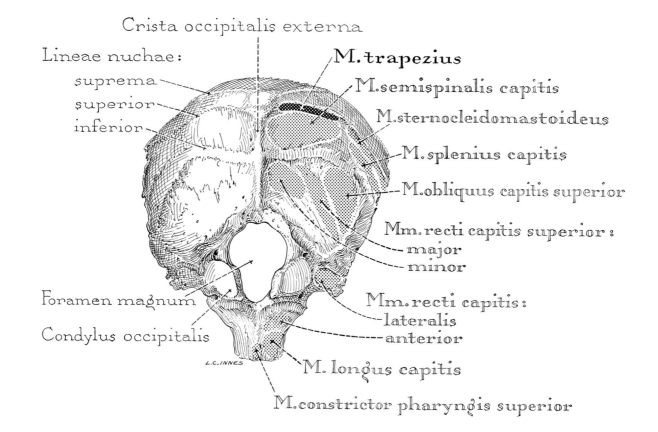

Crista occipitalis externa
Lineae nuchae:
suprema
superior
inferior

M. trapezius
M. semispinalis capitis
M. sternocleidomastoideus
M. splenius capitis
M. obliquus capitis superior
Mm. recti capitis superior:
major
minor
Mm. recti capitis:
lateralis
anterior
M. longus capitis

Foramen magnum
Condylus occipitalis

L.C.INNES

M. constrictor pharyngis superior

Occipital bone.

Base of the skull, showing the areas of attachment (to the occipital bone) of the long cervical muscles and the short msucles of the suboccipital space.

In this figure and in all others which portray the attachment of musculature to bone, areas of origin are indicated in dark pattern and by solid lettering, whereas the areas of insertion are shown in the lighter pattern and by open lettering.

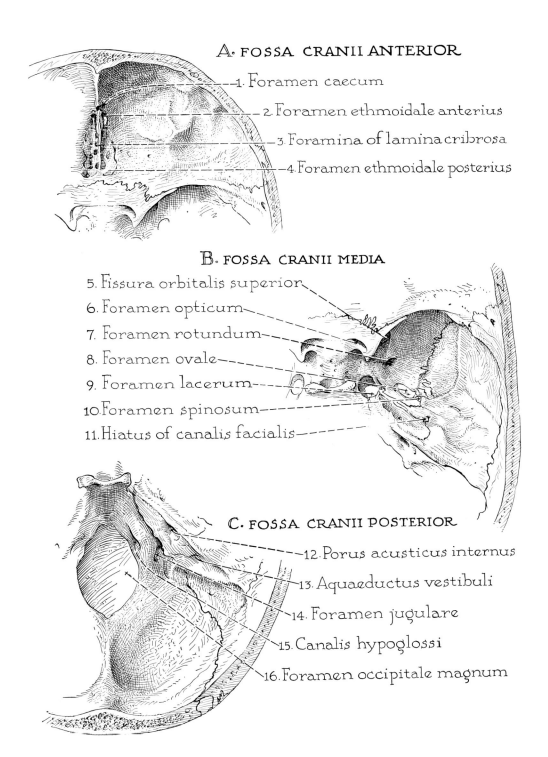

A. FOSSA CRANII ANTERIOR

1. Foramen caecum
2. Foramen ethmoidale anterius
3. Foramina of lamina cribrosa
4. Foramen ethmoidale posterius

B. FOSSA CRANII MEDIA

5. Fissura orbitalis superior
6. Foramen opticum
7. Foramen rotundum
8. Foramen ovale
9. Foramen lacerum
10. Foramen spinosum
11. Hiatus of canalis facialis

C. FOSSA CRANII POSTERIOR

12. Porus acusticus internus
13. Aquaeductus vestibuli
14. Foramen jugulare
15. Canalis hypoglossi
16. Foramen occipitale magnum

Cranial fossae.

Showing the foramina, fissures and canals in each fossa. The descriptive text appears on the following page.

The floor of the anterior cranial fossa is formed by the orbital plates of the frontal bone, the cribriform plate of the ethmoid, and the lesser wings and anterior part of the body of the sphenoid.

The floor of the middle cranial fossa is formed by the body and great wings of the sphenoid bone, and by the anterior surfaces of the petrous portions of the temporal.

The posterior fossa is formed by the dorsum sellae and clivus of the sphenoid bone, the mastoid portions and posterior surfaces of the petrous portions, the temporals, the mastoid angles of the parietals, and the occipital bone.

The foramina of the fossae are hereinbelow listed, together with the structures transmitted by each opening:

Floor of the *cranial* cavity (upper surface of the base of the skull)

A. Anterior Cranial Fossa

1. Foramen caecum
   Emissary vein from nose to superior sagittal sinus
2. Anterior ethmoidal foramen
   Anterior ethmoidal vessels (from ophthalmics)
   Nasociliary nerve (from ophthalmic division of trigeminal)
3. Foramina in cribriform plate
   Filaments of olfactory nerve (coursing from nasal mucous membrane to olfactory bulb)
4. Posterior ethmoidal foramen
   Posterior ethmoidal vessels (from ophthalmics)
   Posterior ethmoidal nerve (from nasociliary branch of ophthalmic)

B. Middle Cranial Fossa

5. Superior orbital fissure
   Ophthalmic veins (coursing to cavernous sinus)
   Oculomotor nerve (supply to seven of muscles of ocular bulb)
   Trochlear nerve (supply to one ocular muscle)
   Abducent nerve (supply to one ocular muscle)
   Ophthalmic nerve (first division of trigeminal)
   Orbital branch of middle meningeal artery (latter from internal maxillary)
   Recurrent (dural) branch of lacrimal artery (latter from ophthalmic)
6. Optic foramen
   Optic nerve (from ganglion cells of retina)
   Ophthalmic artery (from intracranial part of internal carotid)
7. Foramen rotundum
   Maxillary nerve (second division of trigeminal)
8. Foramen ovale
   Mandibular nerve (third division of trigeminal)
   Accessory meningeal artery (from first part of internal maxillary)
   Lesser superficial petrosal nerve (from glossopharyngeal)
9. Foramen lacerum
   Internal venous carotid plexus (ends in internal jugular vein)
   Internal nervous carotid plexus (sympathetic, surrounding artery)
   Superficial petrosal nerve (from glossopalatine part of facial)
10. Foramen spinosum
    Middle meningeal artery (from first part of internal maxillary)

Middle meningeal veins (end in pterygoid plexus)
Recurrent nerve (from mandibular division of trigeminal)
11. Hiatus of facial canal
    Greater superficial petrosal nerve (from glossopalatine part of facial)
    Superficial petrosal branch of middle meningeal artery

C. Posterior Cranial Fossa

12. Internal acoustic meatus
    Internal auditory artery (from basilar artery)
    Internal auditory veins (end in transverse sinus)
    Facial nerve (*en route* to facial canal in temporal bone)
    Cochlear part of stato-acoustic nerve (from spiral organ of Corti)
    Vestibular part of stato-acoustic nerve
13. Vestibular aqueduct (external or cranial aperture)
    Endolymphatic sac (emerges in subdural position)
    Small arteries and veins
14. Jugular foramen (formed with occipital bone)
    Inferior petrosal sinus (terminates in internal jugular vein)
    Transverse sinus (terminates in internal jugular vein)
    Internal jugular vein (terminates in subclavian vein)
    Glossopharyngeal nerve (carrying chiefly sensory fibers from tongue)
    Vagus nerve (chiefly from the lungs and stomach)
    Accessory nerve (chiefly motor supply to trapezius and sternocleidomastoid muscles)
    Meningeal branches of occipital artery (latter from external carotid)
    Meningeal branches of ascending pharyngeal artery (latter from external carotid)
15. Hypoglossal canal
    Hypoglossal nerve (motor supply to lingual muscles)
    Meningeal branch of ascending pharyngeal artery (latter from external carotid)
    Emissary vein from transverse sinus
16. Foramen magnum
    Vertebral arteries (from subclavians)
    Spinal or inferior portion of accessory nerves (ascending to join superior portion)
    Medulla oblongata and meningeal coverings
    Anterior and posterior spinal arteries (from vertebrals)
    Membrana tectoria (descends from clivus of occipital bone to vertebral attachment)

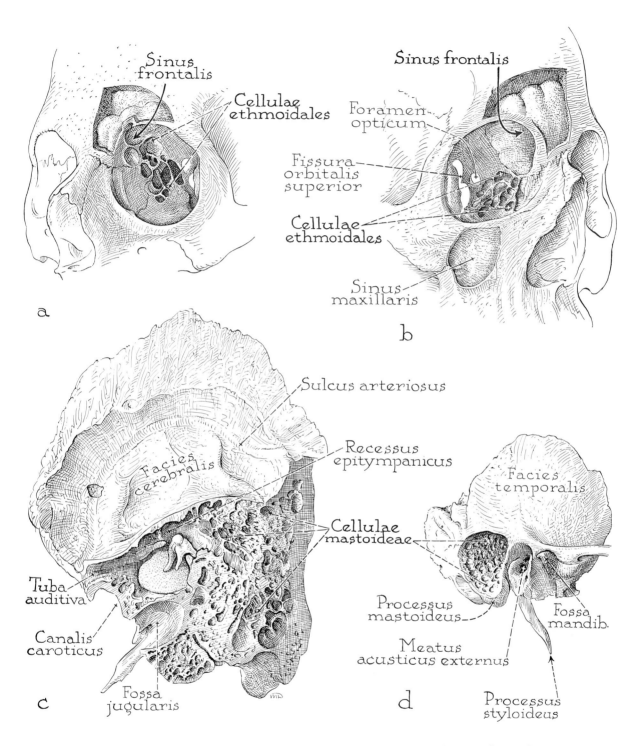

Paranasal sinuses (frontal and maxillary), and the ethmoid and mastoid air cells.

a, The mucous membrane that lines the frontal sinus has been exposed by removal of the overlying outer plate of bone; an artificial opening has been made into the sinus through its orbital wall. The intercommunicating ethmoid cells are shown by extending the dissection along the medial wall of the orbit. *b*, The frontal sinus and the ethmoidal cells are exposed by removal of their orbital wall; the maxillary sinus has been opened anteriorly. *c*, The mastoid air-cells demonstrated by cutting through the temporal bone vertically, in the plane of the auditory tube. *d*, The mastoid air-cells exposed by removal of the lateral wall.

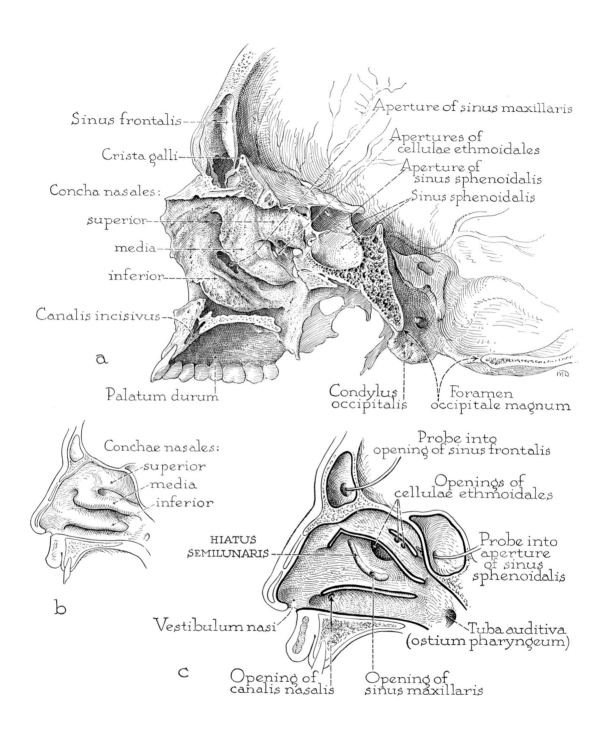

Nasal cavity and paranasal sinuses.

a, Nasal cavity and sinuses accessory thereto, demonstrated in a hemisected skull. *b*, Nasal conchae intact; schematic. *c*, Nasal cavity with the openings of the frontal, sphenoidal, and maxillary sinuses, and of the ethmoid cells; semischematic, as exposed by removal of the nasal conchae.

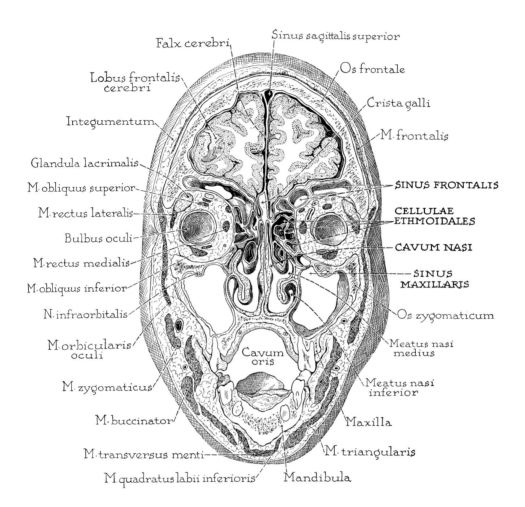

Falx cerebri
Sinus sagittalis superior
Lobus frontalis cerebri
Os frontale
Integumentum
Crista galli
M. frontalis
Glandula lacrimalis
M. obliquus superior
SINUS FRONTALIS
M. rectus lateralis
CELLULAE ETHMOIDALES
Bulbus oculi
CAVUM NASI
M. rectus medialis
SINUS MAXILLARIS
M. obliquus inferior
N. infraorbitalis
Os zygomaticum
M. orbicularis oculi
Cavum oris
Meatus nasi medius
M. zygomaticus
Meatus nasi inferior
M. buccinator
Maxilla
M. transversus menti
M. triangularis
M. quadratus labii inferioris
Mandibula

Frontal and maxillary sinuses and ethmoid air cells, shown in a coronal section of the head.

The frontal sinus is related inferiorly to the orbit, superiorly to the cranial cavity and the brain. The ethmoidal cells are related laterally to the orbit. The large maxillary sinus, occupying the body of the maxilla, lies lateral to the nasal cavity, below the orbit and above the molar and premolar teeth.

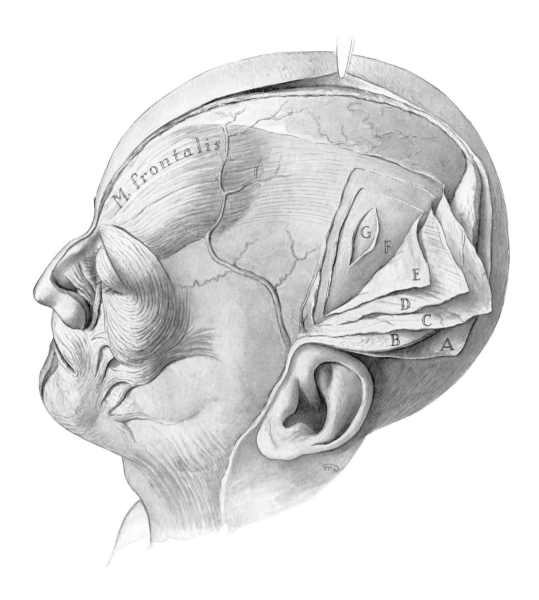

Layers of the scalp.

The layers of the scalp are usually described as being five in number, as follows: skin; fatty subcutaneous layer (containing vessels); epicranius (muscle and aponeurosis); cellular layer, which supports small vessels for the pericranial layer; the pericranium (regarded as a periosteum).

In favorable specimens, however, additional layers are demonstrable. Next below the skin (A) the fatty subcutaneous layer is divisible into two components. The outer one (B) is chiefly fatty and fairly avascular. The third layer (C) or deep component of the subcutaneous tissue is membranous in nature and contains most of the vascular network. The fourth layer (D) is the galea aponeurotica, or epicranius. The fifth layer (E) is the cobweb-like stratum; it is easily separable from the galea on its superficial aspect and the pericranium (F) below it. The periosteum, or pericranium, although fairly well defined, tends to cling to the subjacent bones of the calvarium (G). In some areas small vessels may be seen in the webby stratum (E) and the pericranium (F); they finally quit these strata to pierce the outer table of the skull.

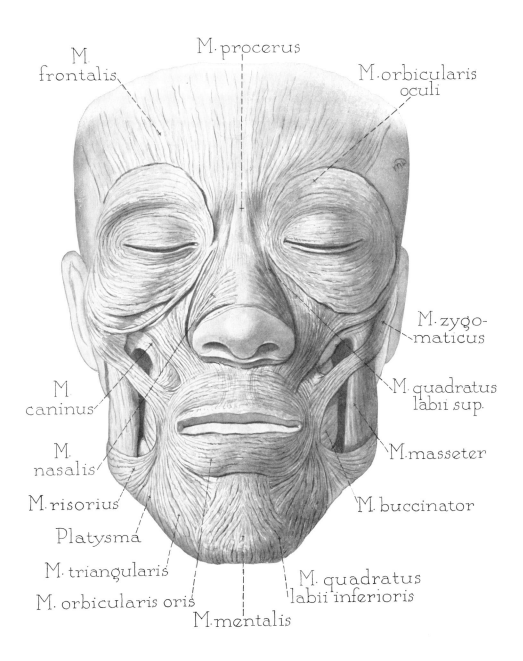

M. frontalis

M. procerus

M. orbicularis oculi

M. zygo- maticus

M. quadratus labii sup.

M. caninus

M. nasalis

M. masseter

M. risorius

M. buccinator

Platysma

M. triangularis

M. quadratus labii inferioris

M. orbicularis oris

M. mentalis

Muscles of facial expression; anterior view.

The following five figures are based upon the same specimen.

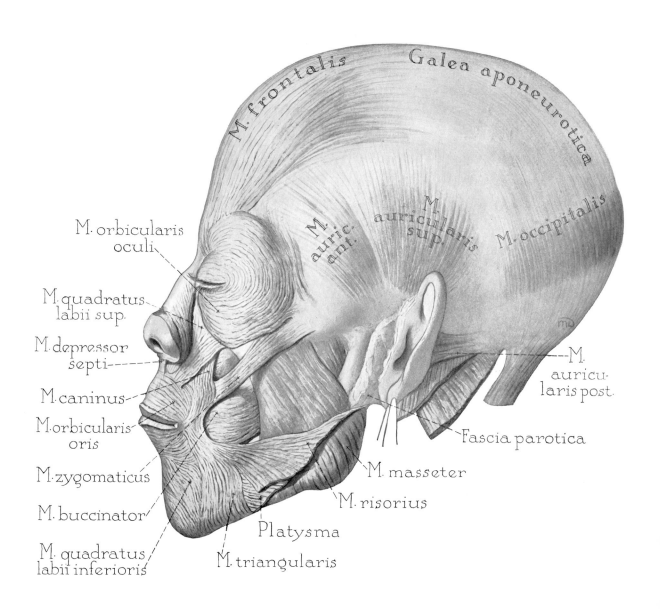

M. frontalis

Galea aponeurotica

M. orbicularis oculi

M. quadratus labii sup.

M. depressor septi

M. caninus

M. orbicularis oris

M. zygomaticus

M. buccinator

M. quadratus labii inferioris

M. auric. ant.

M. auricularis sup.

M. occipitalis

M. auricularis post.

Fascia parotica

M. masseter

M. risorius

Platysma

M. triangularis

Muscles of facial expression; lateral view.

The platysma muscle has been transected at the angle of the mandible, together with the adjacent risorius.

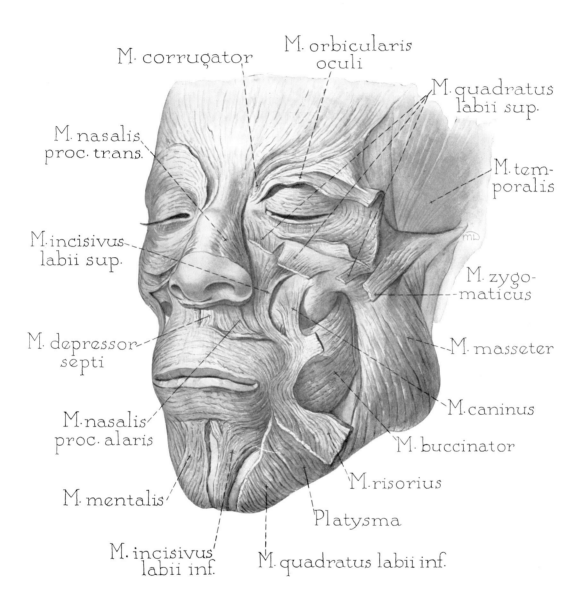

Muscles of facial expression; anterolateral view.

The orbicularis oculi muscle has been reflected; the several heads of the quadratus labii superioris have been transected to expose the underlying caninus and incisivus labii superioris muscles; similarly, the platysma and associated muscles have been partially removed to reveal the subjacent incisivus labii inferioris.

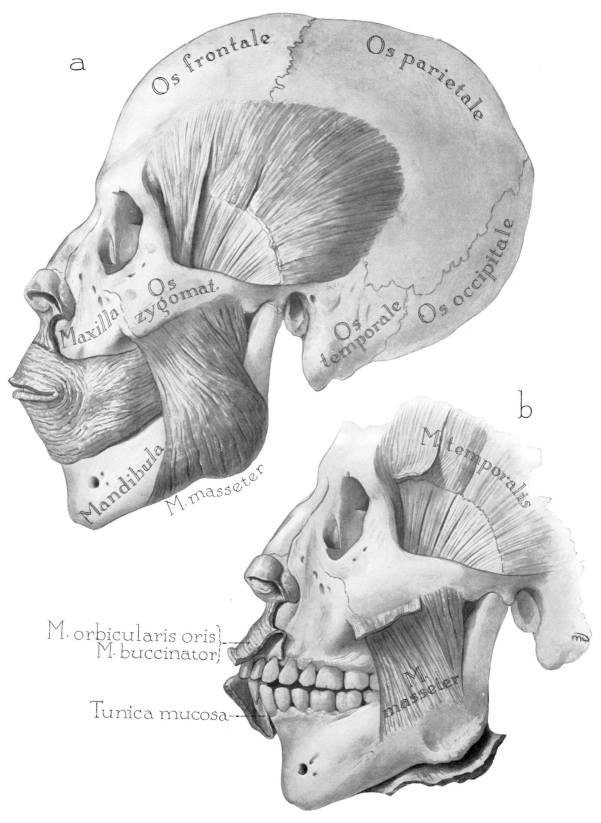

Muscles of mastication; lateral views.

See facing page for legend.

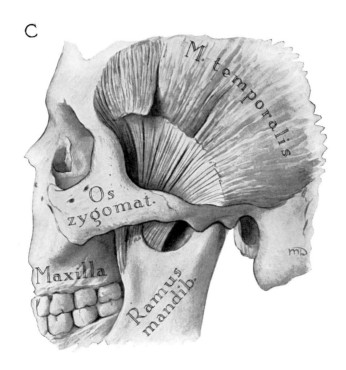

Muscles of mastication; lateral views.

In *a*, the outer leaf of fascicles of the temporalis has been dissected away in the anterior fourth of the muscle, in order to reveal the underlying tendon.

In *b*, the remaining fascicles of the superficial leaf of the temporalis muscle have been removed; similarly, the outer leaf of the masseter has been largely removed, as has also the buccinator muscle of the left side of the mouth.

In *c*, the masseter muscle has been completely dissected away; thereby, the full course of the temporalis has been revealed, from the temporal fossa to the coronoid process of the mandible.

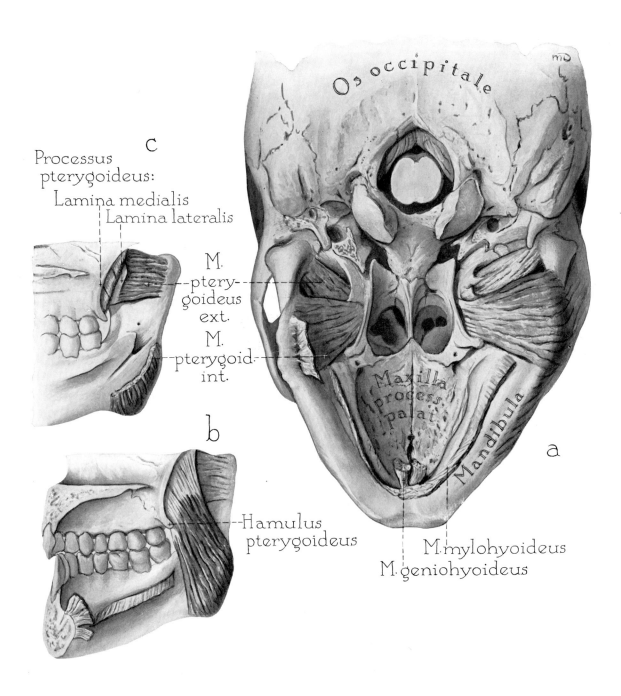

Muscles of mastication; pterygoid group.

Inferior and medial views; complete skull, and hemisected mandible and maxilla.
In *b*, the pterygoideus internus is intact; in *c*, the muscle remains only at its origin and insertion.

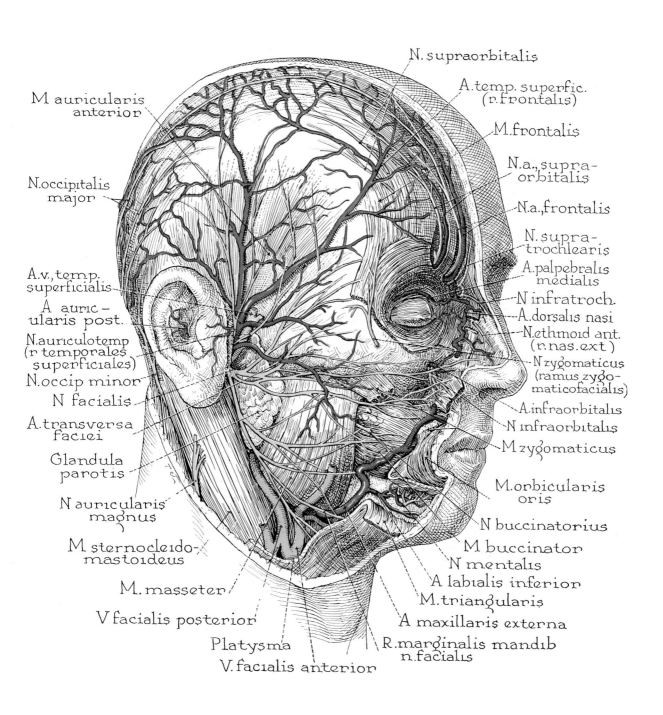

M auricularis
anterior

N.occipitalis
major

A.v.,temp.
superficialis

A auric-
ularis post.

N.auriculotemp
(r temporales
superficiales)

N.occip minor

N facialis

A.transversa
faciei

Glandula
parotis

N auricularis
magnus

M sternocleido-
mastoideus

M. masseter

V facialis posterior

Platysma

V. facialis anterior

N. supraorbitalis

A.temp. superfic.
(r.frontalis)

M.frontalis

N.a., supra-
orbitalis

N.a.frontalis

N. supra-
trochlearis

A.palpebralis
medialis

N infratroch.

A.dorsalis nasi

N.ethmoid ant.
(r.nas.ext)

N zygomaticus
(ramus zygo-
maticofacialis)

A.infraorbitalis

N infraorbitalis

M zygomaticus

M.orbicularis
oris

N buccinatorius

M buccinator

N mentalis

A labialis inferior

M.triangularis

A maxillaris externa

R.marginalis mandib
n.facialis

Arteries, veins and nerves of the face and scalp; superficial level.

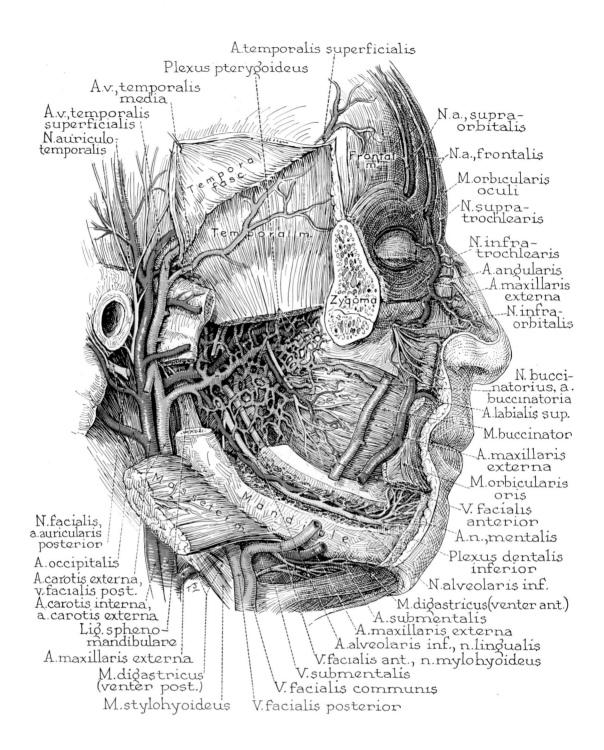

Arteries, veins and nerves of the face; infratemporal and alvolar level.

The zygomatic process and the origin of the masseter muscle have been cut away, and the distal portion of the temporalis muscle removed with the ramus of the mandible. The mandible has been dissected to expose the inferior alveolar nerve, the latter's dental and mental branches.

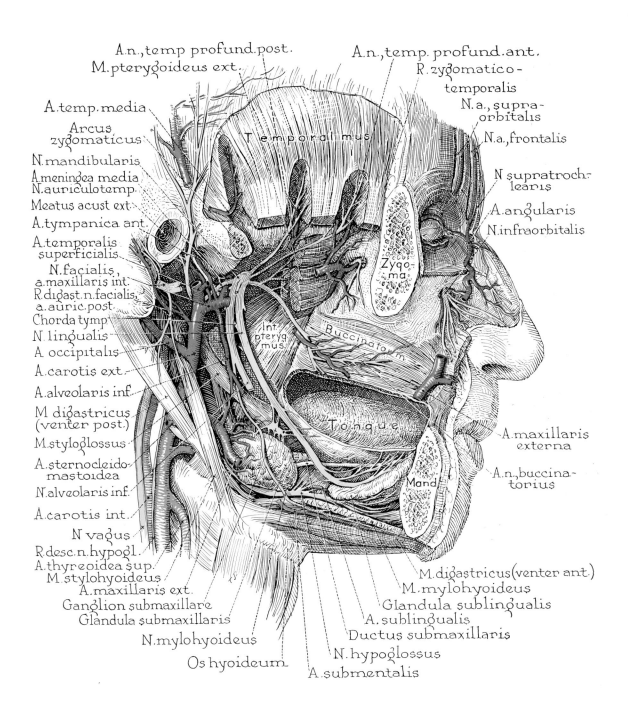

Arteries and nerves of the face.

Portions of the temporalis and pterygoideus lateralis muscles have been dissected away; the mandible has been removed to a point lateral to the symphysis; an opening has been made in the buccinator muscle and the related oral mucous membrane. By these means, the mandibular and the hypoglossal nerves and their branches have been traced to the muscles of mastication, and to the structures of the mouth.

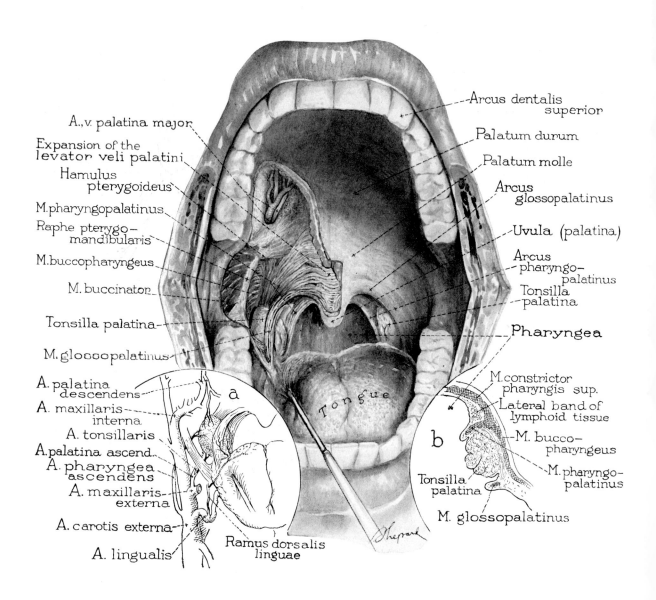

Oral pharynx, with special reference to the palatine tonsil and the musculature of the palate.

In the main figure the palatine muscles and vessels are exposed on the specimen's left through removal of a plaque of the oral mucous membrane. In the insets the anatomy of the tonsil is depicted: *a*, the arterial supply (diagrammatically); *b*, the walls of the tonsillar fossa (in section).

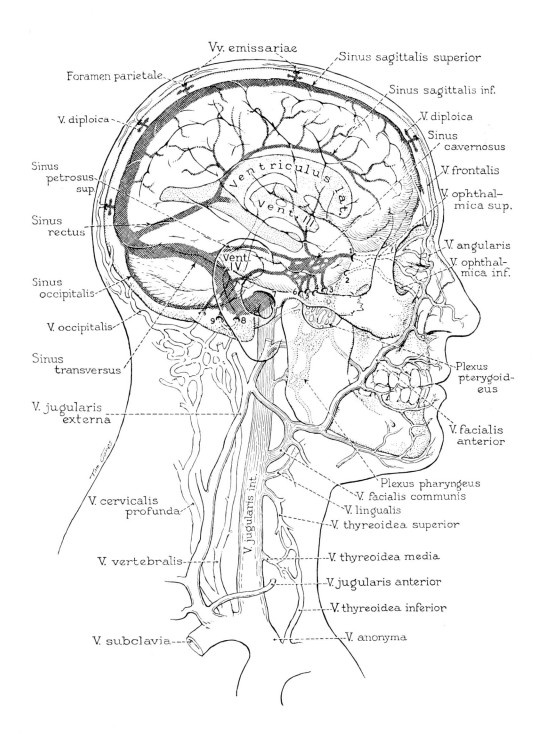

Venous drainage of the head and neck.

The numbers indicate the foramina through which these veins enter the cranium: *1*, fissura orbitalis superior; *2*, fissura orbitalis inferior; *3*, foramen ovale; *4*, foramen spinosum; *5*, foramen lacerum; *6*, canalis caroticus; *7*, foramen jugulare; *8*, canalis hypoglossi; *9*, canalis condyloideus. The black inverted crescents indicate openings through which emissary veins pass. (Adapted from Jones and Shepard: Manual of Surgical Anatomy.)

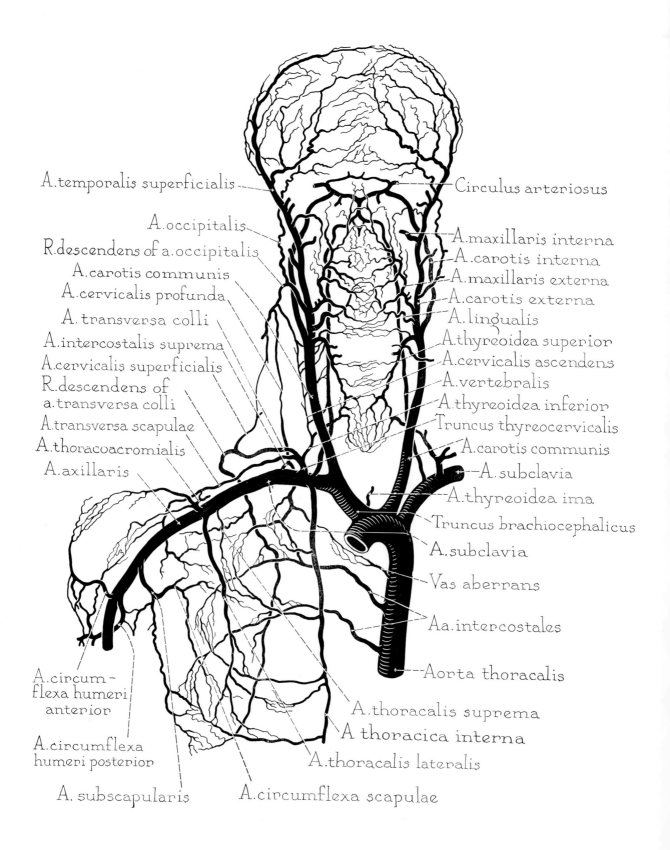

A.temporalis superficialis

A.occipitalis

R.descendens of a.occipitalis

A.carotis communis

A.cervicalis profunda

A.transversa colli

A.intercostalis suprema

A.cervicalis superficialis

R.descendens of
a.transversa colli

A.transversa scapulae

A.thoracoacromialis

A.axillaris

A.circum-
flexa humeri
anterior

A.circumflexa
humeri posterior

A. subscapularis

Circulus arteriosus

A.maxillaris interna

A.carotis interna

A.maxillaris externa

A.carotis externa

A.lingualis

A.thyreoidea superior

A.cervicalis ascendens

A.vertebralis

A.thyreoidea inferior

Truncus thyreocervicalis

A.carotis communis

A.subclavia

A.thyreoidea ima

Truncus brachiocephalicus

A.subclavia

Vas aberrans

Aa.intercostales

Aorta thoracalis

A.thoracalis suprema

A thoracica interna

A.thoracalis lateralis

A.circumflexa scapulae

Channels of collateral circulation in the head, neck, and thorax. (Adapted from Deaver.)

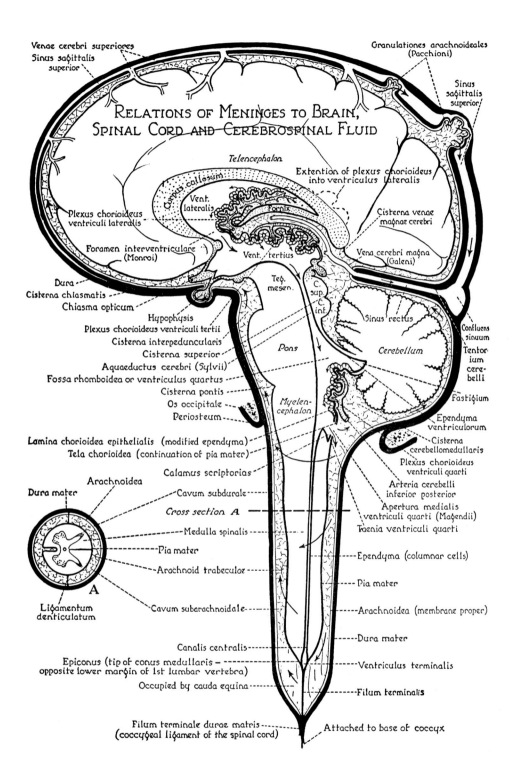

Meninges, brain ventricles and subarachnoid spaces; diagrammatic.

The arrows indicate the direction of the flow of the cerebrospinal fluid. (From Rasmussen: The Principal Nervous Pathways. Macmillan Company.)

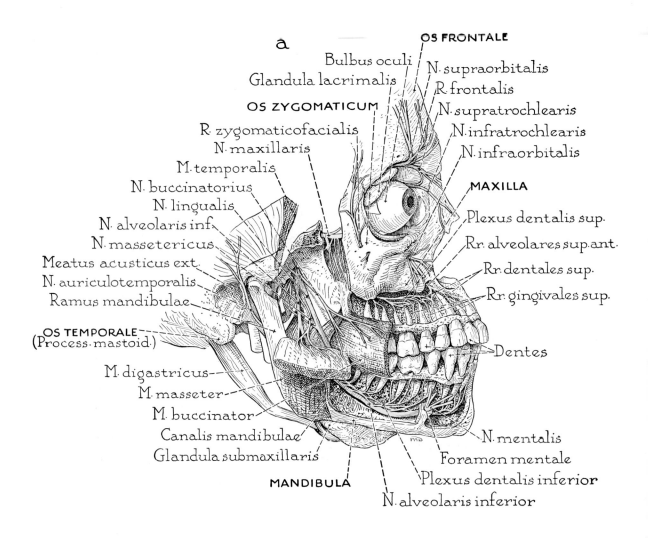

a

Bulbus oculi
Glandula lacrimalis

OS FRONTALE
N. supraorbitalis
R. frontalis

OS ZYGOMATICUM
R. zygomaticofacialis
N. maxillaris
M. temporalis
N. buccinatorius
N. lingualis
N. alveolaris inf.
N. massetericus
Meatus acusticus ext.
N. auriculotemporalis
Ramus mandibulae

N. supratrochlearis
N. infratrochlearis
N. infraorbitalis

MAXILLA
Plexus dentalis sup.
Rr. alveolares sup. ant.
Rr. dentales sup.
Rr. gingivales sup.

OS TEMPORALE
(Process. mastoid.)
M. digastricus
M. masseter
M. buccinator
Canalis mandibulae
Glandula submaxillaris

Dentes

MANDIBULA

N. mentalis
Foramen mentale
Plexus dentalis inferior
N. alveolaris inferior

Trigeminal nerve; deep dissection of the divisions of the nerve, and of the branches of each.

In order to expose the maxillary division of the trigeminal nerve where it enters the temporal fossa, through the foramen ovale in the large wing of the sphenoid bone, the temporalis muscle was cut and reflected upward; the masseter muscle was transected, its mandibular portion turned downward. The contiguous zygomatic process of the temporal bone and the temporal process of the zygomatic bone were cut away, together with the anterior portion of the ramus of the mandible (to include the coronoid process). On a deeper level, and in order to show the maxillary nerve, a portion of the large wing of the sphenoid bone was chiselled away, thus opening into the foramen rotundum. The intraosseous course of the nerves of supply to the upper and lower teeth and gums was revealed by dissection of the alveolar process of the maxilla and of the alveolar part of the mandible. In the territory of the cutaneous nerves derived from the ophthalmic nerve, the contents of the orbital cavity were exposed by removal of the orbital septum and fatty tissue.

The Ophthalmic Nerve. After entering the orbit through the superior orbital fissure, the ophthalmic nerve divides into three branches, the lacrimal, the nasociliary, and the frontal.

The Maxillary Nerve. The maxillary nerve makes exit from the cranial cavity through the foramen rotundum. It continues obliquely forward and downward through the superior part of the pterygopalatine fossa to the infraorbital canal; therein it is similarly named, as is also the foramen in the maxilla through which the nerve ultimately reaches the face.

Within the pterygopalatine fossa the zygomatic nerve arises from the maxillary nerve. The nerve enters the orbit through the inferior orbital fissure. On the lateral wall of the orbit the zygomatic nerve divides into a zygomaticotemporal branch and a zygomaticofacial branch, which, upon reaching the malar surface of the zygomatic bone, supplies the overlying and neighboring skin as far medialward as the eye.

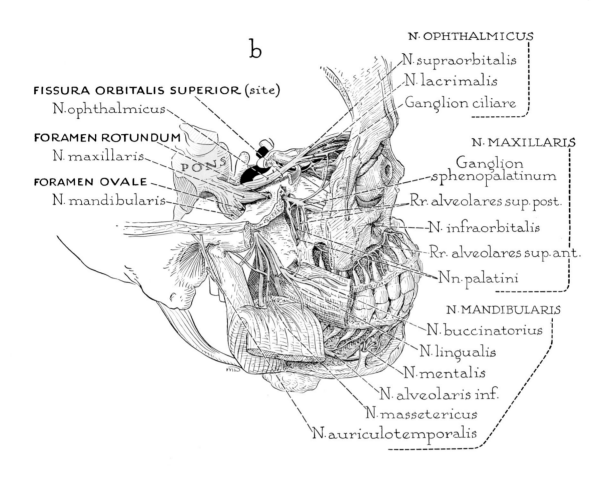

b

FISSURA ORBITALIS SUPERIOR (site)
N. ophthalmicus

FORAMEN ROTUNDUM
N. maxillaris

FORAMEN OVALE
N. mandibularis

PONS

N. OPHTHALMICUS
N. supraorbitalis
N. lacrimalis
Ganglion ciliare

N. MAXILLARIS
Ganglion sphenopalatinum
Rr. alveolares sup. post.
N. infraorbitalis
Rr. alveolares sup. ant.
Nn. palatini

N. MANDIBULARIS
N. buccinatorius
N. lingualis
N. mentalis
N. alveolaris inf.
N. massetericus
N. auriculotemporalis

Within the fossa, fibers are sent to the sphenopalatine ganglion; there, too, arise the posterior members of three sets of superior alveolar rami. These posterior superior alveolar branches arise from the maxillary nerve just before the latter enters the orbit; the branches of the middle set arise from infraorbital continuation of the maxillary nerve in the posterior part of the infraorbital canal, and the elements of the anterior set leave the nerve just before the latter reaches the infraorbital foramen. Together all of the branches form a plexus within canals in the alveolar tissue. From the plexus arise the dental and gingival rami.

The Mandibular Nerve. The mandibular nerve leaves the skull cavity through the foramen ovale in the great wing of the sphenoid bone, to reach the temporal fossa. Of the large branches, the auriculotemporal is the most posteriorly placed. It courses backward beneath the lateral pterygoid muscle to the inner side of the neck of the mandible. Turning upward between the condyle of the mandible and the auricle, it ascends over the zygomatic arch. The lingual nerve courses downward and forward between the medial pterygoid muscle and the ramus of the mandible, then obliquely forward to the side of the tongue. The inferior alveolar nerve descends beneath the external pterygoid muscle to the mandibular foramen in the ramus of the mandible. Before entering the canal the mandibular gives off a branch to the mylohyoid muscle. Within the canal an inferior dental plexus is formed, which is comparable to that described for the upper jaw. Similarly, inferior dental and gingival rami arise from the plexus. The inferior alveolar nerve ends as the mental nerve (upon emergence from a foramen of the same name), which innervates the skin of the chin and the mucous membrane and skin of the lower lip. The buccinator nerve, descending between the pterygoid muscles, sends its branches through the buccinator muscle to mucous membrane of the cheek. The masseter nerve supplies the muscle of the same name; other related offsets supply the temporal and pterygoid muscles—these together being termed the masticator nerve.

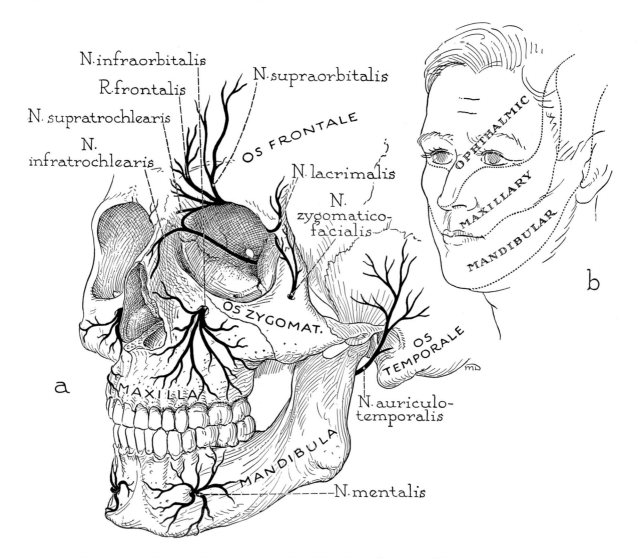

Branches and areas of cutaneous supply of the three divisions of the trigeminal nerve.

a, The branches of the ophthalmic divison reach the face by passing through the orbit. The lacrimal nerve emerges from the orbit to supply the skin at the lateral angle of the eye. The supraorbital nerve, passing through an incisure (in some instances, a fissure) of the same name, supplies the skin of the forehead as far back as the vertex. The supratrochlear nerve, named for its relation to the trochlea of the superior oblique muscle, courses forward on the medial wall of the orbit; emerging, its rami care for the innervation of the skin at the root of the nose, of the upper eyelid, and of the forehead. The infratrochlear nerve sends its cutaneous rami to the caruncula, both lids, and the nose. In addition to the branches illustrated, the external nasal ramus of the anterior ethmoidal nerve also contributes to the innervation of the nose; it attains a superficial position by emerging from the nasal bone and cartilage.

The maxillary division of the trigeminal contributes the infraorbital and zygomatic nerves to the innervation of the face. The former, passing through the infraorbital canal, supplies the lower eyelid and the ala of the nose. The latter, along the lateral wall of the orbit, divides into zygomaticotemporal and zygomaticofacial branches—each emerging through a foramen of corresponding name. The infraorbital nerve innervates the lower eyelid, the angle of the eye, the ala of the nose, and the upper lip. The zygomatic nerve cares for the temporal region, the malar surface of the zygomatic bone, and the lateral angle of the eye.

The mandibular division sends its auriculotemporal nerve around the condyloid process of the mandible; ascending vertically, the nerve supplies the skin of the temporal region. The mental nerve, after traversing the mandibular canal, emerges through the mental foramen; its filaments supply the skin of the chin and the lower lip.

b, Areas of cutaneous innervation served by the divisions of the trigeminal nerve.

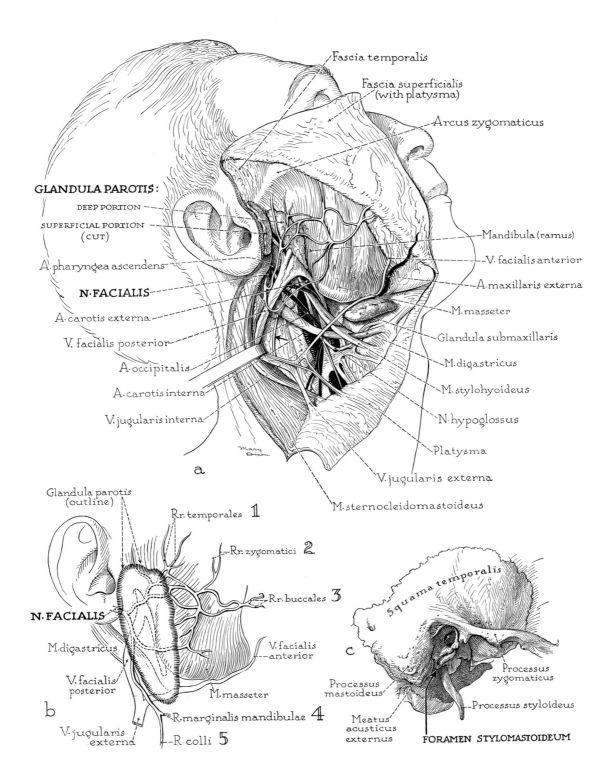

Fascia temporalis

Fascia superficialis (with platysma)

Arcus zygomaticus

GLANDULA PAROTIS:

DEEP PORTION

SUPERFICIAL PORTION (CUT)

A. pharyngea ascendens

N·FACIALIS

A. carotis externa

V. facialis posterior

A. occipitalis

A. carotis interna

V. jugularis interna

Mandibula (ramus)

V. facialis anterior

A. maxillaris externa

M. masseter

Glandula submaxillaris

M. digastricus

M. stylohyoideus

N. hypoglossus

Platysma

V. jugularis externa

M. sternocleidomastoideus

a

Glandula parotis (outline)

Rr. temporales 1

Rr. zygomatici 2

Rr. buccales 3

N·FACIALIS

M. digastricus

V. facialis posterior

V. facialis anterior

M. masseter

R. marginalis mandibulae 4

V. jugularis externa

R. colli 5

b

squama temporalis

c

Processus zygomaticus

Processus mastoideus

Processus styloideus

Meatus acusticus externus

FORAMEN STYLOMASTOIDEUM

Facial nerve.

a, The branches of the nerve in relation to the parotid gland and the blood vessels of the neck. A communicating branch is indicated by arrow. *b*, The gland in relation to the several rami. *c*, The temporal bone, indicating the foramen for exit of the facial nerve. (With the permission of Surgery, Gynecology and Obstetrics.)

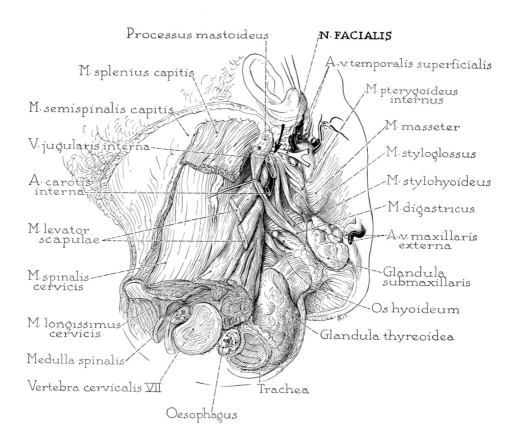

Structures that form, or are closely related to, the fossa for the parotid gland.

The parotid gland has been wholly removed, the sternocleidomastoid muscle cut away from the mastoid process of the temporal bone (at *); the great vessels (together with arterial branches and venous tributaries) have been transected; the facial nerve has been cut just distal to the point at which the trunk divides into temporofacial and cervicofacial portions. Superficially the parotid gland overlaps the masseter muscle in front, the sternocleidomastoid muscle behind. On deeper level it rests upon the styloid group of muscles, the styloid process (at arrow), the medial pterygoid, and digastric muscles. The following neighboring structures are also shown: muscles of the head, neck, and shoulder; hyoid bones; thyroid cartilage; submaxillary gland; and mastoid process of the temporal bone. (With the permission of Surgery, Gynecology and Obstetrics.)

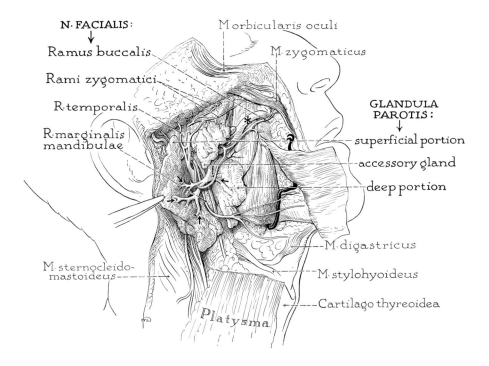

Facial nerve and parotid gland and duct.

Removal of the superficial fascia in the region of the face inferior to the zygomatic arch, and retraction of the outer leaf of the parotid gland permit demonstration of the following features: the location of the temporal and zygomatic rami of the facial nerve in the deep substance of the fat-laden superficial fascia (thus near the muscles which they supply); the intimate relation of the several rami to the tributaries (at arrows) of the parotid duct (at *); the manner in which the rami pass to the deep aspect of the layers of facial musculature (see especially the zygomaticus and the platysma); the independence of the accessory lobe of the parotid gland (its ductule being sent into the main duct as a wholly separate unit, the parenchyma being dissociated from the deep lobe); the close relation of the buccal ramus to the parotid duct. (With the permission of Surgery, Gynecology and Obstetrics.)

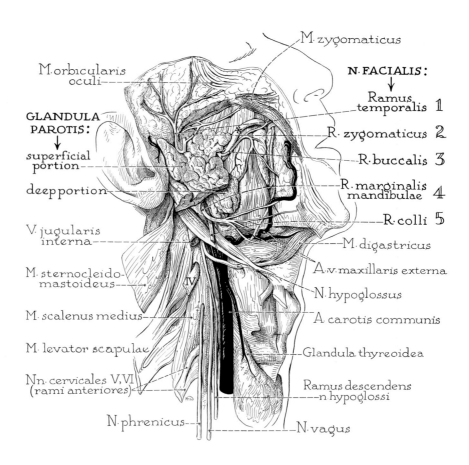

M·zygomaticus

M·orbicularis oculi

GLANDULA PAROTIS:
↓
superficial portion

deep portion

V·jugularis interna

M·sternocleido-mastoideus

M·scalenus medius

M·levator scapulae

Nn·cervicales V,VI (rami anteriores)

N·phrenicus

N·FACIALIS:
↓
Ramus temporalis 1
R·zygomaticus 2
R·buccalis 3
R·marginalis mandibulae 4
R·colli 5
M·digastricus
A·v·maxillaris externa
N·hypoglossus
A·carotis communis
Glandula thyreoidea
Ramus descendens n·hypoglossi
N·vagus

Facial nerve and parotid gland (dissection continued).

The superficial lobe of the parotid gland has been restored to its normal position, the lower portion cut away in order to demonstrate the relation of the facial nerve to the cleavage plane, which intervenes between the superficial and deep lobes. In the region cranial to the zygomatic arch, fatty tissue has been dissected along the course of the temporal rami of the nerve, in order to make clear the depth at which the nerve branches course in the superficial fascia. The parotid duct is marked by *. In addition to the temporal rami sent dorsalward to the auricular muscles and ventralward to the muscles of the eyelid, rami pass to the frontalis portion of the epicranius. Zygomatic branches supply the inferior portion of the orbicularis oculi as well as the zygomaticus. The latter muscle, together with the musculature of the nose and mouth, receive supply from the buccal rami. The marginal mandibular branch sends twigs to the quadratus labii inferioris and to the mentalis. The cervical ramus, covered by the platysma, supplies that muscle. (With the permission of Surgery, Gynecology and Obstetrics.)

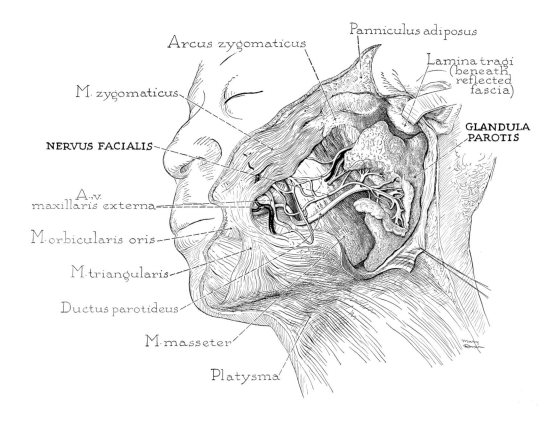

Facial nerve, parotid gland, parotid duct, and fascia.

The outer leaf of the parotid gland has been freed and rolled aside along a curving line which, anteriorly, marks the line of emergence of the several tributaries of the parotid duct from the parenchyma of the gland. The tributaries and the duct itself are closely related (in the area pictured) to the buccal branch of the facial nerve. A membranous portion of the fascia of the face, together with contained fascicles of the facial muscula- ture, constitutes an outer layer of the "capsule" of the gland. This layer lies just beneath a stratum that may contain a moderate amount of fat (see panniculus adiposus), still present in the dissection, cranial to the zygomatic arch. Over the greater portion of its extent, the parotid gland is covered on its superficial aspect by a membranous layer of fascia, which, not being capsular in the usual sense, merely passes over the tri- angular area bounded by the sternocleidomastoideus dorsally, by the zygomaticus cranially, and by the platysma and triangularis caudally. (With the permission of Surgery, Gynecology and Obstetrics.)

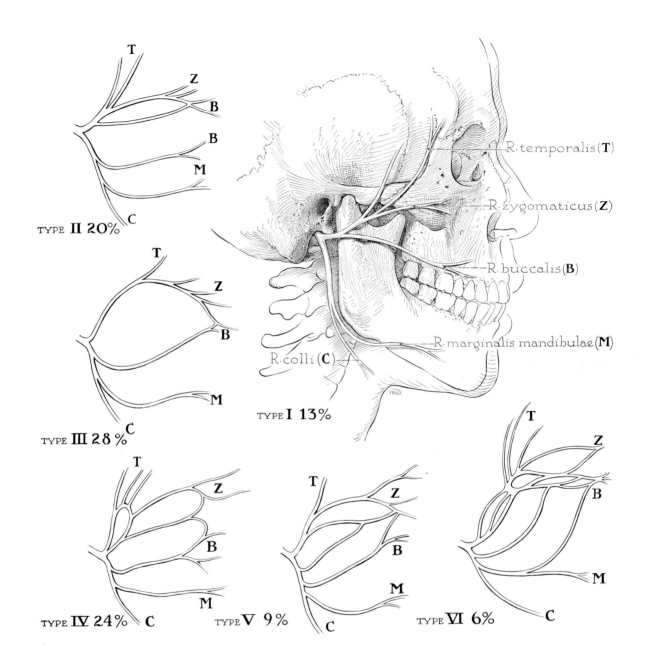

Facial nerve.

Major types of branching and intercommunication, with percentage occurrence of each pattern. From records on 350 cervicofacial halves.

Schematically shown, as of the right side of the head. Note that Types III, IV, V, and VI together represent almost 70 per cent of specimens. *Type I*, Absence of anastomosis between the branches of the two divisions (temporofacial and cervicofacial) of the facial nerve; although regularly pictured, actually a least common type. *Type II*, Anastomoses within the temporofacial division. *Type III*, Anastomosis between chief divisions. *Type IV*, Two anastomotic loops within the temporofacial part. *Type V*, Two loops from the cervicofacial division, intertwined with branches of the temporofacial. *Type VI*, Extensive intermixture. (With the permission of Surgery, Gynecology and Obstetrics.)

The external nose (*nasus externus*) is formed like an irregular, three-sided pyramid. The lower part, which is movable, corresponds to the nasal wings (*alae nasi*). The lower, free margin of the wings surrounds the nasal openings (*nares*), which are separated by the anterior, mobile part of the nasal septum.

The framework of the external nose is formed by the nasal bones (page 64) and the nasal cartilages (*cartilagines nasi*), covered externally by muscles (page 41) and skin. The inner surface is clothed by mucous membrane.

The nasal cavity (*cavum nasi*) opens in front through the nares; behind, it communicates with the pharynx through adjacent *choanae*. It is divided into approximately symmetrical halves by the medially-placed nasal septum (*septum nasi*). The upper and posterior part of the septum is bony (*septum nasi osseum*); the anterior part is cartilaginous (*septum cartilageum*); attached thereto in front and below is a membranous portion (*septum membranaceum*). This part, lying between the nares, is the mobile nasal septum described above.

The lateral wall presents three or four turbinated bones (*conchae nasales*), which are related to communications with the accessory cavities of the nose (*sinus paranasales*). They are the frontal, ethmoidal, maxillary, and sphenoidal cavities (pages 37 to 39).

Apart from the special sense of smell, the general sensory innervation of the nose comes from the first and second divisions of the trigeminal nerve. The blood supply of the internal nose comes from branches of the ophthalmic, and the internal and external maxillary arteries.

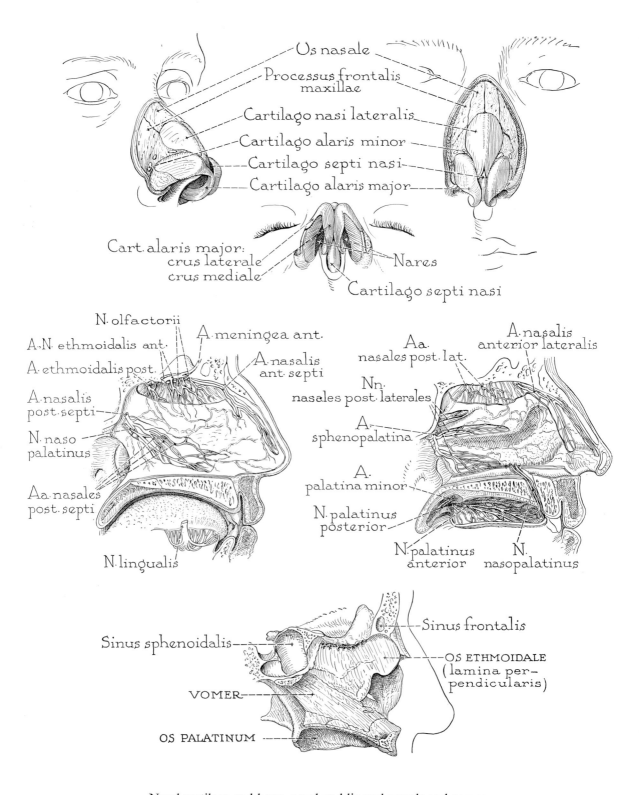

Os nasale

Processus frontalis maxillae

Cartilago nasi lateralis

Cartilago alaris minor

Cartilago septi nasi

Cartilago alaris major

Cart. alaris major:
crus laterale
crus mediale

Nares

Cartilago septi nasi

N. olfactorii

A.N. ethmoidalis ant.

A. meningea ant.

A. ethmoidalis post.

A. nasalis ant. septi

A. nasalis post. septi

N. naso palatinus

Aa. nasales post. septi

N. lingualis

Aa. nasales post. lat.

A. nasalis anterior lateralis

Nn. nasales post. laterales

A. sphenopalatina

A. palatina minor

N. palatinus posterior

N. palatinus anterior

N. nasopalatinus

Sinus sphenoidalis

Sinus frontalis

OS ETHMOIDALE (lamina perpendicularis)

VOMER

OS PALATINUM

Nasal cartilage and bone, nasal and lingual vessels and nerves.

Upper figures picture the nasal bones and cartilages, as seen from the side, from the front, and from below. Middle figures, the nerves and blood vessels of the septum and of the lateral wall of the nose, together with those of the tongue. Lower figure, the bones of the septum. (Adapted from Sobotta-McMurrich.)

The stato-acoustic organ (NA, *organum vestibulocochleare*) may be divided into three parts: external, middle, and inner ear.

The external ear consists of the auricle and the external acoustic meatus, the latter being a passage through which the auricle collects the sound waves. The meatus, lined with skin, leads inward from the bottom of the concha of the auricle to the tympanic membrane.

The middle ear (tympanic cavity) is a narrow chamber lined with mucous membrane. It lies between the external acoustic meatus and the internal ear (labyrinth). The auditory ossicles, a chain of three small bones, cross the cavity, which communicates with the mastoid air cells through the tympanic antrum and with the nasal pharynx through the auditory (eustachian) tube.

The internal ear is the most essential part of the ear; it holds the sensory organs of hearing and equilibrium. The labyrinth is a complicated system of cavities lodged within the petrous portion of the temporal bone. These cavities, with osseous walls, contain fluid called perilymph and a membranous counterpart of the bony chambers; the membranous labyrinth contains a fluid known as endolymph.

The osseous (periotic) labyrinth consists of the cochlea, three semicircular canals, and an ovoid chamber called the vestibule. The latter lies between the medial wall of the tympanic cavity and the fundus of the internal acoustic meatus. Three semicircular canals, by means of five round apertures, open into its posterior part, while the *scala vestibuli* of the cochlea opens into the lower and anterior part. On the lateral wall is the oval window (*fenestra vestibuli*), closed by the base of the stapes. On the medial wall is located the vestibular aqueduct, which passes backward to the posterior surface of the petrous part of the temporal bone and opens under the dura.

The three semicircular canals are placed posterior to the vestibule, at right angles to each other. They open into the vestibule through five round orifices, the number reduced to five because the adjoining extremities of the superior and posterior canals are fused into a common canal (crus commune) that opens by a single orifice. One extremity of each, where it joins the vestibule, expands into an ampulla.

The cochlea is a tapering tube coiled spirally for three and a half turns around a central pillar, the *modiolus*. The cochlea lies anterior to the vestibule, its base directed toward the bottom of the internal acoustic meatus. As the cochlea winds upward toward the apex, its diameter diminishes rapidly. The modiolus forms the inner wall of the cochlear tube; winding around it like a thread of a screw is a thin ledge of bone, the spiral lamina, which partly subdivides the space of the osseous tube into two passages. The spiral lamina is tunneled by small canals that transmit filaments of the cochlear nerve to a larger canal within the central pillar of the cochlea.

The membranous (otic) labyrinth is housed within the periotic labyrinth, whose walls consist of bone. The membranous labyrinth, less capacious, has epithelial walls.

The vestibule of the periotic system contains two membranous sacs of the otic labyrinth: the saccule and the utricle. They communicate indirectly by ducts that are comparably termed utricular and saccular, and by the endolymphatic duct, into which these open directly. The endolymphatic duct continues through a channel in the osseous capsule known as the vestibular aqueduct and ends in a sac-like enlargement in the cranial cavity, on the posterior surface of the petrous part of the temporal bone.

Three membranous semicircular ducts open from the utricle. They are contained within the semicircular canals; although similar in form, they are smaller in diameter.

The saccule communicates with the membranous cochlear duct by means of a short slender tube, the *ductus reuniens*. The cochlear duct occupies the osseous cochlea. Like the three ducts of the canalicular division of the internal ear, it is smaller than the periotic labyrinth in which it is housed. Each of the semicircular ducts lies within an undivided canal, but the cochlear duct, lying between the free margin of the osseous spiral lamina and the opposite wall of the bony cochlea, divides the latter into two compartments: the tympanic scala and the vestibular scala. As its name indicates, the vestibular scala begins in the vestibule, where this portion of the internal ear is closed off from the middle ear (tympanic cavity) by the base of the stapes. At the apex of the cochlea, the *scala vestibuli* communicates with the *scala tympani* by means of an aperture termed the *helicotrema*. The tympanic scala matches the turns of the vestibular scala and ends at the base of the cochlea, where the secondary tympanic membrane in the round window (*fenestra cochleae*) separates the scala from the fossula of the tympanic cavity.

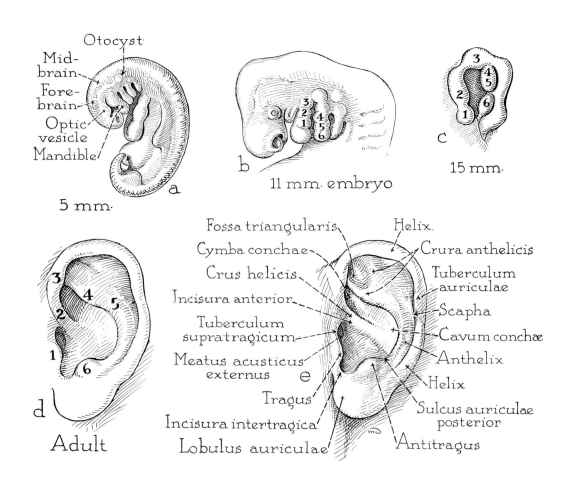

Otocyst
Mid-
brain
Fore-
brain
Optic
vesicle
Mandible
5 mm.
a

11 mm. embryo
b

15 mm.
c

Adult
d

Fossa triangularis
Cymba conchae
Crus helicis
Incisura anterior
Tuberculum
supratragicum
Meatus acusticus
externus
Tragus
Incisura intertragica
Lobulus auriculae
Helix
Crura anthelicis
Tuberculum
auriculae
Scapha
Cavum conchæ
Anthelix
Helix
Sulcus auriculae
posterior
Antitragus
e

Developmental and adult anatomy of the auricle.

a, The primordial elevations on the first (mandibular) and second (hyoid) arches. *b* to *d*, Progress of embryonic fusion of the hillocks and the adult configuration of the auricle (with corresponding numerals on the derived parts). *e*, Adult form of the auricle with the parts identified.

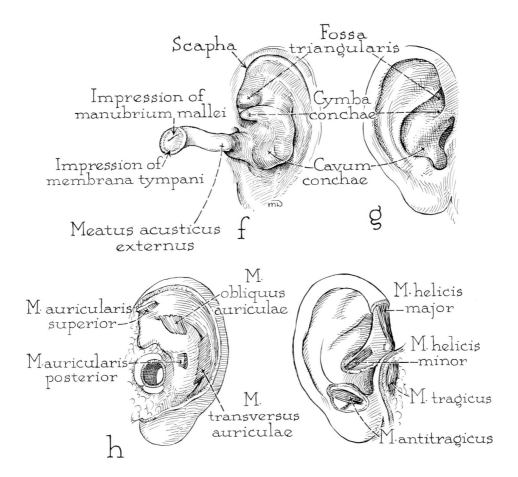

Scapha

Fossa
triangularis

Impression of
manubrium mallei

Cymba
conchae

Impression of
membrana tympani

Cavum
conchae

Meatus acusticus
externus

f

g

M. auricularis
superior

M.
obliquus
auriculae

M. auricularis
posterior

M.
transversus
auriculae

h

M. helicis
major

M. helicis
minor

M. tragicus

M. antitragicus

Auricle; adult form, intrinsic musculature.

f and *g*, Fossae of the auricle and the external acoustic meatus, shown as a cast (in *f*) viewed from the medial side; and the same foveate depressions, and bounding ridges seen from the lateral aspect (in *g*, *h* and *i*). Intrinsic muscles of the auricle, from the lateral and medial aspects, respectively.

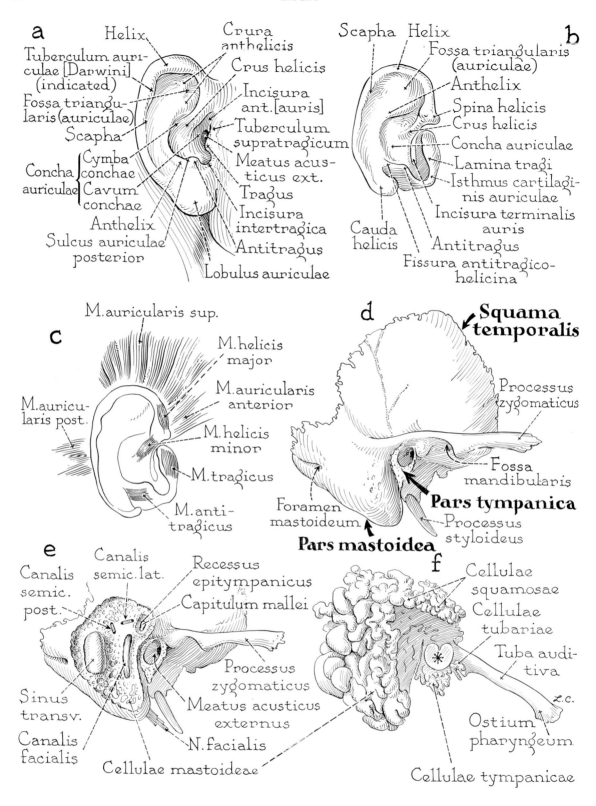

Auricle, temporal bone, air cells and auditory tube.

a, The auricle; *b*, auricular cartilage; *c*, cartilage of the ear, isolated, with the muscles; *d*, temporal bone, external surface; *e*, semicircular canals and related structures exposed by dissection of the mastoid cells; *f*, air cells and auditory tube in relation to the site of the tympanic membrane (at *).

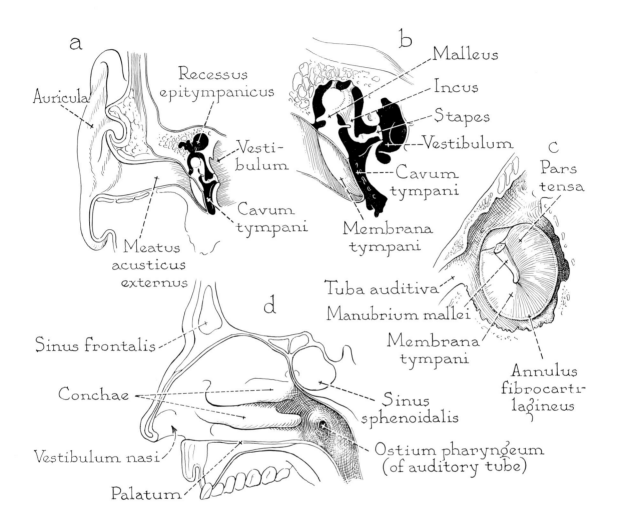

External ear, middle ear and auditory tube.

a, The auricle and external acoustic meatus of the external ear (*auris externa*); the tympanic cavity, epitympanic recess, vestibular fenestra (oval window), tympanic membrane and auditory ossicles of the middle ear (*auris media*); and the vestibuli of the osseous labyrinth of the internal ear (*auris interna*). *b*, The three parts of the ear, emphasizing the middle division, *auris media*. The tympanic, or eardrum, cavity is crossed by the auditory ossicles. The lateral part of the cavity is occupied by the tympanic membrane (to which the manubrium of the malleus is fixed); on the medial wall is situated the vestibular window (occupied by the base of the stapes). *c*, The lateral wall of the tympanic cavity showing the membrane and the manubrium of the malleus. *d*, The pharyngeal orifice of the auditory tube.

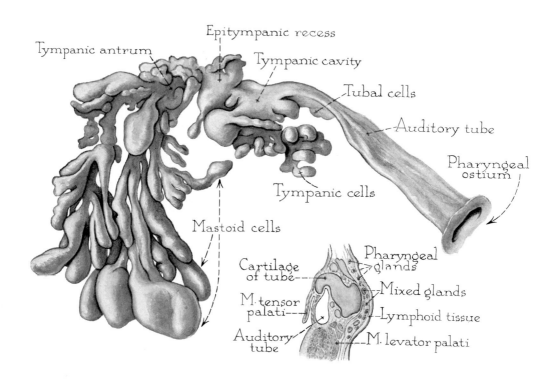

Tympanic cavity, with communicating air cells, recess and auditory tube.
Shown as a cast of the spaces (Siebenmann).

The tympanic, or eardrum, cavity is continuous behind and lateralward with the large air-containing mastoid cells, through the epitympanic recess as an intermediary; in front and medialward it opens into the pharynx through the auditory tube. Small air cells appear on the inferior wall of the cavity and the tube. The auditory tube runs obliquely forward, medialward, and downward, uniting the tympanic cavity with the pharynx. The bony wall of the tube is replaced by cartilage as the pharyngeal ostium is approached (see section in inset).

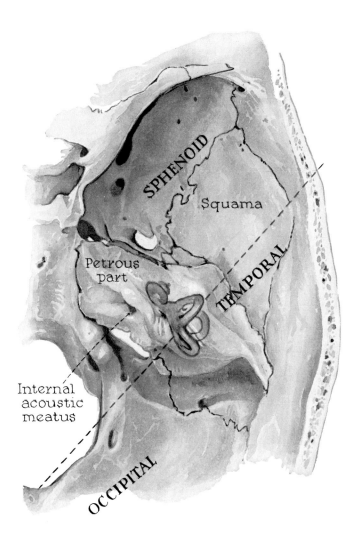

Right bony labyrinth; position in the skull. The labyrinth, drawn from a reconstruction, is shown as if the surrounding part of the temporal bone were transparent.

The bony labyrinth is 20 mm. in length. It lies approximately parallel to the posterior surface of the petrous part of the temporal bone.

The base of the cochlea adjoins the internal acoustic meatus; it lies parallel to the plane of the posterior semicircular canal. Both form an angle of approximately 45 degrees with the median plane, as does also the plane of the superior semicircular canal (in the course of the broken line).

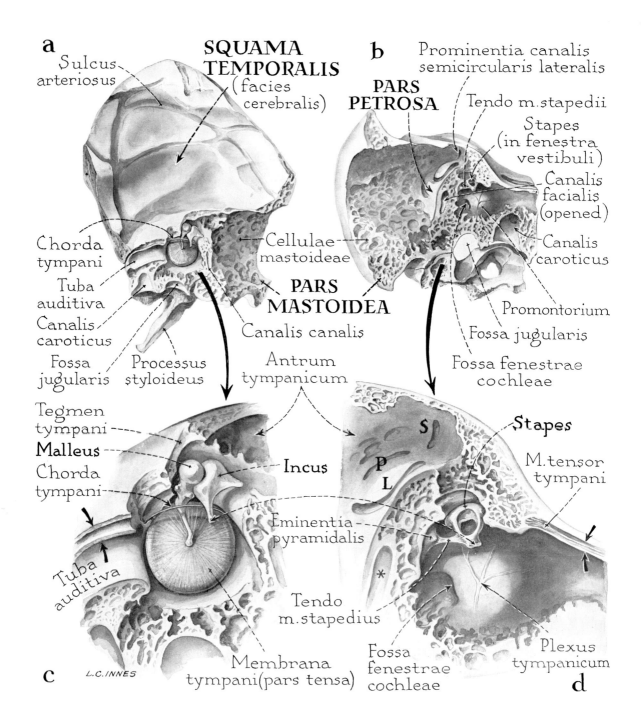

a
Sulcus arteriosus
SQUAMA TEMPORALIS (facies cerebralis)
b
Prominentia canalis semicircularis lateralis
PARS PETROSA
Tendo m. stapedii
Stapes (in fenestra vestibuli)
Canalis facialis (opened)
Canalis caroticus
Chorda tympani
Cellulae mastoideae
Tuba auditiva
Canalis caroticus
PARS MASTOIDEA
Fossa jugularis
Processus styloideus
Canalis canalis
Antrum tympanicum
Promontorium
Fossa jugularis
Fossa fenestrae cochleae
Tegmen tympani
Malleus
Chorda tympani
Incus
Stapes
S
P
L
M. tensor tympani
Tuba auditiva
Eminentia pyramidalis
Tendo m. stapedius
Fossa fenestrae cochleae
Plexus tympanicum
c
L.C. INNES
Membrana tympani (pars tensa)
d

Tympanic cavity, with ossicular contents, related spaces, eminences, and tympanic membrane.

a and *b*, Temporal bone cut through the long axis of the tympanic cavity. *c* and *d*, Details for the areas indicated in the figures above. In *c* and *d* arrows point to the walls of the opened semicanal for the tensor tympani muscle; an unlabelled leader passes from the long crus of the incus to the head of the stapes (articulating in the natural state of the incudostapedial joint). In *d* the exposed lateral, superior, and posterior semicircular canals are indicated, respectively, by *L*, *S*, and *P*.

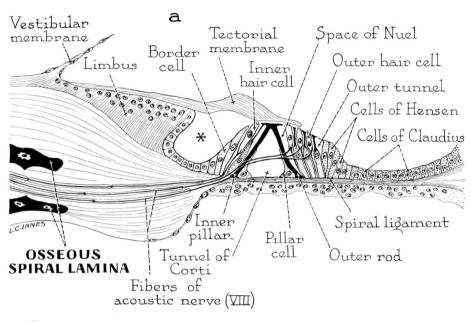

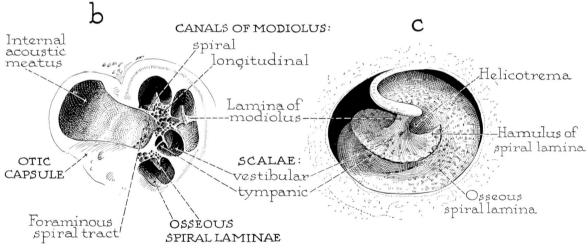

Cochlea and spiral organ.

a, The spiral organ (of Corti), containing the terminal fibers of the cochlear nerve; the fibers reach the sensory cells through the channel in the osseous spiral lamina. The tunnel of Corti is indicated by *. b, The cochlea, shown in section. c, The cupula of the cochlea.

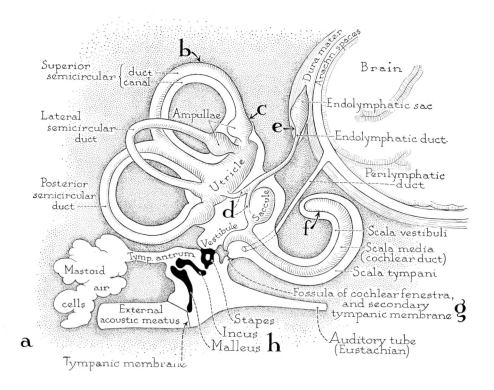

Parts of the ear, shown diagrammatically.

a, The ear, with the exception of the auricle; the parts, depicted on the facing page, are indicated by matching letters (*b* to *h*). *b*, The nonampullated portion of an osseous semicircular canal and its contained membranous duct. *c*, The ampullated part of the canal and duct, with the latter more completely filling the bony space; the *crista ampullaris* projects into the lumen. *d*, The parts of the osseous and membranous labyrinths shown in a transverse section of the temporal bone. *e*, The endolymphatic sac at the external aperture of the vestibular aqueduct and in the fovea on the posterior surface of the petrous part of the temporal bone. *f*, A section through one turn of the cochlea, showing the perilymphatic scalae, the endolymphatic cochlear duct, and the spiral organ within the latter. *g*, The cochlear fenestra, or round window (closed by the secondary tympanic membrane), with the fossula on the outer aspect, the tympanic scala on the inner. *h*, The auditory ossicles. The vestibular fenestra, or oval window, is occupied by the base (footplate) of the stapes; the manubrium of the malleus is fixed to the medial surface of the tympanic membrane.

b and *c* record the late fetal condition of the tissue within the periotic labyrinth; this tissue, between the osseous wall externally and the membranous duct internally, becomes greatly reduced in amount to form mere trabeculate supports for the epithelial duct-system. In *d* the communicating channel (*ductus reuniens*) between the saccule and the cochlear duct is out of the plane of section. In *e* the structures shown are situated between the superior petrosal sulcus and the sigmoid sulcus (page 24). In *f* is demonstrated the relation of the spiral organ (in the cochlear duct) to the tympanic and vestibular scalae; the histological structure is shown in *a* on page 73. In *g* is recorded the relation of the periotic duct to the tympanic scala and the secondary tympanic membrane. In *h* the ossicles of the right ear are viewed from the medial side.

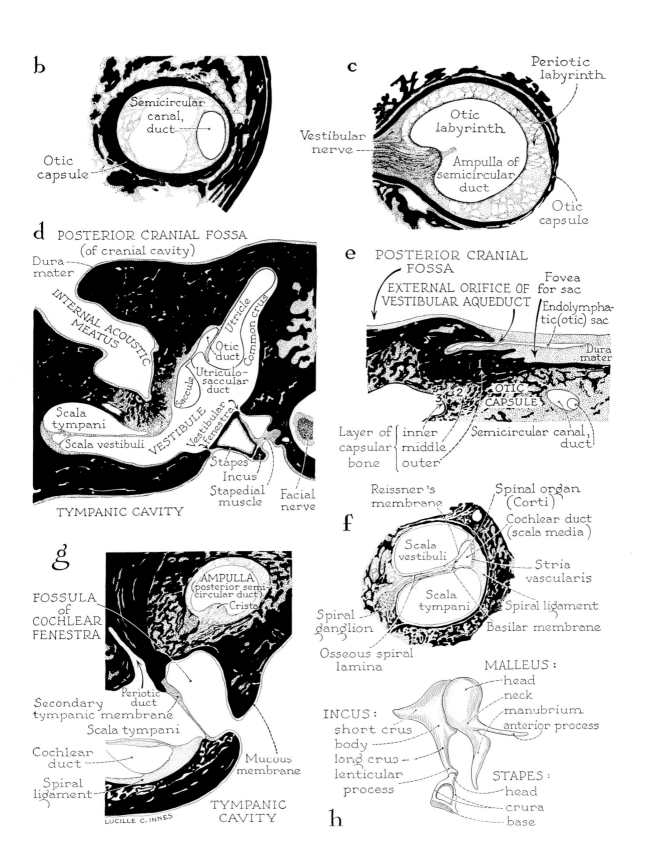

b

Semicircular canal, duct

Otic capsule

c

Periotic labyrinth

Vestibular nerve

Otic labyrinth

Ampulla of semicircular duct

Otic capsule

d POSTERIOR CRANIAL FOSSA
(of cranial cavity)

Dura mater

INTERNAL ACOUSTIC MEATUS

Utricle

Common crus

Otic duct

Utriculo-saccular duct

Saccule

Scala tympani

Scala vestibuli

VESTIBULE

Vestibular fenestra

Stapes

Incus

Stapedial muscle

Facial nerve

TYMPANIC CAVITY

e POSTERIOR CRANIAL FOSSA

EXTERNAL ORIFICE OF VESTIBULAR AQUEDUCT

Fovea for sac

Endolymphatic (otic) sac

Dura mater

1
3 2 OTIC CAPSULE

Layer of capsular bone { inner middle outer }

Semicircular canal, duct

f

Reissner's membrane

Spiral organ (Corti)

Cochlear duct (scala media)

Scala vestibuli

Stria vascularis

Scala tympani

Spiral ligament

Spiral ganglion

Basilar membrane

Osseous spiral lamina

g

FOSSULA of COCHLEAR FENESTRA

AMPULLA (posterior semicircular duct)

Crista

Periotic duct

Secondary tympanic membrane

Scala tympani

Cochlear duct

Spiral ligament

Mucous membrane

TYMPANIC CAVITY

LUCILLE C. INNES

MALLEUS :
head
neck
manubrium
anterior process

INCUS :
short crus
body
long crus
lenticular process

STAPES :
head
crura
base

h

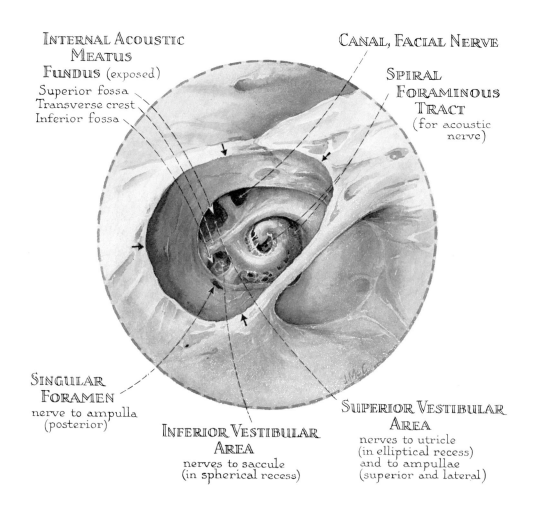

INTERNAL ACOUSTIC
MEATUS
FUNDUS (exposed)
Superior fossa
Transverse crest
Inferior fossa

CANAL, FACIAL NERVE

SPIRAL
FORAMINOUS
TRACT
(for acoustic
nerve)

SINGULAR
FORAMEN
nerve to ampulla
(posterior)

INFERIOR VESTIBULAR
AREA
nerves to saccule
(in spherical recess)

SUPERIOR VESTIBULAR
AREA
nerves to utricle
(in elliptical recess)
and to ampullae
(superior and lateral)

Fundus of the internal acoustic meatus, exposed by removal of the overlying bone
in the area indicated by the arrows.

The fundus is divided into upper and lower portions by a sharp horizontal ridge, the transverse crest. In an anterior depression in the upper, smaller area is situated the internal opening of the facial canal; and a posterior, funnel-shaped depression, the superior vestibular area, contains several small openings of canals that conduct branches of the upper terminal ramus of the vestibular nerve to the *macula cribrosa superior* of the vestibule. Anteriorly the lower, larger area presents a rounded depression, the cochlear area; here begins a spiral band of small openings, the spiral tract of foramina, which transmit the bundles of the cochlear nerve directly to the basal turn or through the longitudinal modiolar canals to the middle and apical turns. In the posterior part of the same area, closely adjacent to the transverse crest, lies a zone with small openings, the inferior vestibular area, for transmission of fibers to the *macula cribrosa media* of the vestibule. Medialward from this area is situated a single, larger opening, the *foramen singulare*, by which the posterior ampullary nerve passes to the *macula cribrosa inferior*.

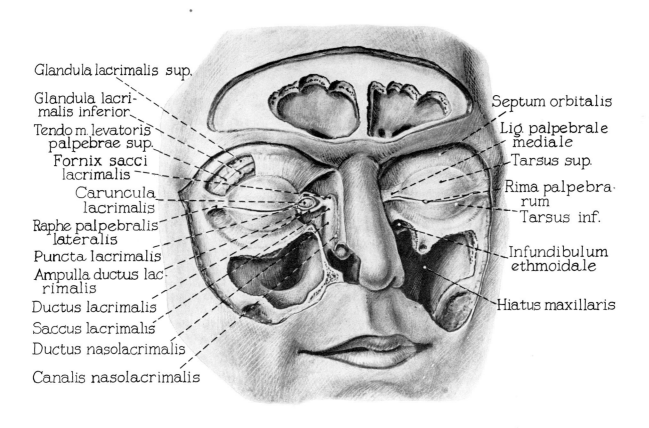

Glandula lacrimalis sup.

Glandula lacrimalis inferior

Tendo m. levatoris palpebrae sup.

Fornix sacci lacrimalis

Caruncula lacrimalis

Raphe palpebralis lateralis

Puncta lacrimalis

Ampulla ductus lacrimalis

Ductus lacrimalis

Saccus lacrimalis

Ductus nasolacrimalis

Canalis nasolacrimalis

Septum orbitalis

Lig. palpebrale mediale

Tarsus sup.

Rima palpebrarum

Tarsus inf.

Infundibulum ethmoidale

Hiatus maxillaris

Frontal and maxillary accessory air sinuses, and the lacrimal apparatus.
Shown in partial dissection of the face.

The paranasal sinuses are cavities hollowed out of several of the flat bones of the skull. The lining of each is directly continuous with the nasal mucous membrane around the lips of small communicating apertures. Developmentally the air spaces replace the cancellous tissue regularly found between the tables of the cranial bones. Excavation of bone occurs simultaneously with advancement of the nasal epithelium.

The frontal sinuses typically occupy the squamous and orbital portions of the frontal bone, and lie as pyramidal spaces behind the superciliary ridges. Rather constantly they are two in number; the thin septum between them is rarely perforated. They are rarely symmetrical, since the septum often deviates to one side or the other of the median line. Occasionally one may be lacking, or either or both present in duplicate or triplicate—totalling any number of spaces from three to six. Encroachment by ethmoidal pneumatization reduces the size of the frontal sinus. On the contrary, either sinus may be enlarged by extension posteriorly in the orbital plate of the frontal bone to the lesser wing of the sphenoid bone, inferolaterally into the zygomatic process of the frontal bone or inferomedially into the nasal spine. The sinus communicates, through the frontonasal duct, with the anterior part of the middle meatus.

The maxillary sinuses are the largest of the accessory air-spaces. Each occupies the entire body of the maxilla and may extend into the zygomatic process. The sinus is situated below the orbit, lateral to the lower part of the nose, and above the molar and premolar teeth (page 39). It opens into the middle meatus of the nasal cavity (page 38). (From Warren: Handbook of Anatomy, Harvard University Press.)

The eyeball consists of a series of concentric layers. The outermost, which is tough, white, and fibrous, is the sclera. In meridional section, the sclera constitutes five-sixths of the circumference of a sphere. The anterior sixth is occupied by the cornea, a thin, bulging, transparent membrane set into the circular gap at the anterior pole of the sclera, with which it fuses at the sclero-corneal junction.

Next within the sclera is the choroid, the vascular layer of the eyeball. The ciliary arteries enter this layer by piercing the posterior aspect of the sclera; then, ramifying in the choroid, they reach all parts of the eyeball. The vortical veins emerge in similar manner from the choroid. This layer does not extend as far forward as the sclero-corneal junction; it merges with a circular structure, the ciliary body, which consists of seventy-two ciliary processes. Each process is a muscular structure containing circular smooth-muscle fibers at its medial portion and radial smooth-muscle fibers at its peripheral part. In this way the ciliary body constitutes a muscular ring that surrounds the anterior margin of the choroid, and the lens is placed within this ring. The lens is held in position by the suspensory ligament, a circular membrane that originates from the anterior aspect of the ciliary body and adheres to the anterior surface of the lens.

Attached to the anterior aspect of the ciliary body but anterior to the suspensory ligament is the iris. This is a pigmented, circular diaphragm with a central orifice, the pupil, which is capable of being dilated or contracted by the action of the radial or concentric smooth-muscle fibers of the iris. The posterior surface of the iris rests upon the convex anterior surface of the lens. Between the posterior surface of the iris, and the suspensory ligament and receding peripheral portion of the lens is a small space known as the posterior chamber, which is filled with aqueous fluid. Between the concave internal surface of the cornea, and the anterior surface of the iris and central anterior surface of the lens is a larger space called the anterior chamber; this also is filled with aqueous fluid. The two chambers communicate with each other through the orifice of the pupil.

The third and innermost layer of the eyeball is the retina, an expansion of the optic nerve. It consists of ten layers of cells, of which the deepest is the layer of rods and cones. Each rod or cone is the terminal filament of one neuraxon of the optic nerve. The retina does not extend as far forward as the choroid but terminates anteriorly in a crenelated margin, the *ora serrata*. At the entrance of the optic nerve is a shallow depression called the blind spot (excavation of the papilla of the optic nerve), in which there are no rods and cones—hence no vision.

At the center of the retina is another shallow depression, the *fovea centralis*, which is known as the *macula lutea* because of its yellowish appearance. This is the area of most intense vision.

The entire space bounded by the retina, ciliary body, and posterior surface of the lens is occupied by the vitreus body (corpus vitreum), which consists of a membrane (*membrana hyaloidea*) filled with a transparent, gelatinous substance (*humor vitreus*). The anterior surface of the vitreous body is a concave depression, the *fossa hyaloidea*, in which the lens rests. The hyaloid membrane is adherent to the posterior surface of the lens and of the ciliary body; with the suspensory ligament, it forms the suspending and compressing apparatus of the lens.

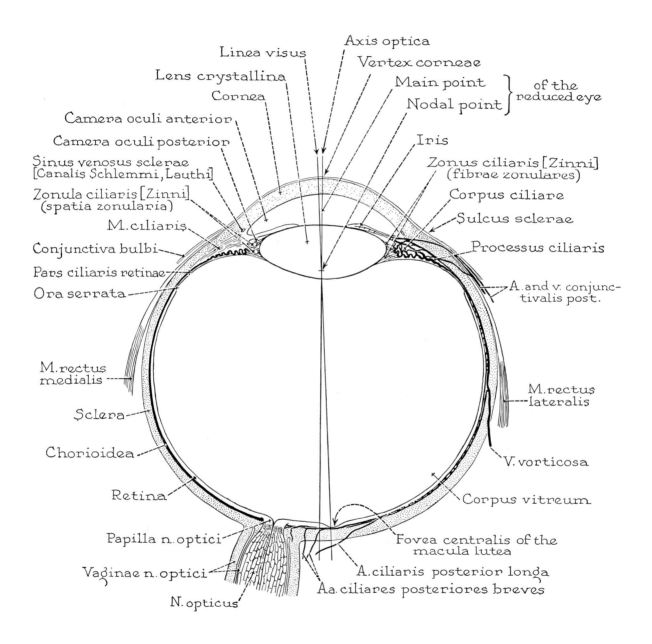

Section through the right eye; schematic (after Spalteholz).

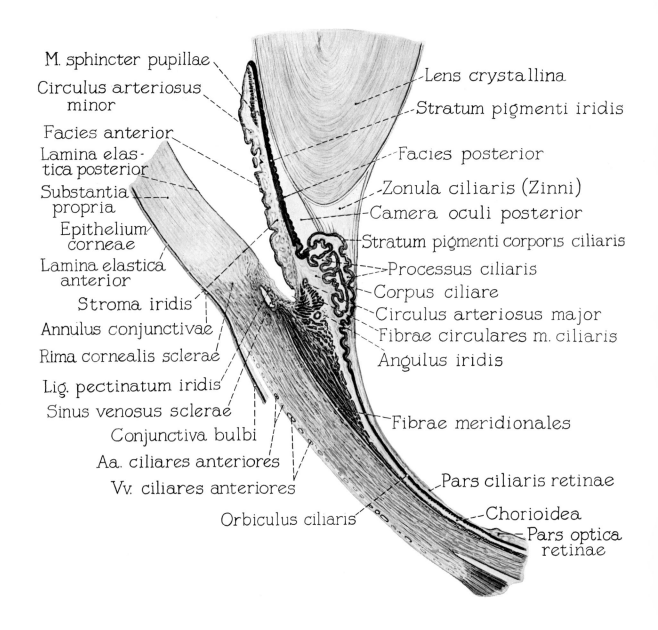

M. sphincter pupillae

Circulus arteriosus minor

Facies anterior

Lamina elastica posterior

Substantia propria

Epithelium corneae

Lamina elastica anterior

Stroma iridis

Annulus conjunctivae

Rima cornealis sclerae

Lig. pectinatum iridis

Sinus venosus sclerae

Conjunctiva bulbi

Aa. ciliares anteriores

Vv. ciliares anteriores

Orbiculus ciliaris

Lens crystallina

Stratum pigmenti iridis

Facies posterior

Zonula ciliaris (Zinni)

Camera oculi posterior

Stratum pigmenti corporis ciliaris

Processus ciliaris

Corpus ciliare

Circulus arteriosus major

Fibrae circulares m. ciliaris

Angulus iridis

Fibrae meridionales

Pars ciliaris retinae

Chorioidea

Pars optica retinae

Bulb of the eye.

Details of structure shown in an anterior radial section. See description on page 78. (From Warren: Handbook of Anatomy. Harvard University Press.)

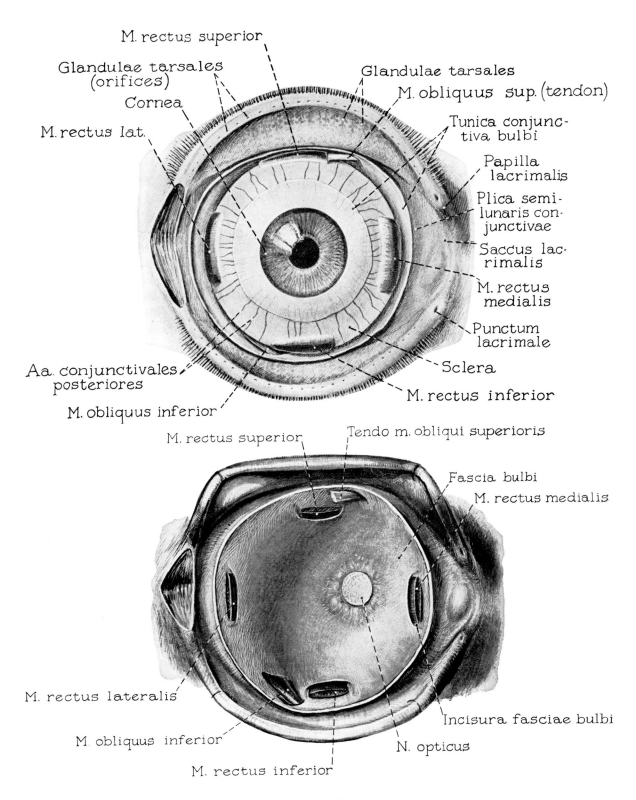

Eye: conjunctiva, fascia, and muscles.

In the upper figure the lateral angle has been cut and the eyelids drawn apart; the conjunctiva has been incised and peeled away to expose the ocular muscles. In the lower figure, the fascia is exposed by removal of the ocular bulb (the optic nerve, cut). (From Warren: Handbook of Anatomy, Harvard University Press.)

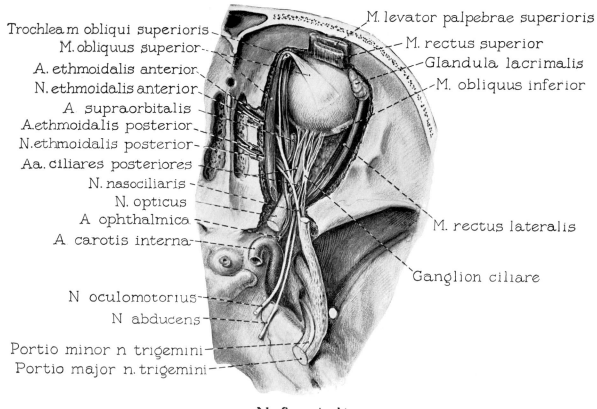

Trochlea m obliqui superioris
M. obliquus superior
A. ethmoidalis anterior
N. ethmoidalis anterior
A. supraorbitalis
A. ethmoidalis posterior
N. ethmoidalis posterior
Aa. ciliares posteriores
N. nasociliaris
N. opticus
A ophthalmica
A carotis interna

N oculomotorius
N abducens

Portio minor n. trigemini
Portio major n. trigemini

M. levator palpebrae superioris
M. rectus superior
Glandula lacrimalis
M. obliquus inferior

M. rectus lateralis

Ganglion ciliare

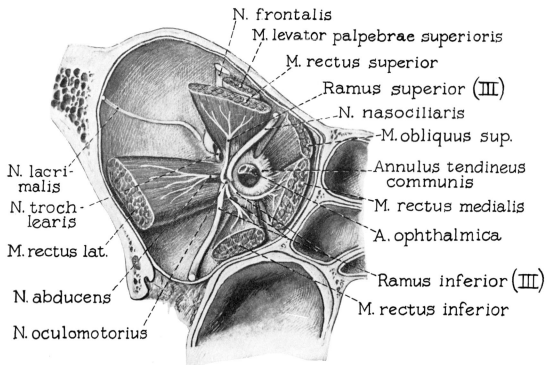

N. frontalis
M. levator palpebrae superioris
M. rectus superior
Ramus superior (III)
N. nasociliaris
M. obliquus sup.

N. lacrimalis
N. trochlearis
M. rectus lat.

N. abducens
N. oculomotorius

Annulus tendineus communis
M. rectus medialis
A. ophthalmica
Ramus inferior (III)
M. rectus inferior

Contents of the orbit and muscles of the ocular bulb.

In the upper figure, the bony roof of the orbit has been removed, and channels cut to demonstrate the course of the ethmoidal arteries and nerves. In the lower illustration, the right orbit has been sectioned coronally to demonstrate the origins of the muscles and the entrance of the nerves. (From Warren: Handbook of Anatomy, Harvard University Press.)

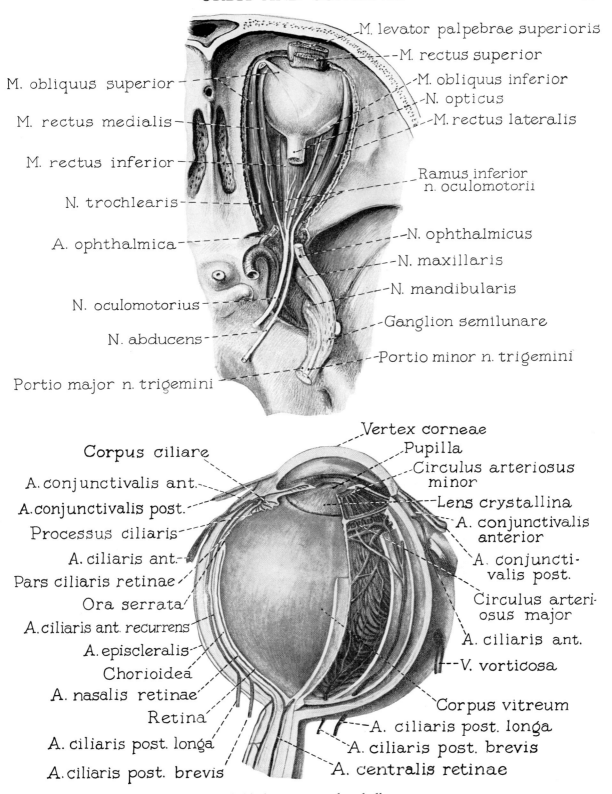

M. levator palpebrae superioris
M. rectus superior
M. obliquus inferior
N. opticus
M. rectus lateralis

M. obliquus superior
M. rectus medialis
M. rectus inferior
N. trochlearis
A. ophthalmica

Ramus inferior
n. oculomotorii

N. ophthalmicus
N. maxillaris
N. mandibularis
Ganglion semilunare

N. oculomotorius
N. abducens

Portio minor n. trigemini

Portio major n. trigemini

Corpus ciliare
A. conjunctivalis ant.
A. conjunctivalis post.
Processus ciliaris
A. ciliaris ant.
Pars ciliaris retinae
Ora serrata
A. ciliaris ant. recurrens
A. episcleralis
Chorioidea
A. nasalis retinae
Retina
A. ciliaris post. longa
A. ciliaris post. brevis

Vertex corneae
Pupilla
Circulus arteriosus minor
Lens crystallina
A. conjunctivalis anterior
A. conjunctivalis post.
Circulus arteriosus major
A. ciliaris ant.
V. vorticosa
Corpus vitreum
A. ciliaris post. longa
A. ciliaris post. brevis
A. centralis retinae

Orbital contents and eyeball.

In the upper figure, the orbit has been opened from above; the semilunar ganglion has been turned lateralward in order to reveal the nerves of supply to the ocular muscles. In the lower illustration, the layers of the eyeball (ocular bulb) are demonstrated, from the sclera successively inward to the retina. (From Warren: Handbook of Anatomy, Harvard University Press.)

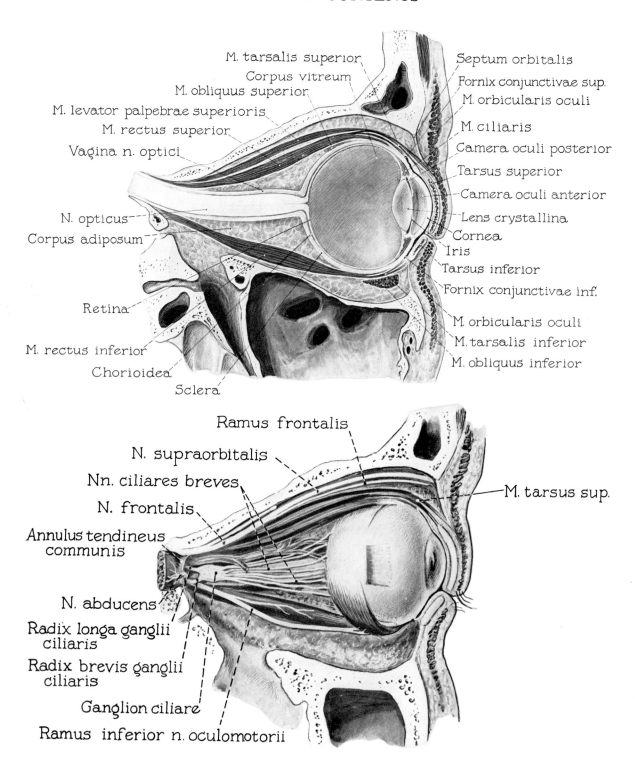

M. tarsalis superior
Corpus vitreum
M. obliquus superior
M. levator palpebrae superioris
M. rectus superior
Vagina n. optici
N. opticus
Corpus adiposum
Retina
M. rectus inferior
Chorioidea
Sclera

Septum orbitalis
Fornix conjunctivae sup.
M. orbicularis oculi
M. ciliaris
Camera oculi posterior
Tarsus superior
Camera oculi anterior
Lens crystallina
Cornea
Iris
Tarsus inferior
Fornix conjunctivae inf.
M. orbicularis oculi
M. tarsalis inferior
M. obliquus inferior

Ramus frontalis
N. supraorbitalis
Nn. ciliares breves
N. frontalis
Annulus tendineus communis
N. abducens
Radix longa ganglii ciliaris
Radix brevis ganglii ciliaris
Ganglion ciliare
Ramus inferior n. oculomotorii

M. tarsus sup.

Orbit; shown in section and in a dissection.

In the upper figure, the contents of the orbit are shown in vertical section taken along the course of the optic nerve. In the lower figure, which is a sagittal section through the bony orbit, the eyeball is shown entire; the related structures are also intact, with the exception of the m. rectus lateralis, from which the middle portion has been excised (the posterior part is then turned outward). (From Warren: Handbook of Anatomy, Harvard University Press.)

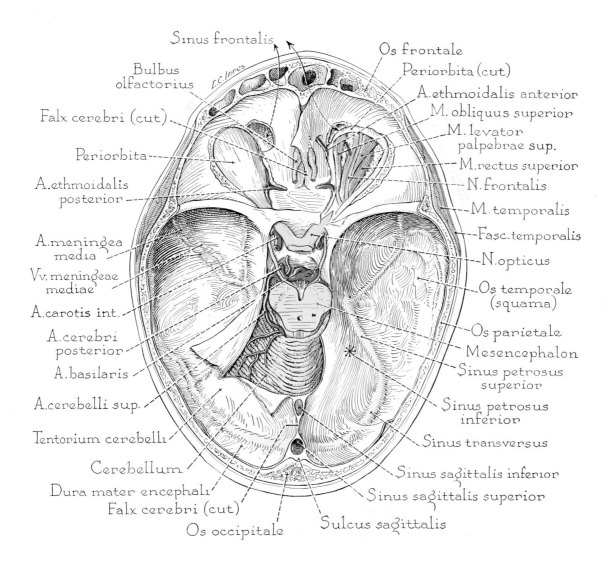

Sinus frontalis

Bulbus olfactorius

Falx cerebri (cut)

Periorbita

A.ethmoidalis posterior

A.meningea media

Vv. meningeae mediae

A.carotis int.

A.cerebri posterior

A.basilaris

A.cerebelli sup.

Tentorium cerebelli

Cerebellum

Dura mater encephali

Falx cerebri (cut)

Os occipitale

Os frontale

Periorbita (cut)

A.ethmoidalis anterior

M. obliquus superior

M. levator palpebrae sup.

M.rectus superior

N.frontalis

M.temporalis

Fasc. temporalis

N.opticus

Os temporale (squama)

Os parietale

Mesencephalon

Sinus petrosus superior

Sinus petrosus inferior

Sinus transversus

Sinus sagittalis inferior

Sinus sagittalis superior

Sulcus sagittalis

Floor of the cranial cavity and the contents of the orbit.

The falx cerebri remains only at its anterior and posterior extremities; the tentorium cerebelli of the left side has been cut and reflected, to expose the cerebellum in the posterior cranial fossa. The dura mater has been removed in the anterior cranial fossa. The roof of each orbital cavity has been dissected away; on the left this dissection has been carried to the level of the periorbita; on the right the latter layer of periorbital periosteum has been removed to reveal the ocular muscles and the nerves which lie medial and superior to the bulb of the eye. The removal of bone, on each side, has been carried to that part of the orbital roof into which the frontal paranasal sinus extends (see arrows).

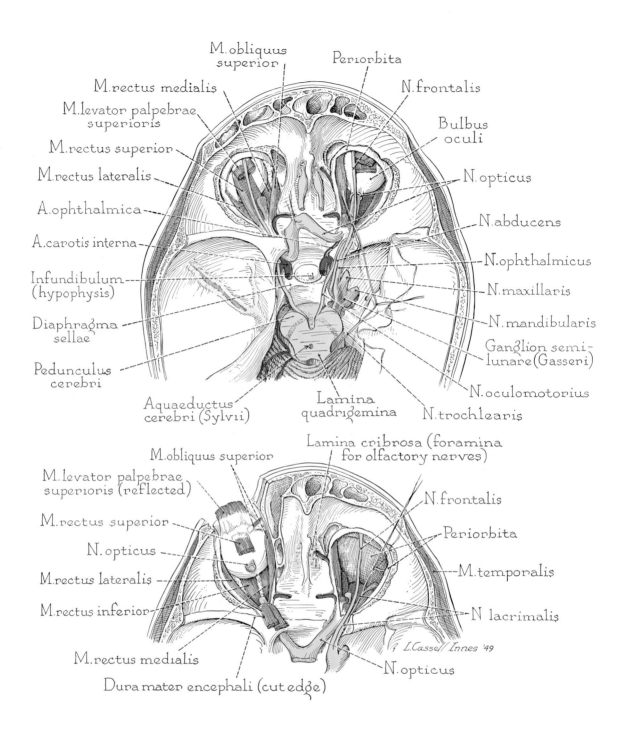

M.obliquus superior
M.rectus medialis
M.levator palpebrae superioris
M.rectus superior
M.rectus lateralis
A.ophthalmica
A.carotis interna
Infundibulum (hypophysis)
Diaphragma sellae
Pedunculus cerebri

Periorbita
N.frontalis
Bulbus oculi
N.opticus
N.abducens
N.ophthalmicus
N.maxillaris
N.mandibularis
Ganglion semilunare (Gasseri)
N.oculomotorius

Aquaeductus cerebri (Sylvii)
Lamina quadrigemina
N.trochlearis

Lamina cribrosa (foramina for olfactory nerves)
M.obliquus superior
M.levator palpebrae superioris (reflected)
M.rectus superior
N.opticus
M.rectus lateralis
M.rectus inferior
M.rectus medialis
Dura mater encephali (cut edge)

N.frontalis
Periorbita
M.temporalis
N lacrimalis
N.opticus

L.Cassel/Innes '49

Floor of the cranial cavity and the contents of the orbit; deeper dissections of the same specimen.

In the upper figure the dura mater of the middle cranial fossa has been reflected on the right half of the skull to expose the semilunar ganglion, the three nerves derived therefrom, and the related abducent, trochlear, and oculomotor nerves. In the anterior cranial fossa the falx cerebri has been removed.

In the lower figure the entire orbital roof has been removed on the left side. In the left orbit the superiorly placed intrinsic muscles have been reflected; in the right orbit the bulb of the eye has been removed.

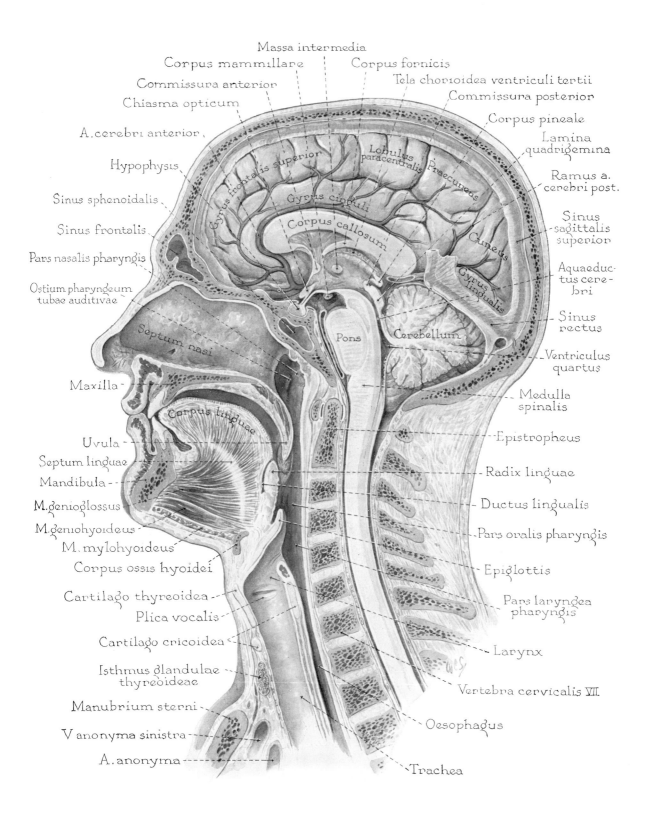

Massa intermedia
Corpus mammillare
Commissura anterior
Chiasma opticum
A. cerebri anterior
Hypophysis
Sinus sphenoidalis
Sinus frontalis
Pars nasalis pharyngis
Ostium pharyngeum tubae auditivae
Septum nasi
Maxilla
Corpus linguae
Uvula
Septum linguae
Mandibula
M. genioglossus
M. geniohyoideus
M. mylohyoideus
Corpus ossis hyoidei
Cartilago thyreoidea
Plica vocalis
Cartilago cricoidea
Isthmus glandulae thyreoideae
Manubrium sterni
V anonyma sinistra
A. anonyma

Corpus fornicis
Tela chorioidea ventriculi tertii
Commissura posterior
Corpus pineale
Lamina quadrigemina
Ramus a. cerebri post.
Sinus sagittalis superior
Aquaeductus cerebri
Sinus rectus
Ventriculus quartus
Medulla spinalis
Epistropheus
Radix linguae
Ductus lingualis
Pars oralis pharyngis
Epiglottis
Pars laryngea pharyngis
Larynx
Vertebra cervicalis VII
Oesophagus
Trachea

Lobulus paracentralis
Praecuneus
Gyrus frontalis superior
Gyrus cinguli
Corpus callosum
Cuneus
Gyrus lingualis
Septum nasi
Pons
Cerebellum

Hemisection of the head and neck.

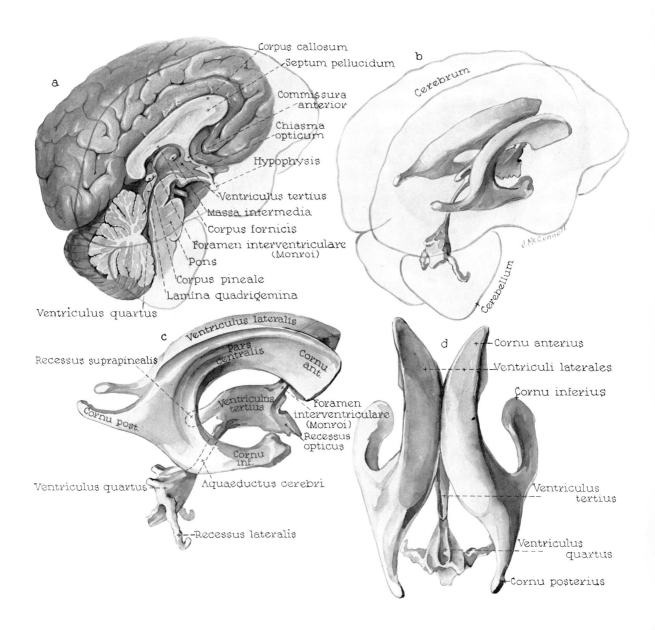

Cerebral ventricles.

a, Median section through the brain; left half, viewed from the right. *b*, The ventricles (shown as casts of the spaces) in relation to the cerebrum and cerebellum; viewed from above, from the side and slightly from behind. *c* and *d*, The ventricles (shown as casts) in lateral and superior views, respectively.

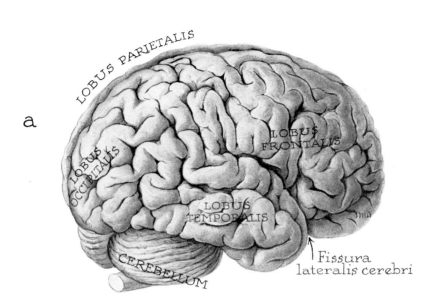

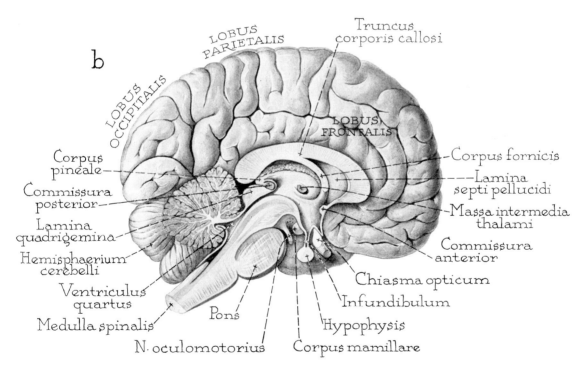

Brain and spinal cord.

a, The brain in lateral view. *b*, The brain and spinal cord in hemisection.

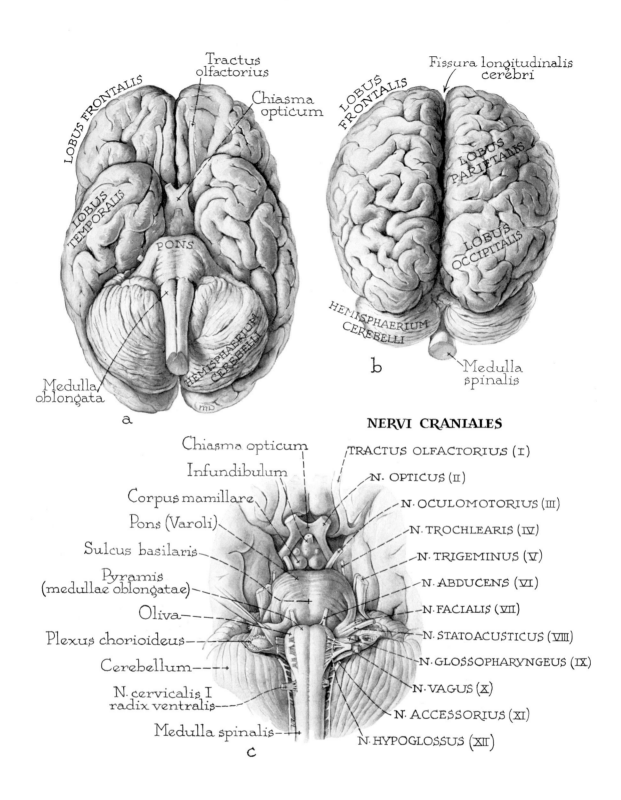

Brain, spinal cord, and cranial nerves.

a, The brain seen from below. *b,* The brain viewed from above and behind. *c,* The cranial nerves and related portions of the brain and spinal cord.

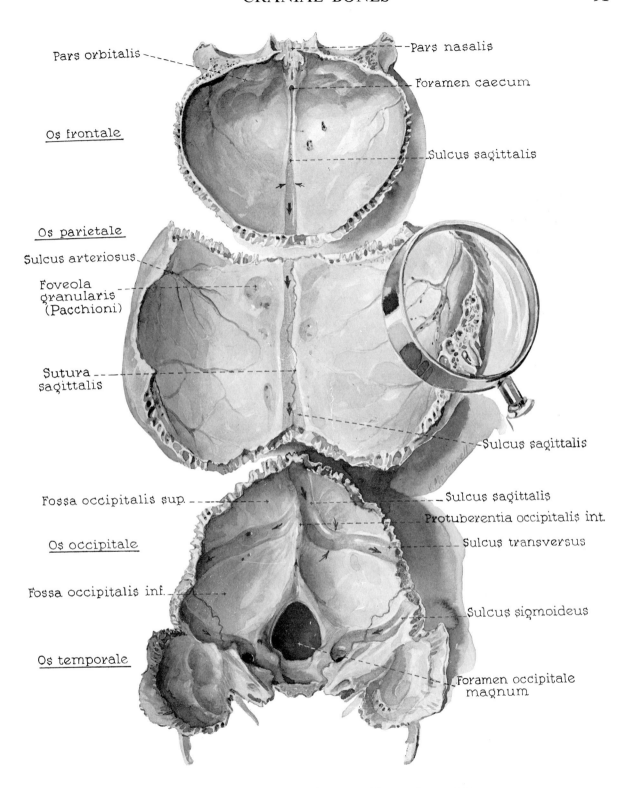

Pars orbitalis

Os frontale

Os parietale

Sulcus arteriosus

Foveola
granularis
(Pacchioni)

Sutura
sagittalis

Fossa occipitalis sup.

Os occipitale

Fossa occipitalis inf.

Os temporale

Pars nasalis

Foramen caecum

Sulcus sagittalis

Sulcus sagittalis

Sulcus sagittalis

Protuberentia occipitalis int.

Sulcus transversus

Sulcus sigmoideus

Foramen occipitale
magnum

Frontal, parietal, occipital and temporal bones, from within.

Showing the lesser sulci for the middle meningeal artery (enlarged on the right parietal bone) and the larger sulci (sagittal, transverse and sigmoid) which accommodate the venous sinuses. The heavy arrows indicate the direction of venous flow; the light arrows point to the elevated margins of the sulci, to which the dural reflections are attached.

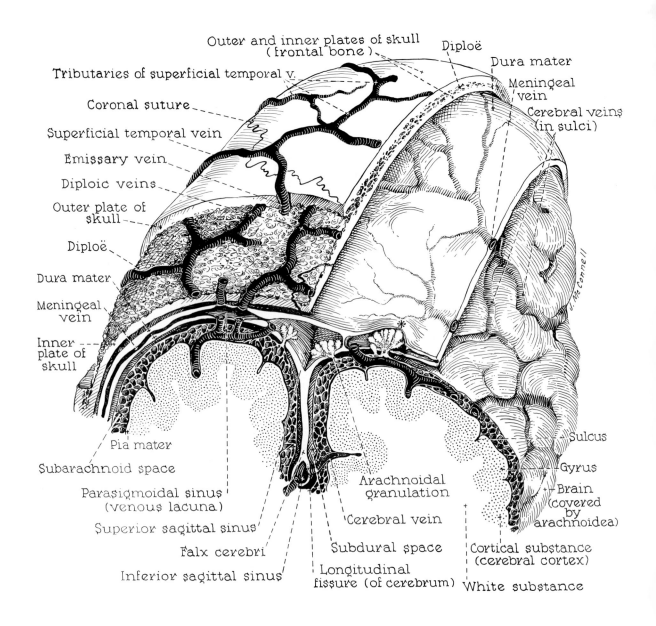

Veins of the scalp, diploic tissue, meninges, and brain. Semidiagrammatic.

From a specimen of skull and brain, sectioned coronally, the succession of vascular levels is recorded from that of the superficial veins of the scalp inward to that of the cortical substance. On the reader's left, the outer plate of the skull has been removed in a rectangular area; on the right all of the calvarium has been cut away along the median line; lateral thereto a portion of the dura remains. On the cut surface, toward the reader, the following layers and structures are shown: the diploic tissue; the meninges and the spaces bounded by these cerebral investments; the gray and white substance of the cerebrum; arachnoidal granulations, one of which (at *) would produce a foveola on the inner table of the skull.

It is clear that connections occur among veins of the several levels. The superficial veins of the scalp communicate with the venous sinuses of the dura either directly, through the emissary veins, or indirectly, by means of the diploic vessels. The venous sinuses receive meningeal veins (from the dura mater) and cerebral veins (from the brain).

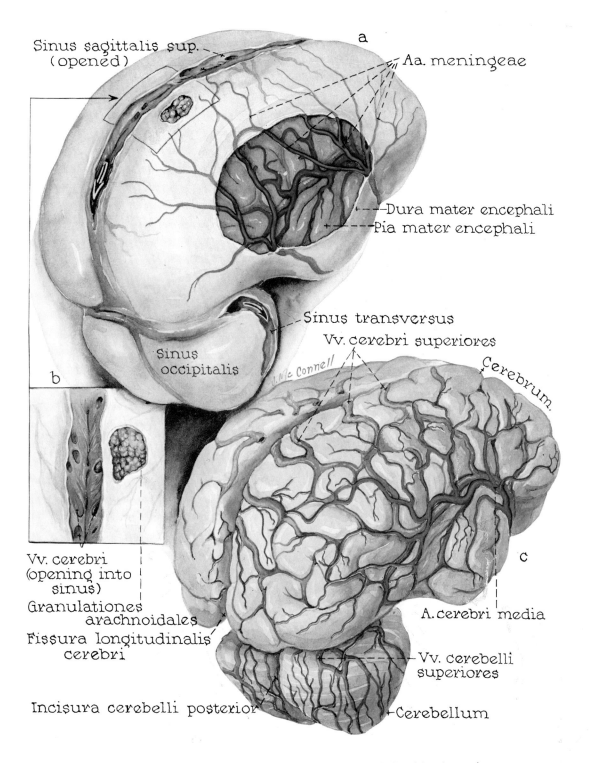

Sinus sagittalis sup.
(opened)

Aa. meningeae

Dura mater encephali
Pia mater encephali

Sinus transversus

Vv. cerebri superiores

Cerebrum

Sinus occipitalis

J. Mc Connell

b

Vv. cerebri
(opening into
sinus)
Granulationes
arachnoidales
Fissura longitudinalis
cerebri

Incisura cerebelli posterior

c

A. cerebri media

Vv. cerebelli
superiores

Cerebellum

Brain and meninges, with dural, cerebral, and cerebellar blood vessels.

a, The dura mater with contained venous sinuses and meningeal veins. Over a portion of the left hemisphere the dural investment has been removed to show the freed meningeal veins superimposed upon the cerebral vessels (the latter lodged in the pia mater). *b*, A detail of the preceding, showing the opened superior sagittal sinus, tributary veins, and arachnoidal granulation. *c*, The brain, with cerebral and cerebellar blood vessels.

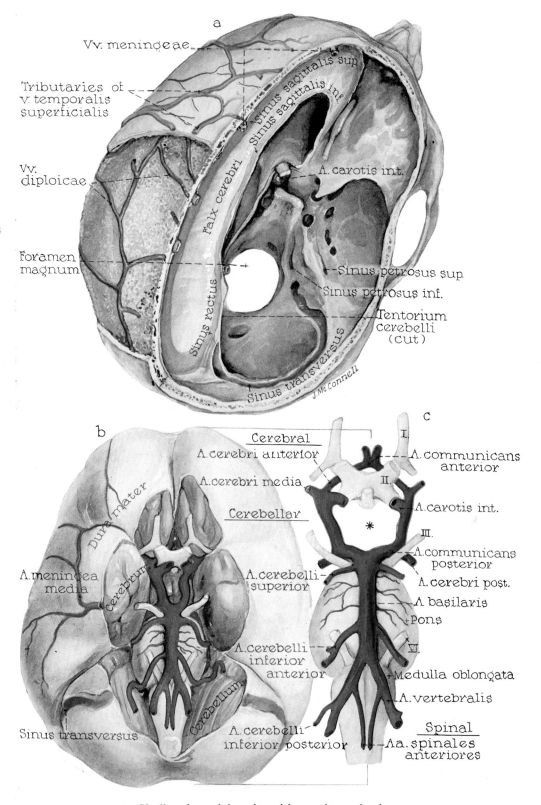

a

Vv. meningeae

Tributaries of
v. temporalis
superficialis

Vv.
diploicae

Foramen
magnum

Sinus sagittalis sup.
Sinus sagittalis inf.
Falx cerebri
A. carotis int.
Sinus rectus
Sinus petrosus sup.
Sinus petrosus inf.
Tentorium
cerebelli
(cut)
Sinus transversus

J. McConnell

b

Cerebral
A. cerebri anterior
A. cerebri media
Cerebellar
Dura mater
A. meningea
media
Cerebrum
A. cerebelli
superior
A. cerebelli
inferior
anterior
Cerebellum
Sinus transversus
A. cerebelli
inferior posterior

c

I.
A. communicans
anterior
II.
A. carotis int.
*
III.
A. communicans
posterior
A. cerebri post.
A. basilaris
Pons
VI.
Medulla oblongata
A. vertebralis
Spinal
Aa. spinales
anteriores

Skull and cranial cavity with arteries and veins.

a, Superficial, diploic and meningeal veins. The outer table of the skull has been partially removed on the left half, in order to demonstrate the diploic veins; on the right half, through removal of the skull cap, the dural reflections and the opened transverse sinus are exposed.

b, Arterial circle (surrounding *) with its contributory vessels and branches.

c, Arteries of the base of the brain, in relation to certain of the cranial nerves (numbered).

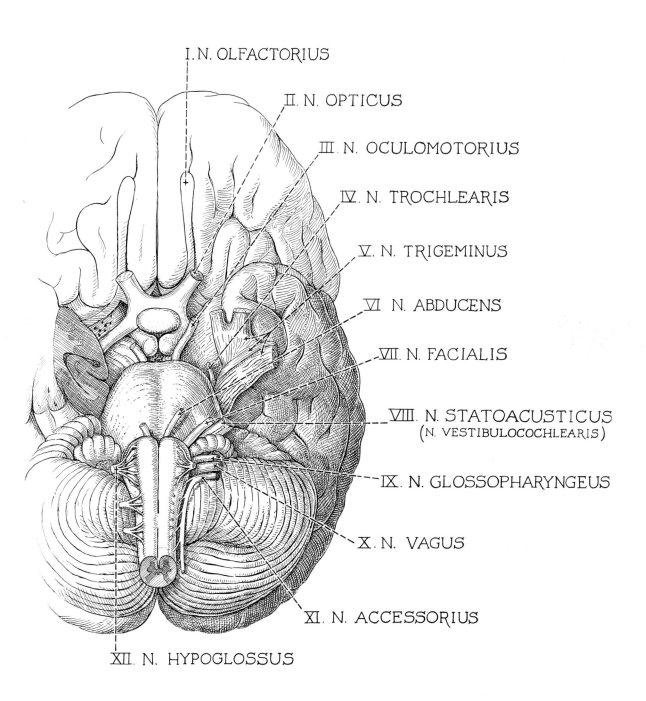

I. N. OLFACTORIUS

II. N. OPTICUS

III. N. OCULOMOTORIUS

IV. N. TROCHLEARIS

V. N. TRIGEMINUS

VI. N. ABDUCENS

VII. N. FACIALIS

VIII. N. STATOACUSTICUS
(N. VESTIBULOCOCHLEARIS)

IX. N. GLOSSOPHARYNGEUS

X. N. VAGUS

XI. N. ACCESSORIUS

XII. N. HYPOGLOSSUS

Base of the brain.

Showing the cranial nerves as they emerge from the brain and spinal cord.
See description on the following page.

I. Olfactory
   From cells in nasal mucosa
   Passage through cribriform plate
   To olfactory bulb
   Sensory: Smell

II. Optic
   Ganglion cells in retina
   Through optic foramen
   Optic chiasm, optic tract
   To lateral geniculate body or superior
      colliculus
   Sensory: Vision

III. Oculomotor
   From midbrain (interpeduncular fossa)
   Through superior orbital fissure
   Motor: Intraorbital muscles except those
      innervated by IV and VI, and levator
      palpebrae superioris.
   Parasympathetic: Sphincter of pupil and
      ciliary muscle.

IV. Trochlear
   Roof of midbrain
   Through superior orbital fissure
   Motor: Superior oblique muscle

V. Trigeminal
   From lateral portion of pons
      Ophthalmic branch
   Through superior orbital fissure
   Sensory: Parts of eye
      Nasal mucous membrane
      Skin of face
      Maxillary branch
   Through foramen rotundum
   Sensory: Skin of face
      Teeth, part of anterior ⅔ of
         oral cavity
      Paranasal sinuses
      Mandibular branch
   Through foramen ovale
   Sensory: Skin of face
      Remainder of anterior ⅔ of
         oral cavity, anterior ⅔ of
         tongue, teeth
   Motor: Muscles of mastication

VI. Abducens
   From lower border of pons (adjacent to
      posterior median sulcus)

Through superior orbital fissure
Motor: Lateral rectus muscle

VII. Facial
   From lower border of pons
   Through stylomastoid foramen
   Parasympathetic: Lacrimal, nasal, palatine,
      submandibular and sublingual glands
   Motor: Muscles of facial expression
   Sensory: Taste, anterior ⅔ of tongue

VIII. Statoacoustic
   From spiral organ, maculae, cristae (coch-
      lea, utricle, saccule, ampullae)
   Through internal acoustic meatus
   To lower border of pons posterior to
      VII
   Sensory: Hearing
            Head position

IX. Glossopharyngeal
   From medulla oblongata (rostral end of
      posterior lateral sulcus)
   Through jugular foramen
   Sensory: Tongue (posterior ⅓), pharynx
            Taste, posterior ⅓ of tongue
   Motor: Part of pharynx

X. Vagus
   From medulla oblongata, in line with IX,
      XI
   Through jugular foramen
   Sensory: Part of external auditory meatus,
      pharynx and larynx—to viscera of thorax
      and abdomen
   Motor: Pharynx and larynx
   Parasympathetic: Thoracic and abdominal
      viscera

XI. Accessory
   From medulla oblongata (caudal to IX, X)
      and cervical cord (I-V)
   Through jugular foramen
   Motor: Upper ½ of trapezius and sterno-
      cleidomastoid muscles

XII. Hypoglossal
   From anterior lateral sulcus between olive
      and pyramid
   Through hypoglossal canal
   Motor: Extrinsic and intrinsic muscles of
      the tongue

Section Three

THE NECK

TRIANGLES OF THE NECK; SCHEMATIC.. 99–100

CERVICAL FASCIA; SCHEMATIC... 101–102

MUSCLES OF THE NECK: SEVEN STAGES IN DISSECTION........................... 103–109

STRUCTURES OF THE NECK: FIVE STAGES IN DISSECTION........................ 110–114

DEEP ANATOMY OF THE NECK: TWO STAGES IN DISSECTION...................... 115–116

DEEP CERVICAL AND THORACIC ANATOMY: RIGHT AND LEFT SIDES................ 117–118

SUBCLAVIAN ARTERY; VARIATIONS.. 119

VERTEBRAL VESSELS... 120

BLOOD VESSELS OF THE NECK.. 121

THYROID GLAND; VARIATIONS... 122

CERVICAL PLEXUS... 123

CERVICAL SYMPATHETIC TRUNK AND GANGLIA; TWO STAGES IN DISSECTION......... 124–125

DEEP ANATOMY OF THE NECK AND THORAX.. 126–127

PHARYNX, OPENED; DORSAL VIEW.. 128

VEINS OF THE NECK... 129

MANDIBLE, HYOID BONE, AND THYROID CARTILAGE: AREAS OF MUSCULAR ATTACHMENT... 130

PHARYNX, LARYNX, AND TRACHEA.. 131–134

CONTENTS OF SUBOCCIPITAL SPACE.. 135

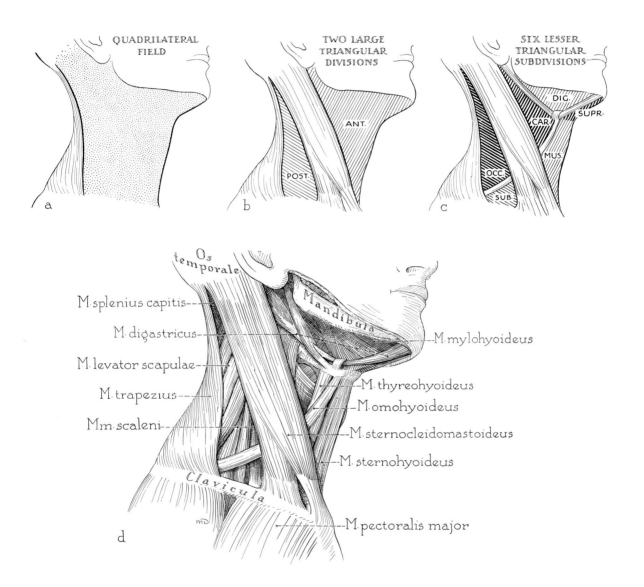

Subdivision of the anterolateral portion of the neck into triangular areas. Diagrammatic.

a, Quadrilateral field bounded by the trapezius muscle (behind), mandible and occipital bone (above), midline of the neck (in front) and clavicle (below). *b*, Subdivision into two triangular areas by the obliquely coursing sternocleidomastoid muscle. *c*, Further subdivision of the posterior (NA, lateral) triangle into occipital and subclavian triangles by the omohyoid muscle; comparable subdivision of the anterior triangle into digastric, carotid, suprahyoid, and muscular triangles by the omohyoid and digastric muscles. *d*, Muscles that form the marginal and the deep boundaries of the several triangular areas of the neck.

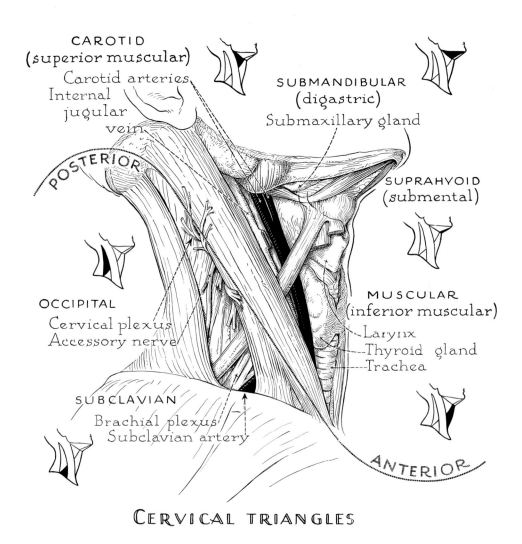

CAROTID
(superior muscular)
Carotid arteries
Internal
jugular
vein

POSTERIOR

SUBMANDIBULAR
(digastric)
Submaxillary gland

SUPRAHYOID
(submental)

OCCIPITAL
Cervical plexus
Accessory nerve

MUSCULAR
(inferior muscular)
Larynx
Thyroid gland
Trachea

SUBCLAVIAN
Brachial plexus
Subclavian artery

ANTERIOR

CERVICAL TRIANGLES

Chief contents of the triangles of the neck.

The contents of the occipital and subclavian triangles are chiefly nervous (cervical plexus, brachial plexus, and spinal accessory nerve). Those of the carotid and digastric triangles are vascular and glandular (carotid arteries; jugular and tributary veins; parotid and submaxillary glands). The contents of the muscular triangle are mainly visceral (larynx, trachea, esophagus, and thyroid gland).

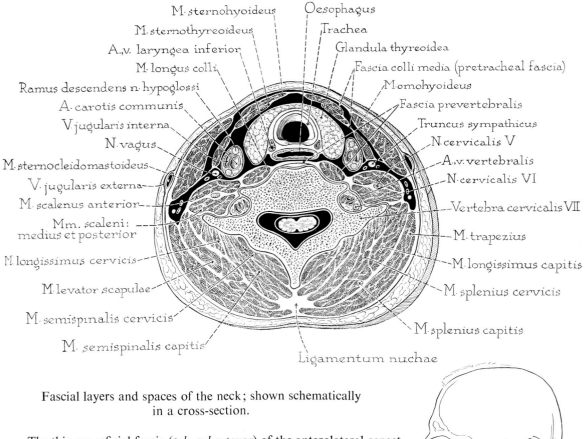

M. sternohyoideus
M. sternothyreoideus
A., v. laryngea inferior
M. longus colli
Ramus descendens n. hypoglossi
A. carotis communis
V. jugularis interna
N. vagus
M. sternocleidomastoideus
V. jugularis externa
M. scalenus anterior
Mm. scaleni: medius et posterior
M. longissimus cervicis
M. levator scapulae
M. semispinalis cervicis
M. semispinalis capitis

Oesophagus
Trachea
Glandula thyreoidea
Fascia colli media (pretracheal fascia)
M. omohyoideus
Fascia prevertebralis
Truncus sympathicus
N. cervicalis V
A., v. vertebralis
N. cervicalis VI
Vertebra cervicalis VII
M. trapezius
M. longissimus capitis
M. splenius cervicis
M. splenius capitis

Ligamentum nuchae

Fascial layers and spaces of the neck; shown schematically
in a cross-section.

The thin superficial fascia (*tela subcutanea*) of the anterolateral aspect of the neck is continuous above with the heavier facial portion, which ascends over the border of the mandible and covers the parotid gland. Below, it is continuous over the clavicle with superficial fascia of the pectoral and deltoid regions; behind, with the superficial fascia of the back of the neck; the latter portion is thick, tough and adherent to the deep fascia.

In the anterior and lateral regions of the neck, the superficial fascia contains the fibers of the platysma. This broad sheet of musculature arises from the fascia that invests the pectoralis major and deltoideus; its fibers course obliquely upward and medialward along the side of the neck. Crossing the mandible, the fibers usually end in the skin and subcutaneous tissue of the lower part of the face; however, in some cases they ascend to the zygomaticus or to the margin of the orbicularis oculi.

The deep cervical fascia (*fascia colli*) forms important connections, because the neck itself is made up of intermediate structures that join the head with the thorax and contribute to the anatomy of the upper limb.

The cervical fascia may be divided, first, into suprahyoid and infrahyoid portions. Both of these, in turn, may be subdivided into smaller portions for the purpose of description. The suprahyoid subdivisions are: the investing fascia, and the deeper portion associated with the mandible and the floor of the mouth. The infrahyoid is divisible into: the investing fascia, the prevertebral fascia, the middle cervical fascia, the visceral fascia, and the carotid sheath.

The fascia of the suprahyoid region extends upward from the hyoid bone to the lower border of the mandible. It covers the anterior segment of the digastric, adheres to its sheath, and is continuous across the middle line. Laterally, it divides to enclose the submandibular gland. The sheets of the superficial and deep surfaces of the submandibular gland come together for a short distance near the angle of the mandible, and separate again to invest the parotid gland. The external layer of the parotid portion extends upward over the masseter muscle for attachment to the zygomatic arch. At the posterior border of the parotid gland, the superficial layer joins the deeper layer but splits again to enclose the sternocleidomastoid muscle. There it is attached to the mastoid process of the temporal bone and is continuous with the fascia of the dorsum of the neck.

(*Continued on next page.*)

The deeper layers of fascia in the anterior portion of the suprahyoid region form individual sheaths for the muscles; below, they are attached to the hyoid bone; above, to the mandible, the styloid process, and the tongue.

The suprahyoid compartment is closed by the attachment of the investing fascia to the border of the mandible above, and to the hyoid bone below. It is continuous across the middle line anteriorly, and reaches the floor of the mouth in the region of the sublingual gland and tongue.

The fascia of the infrahyoid region includes the greater part of what is commonly called the deep cervical fascia.

The investing layer of cervical fascia in the infrahyoid region splits into two sheets to invest the two prominent muscles, the sternocleidomastoideus and the trapezius; however, anteriorly it covers the anterior and posterior triangles as a single sheet except in the area just above the sternum. It is continuous superiorly with the fascia of the suprahyoid region, and inferiorly with the pectoral and deltoid fasciae. It has bony attachments as follows: superiorly, to the hyoid bone; laterally and posteriorly, to the mandible, mastoid process and superior nuchal line (through its continuity with the suprahyoid and posterior cervical fasciae); posteriorly, to the spinous process of the seventh cervical vertebra and the ligamentum nuchae (through the posterior cervical fascia); inferiorly, to the acromion, the clavicle, and the manubrium of the sternum.

The prevertebral fascia is the anterior portion of a larger complex, which encloses the vertebral column and its muscles. Below the first rib, it becomes continuous with the endothoracic fascia. As the spinal nerves emerge between the anterior and the middle scalene muscles on their way to the brachial plexus, they are covered by a prolongation from the scalenus portion of the prevertebral fascia. This prolongation encloses the nerves and the subclavian vessels, and extends deep to the clavicle into the axilla as the axillary sheath.

The middle cervical fascia invests the two layers of infrahyoid muscles, and therefore has a deep and a middle sheet. Superiorly, the three laminae are attached to the hyoid bone. At the lateral border of the omohyoid muscle, the superficial and deep sheets are fused to the under surface of the investing membrane of the neck. Inferiorly, the three layers are attached to the posterior surface of the sternum together with the muscles they invest. In the supraclavicular region, the fascia is securely fastened to the clavicle and is looped over the inferior belly of the omohyoid tendon. Beneath the sternocleidomastoid, the lateral border of the fascia is attached to the carotid sheath. A fascial cleft separates the deep surface of the fascia from the underlying visceral fascia.

The cervical fascia is essentially a tube-like prolongation of the visceral fascia of the mediastinum. It forms a compartment for the esophagus and trachea as they enter the neck from the thorax; farther superiorly, it similarly ensheaths the pharynx, larynx, and thyroid gland. It extends superiorly into the head, and is attached to the base of the skull at the pharyngeal tubercle, the pterygoid hamulus, and the mandible.

A perivisceral fascial cleft separates the visceral fascia from the middle cervical fascia anterolaterally, from the carotid sheath laterally, and from the prevertebral fascia posteriorly. As a result, the esophagus and pharynx are relatively free to move in the act of swallowing. Posterolaterally the visceral fascia has an attachment along its entire length to the tips of the transverse processes; here it is fused also with the carotid sheath and prevertebral fascia. In this way the entire perivisceral fascial cleft is divided into anterior and posterior portions. The anterior portion (the previsceral cleft) is in relation to the part of the visceral fascia that covers the trachea, larynx, and thyroid gland; the posterior portion, between the pharynx and the prevertebral fascia, is continuous downward, behind the esophagus, into the thorax.

The carotid sheath forms a tubular investment for the carotid artery, internal jugular vein, and vagus nerve. It is attached as follows: medially, to the visceral fascia; posteriorly, to the prevertebral fascia along the line of the tips of the transverse processes; laterally, to the investing fascia on the deep surface of the sternocleidomastoid; anteriorly to the middle cervical fascia along the lateral border of the sternothyreoideus. In the upper part of the neck, the sheath is fused with the fascia of the stylohyoideus and posterior belly of the digastric. With these structures, it is fastened to the skull. In the root of the neck, the sheath is adherent to the sternum and first rib; finally it becomes continuous with the fibrous pericardium. The cervical sympathetic trunk is imbedded in the fascia of the posterior wall of the sheath, and hence is not actually within the sheath.

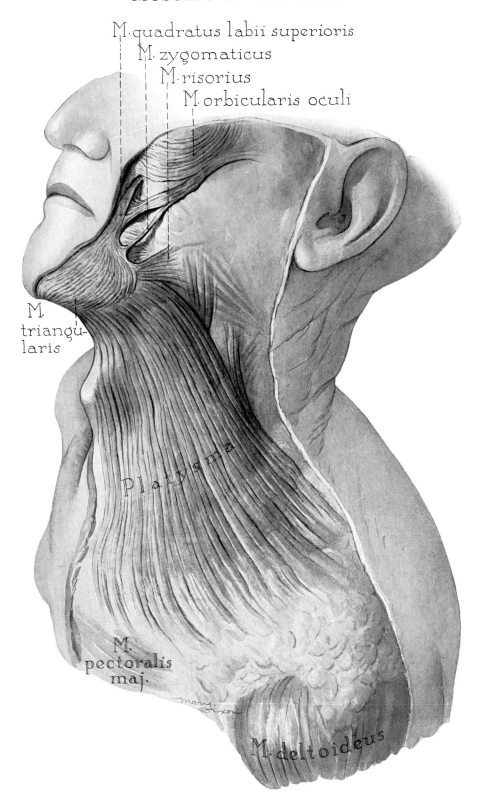

M. quadratus labii superioris
M. zygomaticus
M. risorius
M. orbicularis oculi

M. triangularis

Platysma

M. pectoralis maj.

M. deltoideus

Platysma muscle, and related muscles of facial expression.

The platysma, like the corresponding muscles of the face and scalp, is situated in the superficial fascia. This layer of tissue has been dissected away to expose the platysma muscle, the related triangularis and other facial muscles in the subcutaneous stratum.

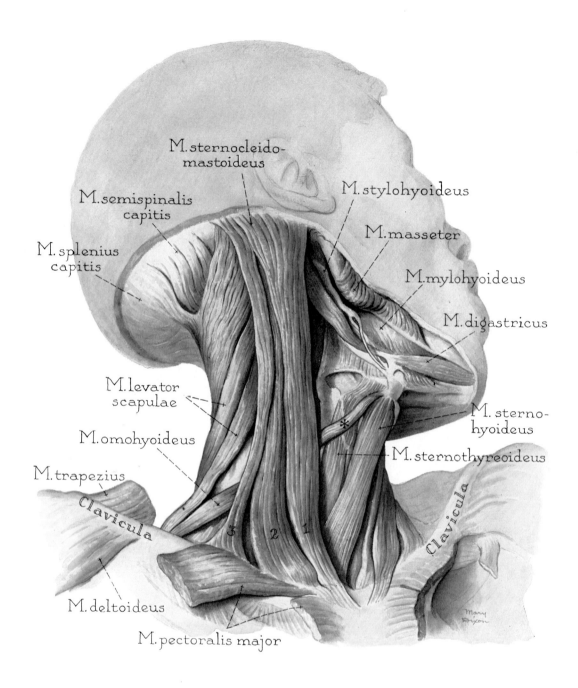

M.sternocleido-
mastoideus

M.semispinalis
capitis

M.splenius
capitis

M.stylohyoideus

M.masseter

M.mylohyoideus

M.digastricus

M.levator
scapulae

M.omohyoideus

M.trapezius

Clavicula

M. sterno-
hyoideus

M.sternothyreoideus

Clavicula

M.deltoideus

M.pectoralis major

Musculature of the neck; anterolateral view.
The following three figures record myological anatomy at successively deeper levels.

The trapezius has been removed; otherwise the cervical muscles remain in their natural positions. The subdivisions of the sternocleidomastoideus are numbered; * marks the anterior portion of the omohyoideus.

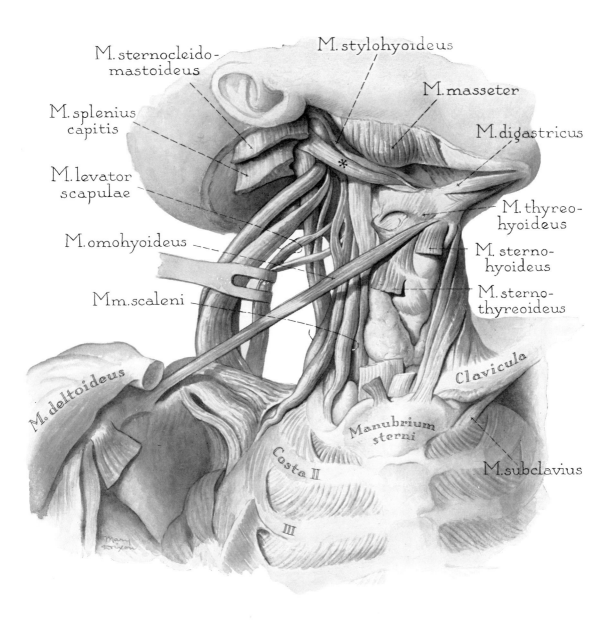

Musculature of the neck; anterolateral view. Dissection continued.

The sternocleidomastoideus muscle remains only at its origin and insertion; dorsally, the semispinalis and splenius muscles have been removed. The several bands which comprise the levator scapulae are retracted; the omohyoideus is drawn taut by abduction of the shoulder (the pectoralis major and pectoralis minor having been removed). In the anterior part of the neck the sternohyoideus and sternothyreoideus muscles have been removed, except at their extremities; in this way the underlying thyroid gland and related structures are exposed. The suprahyoid muscles remain intact. * indicates the posterior portion of the digastricus.

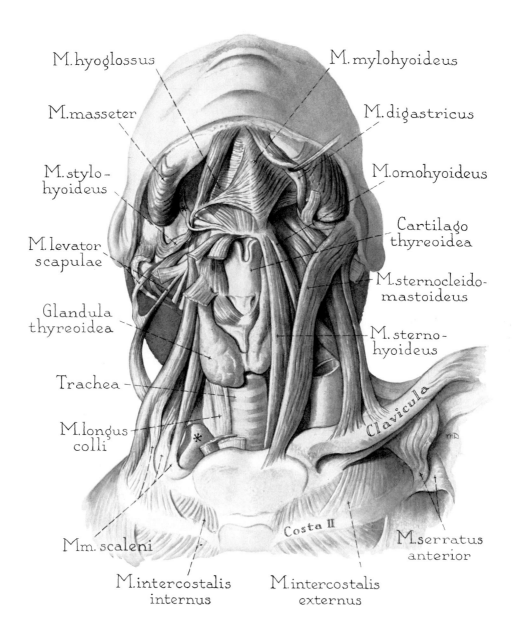

M.hyoglossus

M.masseter

M.stylo-
hyoideus

M.levator
scapulae

Glandula
thyreoidea

Trachea

M.longus
colli

M.mylohyoideus

M.digastricus

M.omohyoideus

Cartilago
thyreoidea

M.sternocleido-
mastoideus

M.sterno-
hyoideus

Clavicula

Costa II

Mm. scaleni

M.intercostalis
internus

M.intercostalis
externus

M.serratus
anterior

Musculature of the neck; anterior view. Dissection continued.

The infrahyoid muscles remain as they were in the preceding stage of the dissection, except for removal of the omohyoideus. In the suprahyoid region the anterior portion of the digastricus has been retracted on the specimen's left, to expose the mylohyoideus. The latter muscle, in this specimen, is anomalous; its right half is triangular in outline, with a narrow apical attachment to the digastricus. Because of the deficiency, a portion of the subjacent hyoglossus muscle is in view. The cupula of the pleura (at *) ascends into the basal part of the neck.

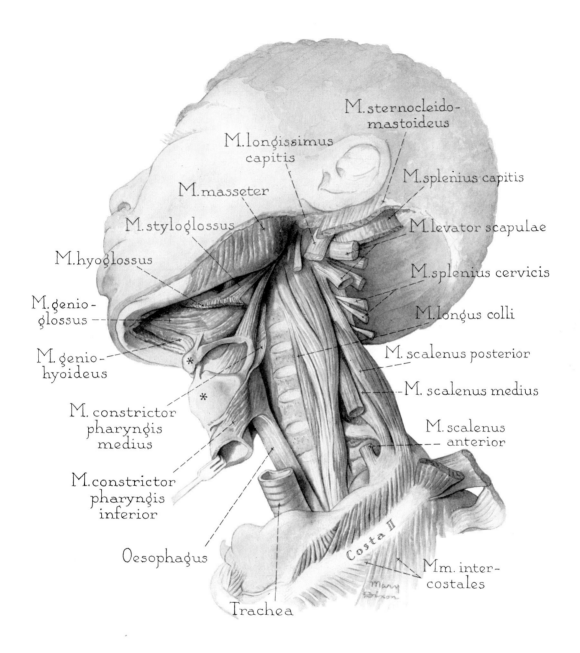

M.sternocleido-
mastoideus

M.longissimus
capitis

M.masseter

M.styloglossus

M.hyoglossus

M.genio-
glossus

M.genio-
hyoideus

M.constrictor
pharyngis
medius

M.constrictor
pharyngis
inferior

Oesophagus

M.splenius capitis

M.levator scapulae

M.splenius cervicis

M.longus colli

M.scalenus posterior

M.scalenus medius

M.scalenus
anterior

Costa II

Mm. inter-
costales

Trachea

Musculature of the neck; lateral view. Dissection concluded.

On the specimen's left side the dissection has been carried to vertebral level. Overlying muscles have been removed in order to expose the longus colli, the scaleni, the trachea (transected), and the esophagus. The thyroid cartilage and the hyoid bone (each indicated by *) are shown. In the suprahyoid region the hyoglossus muscle has been removed in its inferior, or hyoid, portion, with consequent exposure of the genioglossus.

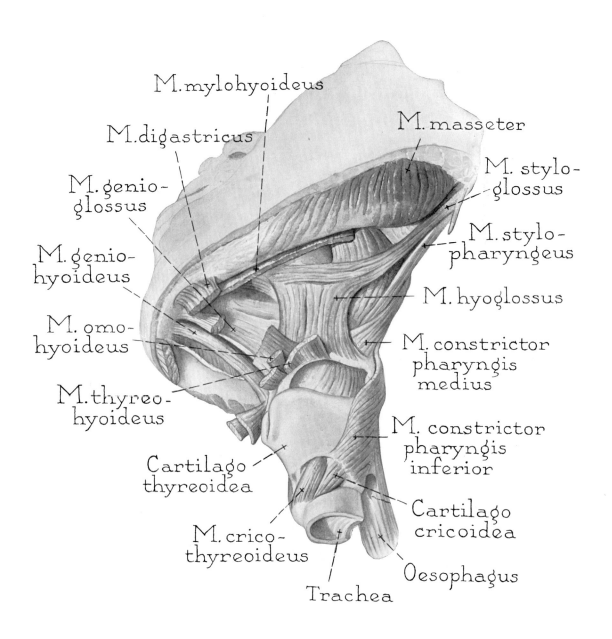

M.mylohyoideus

M.digastricus

M.genio-
glossus

M.genio-
hyoideus

M. omo-
hyoideus

M.thyreo-
hyoideus

Cartilago
thyreoidea

M. crico-
thyreoideus

Trachea

M.masseter

M. stylo-
glossus

M.stylo-
pharyngeus

M. hyoglossus

M. constrictor
pharyngis
medius

M. constrictor
pharyngis
inferior

Cartilago
cricoidea

Oesophagus

Musculature of the neck, especially the suprahyoid region. Inferolateral view, left side.

The midportion of the geniohyoideus has been excised; the thyroid cartilage has been freed of the thyreohyoideus, and the thyroid gland has been excised.

The mylohyoideus, which constitutes the muscular floor of the mouth, has been cut near to the mandible,
where its origin is close to the insertion of the masseter, of the masticator group of muscles. The following
extrinsic muscles of the tongue are exposed: the hyoglossus, genioglossus, and styloglossus. The stylopharyngeus and the constrictor pharyngis, of the pharyngeal group, are also seen.

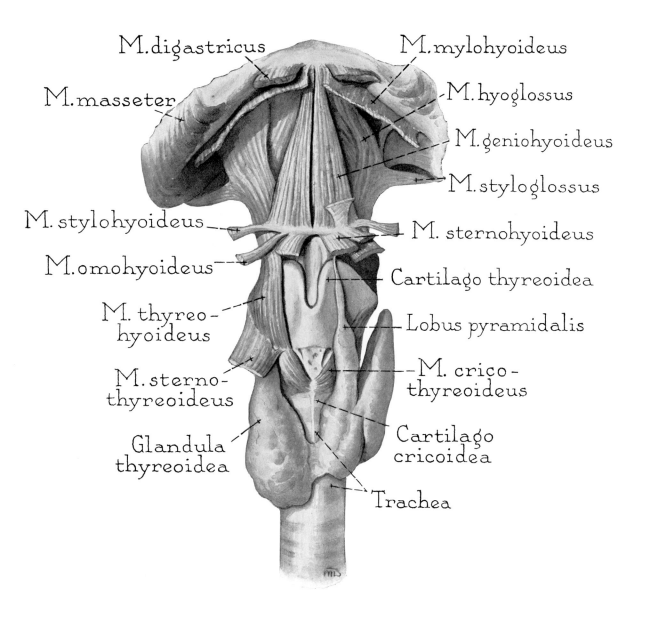

M.digastricus

M.mylohyoideus

M.masseter

M.hyoglossus

M.geniohyoideus

M.styloglossus

M.stylohyoideus

M. sternohyoideus

M.omohyoideus

Cartilago thyreoidea

M. thyreo-
hyoideus

Lobus pyramidalis

M.sterno-
thyreoideus

M. crico-
thyreoideus

Glandula
thyreoidea

Cartilago
cricoidea

Trachea

Musculature of the neck, especially the suprahyoid region. Anterior view.

Of the suprahyoid group of muscles, the following members have been removed: the digastricus, the mylohyoideus, and the stylohyoideus. In this way, the deeper muscles have been brought into view; from the lateral aspect to the midline, these muscles are in succession the styloglossus, hyoglossus, and geniohyoideus.

In the infrahyoid region, the omohyoideus, sternohyoideus, and sternothyreoideus remain at their insertions into the hyoid bone and thyroid cartilage. The short muscles that pass from the thyroid to the cricoid cartilage and the hyoid bone are exposed by the removal of the above-mentioned longer muscles.

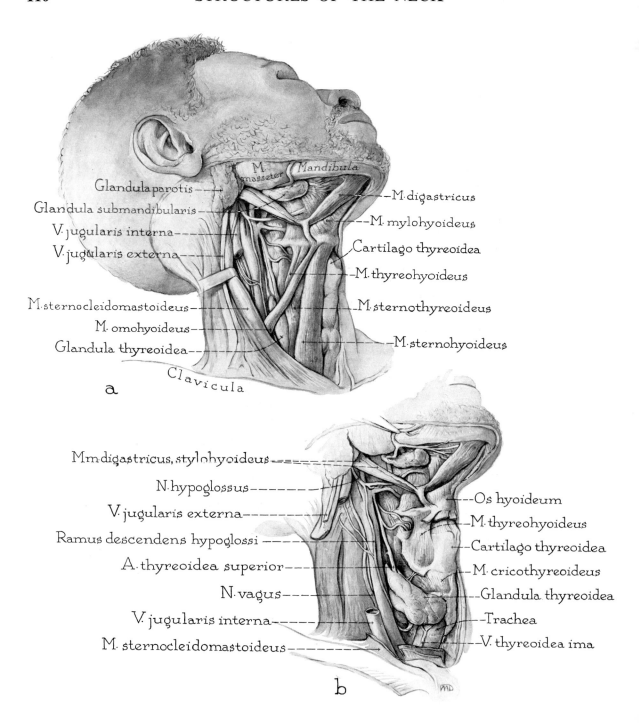

Glandula parotis---

Glandula submandibularis---

V. jugularis interna---

V. jugularis externa---

M. sternocleidomastoideus---

M. omohyoideus---

Glandula thyreoidea---

Clavicula

M. masseter   Mandibula

---M. digastricus

---M. mylohyoideus

Cartilago thyreoidea

---M. thyreohyoideus

---M. sternothyreoideus

---M. sternohyoideus

a

Mm. digastricus, stylohyoideus---

N. hypoglossus---

V. jugularis externa---

Ramus descendens hypoglossi---

A. thyreoidea superior---

N. vagus---

V. jugularis interna---

M. sternocleidomastoideus---

---Os hyoideum

---M. thyreohyoideus

---Cartilago thyreoidea

---M. cricothyreoideus

---Glandula thyreoidea

---Trachea

---V. thyreoidea ima

b

Muscles, vessels and nerves of the neck; lateral view.

In *a*, the sternocleidomastoid muscle has been reflected, the lymph nodes excised, thereby revealing the contents and the triangular spaces of the neck, and the muscles that form the boundaries of these topographical areas (see page 100).

In *b*, the infrahyoid muscles have been cut away to expose the thyroid gland and blood vessels. The fascia that constitutes the carotid sheath has been dissected away in order to demonstrate the internal jugular vein, the common carotid artery, and the accompanying vagus and hypoglossal nerves. In the suprahyoid area the chief contents of the digastric triangle lie *in situ*.

The following four figures carry the dissection to successively deeper levels.

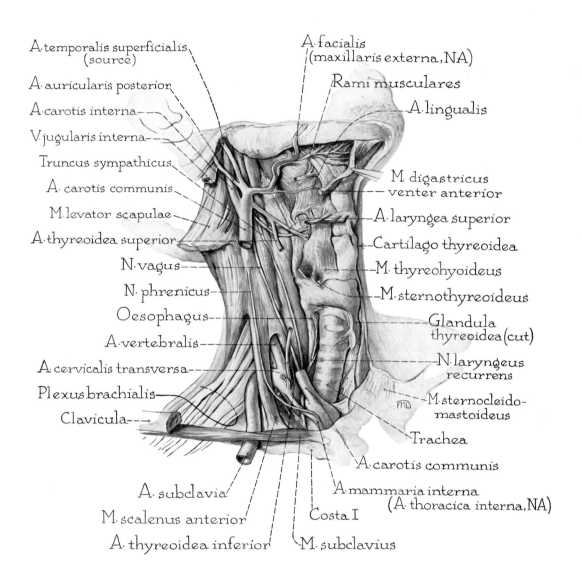

A·temporalis superficialis,
(source)

A·auricularis posterior,

A·carotis interna---

V·jugularis interna---

Truncus sympathicus,

A·carotis communis,

M·levator scapulae,

A·thyreoidea superior,

N·vagus---

N·phrenicus---

Oesophagus---

A·vertebralis---

A·cervicalis transversa---

Plexus brachialis---

Clavicula---

A·facialis
(maxillaris externa, NA)

Rami musculares

A·lingualis

M·digastricus
venter anterior

A·laryngea superior

Cartilago thyreoidea

M·thyreohyoideus

M·sternothyreoideus

Glandula
thyreoidea (cut)

N·laryngeus
recurrens

M·sternocleido-
mastoideus

Trachea

A·carotis communis

A·mammaria interna
(A·thoracica interna, NA)

A·subclavia

M·scalenus anterior

A·thyreoidea inferior

Costa I

M·subclavius

Structures of the neck; dissection continued.

The thyroid gland has been removed to expose the trachea, the middle two fourths of the common carotid artery excised to show the phrenic and vagus nerves and sympathetic trunk. Removal of the sternal part of the clavicle reveals the subclavius muscle, and the relation thereto of the brachial plexus and subclavian artery.

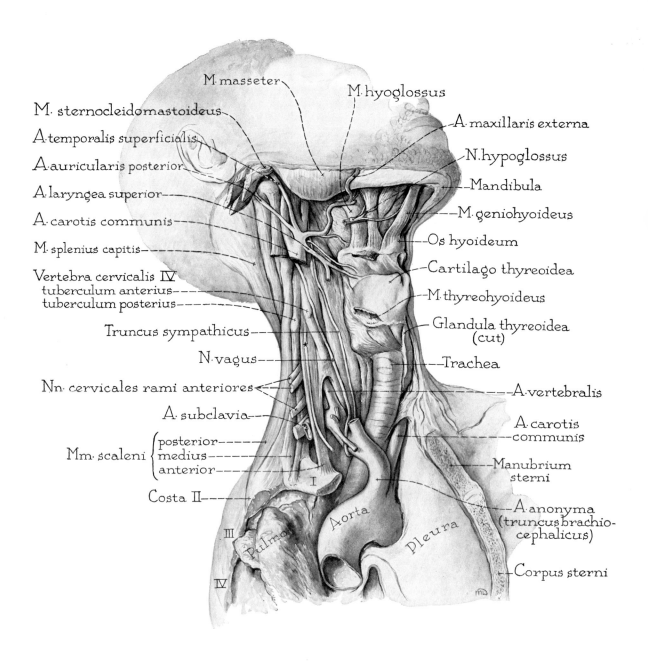

M. masseter

M. hyoglossus

M. sternocleidomastoideus

A. temporalis superficialis

A. auricularis posterior

A. laryngea superior

A. carotis communis

M. splenius capitis

Vertebra cervicalis IV
tuberculum anterius
tuberculum posterius

Truncus sympathicus

N. vagus

Nn. cervicales rami anteriores

A. subclavia

Mm. scaleni { posterior / medius / anterior

Costa II

III

IV

Pulmo

Aorta

I

Pleura

A. maxillaris externa

N. hypoglossus

Mandibula

M. geniohyoideus

Os hyoideum

Cartilago thyreoidea

M. thyreohyoideus

Glandula thyreoidea
(cut)

Trachea

A. vertebralis

A. carotis
communis

Manubrium
sterni

A. anonyma
(truncus brachio-
cephalicus)

Corpus sterni

Structures of the neck and thorax; dissection continued.

The thoracic cage has been opened to demonstrate the course of the branches of the aortic arch; the subclavian artery and the rami contributing to the brachial plexus are shown (transected) as they leave the triangular space between the scalene muscles.

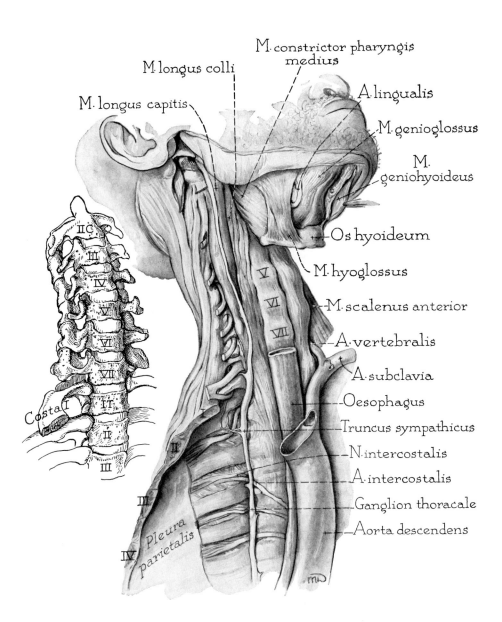

M. constrictor pharyngis medius

M. longus colli

M. longus capitis

A. lingualis

M. genioglossus

M. geniohyoideus

Os hyoideum

M. hyoglossus

M. scalenus anterior

A. vertebralis

A. subclavia

Oesophagus

Truncus sympathicus

N. intercostalis

A. intercostalis

Ganglion thoracale

Aorta descendens

Pleura parietalis

Costa I

Structures of the neck and thorax; dissection continued.

In the neck the dissection has been carried to prevertebral and paravertebral level by excision of the trachea and esophagus. In the thorax are shown the structures of the posterior mediastinum. *Inset:* Cervical and upper thoracic vertebrae.

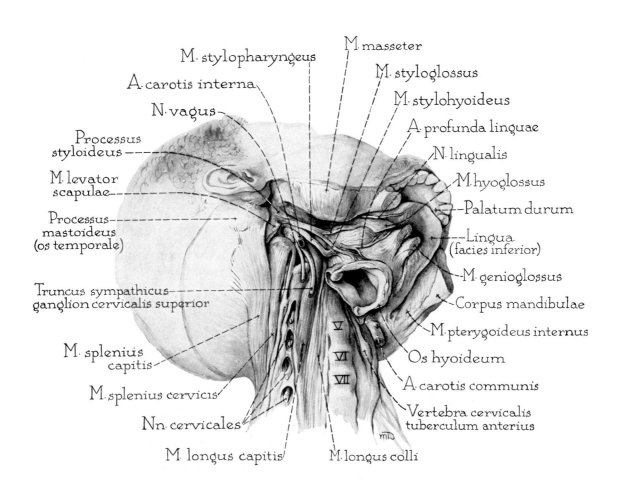

M. stylopharyngeus

M. masseter

A. carotis interna

M. styloglossus

N. vagus

M. stylohyoideus

Processus
styloideus

A. profunda linguae

N. lingualis

M. levator
scapulae

M. hyoglossus

Processus
mastoideus
(os temporale)

Palatum durum

Lingua
(facies inferior)

Truncus sympathicus
ganglion cervicalis superior

M. genioglossus

Corpus mandibulae

M. pterygoideus internus

M. splenius
capitis

V

VI

VII

Os hyoideum

M. splenius cervicis

A. carotis communis

Nn. cervicales

Vertebra cervicalis
tuberculum anterius

M. longus capitis

M. longus colli

Structures of the neck; dissection concluded.

Dissection of the anterior rami of the cervical nerves is carried to the level at which they emerge through the intervertebral foramina. The head is tilted to demonstrate the glossal as well as the upper portions of the deep cervical muscles.

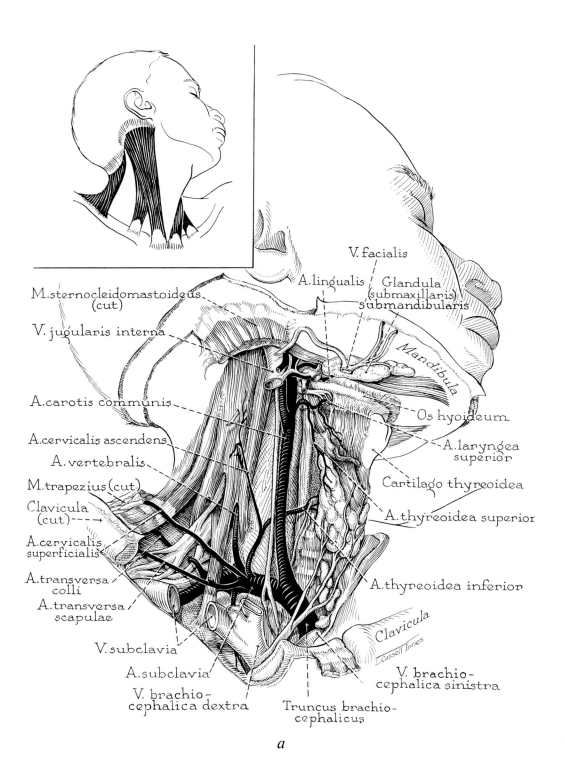

M.sternocleidomastoideus (cut)

V. jugularis interna

A.carotis communis

A.cervicalis ascendens

A. vertebralis

M.trapezius (cut)

Clavicula (cut)

A.cervicalis superficialis

A.transversa colli

A.transversa scapulae

V.subclavia

A.subclavia

V. brachio-cephalica dextra

Truncus brachio-cephalicus

V. facialis

A.lingualis

Glandula (submaxillaris) submandibularis

Mandibula

Os hyoideum

A.laryngea superior

Cartilago thyreoidea

A.thyreoidea superior

A.thyreoidea inferior

Clavicula

V. brachio-cephalica sinistra

E.Cassell Innes

a

The deep anatomy of the neck, in anterolateral view. See following page for discussion.

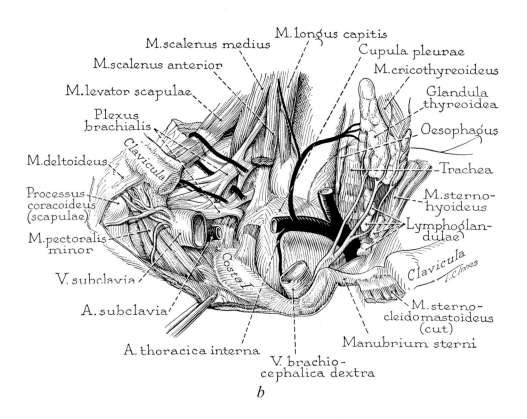

b

The deep anatomy of the neck, in anterolateral view (continued).

In *a*, the sternocleidomastoideus muscle (see inset) and the clavicle have been removed, together with the infrahyoid muscles. The internal jugular vein has been excised; a segment has been removed from the right subclavian vein, in order to expose laterally the subclavian artery in its relation to the scalene muscles and the brachial plexus. Medially, the thyroid gland and its blood vessels are revealed.

In *b*, an additional segment of the vein has been excised to include a portion of the brachiocephalic. Similarly, a piece has been cut from the subclavian artery. In this way, the cupula of the pleura is exposed as it rises to an appreciable extent above the level of the first rib.

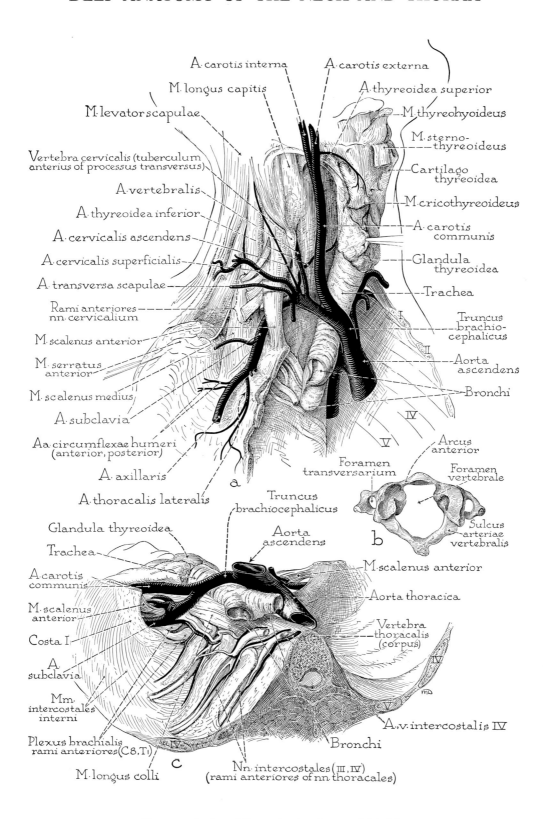

A. carotis interna

A. carotis externa

M. longus capitis

A. thyreoidea superior

M. levator scapulae

M. thyreohyoideus

M. sterno-
thyreoideus

Vertebra cervicalis (tuberculum
anterius of processus transversus)

Cartilago
thyreoidea

A. vertebralis

M. cricothyreoideus

A. thyreoidea inferior

A. carotis
communis

A. cervicalis ascendens

A. cervicalis superficialis

Glandula
thyreoidea

A. transversa scapulae

Trachea

Rami anteriores
nn. cervicalium

Truncus
brachio-
cephalicus

M. scalenus anterior

Aorta
ascendens

M. serratus
anterior

Bronchi

M. scalenus medius

A. subclavia

Aa. circumflexae humeri
(anterior, posterior)

Arcus
anterior

A. axillaris

Foramen
vertebrale

Foramen
transversarium

A. thoracalis lateralis

a

Sulcus
arteriae
vertebralis

b

Truncus
brachiocephalicus

Glandula thyreoidea

Aorta
ascendens

Trachea

M. scalenus anterior

A. carotis
communis

Aorta thoracica

M. scalenus
anterior

Vertebra
thoracalis
(corpus)

Costa I

A.
subclavia

Mm.
intercostales
interni

A. v. intercostalis IV

Plexus brachialis
rami anteriores (C8, T1)

c

Bronchi

M. longus colli

Nn. intercostales (III, IV)
(rami anteriores of nn. thoracales)

Deep cervical and thoracic structures; right side.

a and *c*, The neck, subclavian region, and upper mediastinum; viewed from the side and below. *b*, The atlas, showing foramen and sulcus for the vertebral branch of the subclavian artery.

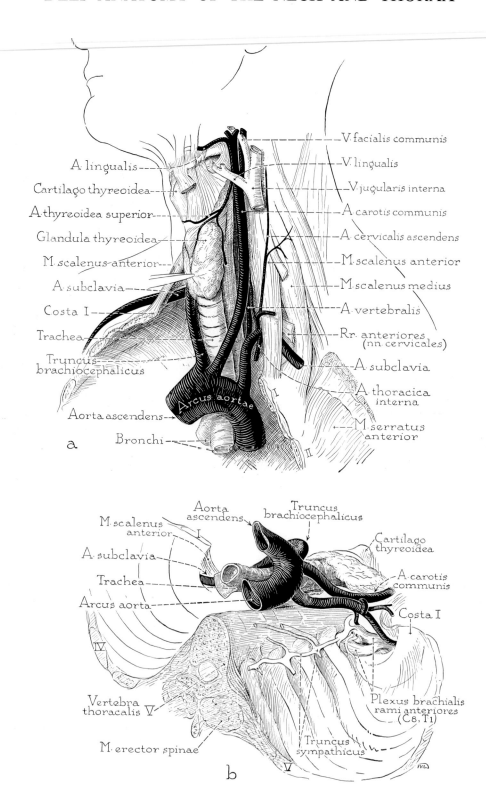

A lingualis
Cartilago thyreoidea
A thyreoidea superior
Glandula thyreoidea
M scalenus anterior
A subclavia
Costa I
Trachea
Truncus brachiocephalicus
Aorta ascendens
Bronchi

V facialis communis
V lingualis
V jugularis interna
A carotis communis
A cervicalis ascendens
M scalenus anterior
M scalenus medius
A vertebralis
Rr anteriores (nn cervicales)
A subclavia
A thoracica interna
M serratus anterior

a

M scalenus anterior
A subclavia
Trachea
Arcus aorta

Aorta ascendens
Truncus brachiocephalicus
Cartilago thyreoidea
A carotis communis
Costa I
Plexus brachialis rami anteriores (C8, T1)

Vertebra thoracalis V
M erector spinae
Truncus sympathicus

b

Deep cervical and thoracic structures; left side.

a, Prevertebral and paravertebral anatomy; anterolateral view. *b*, Superior mediastinal part of the aorta, its major branches, and the trachea at its bifurcation; inferolateral view.

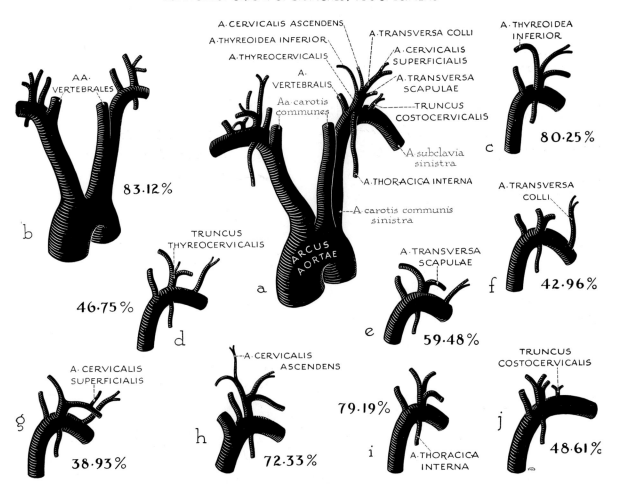

ARTERIA SUBCLAVIA
COMMONEST ORIGIN OF BRANCHES, 400 SPECIMENS

Most frequent origin of each of the branches of the subclavian artery.

Other origins occur with varying frequency. For example, in the case of the vertebral artery, 5 other sites of origin were encountered in the examination of 400 specimens, the lowest frequency being 0.72 per cent.

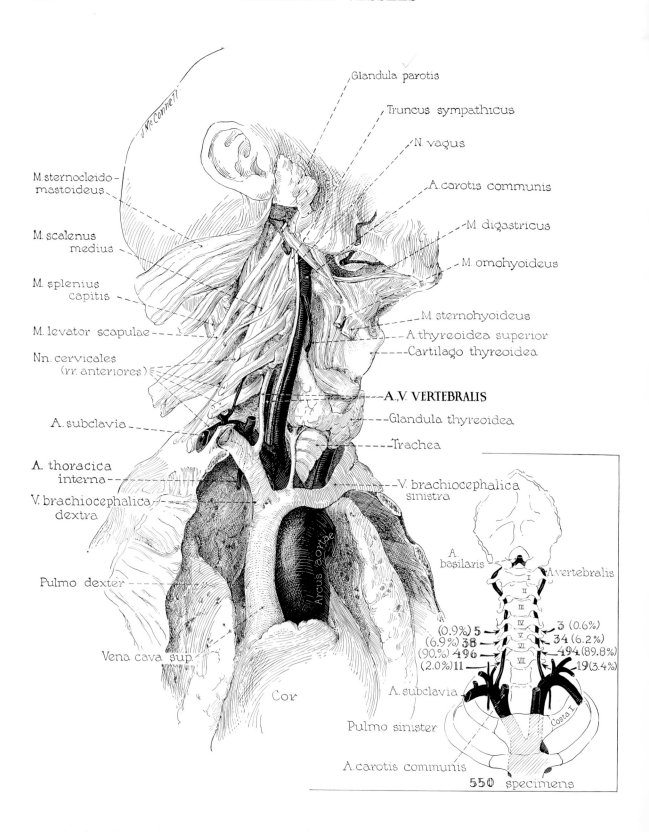

Glandula parotis

Truncus sympathicus

N. vagus

A. carotis communis

M. digastricus

M. omohyoideus

M. sternocleido-mastoideus

M. scalenus medius

M. splenius capitis

M. levator scapulae

Nn. cervicales (rr. anteriores)

M. sternohyoideus

A. thyreoidea superior

Cartilago thyreoidea

A. V. VERTEBRALIS

Glandula thyreoidea

Trachea

A. subclavia

A. thoracica interna

V. brachiocephalica dextra

V. brachiocephalica sinistra

Arcus aortae

Pulmo dexter

Vena cava sup.

Cor

A. basilaris

A. vertebralis

(0.9%) 5   3 (0.6%)

(6.9%) 38   34 (6.2%)

(90.%) 496   494 (89.8%)

(2.0%) 11   19 (3.4%)

A. subclavia

Pulmo sinister

Costa I.

A. carotis communis

550 specimens

Aortic arch, superior vena cava, and their major arterial branches and venous tributaries; emphasizing the vertebral vessels. Anterolateral view. *Inset* (lower right): Levels of entry of the vertebral artery into the transverse foramina of the cervical vertebrae; percentage occurrence in 550 specimens.

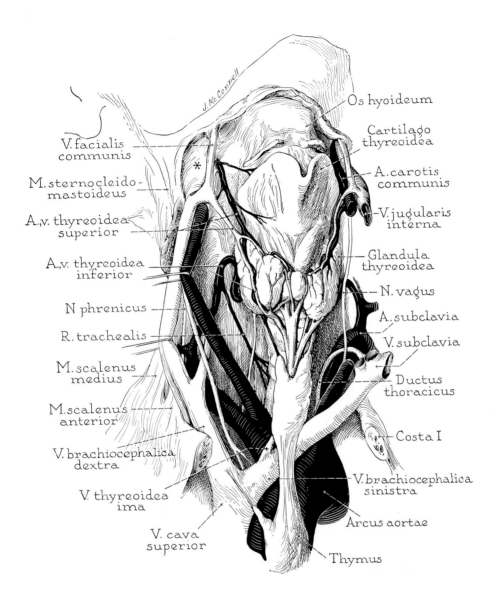

Os hyoideum

Cartilago thyreoidea

V. facialis communis

M. sternocleido-mastoideus

A.,v. thyreoidea superior

A.,v. thyreoidea inferior

N phrenicus

R. trachealis

M. scalenus medius

M. scalenus anterior

V. brachiocephalica dextra

V. thyreoidea ima

V. cava superior

A. carotis communis

V. jugularis interna

Glandula thyreoidea

N. vagus

A. subclavia

V. subclavia

Ductus thoracicus

Costa I

V. brachiocephalica sinistra

Arcus aortae

Thymus

J. McConnell

Blood vessels, glands and related structures in the neck. Anterolateral view.

The sternocleidomastoid muscle, the infrahyoid musculature and the cervical fascia (including the carotid sheath), the sternum, clavicles, and sternal portions of the ribs have been removed. Showing, especially, the arteries and veins of the thyroid gland and thymus, and the vessels related to the terminal portion of the thoracic duct (lower right) and the submaxillary gland (upper left, at *).

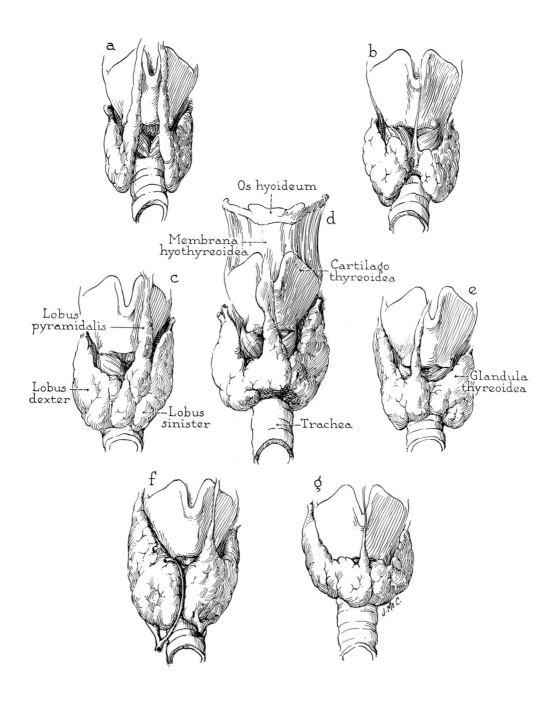

Thyroid gland: variation in form and size.

The gland may be disposed in two separate portions (*a*); the pyramidal lobe may lie in or near the median plane (*b*, *c* and *g*), to either the right (*e*) or to the left thereof (*c* and *f*).

PLEXUS CERVICALIS
(RAMI VENTRALES)

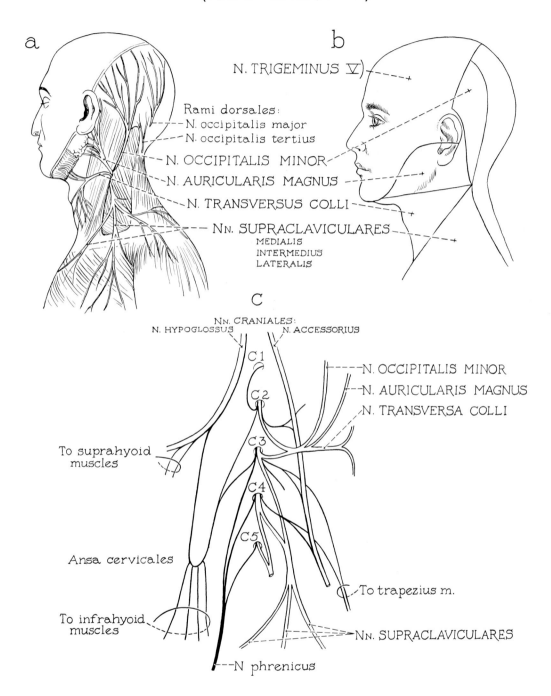

a

b

N. TRIGEMINUS V)

Rami dorsales:
N. occipitalis major
N. occipitalis tertius
N. OCCIPITALIS MINOR
N. AURICULARIS MAGNUS
N. TRANSVERSUS COLLI
Nn. SUPRACLAVICULARES
MEDIALIS
INTERMEDIUS
LATERALIS

c

Nn. CRANIALES:
N. HYPOGLOSSUS   N. ACCESSORIUS

C1

C2

C3

C4

C5

To suprahyoid muscles

Ansa cervicales

To infrahyoid muscles

N phrenicus

N. OCCIPITALIS MINOR
N. AURICULARIS MAGNUS
N. TRANSVERSA COLLI

To trapezius m.

Nn. SUPRACLAVICULARES

Cervical plexus.

a, The course of the branches (in capital lettering) from the point of their emergence along the dorsal border of the sternocleidomastoid muscle. b, The areas of cutaneous supply. c, The plexus, shown schematically.

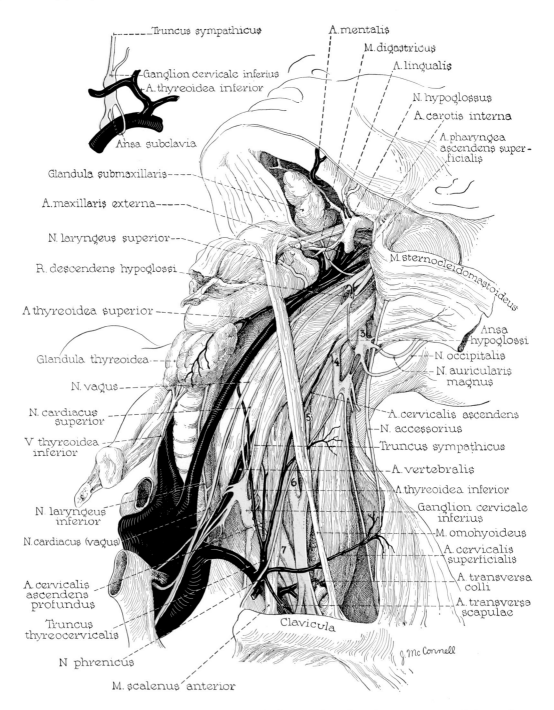

Cervical sympathetic trunk and ganglia in relation to the other deep structures of the neck.

The contents of both the anterior and posterior triangles of the neck have been exposed by reflection of the sternocleidomastoideus; the omohyoideus is drawn taut by elevation of the head. The infrahyoid muscles remain as cut extremities at the hyoid bone and thyroid cartilage. The aortic arch, together with its main branches and the derived arteries, are retained, but the corresponding veins have been excised. The pulmonary artery has been transected near the point at which it is connected with the aortic arch by the arterial ligament (at *). The innominate (NA, bracheocephalic) vein remains as a segment where it receives the inferior thyroid vein. Certain of the contributory rami (numbered 3 to 7) and derived nerves of the cervical and brachial plexuses are shown, as well as the cervical sympathetic trunk and its larger ganglia and related nerve.

Inset (upper left): Inferior cervical ganglion and the ansa subclavia in the same specimen.

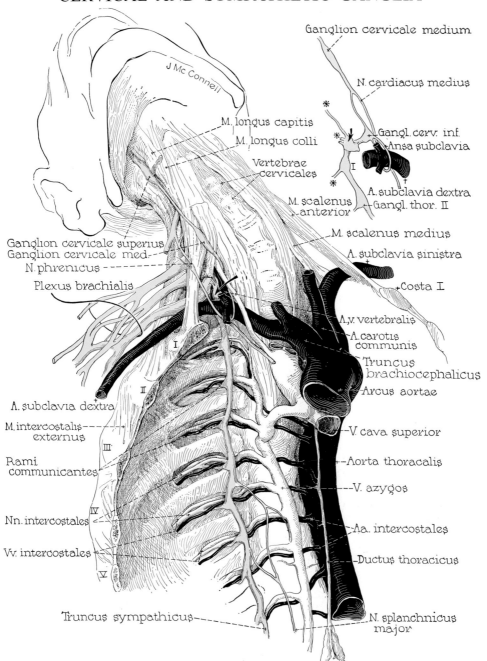

Cervical sympathetic ganglia, with related deep muscles and vessels of the neck and the thoracic sympathetic ganglia.

Showing the ganglionated chain in the neck in relation to the vertebral artery and vein, the longus capitis, longus colli, and scaleni; comparably, in the thorax, the segmental continuation of the chain is shown in relation to the vertebral column, the aorta with its intercostal branches, azygos vein and its tributaries, and the thoracic duct. For exposure of these structures, the following were removed; the upper extremities and the pectoral girdle; the front of the thoracic cage; the cervical and thoracic organs; all musculature dorsalward to the level of the scaleni and longus colli; the arteries, with the exception of those which give origin to deep branches; the nerves, except the sympathetic elements and the brachial plexus.

Inset (upper right): Middle and inferior cervical sympathetic ganglia (at arrow), first and second thoracic ganglia, and the communicating rami (at *). In this specimen there occurred partial fusion of the inferior cervical and first thoracic ganglia, a portion of each of these contributing to the bulk of the stellate ganglion (at arrow). The ansa subclavia passed between cranial and caudal parts of the inferior ganglion.

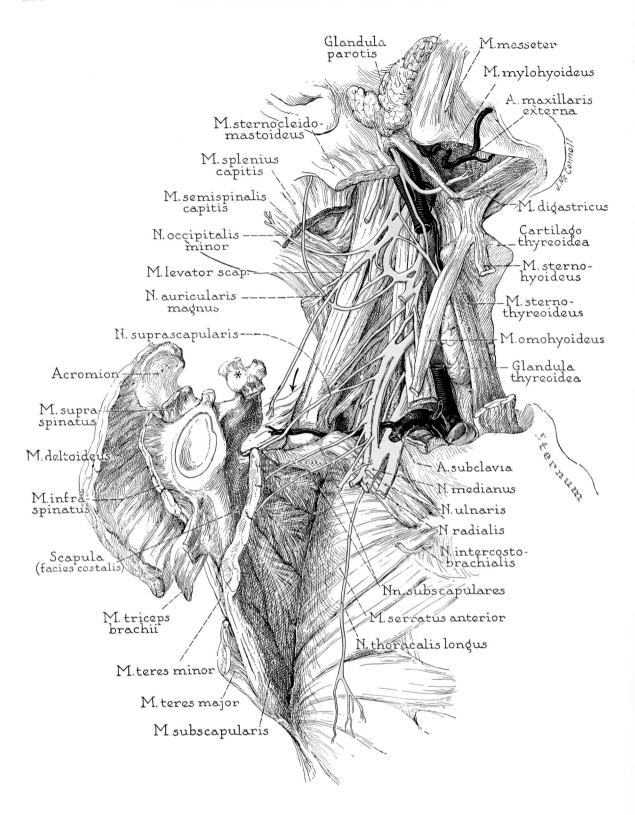

Deep structures of the neck and axilla; anterolateral view.

The dissection pictured in the preceding figure has been extended to include the dorsum of the neck, the medial and dorsal walls of the axilla, and the deeper aspect of anterolateral portion of the neck.

On the side of the neck the scaleni, the levator scapulae, and the splenius capitis have been exposed, where these muscles form the floor of the posterior triangle. The last-named muscle has been partially removed, to reveal the subjacent semispinalis capitis muscle.

In the anterior portion of the neck, on the floor of the anterior triangle, the sternothyreoideus muscle has been exposed through partial removal of the sternohyoideus. A segment of the costal extremity of the scalenus anterior has been excised, to reveal the brachial artery. In the area which lies deep to the sternocleidomastoideus muscle, the anterior rami of the cervical nerves are seen, as they emerge from the scalene muscles to form the cervical and brachial plexuses of nerves.

The arm has been removed at the shoulder joint; the clavicle has been disarticulated at the acromioclavicular and sternoclavicular joints and, like the arm, has been removed from the body. In this removal, the following muscles have been transected or partially removed: the trapezius (cut at arrow); the deltoideus, as it descends from the spine of the scapula; the supraspinatus and infraspinatus muscle, as they emerge, respectively, from the supraspinous and infraspinous fossae on the dorsum of the scapula; the teres minor and teres major, as these muscles extend toward the humerus from the axillary border of the scapula; and the subscapularis, as it passes lateralward from the costal surface of the scapula. The muscles of the chest have been removed. In disarticulating the arm the following brachial muscles were cut at their proximal extremities: the long head of the triceps brachii, as it arises (in two laminae) from the infraglenoid area of the scapula; the biceps brachii, as it takes origin from the supraglenoid tuberosity and the coracoid process of the scapula; the coracobrachialis, as it arises in common with the long head of the preceding (these muscles unlabelled). In this way, the axillary space has been widened. As shown, the posterior boundary is formed by the subscapularis and teres major muscles; the muscles which form the medial boundary are the serratus anterior and the intercostales externi.

Through removal of the sternocleidomastoideus muscle and abduction of the scapula, the nerves, derived from the cervical and brachial plexuses, which supply structures in the area between the occiput and the caudal limit of the axillae, have been traced to their terminations. The long thoracic nerve is followed downward to its thoracic termination in the serratus anterior muscle. In the more cranial area the lesser occipital and great auricular nerves are shown, from their points of origin as cervical rami to the areas where they attain the occiput and the ear. The nerves which cross the neck and which descend upon the chest (cutaneous colli, supraclaviculares) have been cut near their points of origin from the cervical plexus. At the base of the neck are seen the subclavian vessels, the costocervical trunk and its branches, and the transverse cervical and transverse scapular arteries.

In this specimen the first cervical nerve sends most of its fibers (with the accessory nerve) to the sternocleidomastoideus muscle; in the area exposed, it sends no communicating fibers to the cervical plexus. The second, third and fourth nerves contribute to the formation of the plexiform loop; in addition to nerves pictured in the preceding figures, a branch to the trapezius muscle is shown; this cervical contribution is auxiliary to that derived from the accessory nerve (latter removed).

The following nerves from the brachial plexus which supply the arm, forearm and hand are shown transected: musculocutaneous, axillary, median and ulnar.

On the coracoid process (at *) of the scapula the cut ends of the following muscles are shown: pectoralis minor (insertion); coracobrachialis and the long head of the biceps brachii (origins).

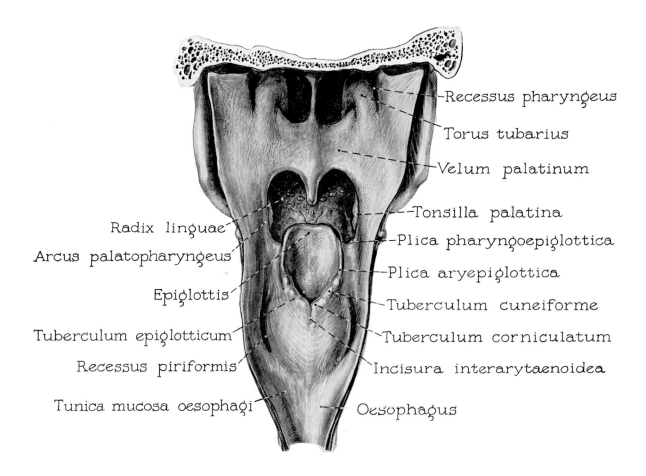

Recessus pharyngeus

Torus tubarius

Velum palatinum

Tonsilla palatina

Plica pharyngoepiglottica

Plica aryepiglottica

Tuberculum cuneiforme

Tuberculum corniculatum

Incisura interarytaenoidea

Oesophagus

Radix linguae

Arcus palatopharyngeus

Epiglottis

Tuberculum epiglotticum

Recessus piriformis

Tunica mucosa oesophagi

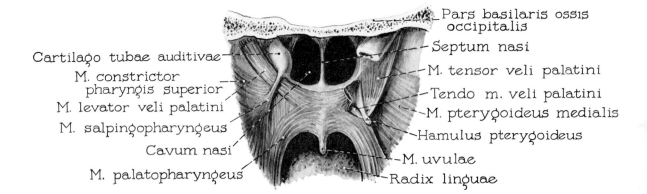

Pars basilaris ossis occipitalis

Septum nasi

M. tensor veli palatini

Tendo m. veli palatini

M. pterygoideus medialis

Hamulus pterygoideus

M. uvulae

Radix linguae

Cartilago tubae auditivae

M. constrictor pharyngis superior

M. levator veli palatini

M. salpingopharyngeus

Cavum nasi

M. palatopharyngeus

Pharynx, opened and viewed from behind.

Upper figure, The mucous membrane is intact.
Lower figure, The muscles and tendons of the palate and pharynx are shown by removal of the mucous membrane. (From Warren: Handbook of Anatomy, Harvard University Press.)

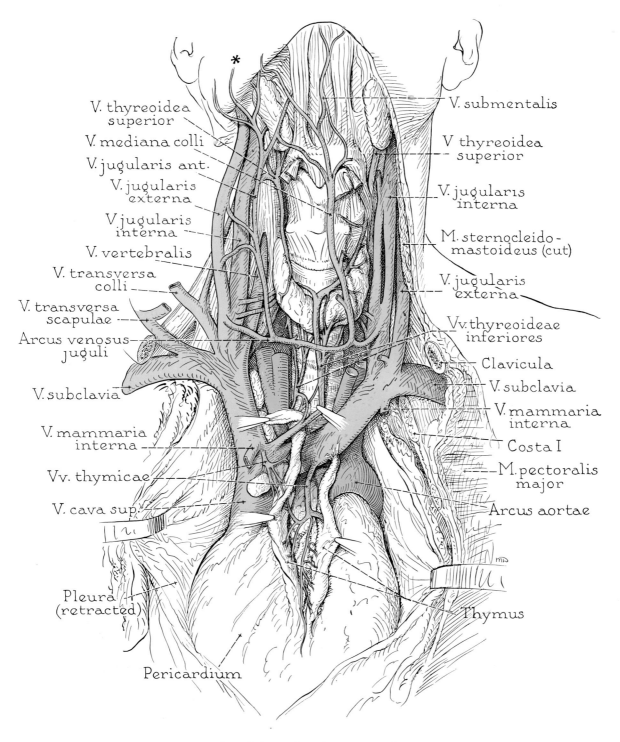

*

V. thyreoidea
superior

V. mediana colli

V. jugularis ant.

V. jugularis
externa

V. jugularis
interna

V. vertebralis

V. transversa
colli

V. transversa
scapulae

Arcus venosus
juguli

V. subclavia

V. mammaria
interna

Vv. thymicae

V. cava sup.

Pleura
(retracted)

Pericardium

V. submentalis

V thyreoidea
superior

V. jugularis
interna

M. sternocleido-
mastoideus (cut)

V. jugularis
externa

Vv. thyreoideae
inferiores

Clavicula

V. subclavia

V. mammaria
interna

Costa I

M. pectoralis
major

Arcus aortae

Thymus

Veins of the neck and upper member.

The veins of cervical, axillary, and precordial source converge upon the brachiocephalic veins; the latter join to form the superior vena cava.

The thoracic wall has been removed and the pericardial sac opened; in the neck, the dissection has been carried to the level of the thyroid gland. Both the superficial and deep veins are shown, including the vessels of superficial level (cranialward to those which, at *, descend from the mandibular region), the veins which drain the thyroid gland and the thymus. The internal mammary (NA, thoracic) and other small veins have been cut.

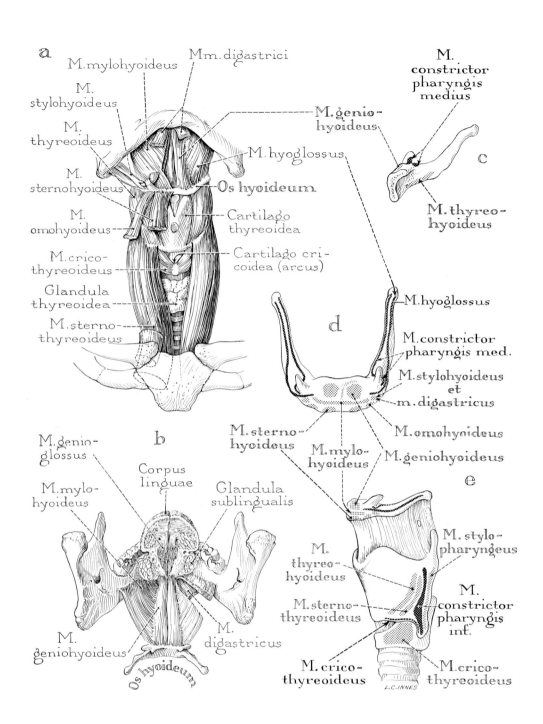

Mandible, hyoid bone, and thyroid cartilage; areas of attachment of glossal, suprahyoid, and infrahyoid muscles.

a, The musculature, seen from the front. *b*, Glossal and related muscles, seen from behind. *c*, Hyoid bone, right half, in medial view. *d*, Hyoid bone, entire, in anterior view. *e*, Hyoid bone and thyroid cartilage, anterolateral aspect.

Origins indicated by dark pattern on areas of attachment and by heavy lettering; insertions by light pattern and open lettering.

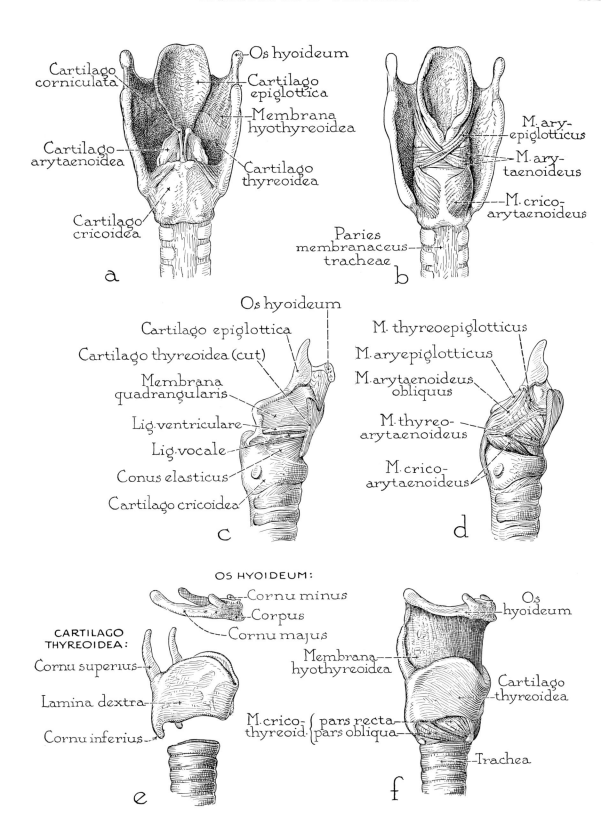

Larynx and trachea: musculature, membrane and supporting cartilaginous and osseous framework.
a and *b* are posterior views; *c* to *f* are seen from the right side.

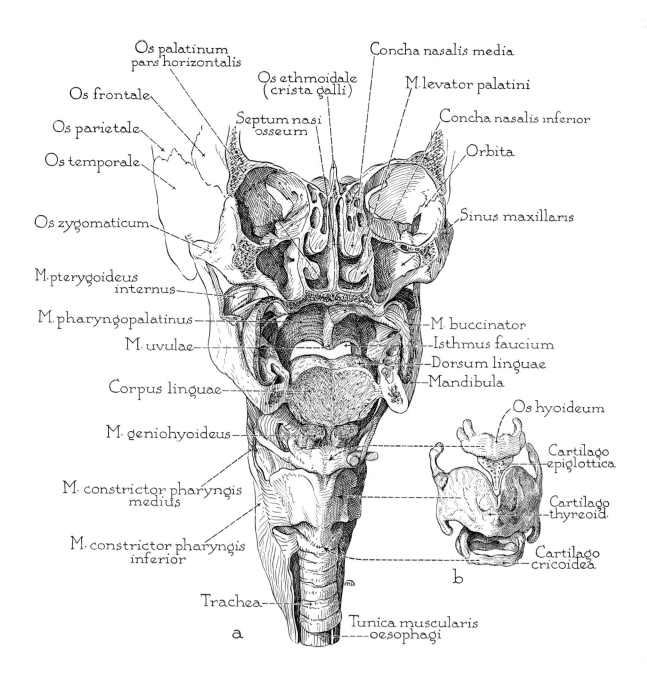

Nasal and oral portions of the pharynx with supporting and other related structures.

a, The pharynx shown in a frontal section of the head. Except in the pharyngeal region, the bones of the skull are shown freed of all soft tissue. The mucous membrane has been removed from the palate. A portion of the hyoglossus muscle has been cut away in order to expose the lesser cornu of the hyoid bone.

b, The hyoid bone and the larger cartilages of the larynx. Seen from the front.

The hyoid bone presents a body (*corpus*) which is convex forward, and two pairs of horn-like projections (*cornua*). The thyroid cartilage is made up of two symmetrical plates of quadrilateral form which are together in the median line; the posterior edge of each plate is prolonged upward and downward into a process (cornu), of which the upper is the longer. The cricoid cartilage possesses the form of a signet ring; its broader part (*lamina*) is behind, while the narrower, arciform portion (*arcus*) is in front.

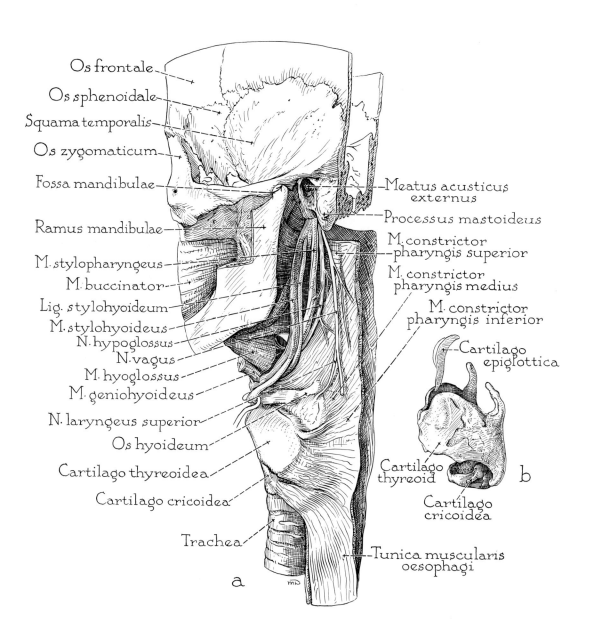

Os frontale
Os sphenoidale
Squama temporalis
Os zygomaticum
Fossa mandibulae
Ramus mandibulae
M. stylopharyngeus
M. buccinator
Lig. stylohyoideum
M. stylohyoideus
N. hypoglossus
N. vagus
M. hyoglossus
M. geniohyoideus
N. laryngeus superior
Os hyoideum
Cartilago thyreoidea
Cartilago cricoidea
Trachea

Meatus acusticus externus
Processus mastoideus
M. constrictor pharyngis superior
M. constrictor pharyngis medius
M. constrictor pharyngis inferior
Cartilago epiglottica
Cartilago thyreoid
Cartilago cricoidea
Tunica muscularis oesophagi

a

b

Pharynx with supporting and related structures; continued.
Lateral view of the preparations pictured in the preceding plate of figures.

a, The musculature and the skeletal supports of the pharynx together with the nerves of laryngeal supply.
The pharynx and the esophagus have been opened from behind in the median line.
b, The thyroid, epiglottic, and cricoid cartilages.

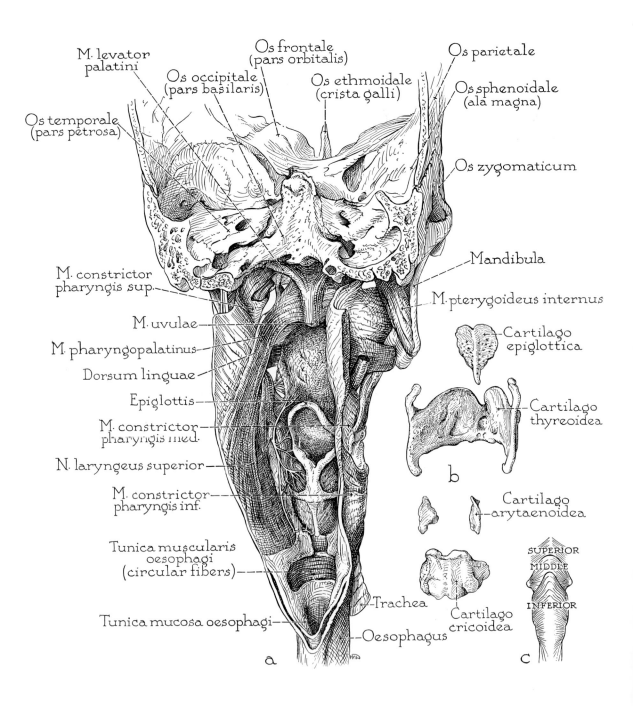

M. levator palatini

Os frontale (pars orbitalis)

Os parietale

Os occipitale (pars basilaris)

Os ethmoidale (crista galli)

Os sphenoidale (ala magna)

Os temporale (pars petrosa)

Os zygomaticum

Mandibula

M. constrictor pharyngis sup.

M. pterygoideus internus

M. uvulae

Cartilago epiglottica

M. pharyngopalatinus

Dorsum linguae

Cartilago thyreoidea

Epiglottis

b

M. constrictor pharyngis med.

N. laryngeus superior

Cartilago arytaenoidea

M. constrictor pharyngis inf.

Tunica muscularis oesophagi (circular fibers)

SUPERIOR
MIDDLE

INFERIOR

Trachea

Tunica mucosa oesophagi

Cartilago cricoidea

Oesophagus

a

c

Pharynx with supporting and related portions of skull and laryngeal cartilages; concluded.
Posterior view of the preparations shown in the two preceding plates.

a, The musculature of the pharynx, larynx, and esophagus. The pharynx and the esophagus have been opened from behind by a median cut, in order to show the oral and laryngeal divisions of the former; the nasal portion of the pharynx is out of view (above the palate). The mucous membrane has been removed except where it covers the tongue, epiglottis, and a portion of the esophagus.

b, The epiglottic, thyroid, arytenoid, and cricoid cartilage in pairs.

c, The three portions of the pharyngeal constrictor. Schematic.

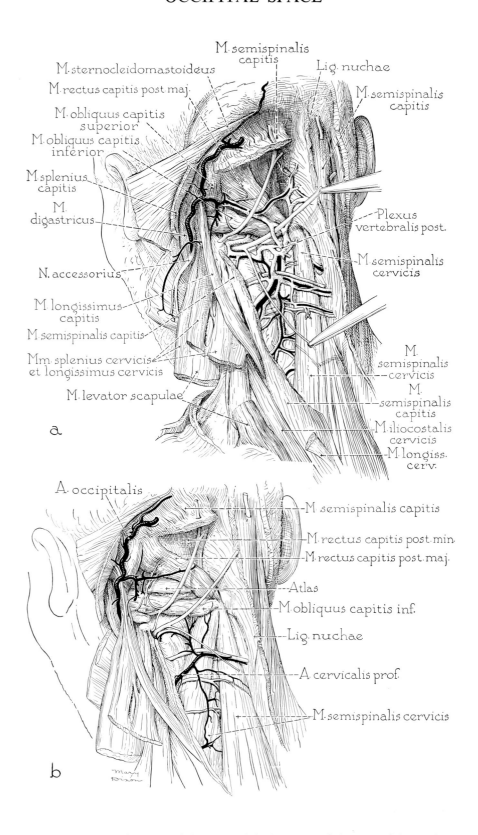

Blood vessels and nerves of the suboccipital space and dorsum of the neck.

The trapezius, semispinalis, splenius, and associated muscles have been cut and reflected.

Section Four

THE UPPER MEMBER

BONES OF SHOULDER AND UPPER MEMBER..................................... 139–142
    Scapula... 139
    Clavicle, Sternum, and Scapula......................... 140
    Humerus.. 141
    Radius and Ulna.. 142

ARTICULATIONS, LIGAMENTS.. 143–146
    Shoulder Joint... 143
    Elbow and Radio-ulnar Joints........................... 144
    Wrist and Hand... 145–146

TERMINOLOGY OF MUSCLES.. 147–148

SCAPULA AND CLAVICLE: AREAS OF MUSCULAR ATTACHMENT..................... 149

HUMERUS: AREAS OF MUSCULAR ATTACHMENT................................. 150

RADIUS AND ULNA: AREAS OF MUSCULAR ATTACHMENT......................... 151

HAND: AREAS OF MUSCULAR ATTACHMENT.................................... 152–154

ACTIONS OF MUSCLES; SCHEMATIC: ARM AND FOREARM........................ 155

AXILLARY SPACE; BOUNDARIES... 156

MUSCLES OF THE CHEST AND SHOULDER: THREE STAGES IN DISSECTION............ 157–160

MUSCLES OF THE SHOULDER, NECK, AND BACK: THREE STAGES IN DISSECTION....... 161–163

MUSCLES OF THE SHOULDER: THREE STAGES IN DISSECTION...................... 164–166

MUSCLES OF THE SHOULDER AND ARM: FOUR STAGES IN DISSECTION.............. 167–170

BICEPS BRACHII MUSCLE; TYPES... 171

MUSCLES OF THE FOREARM: SEVEN STAGES IN DISSECTION...................... 172–178

PALMARIS LONGUS MUSCLE; TYPES... 179

ABDUCTOR POLLICIS LONGUS MUSCLE; TYPES................................. 180

ACTIONS OF MUSCLES; SCHEMATIC: WRIST; ANTEBRACHIAL MUSCULATURE......... 181

SYNOVIAL SHEATHS, SULCI AND COMPARTMENTS; SCHEMATIC: WRIST AND HAND..... 182–186

SUPERFICIAL VEINS... 187

ARTERIES OF THE SHOULDER; SEMIDIAGRAMMATIC............................. 188

VESSELS AND NERVES OF THE AXILLA: TWO STAGES IN DISSECTION.............. 189–190

VESSELS AND NERVES OF THE NECK AND SHOULDER: TWO STAGES IN DISSECTION..... 191–192

137

(Continued)

VESSELS AND NERVES OF THE SHOULDER AND ARM: FOUR STAGES IN DISSECTION...... 193–196

VESSELS AND NERVES OF THE FOREARM: EIGHT STAGES IN DISSECTION.............. 197–200

BRACHIAL ARTERY; TYPES... 201

AXILLARY SPACE AND BRACHIAL PLEXUS....................................... 202–203

MUSCLES OF THE HAND: TWO STAGES IN DISSECTION............................ 204

VESSELS AND NERVES OF THE VOLAR FOREARM; SCHEMATIC...................... 205

PRONATOR TERES MUSCLE AND MEDIAN NERVE; VARIATIONS..................... 206

EXTENSOR MUSCLES OF THE HAND; TYPES..................................... 207

MIDPALMAR COMPARTMENT: THREE STAGES IN DISSECTION...................... 208–210

INTEROSSEOUS SPACE... 211

ARTERIES AND NERVES OF THE HAND: FOUR STAGES IN DISSECTION.............. 212–213

ARTERIES OF THE HAND, DORSAL SURFACE; SCHEMATIC......................... 214

ARTERIES OF THE HAND, PALMAR SURFACE; SCHEMATIC........................ 215

VESSELS AND NERVES OF THE FOREARM; SCHEMATIC........................... 216

ARTERIES OF THE PALM; VARIATIONS.. 217–218

NERVES OF THE HAND; PALMAR SURFACE; SCHEMATIC.......................... 219

NERVES OF THE HAND; DORSAL SURFACE; SCHEMATIC.......................... 220

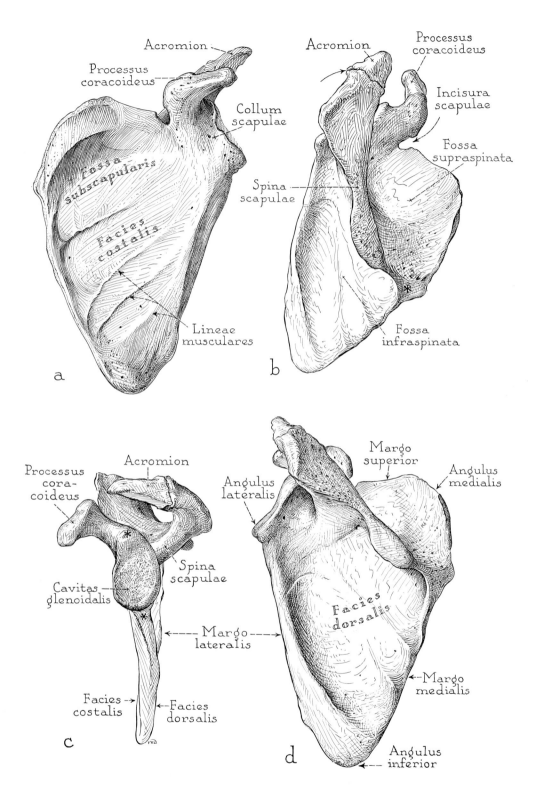

Scapula, left shoulder.

a, Scapula, costal surface. *b* and *d*, Dorsal surface of the bone; unlabelled arrow (in *b*) points to an epiphyseal line. *c*, Medial or vertebral aspect; asterisks indicate the supraglenoid and infraglenoid tuberosities.

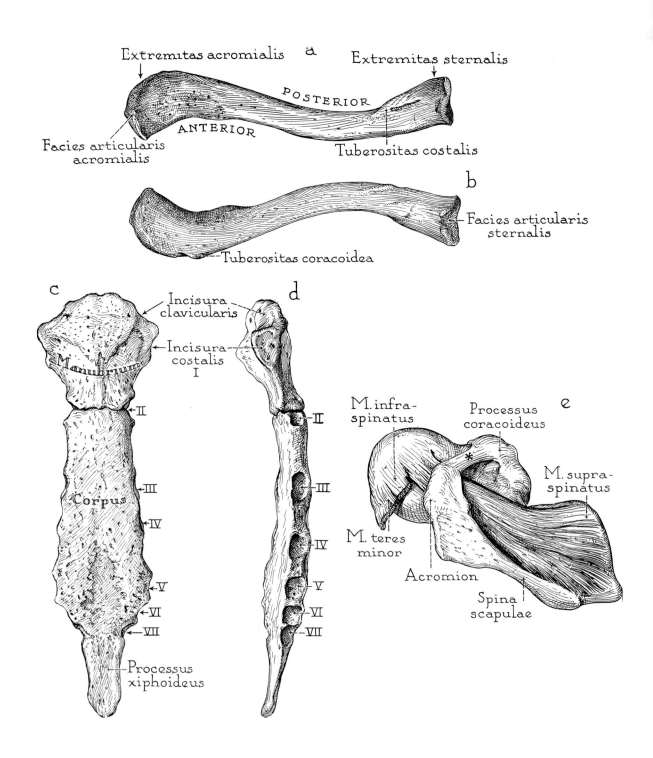

Clavicle, sternum, and scapula.

a and *b*, Left clavicle, inferior and superior surfaces, respectively.

c and *d*, Sternum, anterior and lateral views.

e, Left scapula, seen from above. The supraspinatus muscle occupies the supraspinous fossa; the infraspinatus and teres minor muscles remain only at their humeral insertions. The coracoacromial ligament is indicated by *.

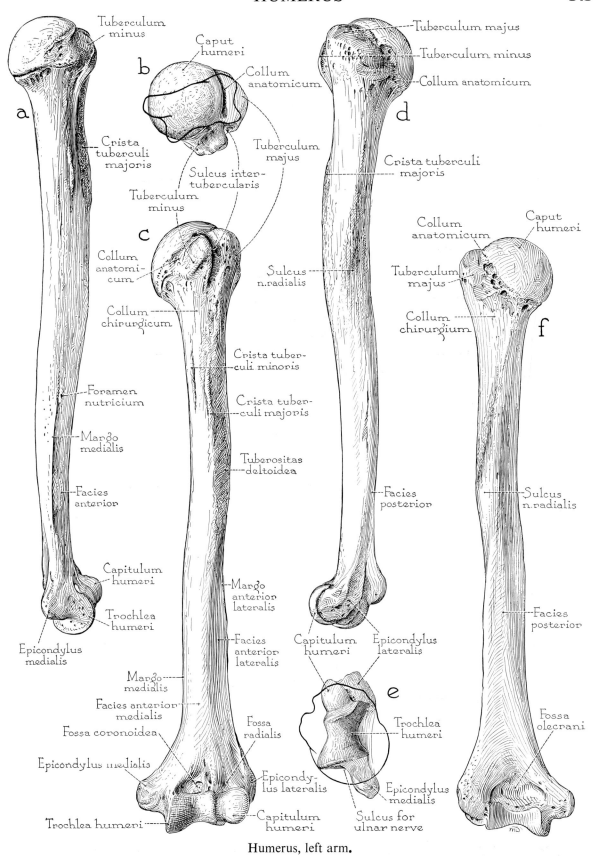

Humerus, left arm.

a, Humerus, medial view. *b*, Upper extremity of the bone, seen from above. *c*, Anterior view. *d*, Lateral view. *e*, Lower extremity of the humerus, from below. *f*, Posterior view.

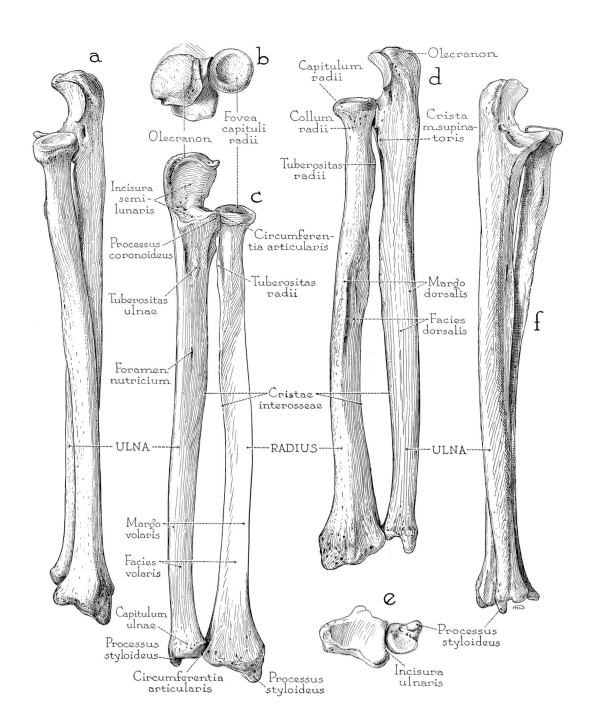

Radius and ulna, left forearm.

a, Radius and ulna, lateral view. *b*, Both bones, from above. *c*, Anterior view. *d*, Posterior view. *e*, Both bones, from below. *f*, Medial view.

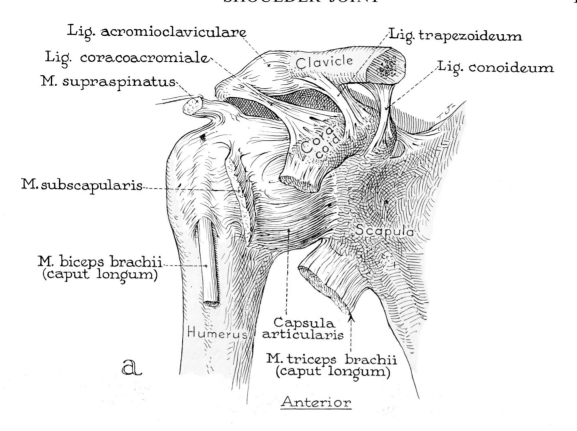

Lig. acromioclaviculare

Lig. coracoacromiale

M. supraspinatus

Lig. trapezoideum

Clavicle

Lig. conoideum

M. subscapularis

Cora cod

Scapula

M. biceps brachii
(caput longum)

Humerus

Capsula
articularis

M. triceps brachii
(caput longum)

a

Anterior

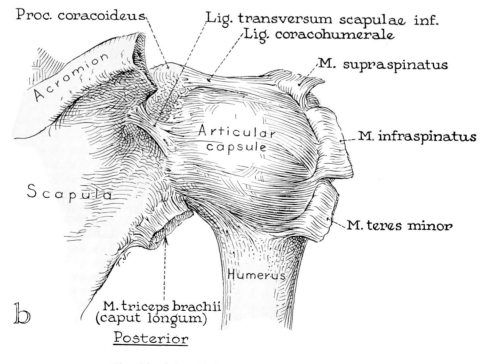

Proc. coracoideus

Lig. transversum scapulae inf.

Lig. coracohumerale

M. supraspinatus

Acromion

Articular
capsule

M. infraspinatus

Scapula

M. teres minor

Humerus

b

M. triceps brachii
(caput longum)

Posterior

Shoulder joint; right extremity.

a, Anterior view of the articulation. *b*, Posterior view.

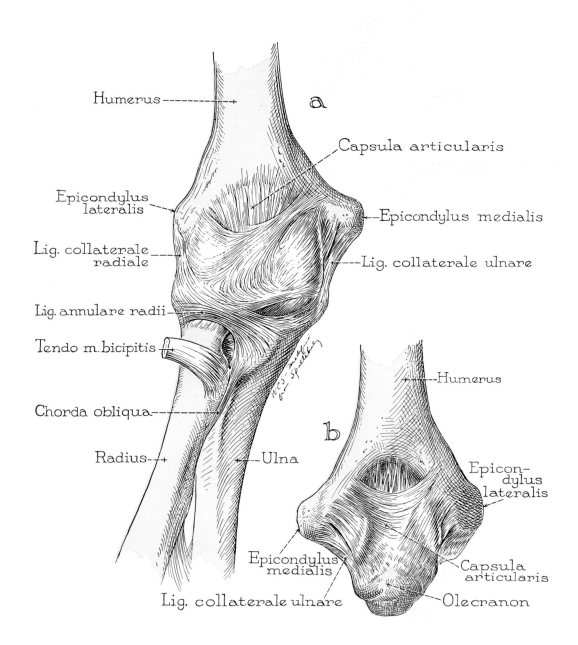

Elbow and radio-ulnar joints; right extremity.

a, Anterior (ventral) view. *b*, Posterior (dorsal) view of the articulation, forearm in the flexed position.

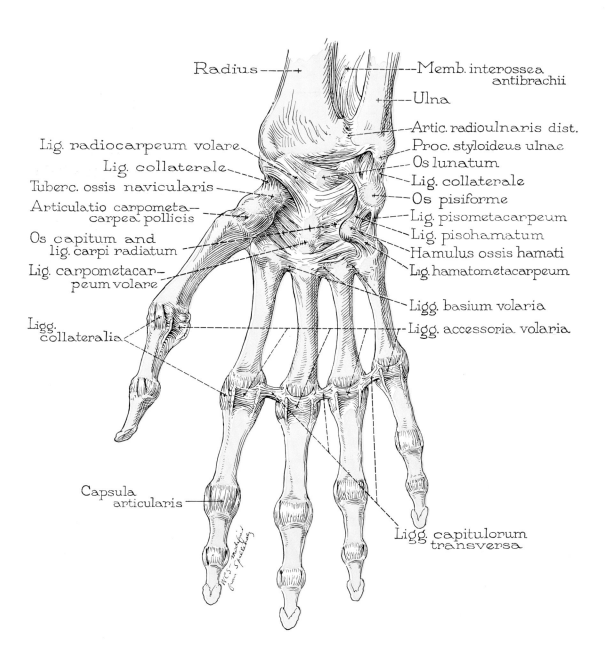

Radius

Memb. interossea antibrachii

Ulna

Artic. radioulnaris dist.

Lig. radiocarpeum volare

Proc. styloideus ulnae

Lig. collaterale

Os lunatum

Tuberc. ossis navicularis

Lig. collaterale

Articulatio carpometa-carpea pollicis

Os pisiforme

Lig. pisometacarpeum

Os capitum and lig. carpi radiatum

Lig. pisohamatum

Hamulus ossis hamati

Lig. carpometacar-peum volare

Lig. hamatometacarpeum

Ligg. basium volaria

Ligg. collateralia

Ligg. accessoria volaria

Capsula articularis

Ligg. capitulorum transversa

Joints of the distal forearm, wrist, and hand; palmar (ventral) aspect.

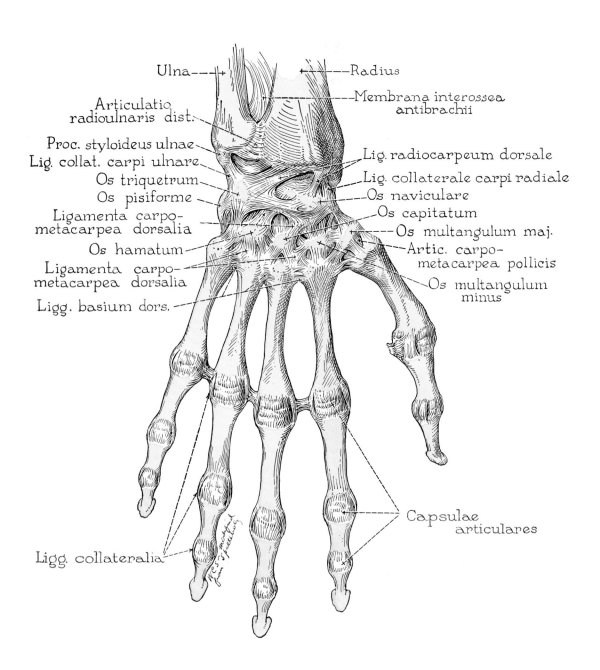

Ulna

Articulatio radioulnaris dist.

Proc. styloideus ulnae

Lig. collat. carpi ulnare

Os triquetrum

Os pisiforme

Ligamenta carpo-metacarpea dorsalia

Os hamatum

Ligamenta carpo-metacarpea dorsalia

Ligg. basium dors.

Radius

Membrana interossea antibrachii

Lig. radiocarpeum dorsale

Lig. collaterale carpi radiale

Os naviculare

Os capitatum

Os multangulum maj.

Artic. carpo-metacarpea pollicis

Os multangulum minus

Capsulae articulares

Ligg. collateralia

Joints of the distal forearm, wrist, and hand; dorsal aspect.

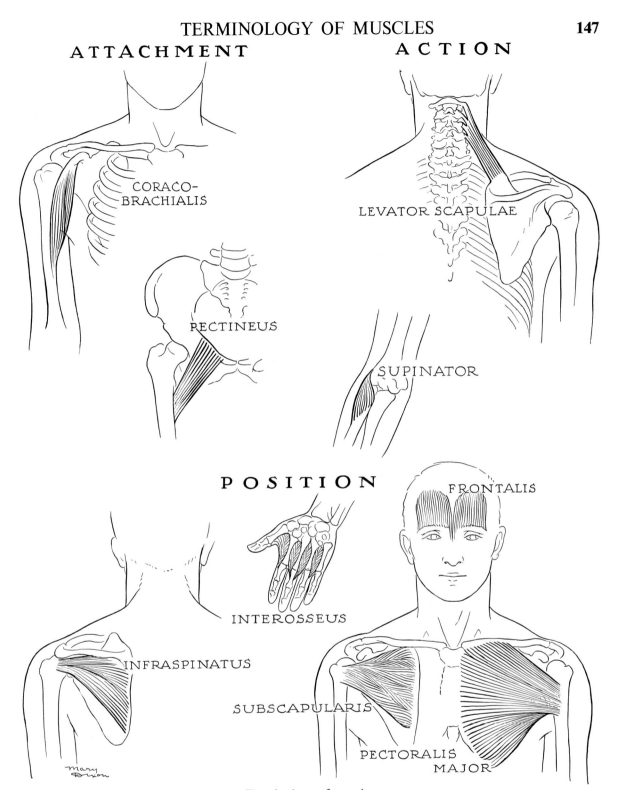

ATTACHMENT   ACTION

CORACO-BRACHIALIS

PECTINEUS

LEVATOR SCAPULAE

SUPINATOR

POSITION   FRONTALIS

INTEROSSEUS

INFRASPINATUS

SUBSCAPULARIS

PECTORALIS MAJOR

Terminology of muscles.

Examples of names based upon the attachments of the particular muscle, upon its action, or upon its position. The *coracobrachialis* arises from the coracoid process of the scapula and inserts into the bone (humerus) of the brachium (arm). The pectineus arises from the pecten, or comb-like crest, on the superior ramus of the pubis. The *levator scapulae* is the lifter of the scapula. The *supinator* acts upon the forearm, at the radioulnar joints, in such a way as to bring the hand into the palm-upward, or supine, position. Each *interosseus* is situated in a position between adjacent metacarpal bones. The *infraspinatus* lies inferior to the spine of the scapula, the *subscapularis* under the same bone. The *frontalis* covers a bone of the same name; the *pectoralis* is a muscle of the *pectus*, or chest.

FORM

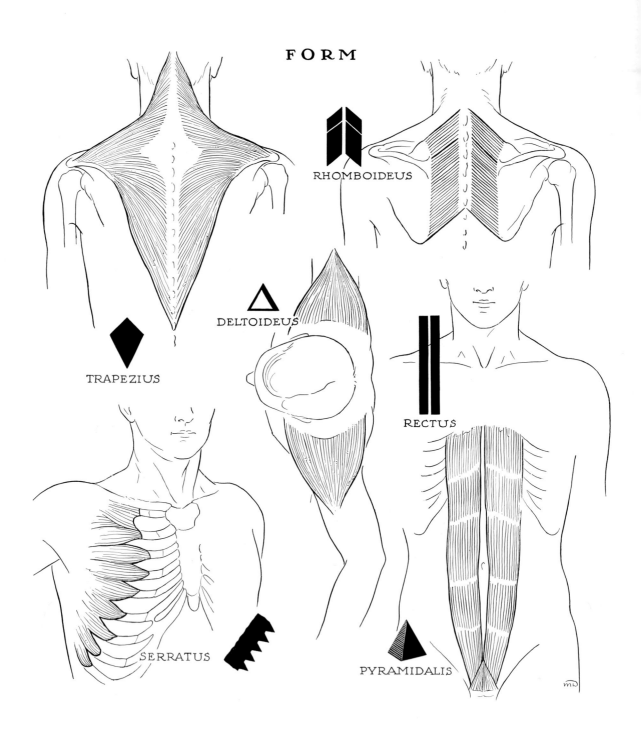

Terminology of muscles.

Examples of names based upon the form of the muscle. *Trapezium:* a plane geometric figure formed by four straight lines, of which no two are parallel. *Rhombus:* an equilateral parallelogram having its angles oblique. *Deltoid:* shaped like the capital letter delta of the Greek alphabet. *Serrate:* possessing a notched or saw-toothed edge. *Rectus:* straight. *Pyramidal:* having the form of a pyramid.

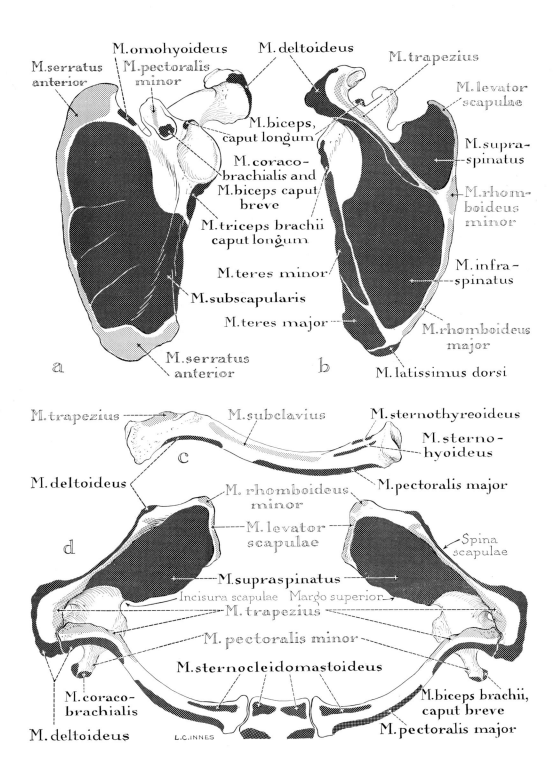

Bones of the pectoral girdle, showing the areas of muscular attachments.

a and *b*, The scapula, anterior and posterior views, respectively. *c*, The cavicle, inferior surface. *d*, The scapula, clavicle, and sternum, seen from above.

Dark pattern and heavy lettering indicate the origin of a muscle; light pattern and open lettering indicate the insertion.

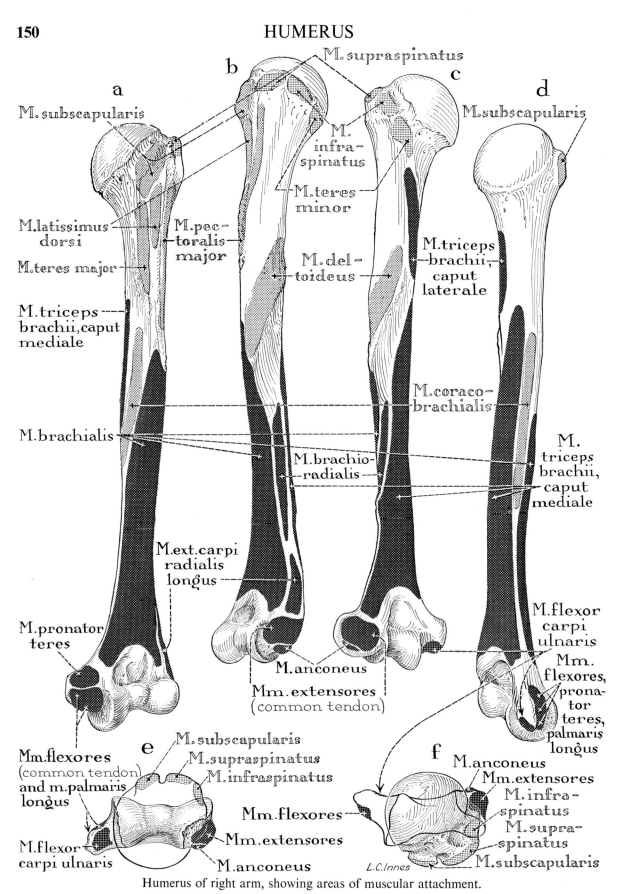

a, Anterior view. **b**, Anterolateral view. **c**, Posterior view. **d**, Posterolateral view. **e** and **f**, Distal and proximal extremities, with the opposite extremity in each instance shown by outline. (Compare page 141.)

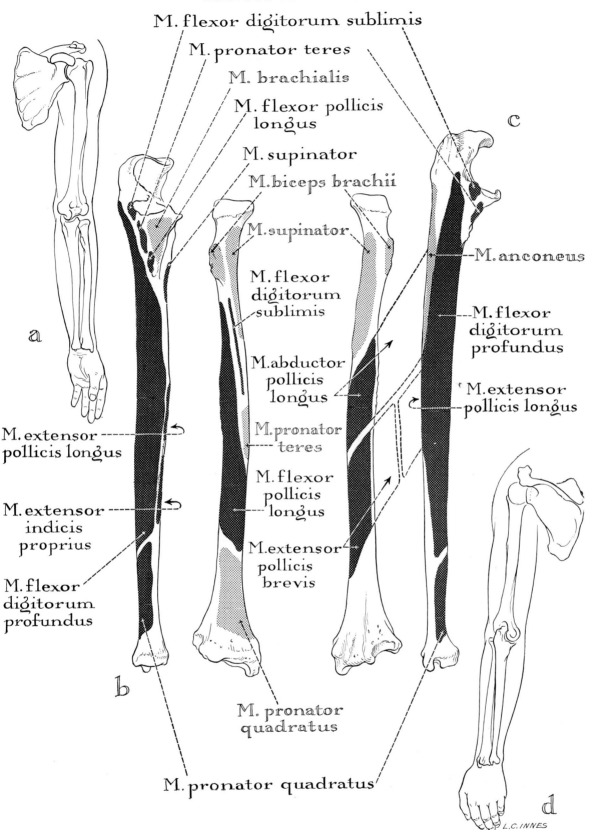

M. flexor digitorum sublimis

M. pronator teres

M. brachialis

M. flexor pollicis longus

M. supinator

M. biceps brachii

M. supinator

M. flexor digitorum sublimis

M. abductor pollicis longus

M. pronator teres

M. flexor pollicis longus

M. extensor pollicis brevis

M. anconeus

M. flexor digitorum profundus

M. extensor pollicis longus

M. extensor pollicis longus

M. extensor indicis proprius

M. flexor digitorum profundus

M. pronator quadratus

M. pronator quadratus

a

b

c

d

L.C. INNES

Radius and ulna of the right forearm, showing areas of muscular attachment.

a, The extremity seen in ventral view; *b*, the radius and ulna similarly placed. *d*, The extremity from the opposite aspect; *c*, the bones similarly viewed.

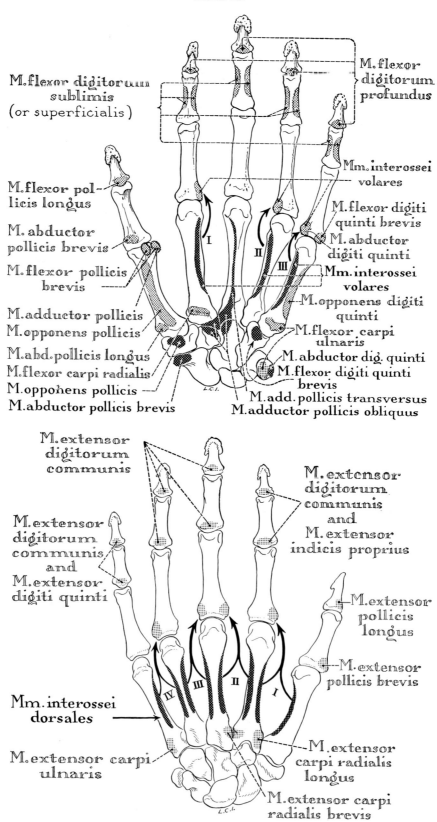

M.flexor digitorum
sublimis
(or superficialis)

M.flexor
digitorum
profundus

M.flexor pol-
licis longus

M. abductor
pollicis brevis

M.flexor pollicis
brevis

Mm.interossei
volares

M.flexor digiti
quinti brevis

M. abductor
digiti quinti

Mm.interossei
volares

M.opponens digiti
quinti

M.flexor carpi
ulnaris

M.abductor dig. quinti

M.flexor digiti quinti
brevis

M.adductor pollicis
M.opponens pollicis
M.abd.pollicis longus
M.flexor carpi radialis
M.opponens pollicis
M.abductor pollicis brevis

M.add. pollicis transversus
M.adductor pollicis obliquus

M.extensor
digitorum
communis

M.extensor
digitorum
communis
and
M.extensor
indicis proprius

M.extensor
digitorum
communis
and
M.extensor
digiti quinti

M.extensor
pollicis
longus

M.extensor
pollicis
brevis

Mm.interossei
dorsales

M.extensor carpi
ulnaris

M.extensor
carpi radialis
longus

M.extensor carpi
radialis brevis

Bones of the right hand, showing areas of muscular attachment.

Upper figure, the palmar aspect. *Lower figure*, the dorsal aspect.

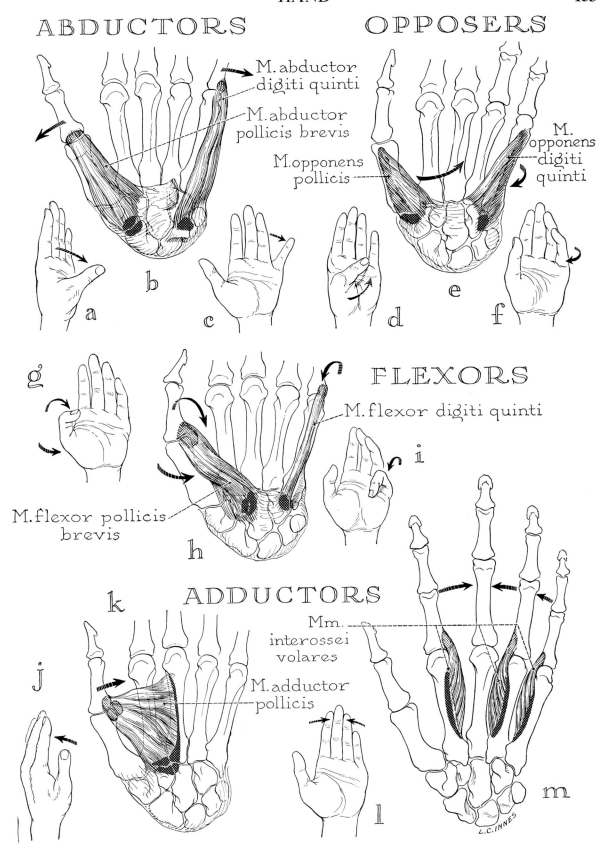

ABDUCTORS

OPPOSERS

M. abductor
digiti quinti

M. abductor
pollicis brevis

M. opponens
pollicis

M.
opponens
digiti
quinti

a

b

c

d

e

f

g

FLEXORS

M. flexor digiti quinti

i

M. flexor pollicis
brevis

h

k

ADDUCTORS

Mm.
interossei
volares

M. adductor
pollicis

j

l

m

L.C.INNES

Intrinsic muscles of the hand, with their actions indicated by arrows.

The actions are as follows: *a* to *c*, abduction; *d* to *f*, opposition; *g* to *i*, flexion; *j* to *m*, adduction.

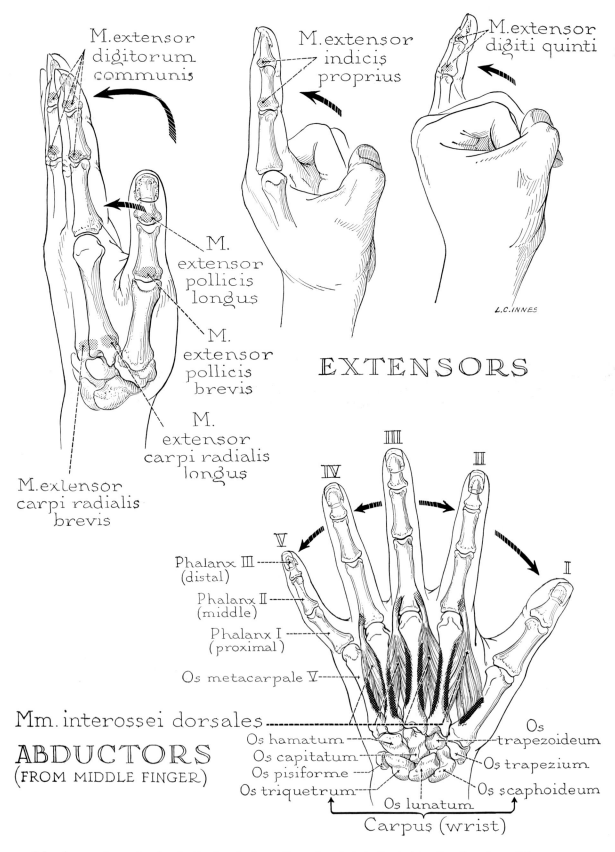

M.extensor digitorum communis

M.extensor indicis proprius

M.extensor digiti quinti

M. extensor pollicis longus

M. extensor pollicis brevis

M. extensor carpi radialis longus

M.extensor carpi radialis brevis

L.C.INNES

EXTENSORS

III

IV

II

V

II

Phalanx III (distal)

Phalanx II (middle)

Phalanx I (proximal)

Os metacarpale V

Mm. interossei dorsales

ABDUCTORS (FROM MIDDLE FINGER)

Os hamatum
Os capitatum
Os pisiforme
Os triquetrum
Os lunatum

Os trapezoideum
Os trapezium
Os scaphoideum

Carpus (wrist)

Muscles causing extension in the hand; the action of each is indicated by the direction of the arrow.

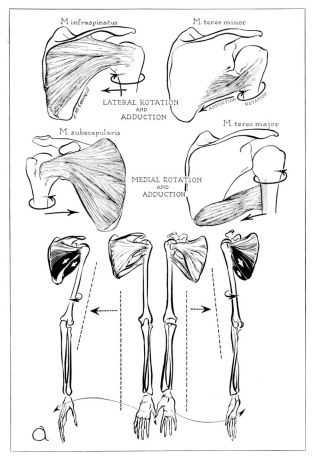

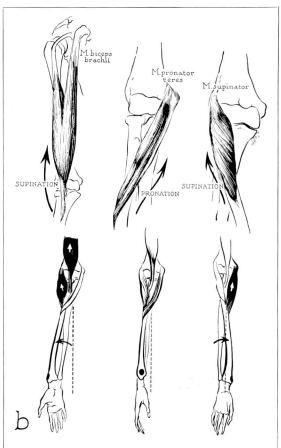

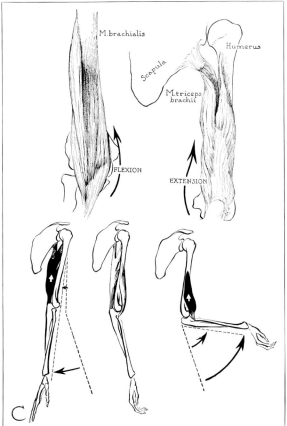

Muscles of the upper member, with schematized demonstration of the sole or chief action of each.

a, The infraspinatus, teres minor, teres major, and subscapularis.

b, The biceps brachii, pronator teres, and supinator.

c, The brachialis and triceps brachii.

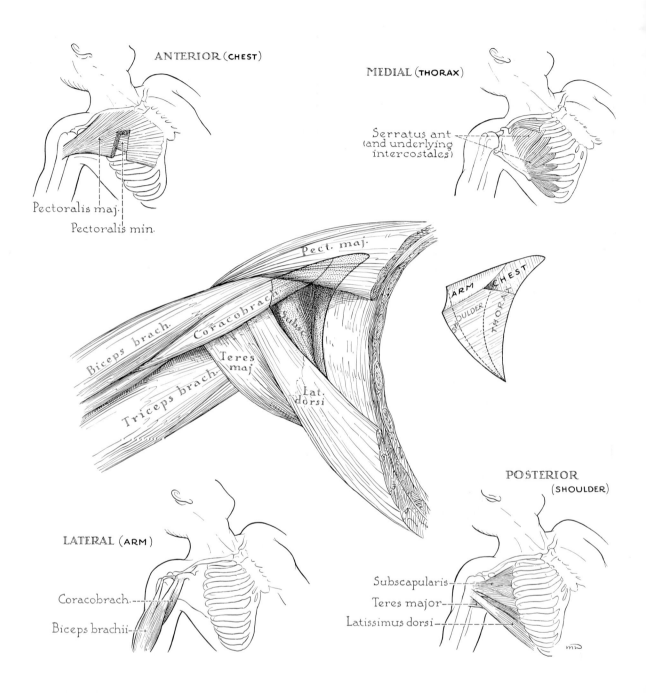

ANTERIOR (CHEST)

MEDIAL (THORAX)

Serratus ant.
(and underlying
intercostales)

Pectoralis maj.
Pectoralis min.

Pect. maj.

Biceps brach.

Coracobrach.

Subsc.

Teres
maj.

Triceps brach.

Lat.
dorsi

ARM　CHEST
SHOULDER　THORAX

POSTERIOR
(SHOULDER)

LATERAL (ARM)

Coracobrach.
Biceps brachii

Subscapularis
Teres major
Latissimus dorsi

Boundaries of the axillary space.

The central figure depicts the axilla as viewed from an inferolateral position; the inset represents a cast of the space, with surfaces labelled. The figures in the four corners show diagrammatically, and in succession, the anterior, medial, lateral, and posterior boundaries.

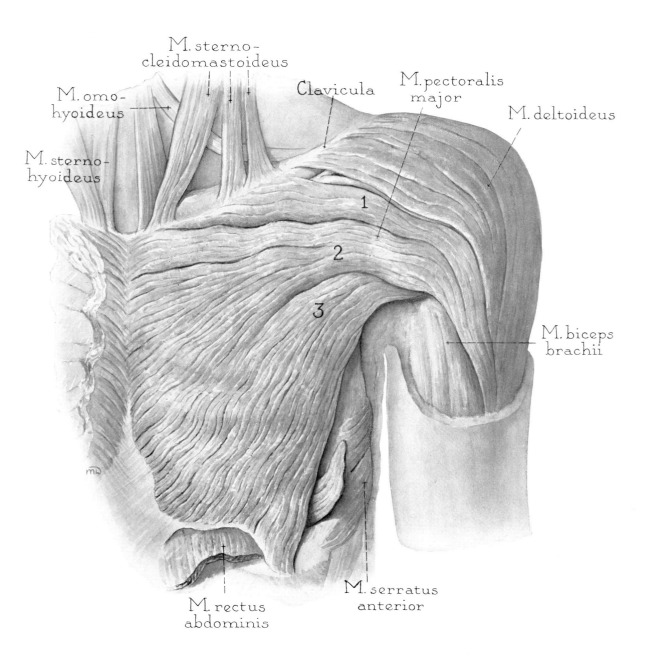

Muscles of the chest: pectoralis major muscle.

The pectoralis major takes origin in three main portions, as follows: from the clavicle (at 1); from the sternoclavicular joint and the sternum (at 2); from the sternum and the sheath of the rectus muscle (at 3). The three portions are separated by clefts. Lesser slips of costal origin (not exposed) are implanted into the deep surface of the muscle. The portion (at 1) which arises from the clavicle narrows as it approaches the humerus. The sternal part (at 2) blends with the preceding as the insertion is approached. The third, or sterno-vaginal, portion (at 3) passes beneath the other two, forming a second leaf of humeral insertion. In coursing toward the humerus, the cranial division passes somewhat downward from its origin, as well as lateralward; the caudal division inclines upward; the intermediate portion is, at least in part, transverse (see following figures). The portions converge as would the blades of a fan.

The pectoralis major muscle constitutes the anterior wall of the axilla. In the succeeding three plates of figures the dissection is carried to progressively deeper levels, terminating with full exposure of the scapular, thoracic, and brachial boundaries of the axillary space.

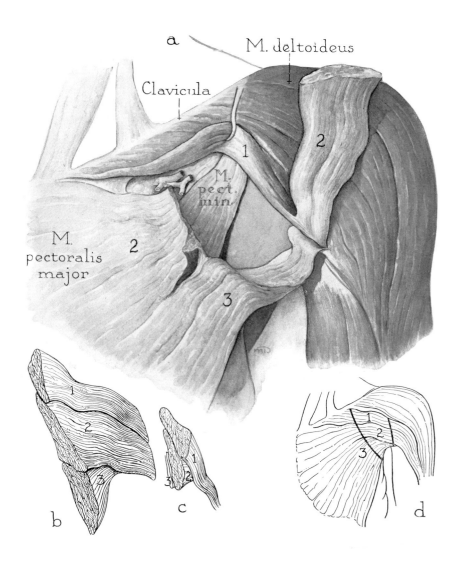

Muscles of the chest: pectoralis major and pectoralis minor muscles.

a, The middle segment (at 2) of the pectoralis major has been reflected to expose the structures beneath, namely, the pectoralis minor, the costocoracoid membrane, and the thoraco-acromial vessels. The upper piece (at 1), here retracted toward the clavicle, forms the inferior boundary of the deltopectoral cleft through which the cephalic vein reaches the axilla; its lower border overlaps the second piece of the same muscle. The second piece, as it approaches the axilla, covers progressively more of the third piece (at 3). The first and second parts fuse at their insertions, being entirely separate near their origins. The second and third portions are continuous in their medial half, but separate as they approach the humerus. The distal half of the pectoralis minor is seen in the opening in the pectoralis major. The vessels and nerves of supply have been removed, except where they enter the field of dissection superior to the pectoralis minor, by perforating the costocoracoid membrane.

b, Pectoralis major; divisions as marked in *d*.

c, Pectoralis major; segment near the insertion. Showing the imbricated arrangement near the humeral insertion. At this level the second piece is overlapped by the first for one-half of its height; the third is completely obscured by the second.

d, Pectoralis major. Showing the lines of section in the two preceding figures, and the three major subdivisions of the muscle. Semidiagrammatic.

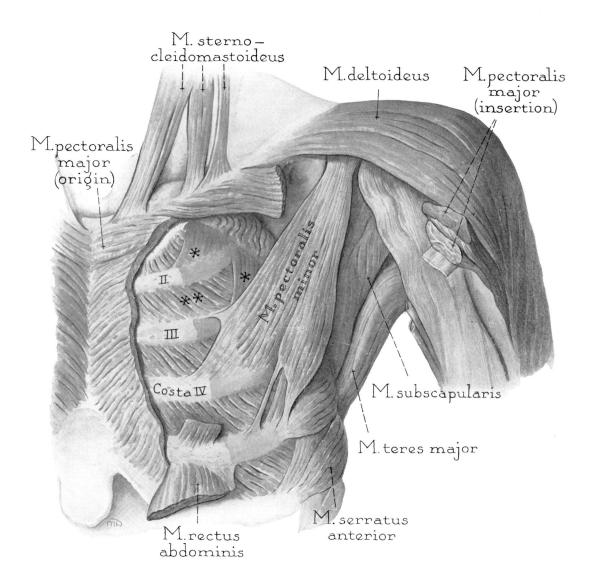

Muscles of the chest: pectoralis minor and related muscles.

The pectoralis major has been removed, except for the portions that constitute its attachments. The pectoralis minor is revealed throughout its entire extent. The following areas and structures are exposed: the thorax, in the area of junction of the ribs and costal cartilages; the attachment of the rectus muscle to the fifth rib, and a costal slip of the pectoralis major (pointing upward from the superior surface of the same rib); the intercostales (external at * and internal at **), after removal of the external intercostal membrane; several digitations of the serratus anterior; the subscapularis muscle, on the anterior (costal) surface, and the teres major on the lateral (axillary) border of the scapula; the coracobrachialis and biceps brachii muscles on the medial aspect of the humerus.

The origin of the pectoral minor is aponeurotic, by means of slips from the third, fourth, and fifth ribs; the muscle ends in a strong tendon, which is inserted into the coracoid process of the scapula.

The pectoralis major, pectoralis minor, and subclavius muscles together bound the axillary space anteriorly. With removal of the pectoralis major muscle, the other muscular boundaries are exposed. Medially are situated muscles of the thorax (external and internal intercostals and the serratus anterior); posteriorly placed are muscles of the shoulder (subscapularis and teres major) and back (latissimus dorsi); on the lateral wall are muscles of the arm (coracobrachialis and biceps brachii).

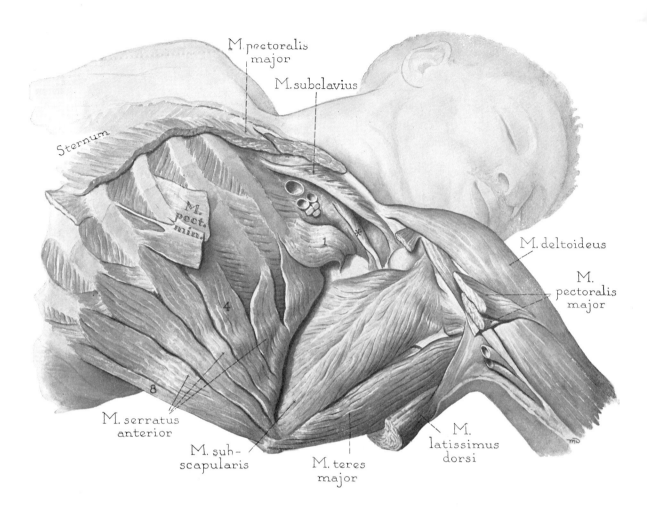

The following structures have been removed: the pectoralis minor, except at its extremities; the pectoralis major, cut proximally at its sternal and clavicular origin, and distally at the humeral insertion; and the latissimus dorsi, except at insertion. The axillary vessels and the brachial plexus appear proximally, and only as cut ends where they enter the axilla beneath the clavicle and upon the first rib; distally, their brachial continuations enter the sulcus situated dorsal to the coracobrachialis muscle. In order to show fully the various structures enumerated and described above, the arm is abducted. With the axillary space opened wide from the front, the serratus anterior is seen in full surface view, from origin to insertion; the posterior wall, formed by the subscapular structures, is also brought into favorable exposure. The bilaminar tendon of insertion of the pectoralis major is shown as it enters the cleft between the deltoid and the biceps brachii muscles. The latissimus dorsi appears near its brachial attachment. The parts of the serratus anterior are numbered. The origin and the pectoral part (at *) of the omohyoideus muscle are shown. The clavicular portion of the deltoid is in view; its anterior margin faces the reader. This margin borders the cleft in which lay the cephalic vein.

The muscles described above form the boundaries of the axilla. The axillary space, between the upper part of the side of the thorax and the proximal part of the arm, assumes the form of a four-sided pyramid when the arm is abducted. The apex reaches the coracoid process of the scapula; the base lies between the free edges of the muscles of the chest and shoulder. The anterior wall is formed by the following three muscles: the pectoralis major, the pectoralis minor and the subclavius. The posterior wall is also made up of three muscles: the subscapularis, the latissimus dorsi, and the teres major. On the medial wall, in addition to parts of the upper five ribs, are situated the intercostales and the serratus anterior. The lateral wall is formed by the coracobrachialis and biceps brachii muscles.

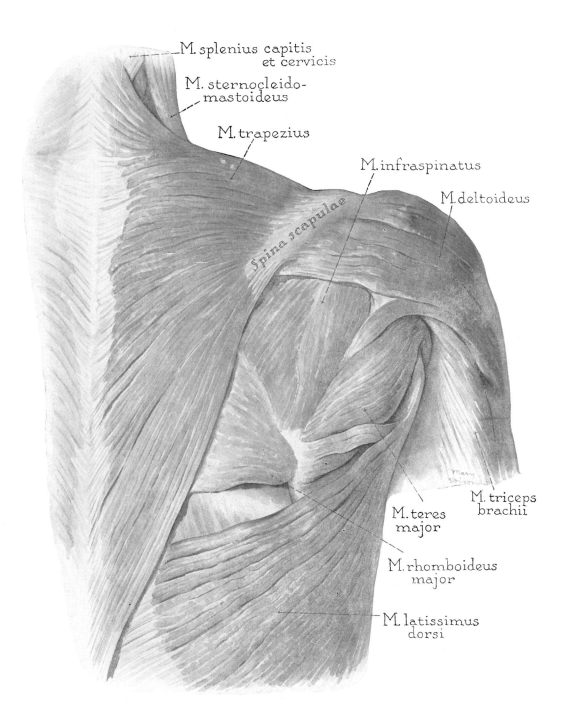

Muscles of the shoulder, neck, and back.

First layer of muscles of the back in relation to the musculature of the upper extremity.

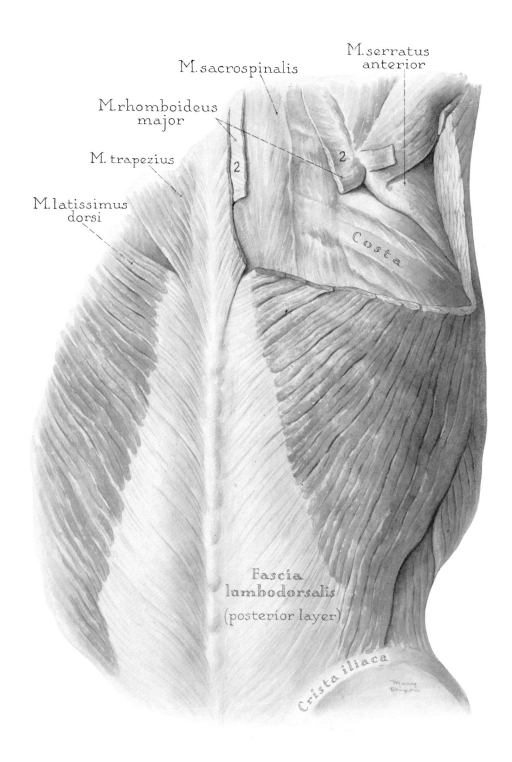

M. serratus
anterior

M. sacrospinalis

M. rhomboideus
major

M. trapezius

M. latissimus
dorsi

Costa

Fascia
lumbodorsalis
(posterior layer)

Crista iliaca

Muscles of the back; first and second layers.

The trapezius muscle has been removed; a triangular segment has been cut from the cranial portion of
the latissimus dorsi. The rhomboideus major (at 2), one of the three constituents of second layer of flat muscles
of the back, has been removed in its middle two fourths to expose the column of long muscles.

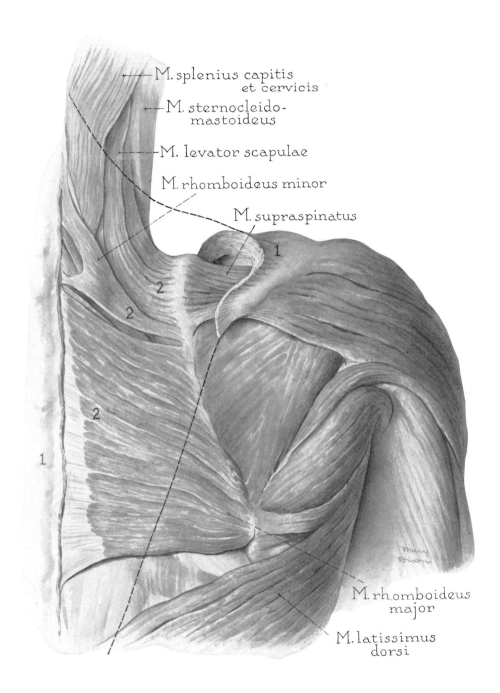

Muscles of the back; second layer.

The trapezius muscle has been removed (cut ends at 1—original extent indicated by broken lines); the latissimus dorsi remains intact. The muscles of the second stratum are now exposed; these, indicated by 2, are the levator scapulae, the rhomboideus major, and the rhomboideus minor.

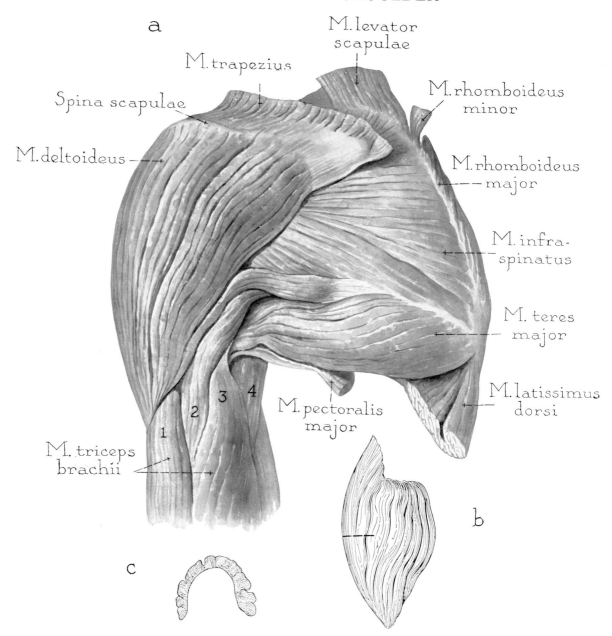

Muscles of the shoulder.

a, Musculature, in dorsal view. *b* and *c*, Form of the deltoideus in lateral view and in section, respectively.

a, Dorsally the deltoideus arises chiefly from the spine of the scapula. The site of the brachial insertion is in view. A large accessory band is present in the inferior part of the infraspinous fossa. The broad convergent fascicles of the infraspinatus are arranged in two incompletely divided portions. The teres major is seen in the area of its origin from the inferior angle of the scapula, to the point where it passes beneath an accessory slip to the triceps brachii muscle (at 3). Of the muscles of the arm, the triceps brachii appears medial to the deltoideus; of the appendicular muscles of the back, the trapezius, levator scapulae, latissimus dorsi, and the two rhomboidei remain at their scapular or humeral attachments. In addition to the lateral and long heads of the triceps (at 1 and 4, respectively) accessory portions are present (at 2 and 3).

b, As is evident in lateral view, the form of the deltoideus muscle is that of the Greek letter Δ. On the left (the anterior part of the muscle) the clavicular origin appears as an extension; on the right (posterior) the scapular, or spinous, origin is horizontal. The insertion into the deltoid tuberosity of the humerus is pointed.

c, In horizontal sections (at the level indicated in *b*) the deltoideus is deeply concave on its medial (inner) surface, where it is moulded against the humerus.

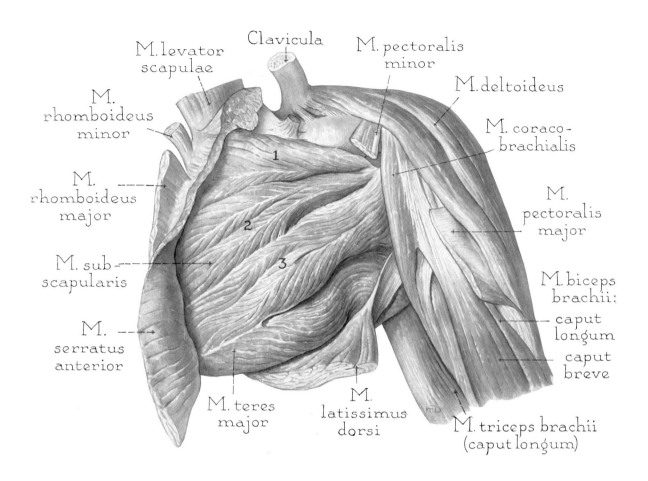

Muscles of the shoulder and proximal portion of the arm, ventral (costal) aspect.

The subscapularis muscle virtually fills the fossa of the same name on the costal surface of the scapula. The muscle consists of three major subdivisions, which fuse at the tendon of insertion into the lesser tubercle of the humerus. The uppermost (at 1) is the smallest; the lowermost portion (at 3) is the largest; the middle (at 2) is of intermediate size. The first subdivision is a single, bipennate, muscle; each of the other two is a pair of such muscles. The muscle arises in part from tendinous bands which are attached to ridges on the scapula; they cross the costal surface and tend to converge upon the articular area (here concealed). The relation between the lineae musculares and the fascial bands is shown in the following figure.

The teres major is demonstrated in its course from the inferior angle of the scapula to the intertubercular groove of the humerus. The teres minor is not in view.

The distal portion of the transected latissimus dorsi is seen, where it is concentrated into a thick, ribbon-like band which winds about the teres major and passes to the anterior surface on the latter muscle, on the way to its humeral insertion.

The deltoideus muscle covers the shoulder joint. This anterior portion arises from the ventral border and upper surface of the lateral third of the clavicle. It narrows toward the humeral insertion.

The coracobrachialis muscle is exposed. Its origin, in common with the short head of the biceps from the tip of the coracoid process, is here just covered by the margin of the deltoideus.

The pectoralis major is represented by its tendon of insertion, cut near the bicipital groove. The pectoralis minor is seen at its insertion into the coracoid process of the scapula.

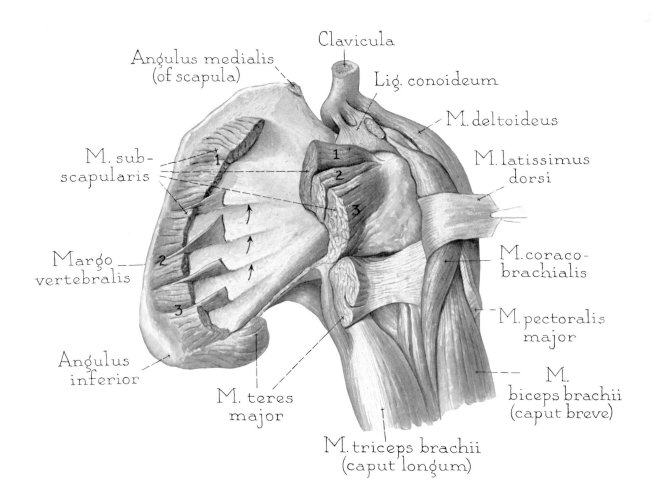

Muscles of the shoulder; ventral (costal) aspect.

The subscapularis muscle has been largely cut away to show its structure and to expose the bony surface to which it was attached. Medially, at the vertebral border of the scapula, the muscular tissue has been removed in such a way as to leave the tendinous laminae projecting distally beyond the segments of the cut muscle. From superior and inferior surfaces of each, fiber bundles arise, each set making up half of adjacent major subdivisions of the muscle, that is, adjacent halves of the feather-like groupings. The bands are attached to the lineae musculares (indicated by arrows), seen extending somewhat beyond the point at which the bands are cut. On the free surface of the muscle these tendinous plates were continuous with the subscapular fascia (here removed), of which they appeared to be septal processes. At the lateral, or humeral, extremity of the muscle, the three principal subdivisions are shown; they are fully exposed by retracting the coracobrachialis and the deltoid. The subdivisions converge in such a way that the first piece (at 1) remains separate; the second and third together form an intermediate piece (at 2); the fourth and the fifth fuse to form a lower piece (at 3). The superior is the smallest, the inferior the largest, of the three.

The teres major has been cut (middle third removed), in order to show its form in section. The latissimus dorsi has been drawn lateralward in order to display the form of the tendon of insertion. The deltoideus has been retracted to expose the origins of the brachial muscles, the omohyoid removed to show the scapular notch. The tendon of origin of the long head of the triceps brachii is seen in the interval between the teres major and the axillary border of the scapula. The serratus anterior has been removed, its marginal area of bony insertion shown (compare preceding figure).

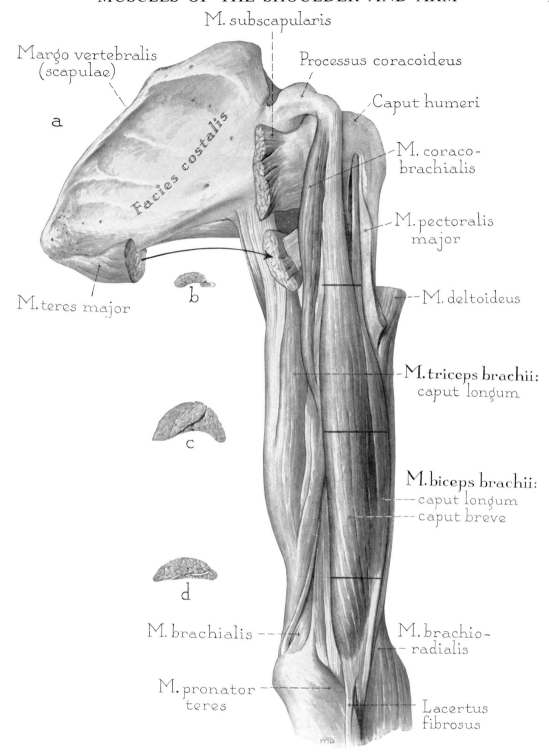

M. subscapularis

Margo vertebralis
(scapulae)

Processus coracoideus

Caput humeri

a

Facies costalis

M. coraco-
brachialis

M. pectoralis
major

M. deltoideus

M. teres major

b

M. triceps brachii:
caput longum

c

M. biceps brachii:
caput longum
caput breve

d

M. brachialis

M. brachio-
radialis

M. pronator
teres

Lacertus
fibrosus

Muscles of the ventral aspect of the shoulder and arm.

a, The subscapularis muscle has been removed except at its humeral insertion into the lesser tubercle of the humerus; the teres major remains only at its proximal and distal extremities. Both heads of the biceps brachii are seen, as well as the coracobrachialis. The deltoideus and the pectoralis major remain only at their insertions.

b to *d,* Successive sections of the biceps brachii muscle, at the levels marked in *a;* each piece shown as if it were moulded against the subjacent bone or musculature, and drawn in natural contour. The first cut passes through the two heads of origin; the second, through the bulkiest portion of the muscle; the third includes the tendon of insertion, which still lies within the muscle belly.

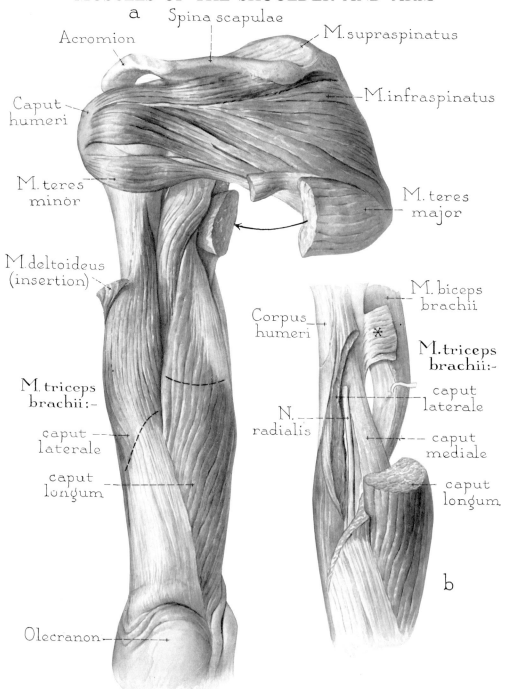

a

Spina scapulae

Acromion

M. supraspinatus

M. infraspinatus

Caput humeri

M. teres minor

M. teres major

M. deltoideus (insertion)

Corpus humeri

M. biceps brachii

M. triceps brachii:-

caput laterale

N. radialis

M. triceps brachii:-

caput laterale

caput mediale

caput longum

caput longum

b

Olecranon

Muscles of the dorsal aspect of the shoulder and arm.

a, The following muscles have been removed: the trapezius, in order to expose the supraspinatus; the deltoideus, to show the insertions of three muscles into the greater tubercle of the humerus; the teres major, in its midportion, to reveal the axillary border of the scapula; the levator scapulae and the rhomboidei, along the medial (vertebral) border of the same bone. An accessory scapular head of the triceps brachii is present. The broken lines indicate points at which the heads of the muscle were cut for the dissection illustrated in b.

b, The lateral head of the triceps brachii has been largely removed to uncover the radial groove; the long head of the muscle has been cut close to its point of implantation into the common tendon of ulnar insertion, thus exposing the medial head of the same muscle. * indicates the tendon of the teres major. The biceps brachii is retracted medialward.

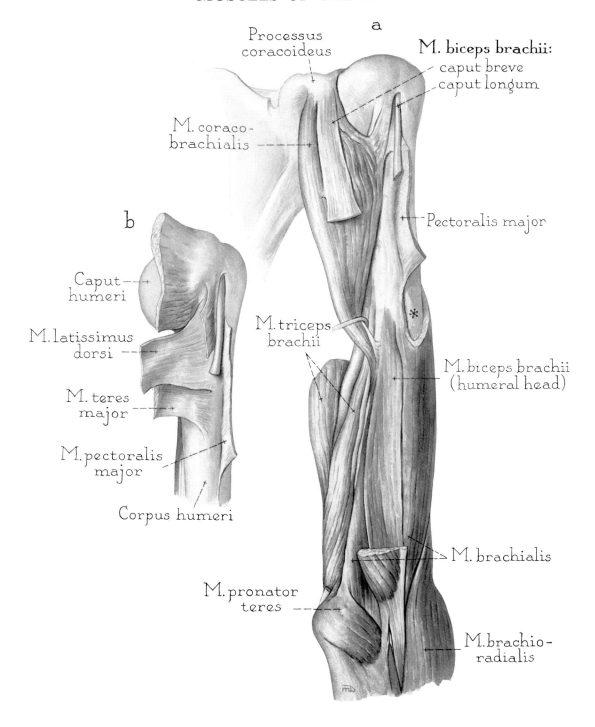

Processus coracoideus

M. biceps brachii:
caput breve
caput longum

M. coraco-brachialis

Pectoralis major

*

M. biceps brachii (humeral head)

b

Caput humeri

M. latissimus dorsi

M. teres major

M. pectoralis major

Corpus humeri

M. triceps brachii

M. brachialis

M. pronator teres

M. brachio-radialis

Dissection of the arm; anterior aspect.

a, The biceps brachii has been removed except at its extremities. An accessory (humeral) head is present. In this specimen the coracobrachialis arises not merely from the coracoid process, but by an accessory head from the medial margin of the intertubercular groove, the latter occupied by the tendon of the long head of the biceps. The deltoideus muscle has been wholly removed (area of its insertion being marked by *).

b, Tendons related to the proximal extremity of the humerus. The subscapularis inserts chiefly into the lesser tubercle of the humerus; the teres major, latissimus dorsi, and accessory head of the coracobrachialis are attached to the medial margin of the intertubercular sulcus (occupied by the bicipital tendon), the pectoralis major to its lateral margin.

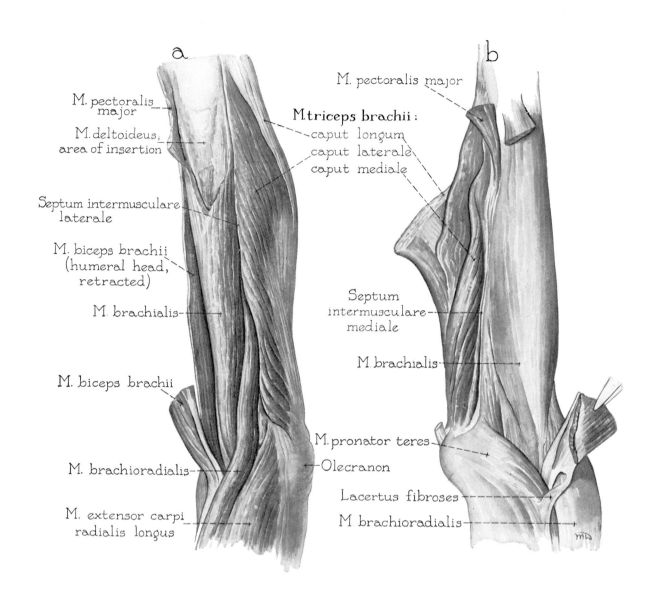

M. pectoralis major

M. deltoideus, area of insertion

Septum intermusculare laterale

M. biceps brachii (humeral head, retracted)

M. brachialis

M. biceps brachii

M. brachioradialis

M. extensor carpi radialis longus

M. pectoralis major

M. triceps brachii:
caput longum
caput laterale
caput mediale

Septum intermusculare mediale

M. brachialis

M. pronator teres

Olecranon

Lacertus fibroses

M. brachioradialis

Deep dissection of the arm, anterolateral and anteromedial views.

   a, The humeral head of the biceps brachii has been reflected to expose the brachialis. The lateral intermuscular septum (cut) is shown as it separates the muscles of the anterior brachial compartment from those in the posterior space.
   b, The heads of the triceps brachii are shown in this view from the opposite side. The medial intermuscular septum has been cut to the level at which it attaches to the brachialis anteriorly and the triceps brachii posteriorly.

M. BICEPS BRACHII
Variations in 150 specimens

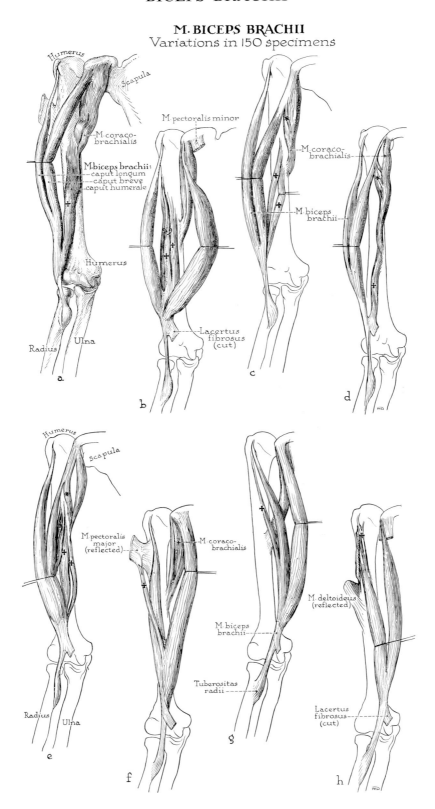

Biceps brachii muscle. Accessory heads (+).

a and *d*, Single accessory humeral head (muscle, therefore, tricipital). *b* and *c*, Two such heads (muscle quadricipital). *e*, Total of five humeral heads. *f*, Accessory head from the tendon of the pectoralis major; *g*, from the articular capsule; *h*, from the bicipital groove.

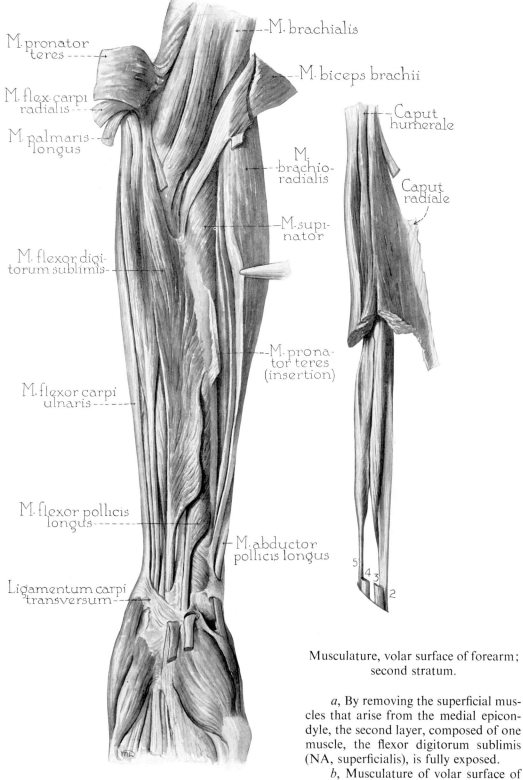

M. brachialis

M. pronator teres

M. biceps brachii

M. flex. carpi radialis

Caput humerale

M. palmaris longus

M. brachio-radialis

Caput radiale

M. supi-nator

M. flexor digitorum sublimis

M. prona-tor teres (insertion)

M. flexor carpi ulnaris

M. flexor pollicis longus

M. abductor pollicis longus

5 4 3 2

Ligamentum carpi transversum

Musculature, volar surface of forearm; second stratum.

a, By removing the superficial muscles that arise from the medial epicondyle, the second layer, composed of one muscle, the flexor digitorum sublimis (NA, superficialis), is fully exposed.

b, Musculature of volar surface of forearm: flexor digitorum sublimis, excised. The fiber bundles of the ulnar and radial heads converge, to form a common belly. The superficial portion of the muscle divides into lateral and medial divisions. The lateral, or radial, division is inserted on a tendon that goes to the middle (third) finger. The medial, or ulnar, division goes to the ring (fourth) finger. The entire deep portion, like the humeral, or medial, part of the superficial portion, is derived from the humeral origin. Its tendons pass to the little (fifth) finger and to the index (second) finger.

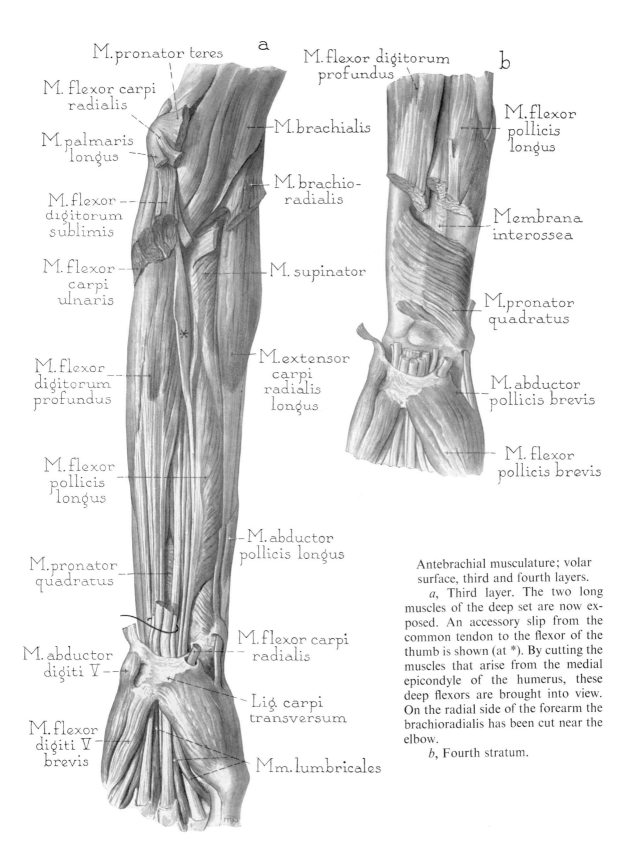

M.pronator teres

a

M. flexor digitorum profundus

b

M. flexor carpi radialis

M.palmaris longus

M. flexor digitorum sublimis

M. flexor carpi ulnaris

M.brachialis

M. brachio-radialis

M. supinator

M.flexor digitorum profundus

M.extensor carpi radialis longus

M.flexor pollicis longus

M.pronator quadratus

M.abductor digiti V

M.flexor digiti V brevis

M.abductor pollicis longus

M.flexor carpi radialis

Lig. carpi transversum

Mm. lumbricales

M.flexor pollicis longus

Membrana interossea

M.pronator quadratus

M.abductor pollicis brevis

M. flexor pollicis brevis

Antebrachial musculature; volar surface, third and fourth layers.

a, Third layer. The two long muscles of the deep set are now exposed. An accessory slip from the common tendon to the flexor of the thumb is shown (at *). By cutting the muscles that arise from the medial epicondyle of the humerus, these deep flexors are brought into view. On the radial side of the forearm the brachioradialis has been cut near the elbow.

b, Fourth stratum.

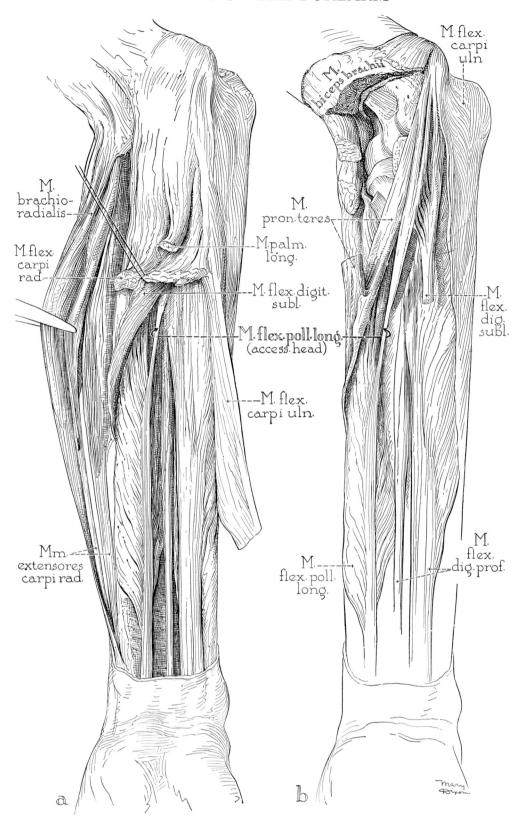

M.
brachio-
radialis

M. flex.
carpi
rad.

Mm.
extensores
carpi rad.

M.
pron. teres

M. palm.
long.

M. flex. digit.
subl.

M. flex. poll. long.
(access. head)

M. flex.
carpi uln.

M. flex. poll.
long.

M. flex.
carpi
uln

M. biceps brachii

M.
flex.
dig.
subl.

M.
flex.
dig. prof.

a   b

Flexor pollicis longus muscle; accessory head of humeral origin.

a, The accessory head, shown by transecting the superficial and intermediate layers of musculature.
b, The epicondylar (accessory or humeral) head, fully exposed.

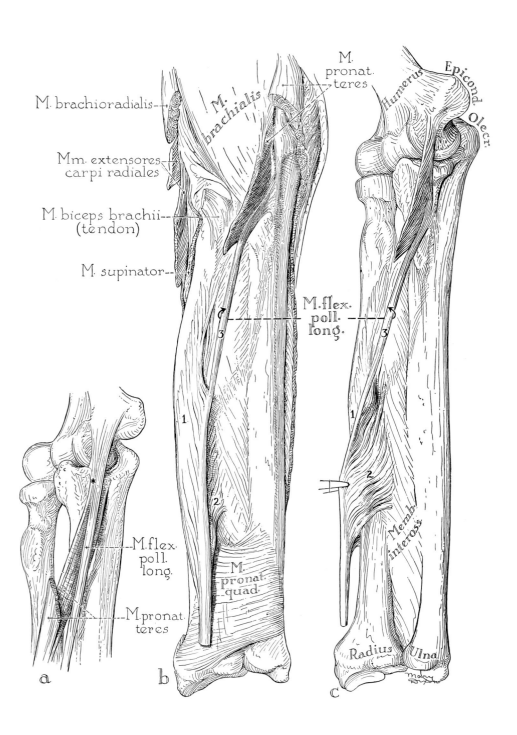

M. brachioradialis

M. pronat. teres

Humerus

Epicond.

Olecr.

M. brachialis

Mm. extensores carpi radiales

M. biceps brachii (tendon)

M. supinator

M. flex. poll. long.

M. pronat. quad.

M. flex. poll. long.

M. pronat. teres

Radius

Ulna

Membr. inteross.

a

b

c

Flexor pollicis longus muscle.

a, The accessory head of the muscle, and its association (at *) with the ulnar head of the pronator teres.
b and *c*, Showing the origin of the muscle from the radius (at 1), the interosseous membrane (at 2) and the ulna and humerus (at 3).

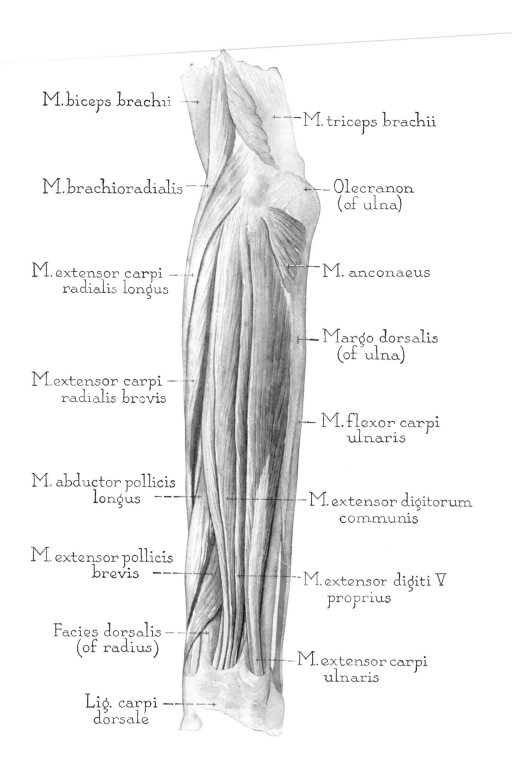

M. biceps brachii

M. triceps brachii

M. brachioradialis

Olecranon
(of ulna)

M. extensor carpi
radialis longus

M. anconaeus

Margo dorsalis
(of ulna)

M. extensor carpi
radialis brevis

M. flexor carpi
ulnaris

M. abductor pollicis
longus

M. extensor digitorum
communis

M. extensor pollicis
brevis

M. extensor digiti V
proprius

Facies dorsalis
(of radius)

M. extensor carpi
ulnaris

Lig. carpi
dorsale

Dorsal antebrachial muscles (radiodorsal division); superficial group. Direct dorsal view.

The muscles of the extensor-supinator group are fully exposed by removal of the antebrachial fascia.

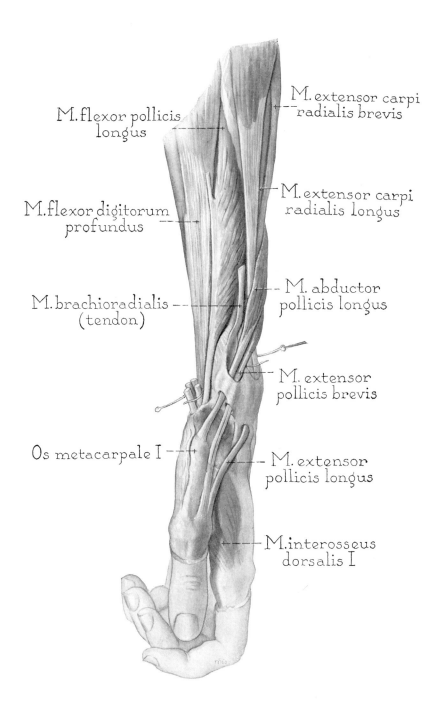

M.flexor pollicis longus

M. extensor carpi radialis brevis

M.flexor digitorum profundus

M. extensor carpi radialis longus

M.brachioradialis (tendon)

M. abductor pollicis longus

M. extensor pollicis brevis

Os metacarpale I

M. extensor pollicis longus

M.interosseus dorsalis I

Dorsal and ventral antebrachial muscles.
Radial margin of the forearm and hand; showing especially the relation of the tendons at the wrist.

The deep flexors are exposed by removal of the flexor digitorum sublimis; the extensors are shown by removal of the brachioradialis. Ventrally (anteriorly) the flexor pollicis longus is shown in its radial origin (with the flexor digitorum profundus in the background). Dorsally (posteriorly) the abductor pollicis longus, extensor pollicis longus and extensor pollicis brevis appear. The tendons of the abductors and the extensors of the thumb cross the radial side of the wrist obliquely; beneath them lie the extensor carpi radialis longus and the extensor carpi radialis brevis. At the wrist, on the volar surface, the cut tendons of the flexor digitorum sublimis are shown.

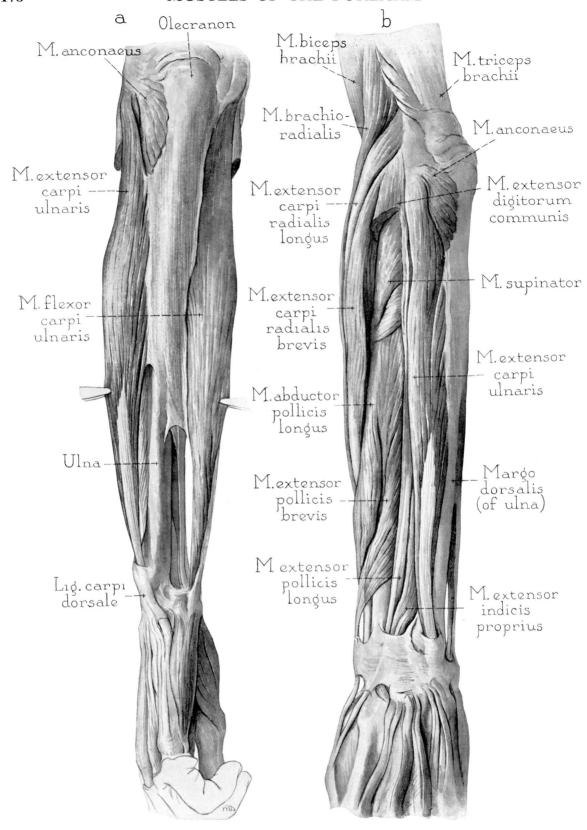

a   Olecranon

M. anconaeus

M. biceps brachii

M. triceps brachii

M. brachio-radialis

M. anconaeus

M. extensor carpi ulnaris

M. extensor carpi radialis longus

M. extensor digitorum communis

M. flexor carpi ulnaris

M. extensor carpi radialis brevis

M. supinator

M. abductor pollicis longus

M. extensor carpi ulnaris

Ulna

M. extensor pollicis brevis

Margo dorsalis (of ulna)

Lig. carpi dorsale

M. extensor pollicis longus

M. extensor indicis proprius

Antebrachial muscles. Medial and posterior views.

a, Extensor and flexor muscles at the ulnar margin of the forearm. *b*, Extensor muscles of the superficial and deep groups; the latter are shown by removal of the extensor digitorum communis.

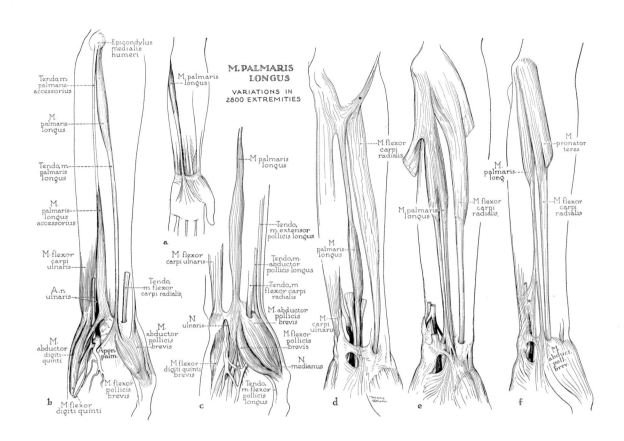

Palmaris longus muscle and tendons. Selected variations in form and attachments.

a, Regular form, course, and attachments. *b*, Doubling of the muscle; the ulnar element possesses a distal muscular portion that receives a slip from the short flexor of the little finger. *c*, A single muscle, the position of the fleshly and the tendinous portions being the reverse of the normal arrangement. *d*, A specimen aberrant in respect to 2 features: a centrally placed muscular segment; a proximal slip (at *) derived from the lacertus fibrosus. *e*, A bifid palmaris longus (partial doubling of the fleshy segment, complete duplication of the tendon). *f*, A tendon separated in its distal third, the accessory (ulnar) slip becoming blended with the antebrachial fascia (at *).

In 1600 extremities the palmaris longus muscle was absent in 205 cases (incidence, 12.9 per cent). The incidence of anomalies of all types, exclusive of agenesis, was 46 in 530 consecutive arms. Variations in position and form constitute half of these (23 in 46). Accessory slips and substitute structures were encountered 15 times in the set of 46 anomalies, while duplication of the palmaris was encountered 4 times, aberrancies of attachment 3 times.

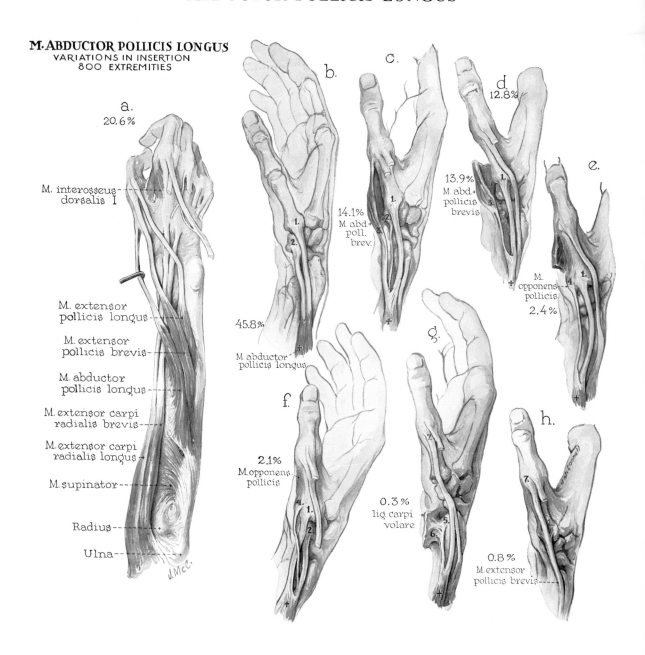

M. ABDUCTOR POLLICIS LONGUS
VARIATIONS IN INSERTION
800 EXTREMITIES

Abductor pollicis longus muscle. Types of insertion.

a, Showing the full extent of the muscle revealed by removal of the extensor digitorum communis, extensor digiti quinti proprius, extensor carpi ulnaris, and anconaeus. In this specimen, insertion is limited to the first metacarpal bone. This regularly described type of attachment occurred in only 20.6 per cent of 800 extremities. *b* to *h*, Variations in the insertion of the tendon of the abductor pollicis longus muscle. The percentage occurrence of each type of insertion is recorded with the illustration of the sample specimens. In all, 7 structures (numbered) receive the insertion of the tendon. *b*, Insertion into both the first metacarpal bone (at 1) and the greater multangular (2). *c*, Insertion into the first metacarpal (1) and, additionally, the abductor pollicis brevis (3) and the greater multangular (2). *d*, Insertion into the metacarpal (1) and the abductor pollicis brevis (3). *e*, Insertion into the metatarsal (1) and the opponens pollicis (4). *f*, Insertion into the first metacarpal bone (1), greater multangular (2) and the opponens pollicis (4). *g*, Insertion into the styloid process of the radius (5), the volar carpal ligament (6) and the proximal phalanx of the thumb (7). *h*, Insertion through an accessory slip from the extensor pollicis brevis (1) in the absence of a muscular part of the abductor itself, the extensor passing to the regular attachment (7).

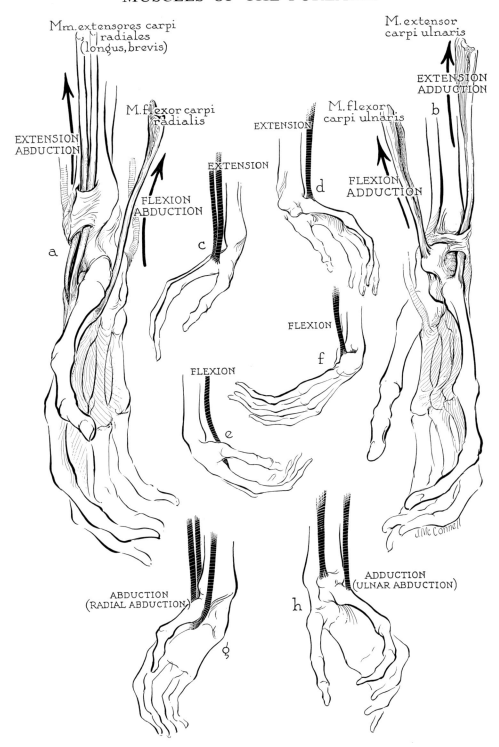

Muscles of the forearm, with their actions at the wrist.

a, The carpal extensors and flexors of the radial side of the antebrachium.

b, The extensors and flexors of the ulnar side.

c and *d*, Demonstrating extension as a combined action of the muscles of radial (*c*) and ulnar (*d*) origin.

e and *f*, Similarly integrated flexor action.

g and *h*, Abduction and adduction produced, respectively, by the carpal extensors and flexors of the radial side (*g*) and by the extensors and flexors of the ulnar side (*h*).

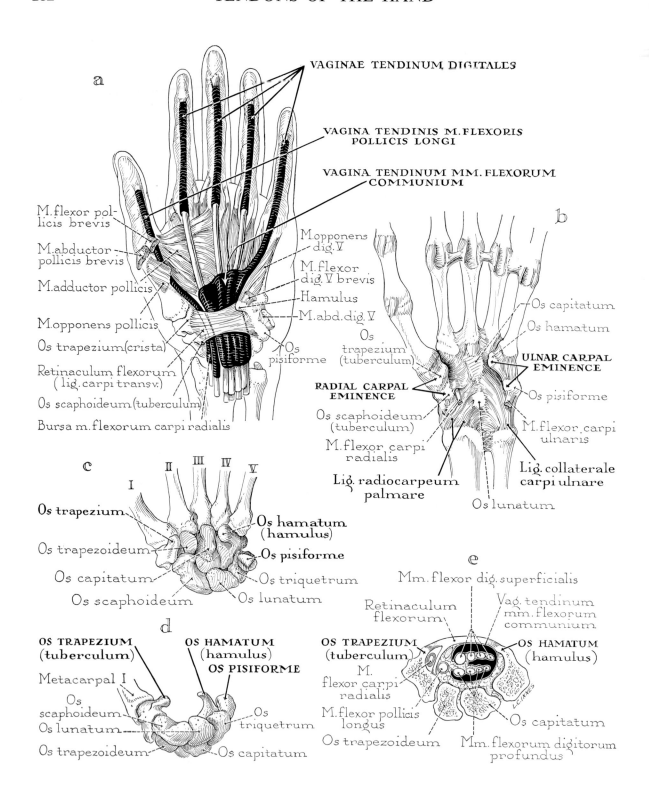

Tendons of the volar antebrachial muscles and their carpal relationships.

a, The synovial sheaths of the flexor tendons. *b*, The ligamentous structures on the floor of the carpal compartment. *c* and *d*, The osseous boundaries of the compartment. *e*, The carpal tunnel, its contents and related skeletal and ligamentous elements.

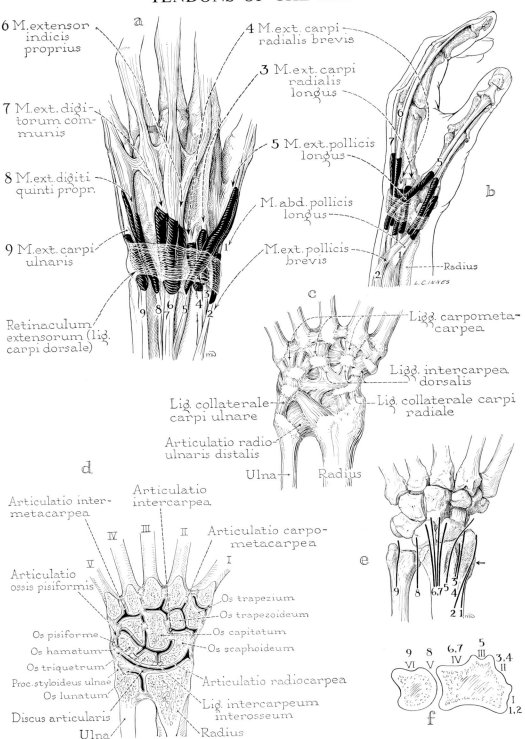

Tendons of dorsal antebrachial muscles and their carpal relationships.

a and *b*, The synovial sheaths of the extensor tendons. *b*, The ligaments of the carpal and distal radio-ulnar articulations to which the extensor tendons are related. *c*, The bones, ligaments, and articular cavities of the hand. *d*, Sulci on the distal extremities of the radius and ulna occupied by the extensor tendons as they pass through osseoligamentous compartments, from the extensor-supinator aspect of the forearm into the hand. *e*, Sulci on the radius and ulna. *f*, The sulci demonstrated by sectioning the bones in the direction of the arrow in *e*. Roman numerals indicate the sulci. Arabic numerals refer to numbers on the tendons of the long extensor muscles of the forearm.

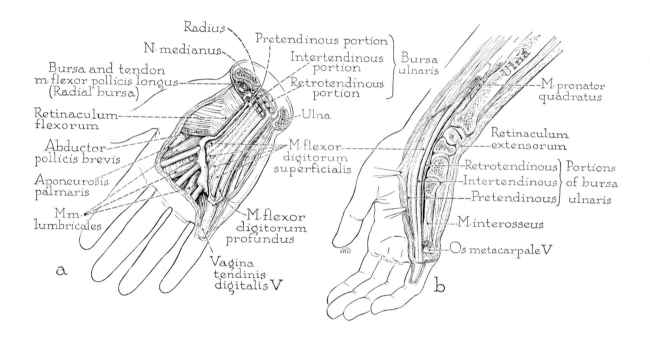

Radius

N. medianus

Bursa and tendon
m. flexor pollicis longus
(Radial bursa)

Retinaculum
flexorum

Abductor
pollicis brevis

Aponeurosis
palmaris

Mm.
lumbricales

a

Pretendinous portion
Intertendinous
portion   Bursa
Retrotendinous   ulnaris
portion

Ulna

M. flexor
digitorum
superficialis

M. flexor
digitorum
profundus

Vagina
tendinis
digitalis V

Ulna

M. pronator
quadratus

Retinaculum
extensorum

Retrotendinous   Portions
Intertendinous   of bursa
Pretendinous   ulnaris

M. interosseus

Os metacarpale V

b

Synovial sheath and bursa of the palm.

In *a* and *b* the synovial cavity has been opened in such a way as to demonstrate the manner in which it is
subdivided into intercommunicating spaces above, below, and between the tiers of tendons. *a*, Viewed from
the palmar aspect; *b*, from the hypothenar side.

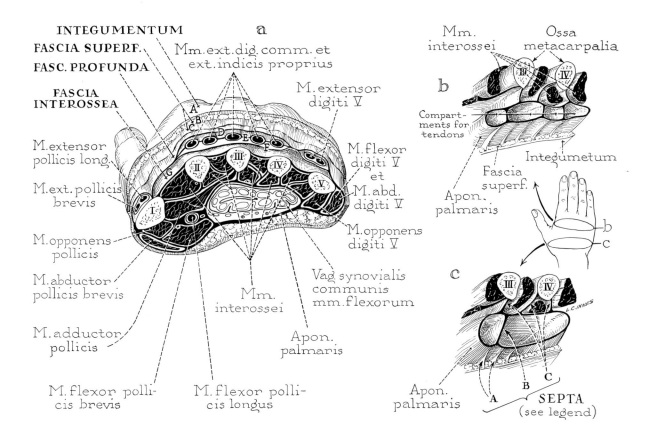

INTEGUMENTUM

FASCIA SUPERF.

FASC. PROFUNDA

FASCIA INTEROSSEA

M.extensor pollicis long.

M.ext.pollicis brevis

M.opponens pollicis

M.abductor pollicis brevis

M.adductor pollicis

M.flexor pollicis brevis

a

Mm.ext.dig.comm. et ext.indicis proprius

M.extensor digiti V

M.flexor digiti V et M.abd. digiti V

M.opponens digiti V

Vag.synovialis communis mm.flexorum

Mm. interossei

Apon. palmaris

M.flexor pollicis longus

Mm. interossei

b

Ossa metacarpalia

Compartments for tendons

Fascia superf.

Apon. palmaris

Integumetum

c

Apon. palmaris

SEPTA (see legend)

Layers and spaces of the hand shown diagrammatically.

a, The layers of the dorsal aspect of the hand, shown in section. (See following page for explanation of the letters.)

b and c, The subdivisions of the midpalmar compartment at the levels indicated in the inset. Compare pages 208 and 209. A, septal connections between integument and aponeurosis. B and C, septa within the compartment.

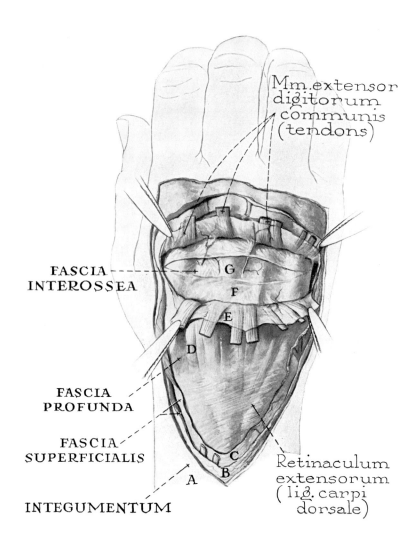

FASCIA
INTEROSSEA

FASCIA
PROFUNDA

FASCIA
SUPERFICIALIS

INTEGUMENTUM

Mm. extensor
digitorum
communis
(tendons)

Retinaculum
extensorum
(lig. carpi
dorsale)

Layers of the dorsum of the hand.

a, In the distal forearm the layers are shown in succession from the skin to the deep fascia; on the metacarpus they are exposed to skeletal level by means of openings in the fascial strata. Key to letters: A, integument; B and C, superficial and deep layers, respectively, of superficial fascia; D and F, supratendinous and
infratendinous laminae, respectively, of deep fascia; E, fascia of tendons; G, interosseous fascia.

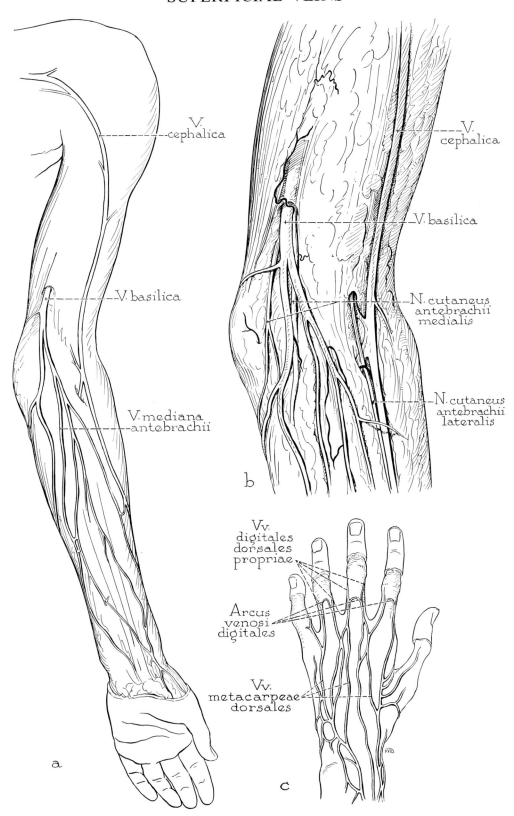

Veins of the upper extremity.

a, Veins of the ventral aspect of the upper extremity. *b*, Veins in the region of the cubital fossa. *c*, Veins of the dorsum of the hand.

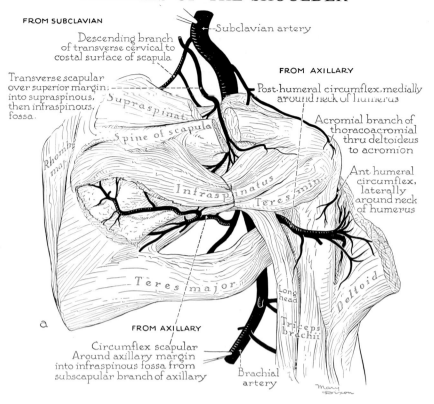

Descending branch
of transverse cervical to
costal surface of scapula

Transverse scapular
over superior margin;
into supraspinous,
then infraspinous,
fossa.

Subclavian artery

FROM AXILLARY

Post. humeral circumflex, medially
around neck of humerus

Acromial branch of
thoracoacromial
thru deltoideus
to acromion

Ant. humeral
circumflex,
laterally
around neck
of humerus

Rhomb major

Supraspinat.

Spine of scapula

Infraspinatus

Teres minor

Teres major

Long head

Triceps brachii

Deltoid

a

FROM AXILLARY

Circumflex scapular
Around axillary margin
into infraspinous fossa from
subscapular branch of axillary

Brachial
artery

Mary Dixon

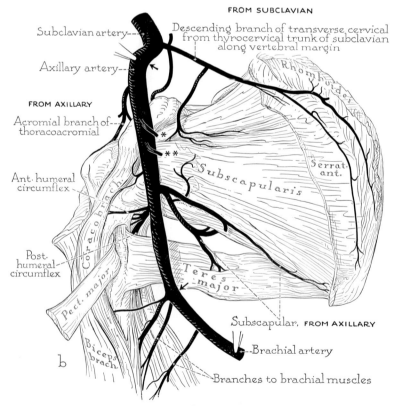

FROM SUBCLAVIAN

Subclavian artery

Descending branch of transverse cervical
from thyrocervical trunk of subclavian
along vertebral margin

Axillary artery

FROM AXILLARY

Acromial branch of
thoracoacromial

Ant. humeral
circumflex

Post.
humeral
circumflex

Coracobrach.

Pect. major

Biceps brach.

b

Rhomboideu

*

**

Subscapularis

Serrat. ant.

Teres major

Subscapular, FROM AXILLARY

Brachial artery

Branches to brachial muscles

Arterial supply of the shoulder.

a, Dorsal view. The spine of the scapula has been cut away, and segments of neighboring muscles excised.

b, Ventral view. Arrows mark lines of division of the artery (subclavian, axillary, brachial); * and ** indicate transected thoracic branches.

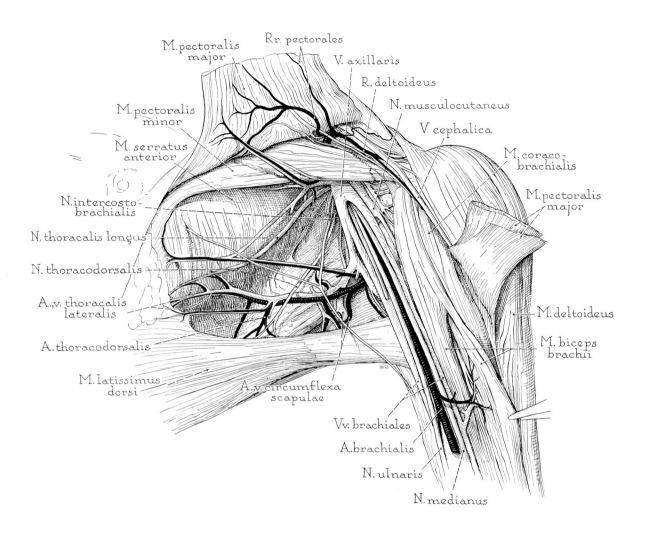

Vessels and nerves of the axilla.

Anteriorly, the pectoralis major muscle has been cut and reflected; the subjacent pectoralis minor is intact. The costacoracoid membrane has been dissected away to expose the cephalic vein, the thoracoacromial artery and its branches to the pectoral and brachial musculature.

The serratus anterior is shown medial to the abducted arm. Descending from the apex of the axilla, upon the muscle, are the long thoracic nerve and the lateral thoracic vessels. From similar source, the thoracodorsal nerve and artery course obliquely backward to supply musculature located along the axillary margin of the scapula. Nearby, the circumflex scapular vessels bend dorsalward, deep to the latissimus dorsi, between the subscapularis and teres major muscles; the vessels then pass to the dorsal surface of the scapula, through the medial axillary, or so-called triangular, space. From the summit of the axilla, the intercostobrachial nerve descends to the medial aspect of the arm.

Along the arm, toward the forearm, pass the axillary vessels and their brachial continuations, together with the radial and the ulnar nerves. These vessels and nerves descend in the sulcus bounded in front by the coracobrachialis and biceps brachii and behind by the triceps brachii. The musculocutaneous nerve pierces the coracobrachialis; attaining the space between the biceps brachii and the brachialis, the nerve descends between the muscles, innervating them en route.

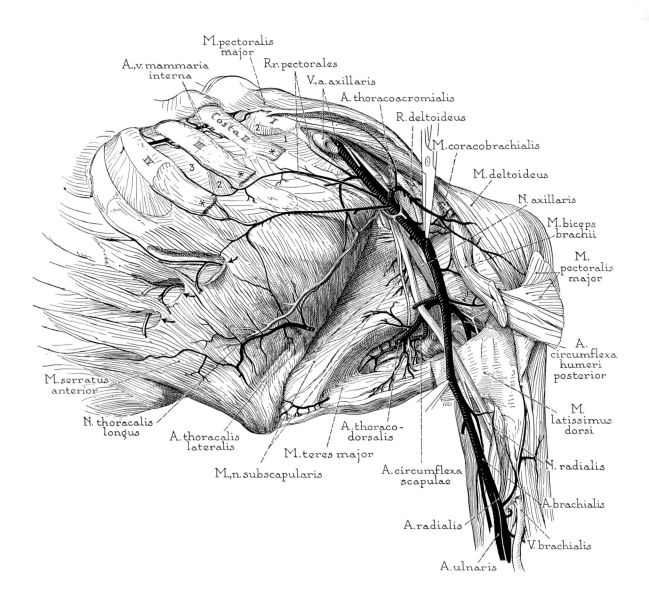

Arteries and nerves of the axilla. Dissection continued.

The pectoralis major remains only in the areas of sternoclavicular origin and humeral insertion. The pectoralis minor has been cut medially at the costal slips of origins, marked by *; the arm, thus freed, has been sharply abducted. On the thoracic wall, toward the sternum, the layers have been removed to successively deeper levels in order to show the external intercostal muscle (at 1), the internal intercostal (at 2), the pleura (at 3), and the internal mammary (NA, thoracic) vessels. In more lateral position, several digitations of the serratus anterior have been dissected away (at arrows), to demonstrate the parietal rami of the intercostal arteries and the accompanying veins.

The lateral thoracic artery has been transected; the axillary and brachial veins have been removed, in order to bring the arterial and nervous elements more prominently into view. In this specimen the brachial artery splits, in the distal third of the arm, into its radial and ulnar divisions.

The coracobrachialis has been excised, the biceps brachii transected and reflected. The axillary nerve is traced to the head of the humerus; the radial nerve is followed into the sulcus bounded by the heads of the triceps brachii.

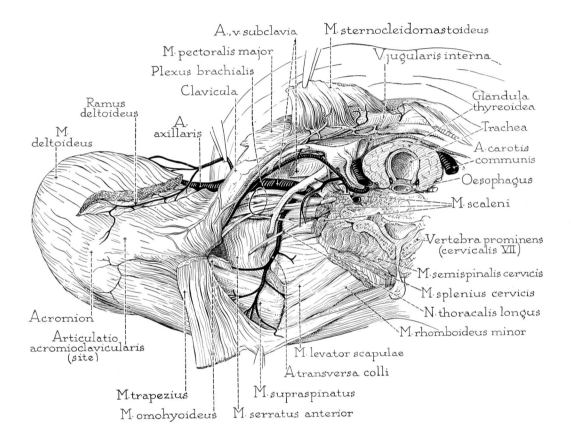

A., v. subclavia

M. sternocleidomastoideus

M. pectoralis major

V. jugularis interna

Plexus brachialis

Clavicula

Glandula thyreoidea

Ramus deltoideus

Trachea

M. deltoideus

A. axillaris

A. carotis communis

Oesophagus

M. scaleni

Vertebra prominens (cervicalis VII)

M. semispinalis cervicis

M. splenius cervicis

N. thoracalis longus

M. rhomboideus minor

Acromion

Articulatio acromioclavicularis (site)

M. levator scapulae

A. transversa colli

M. trapezius

M. supraspinatus

M. omohyoideus

M. serratus anterior

Vessels and nerves of the neck and shoulder.

The trapezius muscle is retracted to demonstrate the course of the transverse cervical artery and the long thoracic nerve. A gutter has been cut in the deltoid muscle along the course of the deltoid ramus of the axillary artery.

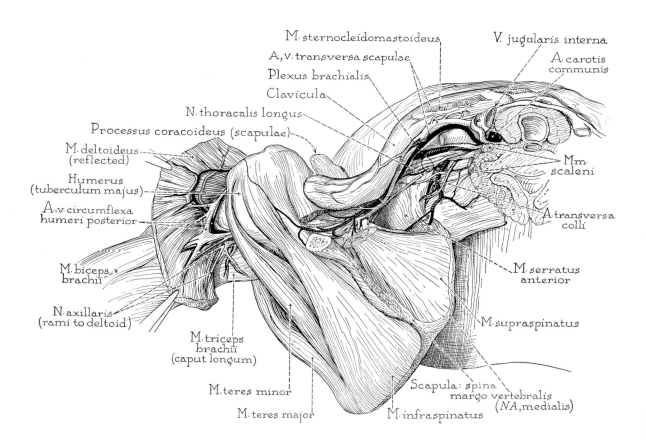

Vessels and nerves of the neck and shoulder; dissection continued.

The trapezius muscle has been removed and a portion of the supraspinatus dissected, in order to reveal the course of the transverse cervical artery and vein. The deltoid muscle has been reflected, demonstrating the axillary nerve and the circumflex humeral blood vessels.

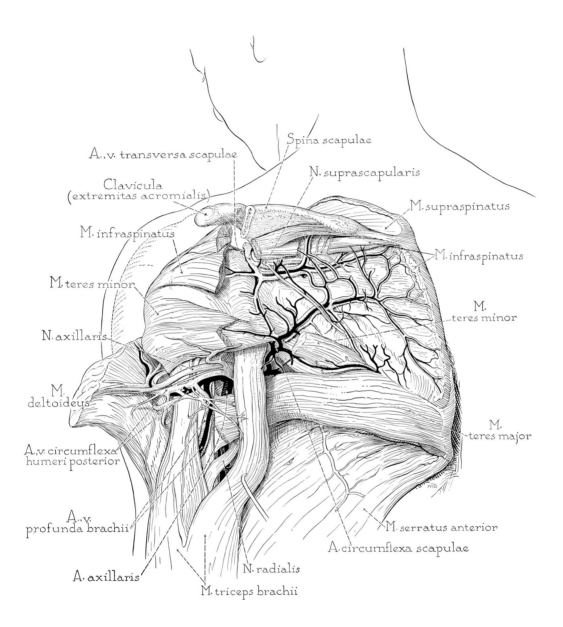

Vessels and nerves of the shoulder. Dorsal aspect.

The arteries, veins, and nerves of the infraspinous fossa, of the axilla and scapula, and of the proximal extremity of the humerus are revealed through removal of the infraspinatus and teres minor muscles. The vessels and nerves of proximal humeral position are exposed through reflection of the deltoideus muscle. The spine of the scapula has been cut away in order to demonstrate the route by which vessels and nerves pass from the supraspinous into the infraspinous fossa.

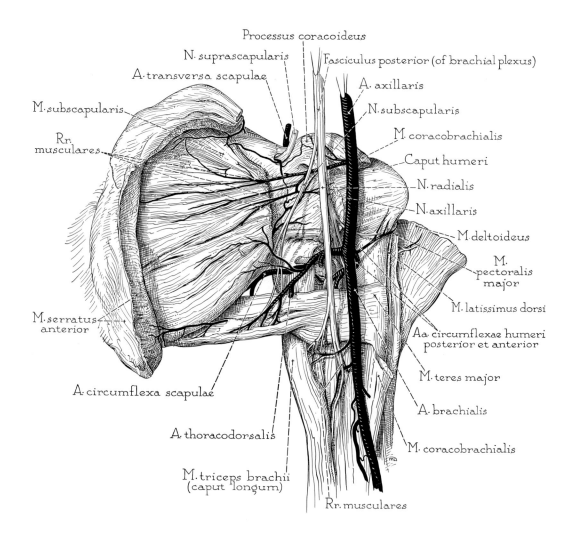

Vessels and nerves of the shoulder. Ventral, or costal, aspect.

In the disarticulated shoulder the serratus anterior and deltoideus muscles have been removed except in the areas of insertion into, respectively, the vertebral (medial) border of the scapula and the deltoid tuberosity of the humerus.

A segment of the subscapularis has been removed in the area where it covers the articular capsule. The scapular foramen, and the triangular and quadrangular spaces are shown, together with the contents of each.

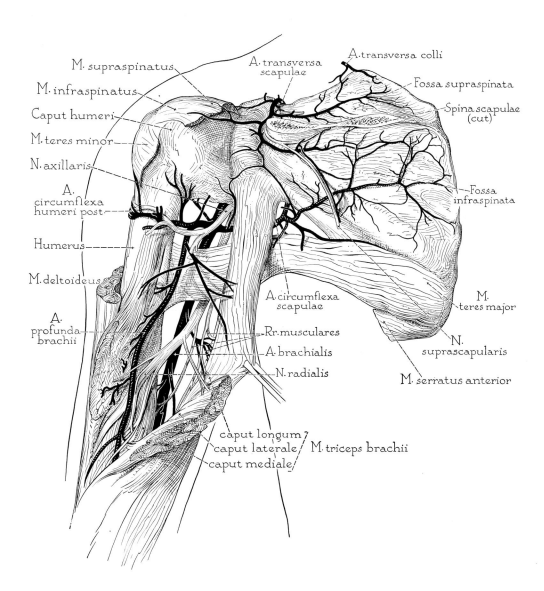

M. supraspinatus

M. infraspinatus

Caput humeri

M. teres minor

N. axillaris

A. circumflexa humeri post

Humerus

M. deltoideus

A. profunda brachii

A. transversa scapulae

A. transversa colli

Fossa supraspinata

Spina scapulae (cut)

Fossa infraspinata

A. circumflexa scapulae

Rr. musculares

A. brachialis

N. radialis

M. teres major

N. suprascapularis

M. serratus anterior

caput longum
caput laterale   } M. triceps brachii
caput mediale

Vessels and nerves of the shoulder and arm. Dorsal aspect, deep dissection.

The supraspinatus, infraspinatus, and teres minor muscles have been removed except at the humeral insertions; the spine of the scapula has been cut away close to its root. The medial head of the triceps brachii has been separated, by oblique cut, from the lateral head. By retraction the combined long head and medial head of the muscle, the deep branch of the brachial artery, and the accompanying radial nerve are brought into view. Additionally, the dissection demonstrates the relation of the axillary nerves and posterior humeral circumflex artery to the quadrangular space, and that of the circumflex scapular artery to the triangular space.

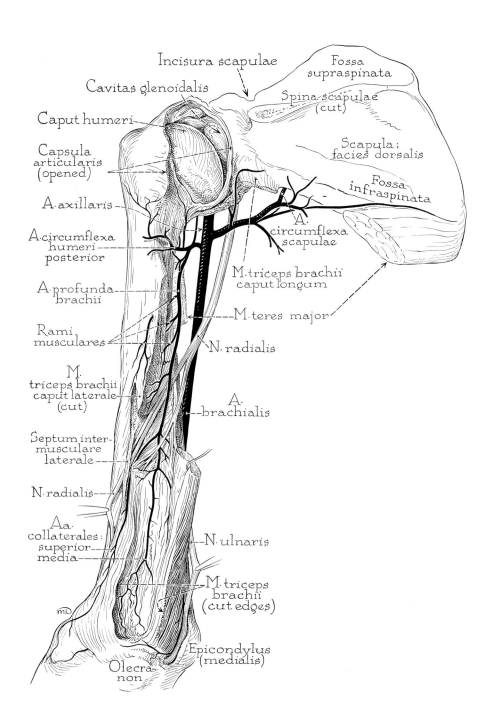

Vessels and nerves of the shoulder and arm, dissection continued.

The long head of the triceps brachii muscle has been removed to reveal the course of the radial nerve and the deep branch of the brachial artery. The radial nerve passes through the lateral intermuscular septum to reach the anterior surface of the forearm; the ulnar nerve, on the opposite aspect of the arm, pierces the medial intermuscular septum to pass behind the medial epicondyle of the humerus.

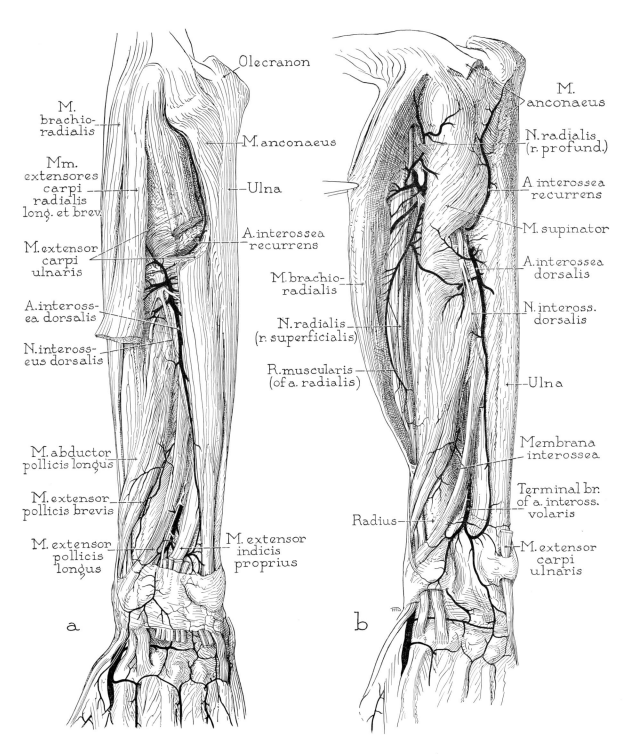

Olecranon

M. brachio-radialis

M. anconaeus

Mm. extensores carpi radialis long. et brev.

M. extensor carpi ulnaris

Ulna

A. interossea recurrens

A. inteross-ea dorsalis

N. inteross-eus dorsalis

M. abductor pollicis longus

M. extensor pollicis brevis

M. extensor pollicis longus

M. extensor indicis proprius

a

M. anconaeus

N. radialis (r. profund.)

A. interossea recurrens

M. supinator

A. interossea dorsalis

N. inteross. dorsalis

M. brachio-radialis

N. radialis (r. superficialis)

R. muscularis (of a. radialis)

Ulna

Membrana interossea

Terminal br. of a. inteross. volaris

Radius

M. extensor carpi ulnaris

b

Vessels and nerves of the forearm and hand. Dorsal surface.

a, The digital extensor muscles have been removed in the forearm. With excision of these members of the superficial layer of dorsal antebrachial muscles, the muscles of the deep set are exposed, together with the dorsal interosseous vessels and nerves (which course between the two muscular strata). In the hand the tendons of the same muscles (extensor digitorum communis and extensor digiti quinti proprius) have been transected near the dorsal carpal ligament and drawn distalward. In this way the carpal rete and metacarpal arteries are exposed.

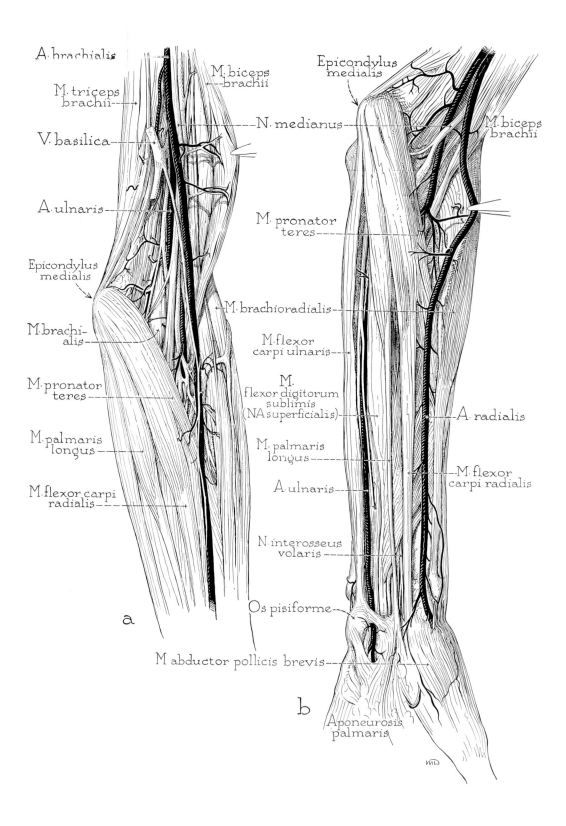

A·brachialis

M·triceps brachii

V·basilica

A·ulnaris

Epicondylus medialis

M·brachi- alis

M·pronator teres

M·palmaris longus

M·flexor carpi radialis

M·biceps brachii

N·medianus

M·brachioradialis

M·flexor carpi ulnaris

M. flexor digitorum sublimis (NA superficialis)

M·palmaris longus

A·ulnaris

N·interosseus volaris

Os pisiforme

M·abductor pollicis brevis

Epicondylus medialis

M·biceps brachii

M·pronator teres

A·radialis

M·flexor carpi radialis

Aponeurosis palmaris

a

b

Vessels and nerves of the forearm.

Arteries and nerves of the forearm. Ventral surface. Two stages in dissection.

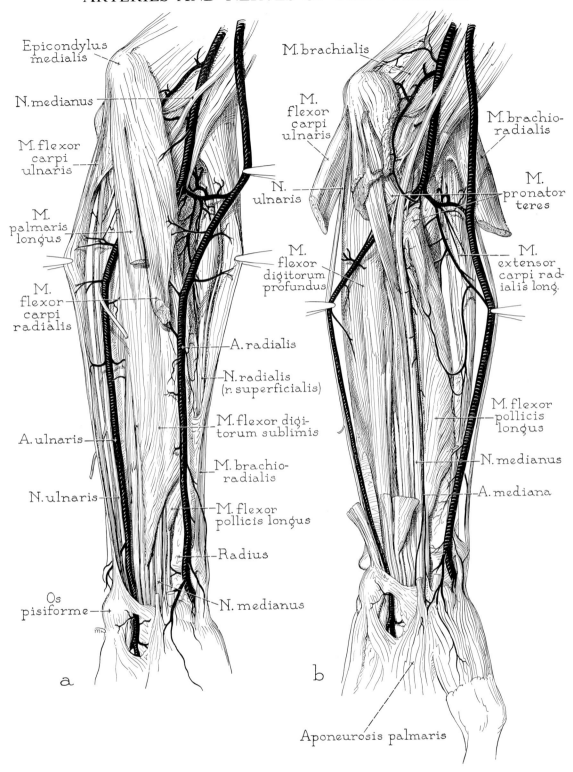

Epicondylus medialis

N. medianus

M. flexor carpi ulnaris

M. palmaris longus

M. flexor carpi radialis

A. ulnaris

N. ulnaris

Os pisiforme

a

M. brachialis

M. flexor carpi ulnaris

N. ulnaris

M. flexor digitorum profundus

A. radialis

N. radialis (n. superficialis)

M. flexor digitorum sublimis

M. brachioradialis

M. flexor pollicis longus

Radius

N. medianus

M. brachioradialis

M. pronator teres

M. extensor carpi radialis long.

M. flexor pollicis longus

N. medianus

A. mediana

b

Aponeurosis palmaris

Arteries and nerves of the forearm. Ventral surface.
Superficial and intermediate levels of dissection.

a, The course of the ulnar division of the brachial artery is shown, as it passes to the ulnar side of the forearm beneath the flexor muscles of medial epicondylar origin. Under cover of the flexor carpi ulnaris muscle (retracted) the artery joins the ulnar nerve. The radial division remains superficial to the flexor digitorum sublimis (NA, superficialis) muscle.

b, The ulnar artery in its course beneath the deep head of the pronator teres; the median, accompanied by a small median artery, passes between the superficial head (cut) and deep head of the same muscle.

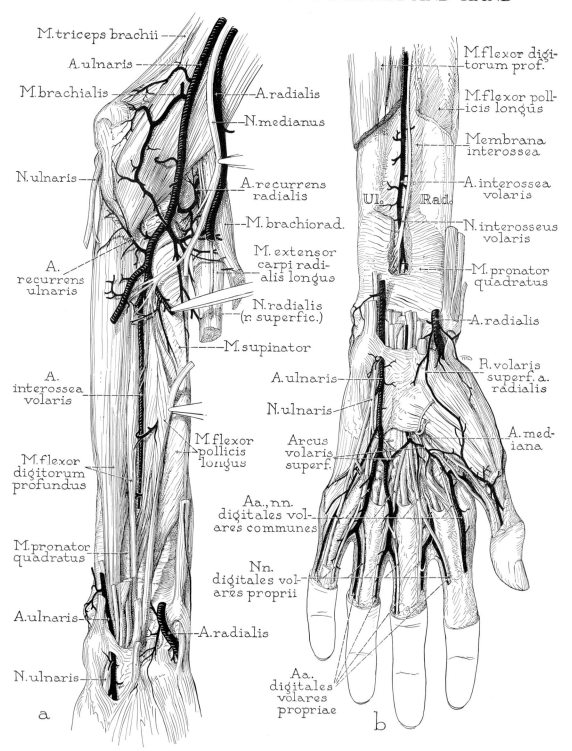

Arteries and nerves of the forearm and hand. Ventral (volar) surface.
Deep dissection of the forearm.

a, The course of the volar interosseous artery, and that of the volar interosseous branch of the median nerve, are shown as they descend in the sulcus between the flexor digitorum profundus and the flexor pollicis longus muscles. The ulnar nerve (transected) distal to the point at which it enters the forearm between the humeral and ulnar heads of the flexor carpi ulnaris.

b, The volar interosseous artery and nerve are followed into the pronator quadratus muscle. In the hand the superficial volar arterial arch is shown, together with the contributory arteries and derived branches. Additionally, the median and ulnar nerves are shown.

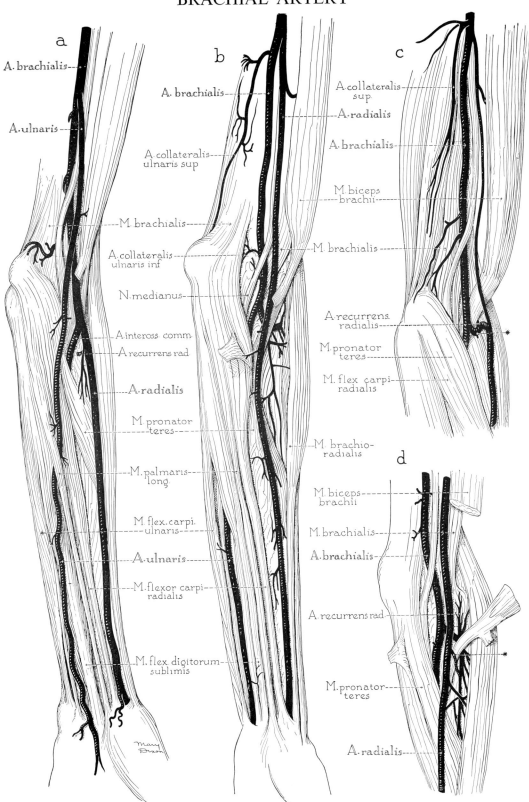

Brachial artery; variations in division.

In addition to variation in the point of origin from the main stem, of the radial and ulnar divisions, the following departures from the anatomic norm are recorded: in *a*, course of the ulnar artery superficial to 3 of the 4 muscles that constitute the first layer of the flexor-pronator set; in *b*, high division of the brachial; in *c*, the occurrence of a superficial radial artery, which continues as a large vessel distal to the point of communication (at *) in the cubital fossa, with the brachial artery; in *d*, the occurrence of a communication (at *), distal to the cubital fossa, between a large radial artery and the volar interosseous artery.

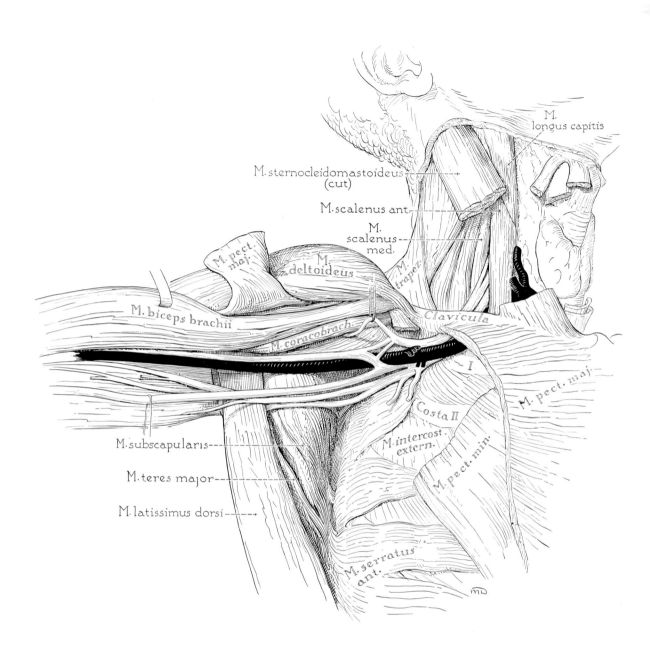

Boundaries and chief contents of the axillary space; anterolateral view.

The pectoralis major and pectoralis minor, which form the anterior boundary of the axilla, have been partially removed; the arm is abducted. In this way the chief arterial and nervous contents of the axilla have been exposed, as well as the muscles which constitute the medial, lateral, and posterior boundaries of the space. The trunks of the brachial plexus are exposed by transection of the sternocleidomastoid muscle; the cords appear distal to the clavicle. The nerves are demonstrated in the following manner: the musculocutaneous has been lifted to demonstrate its short free course to the point where it pierces the coracobrachialis; the median nerve retains its normal relation to the brachial artery; the ulnar and medial antebrachial cutaneous nerves have been drawn slightly downward.

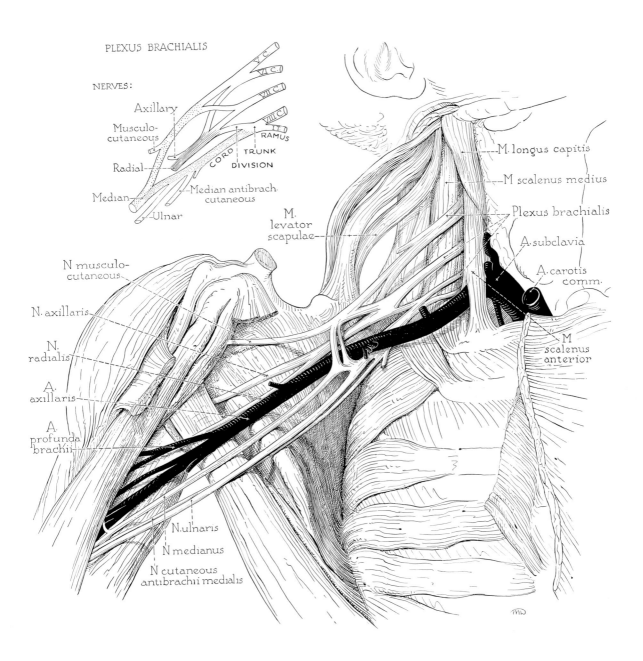

Subclavian artery and its axillary continuation, and the brachial plexus.
Deep dissection of the same specimen; anterolateral view.

The clavicle has been removed; the pectoral girdle has been drawn dorsalward away from the trunk. The pectoral muscles have been further cut away at their origins; the sternocleidomastoid and the trapezius have been removed and the anterior scalene has been retracted to show the cervical rami contributory to the brachial plexus. The levator scapulae has been mobilized, its portions segregated. The subclavian artery is now fully exposed, and its axillary and brachial continuations followed to the arm. The brachial plexus has been mobilized to demonstrate the rami, trunks, divisions, cords, and derived nerves (compare diagram, inset at the upper left). In addition to the nerves seen in the preceding figure, the axillary and the radial are now in view.

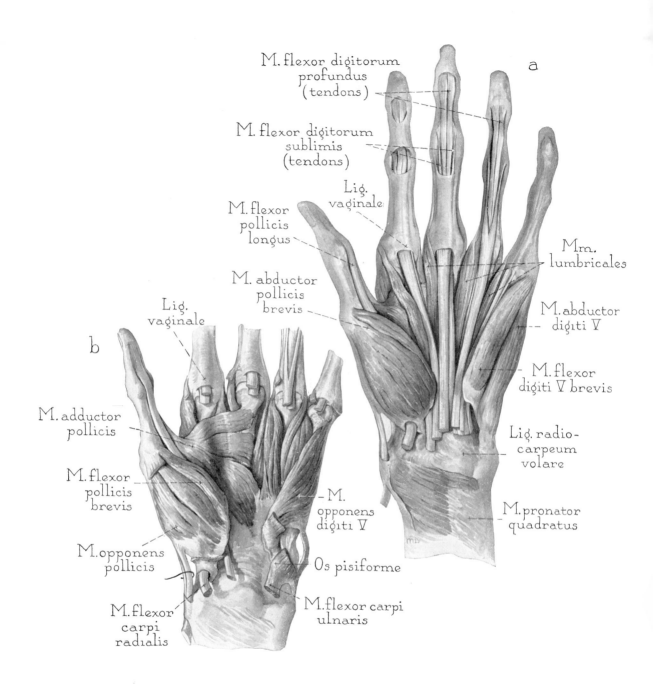

M. flexor digitorum profundus (tendons)

M. flexor digitorum sublimis (tendons)

Lig. vaginale

M. flexor pollicis longus

M. abductor pollicis brevis

Lig. vaginale

b

a

Mm. lumbricales

M. abductor digiti V

M. flexor digiti V brevis

Lig. radio-carpeum volare

M. pronator quadratus

M. adductor pollicis

M. flexor pollicis brevis

M. opponens pollicis

M. flexor carpi radialis

M. opponens digiti V

Os pisiforme

M. flexor carpi ulnaris

Muscles of the palm.

a, The palmar aponeurosis has been removed, and the long tendons exposed; likewise shown are the muscles of the thenar and hypothenar eminences. The fascial sheaths have been opened on the index, middle and ring fingers to demonstrate the marginal attachments of the tendons from the flexor digitorum sublimis (NA, superficialis).

b, On the thenar eminence the abductor pollicis brevis has been reflected to expose the opponens pollicis; correspondingly on the hypothenar eminence the abductor digiti quinti and flexor digiti quinti have been dissected away to show the opponens digiti quinti. In the middle of the hand the adductor pollicis and the interossei of the ulnar side are shown. The muscles form the floor of the midpalmar space.

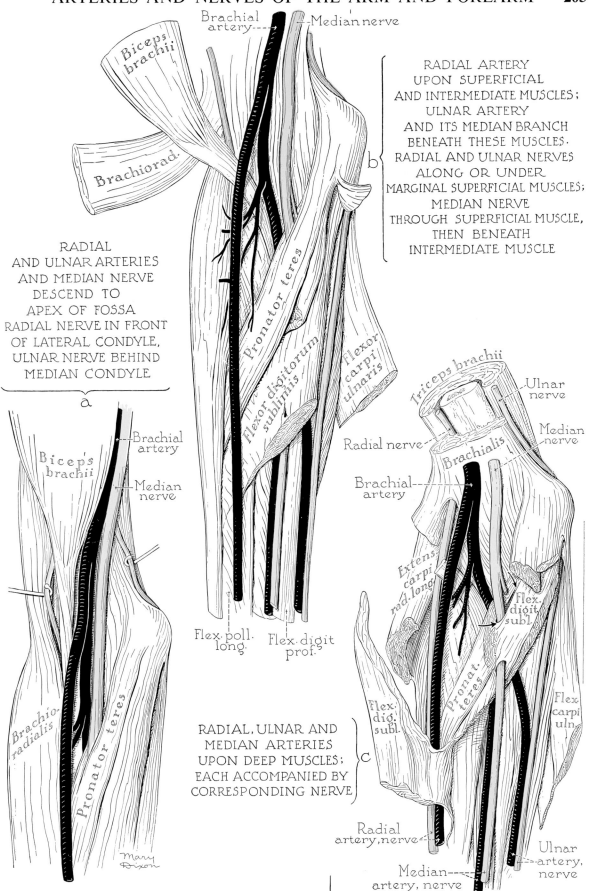

Brachial artery

Median nerve

Biceps brachii

Brachiorad.

RADIAL ARTERY
UPON SUPERFICIAL
AND INTERMEDIATE MUSCLES;
ULNAR ARTERY
AND ITS MEDIAN BRANCH
BENEATH THESE MUSCLES.
RADIAL AND ULNAR NERVES
ALONG OR UNDER
MARGINAL SUPERFICIAL MUSCLES;
MEDIAN NERVE
THROUGH SUPERFICIAL MUSCLE,
THEN BENEATH
INTERMEDIATE MUSCLE

b

RADIAL
AND ULNAR ARTERIES
AND MEDIAN NERVE
DESCEND TO
APEX OF FOSSA
RADIAL NERVE IN FRONT
OF LATERAL CONDYLE,
ULNAR NERVE BEHIND
MEDIAN CONDYLE

a

Pronator teres

Flexor digitorum sublimis

Flexor carpi ulnaris

Biceps brachii

Brachial artery

Median nerve

Triceps brachii

Ulnar nerve

Radial nerve

Median nerve

Brachialis

Brachial artery

Extens. carpi rad. long.

Flex. digit. subl.

Brachioradialis

Pronator teres

Flex. poll. long.

Flex. digit. prof.

Flex. dig. subl.

Pronat. teres

Flex. carpi uln.

RADIAL, ULNAR AND
MEDIAN ARTERIES
UPON DEEP MUSCLES;
EACH ACCOMPANIED BY
CORRESPONDING NERVE

c

Radial artery, nerve

Median artery, nerve

Ulnar artery, nerve

Mary Dixon

Course and relations of the arteries and nerves on the ventral surface of the arm and forearm.

PRONATOR TERES
M·PRONATOR TERES, N·MEDIANUS
VARIATION IN RELATIONSHIP, 1000 SPECIMENS

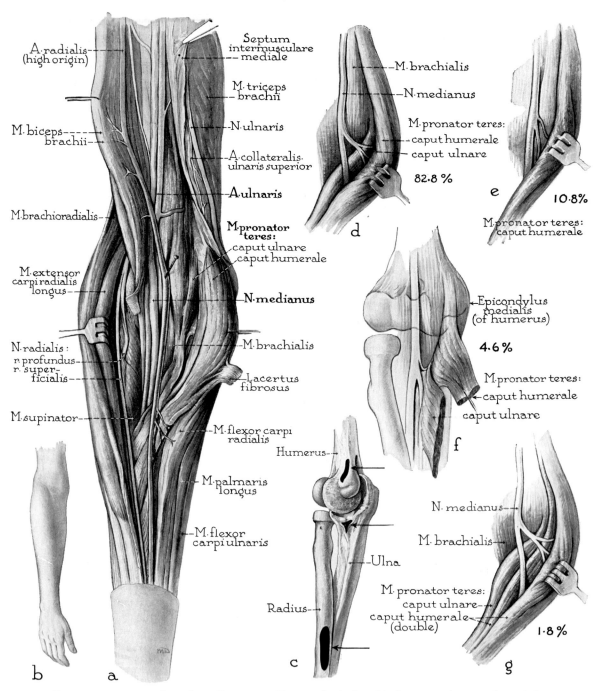

Pronator teres muscle and median nerve. Types of relationship between the muscle and the nerve encountered in 1000 specimens, with percentage occurrence of each type.

b, The forearm in pronated position. *a,* An infrequent type (4.6 per cent, as in *f*), in which the nerve passes beneath the ulnar (deep) head of the muscle. In this specimen there occurred a high (proximal) division of the brachial artery, to send the ulnar and radial divisions separately into the cubital fossa. *d,* The most frequent type (82.8 per cent), in which the nerve passes between the humeral (superficial) and ulnar (deep) heads of the pronator teres (areas of skeletal attachment shown in *c*). *e,* One of the three infrequent types (10.8 per cent) in which the nerve, in the absence of an ulnar head of the pronator, passes to deep level in the antebrachium by coursing distalward under the humeral head. *f,* An even less common relationship (4.6 per cent), in which the nerve courses deep to the regular ulnar head. *g,* The least common arrangement (1.8 per cent), whereby, in the presence of an ulnar head, the nerve passes between subdivisions of a split humeral portion of the muscle.

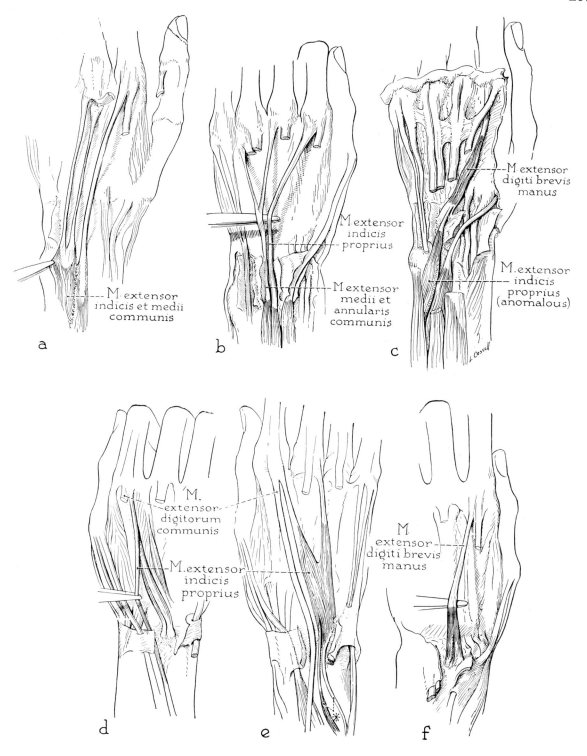

Extensor musculature of the hand. Selected variations from 263 specimens of upper member.

a, An example of extensor of the index and middle fingers in which a lateral tendon inserted into the digit as would a typical extensor indicis proprius, while the other 2 tendons passed to the middle finger. *b*, A case in which a normal extensor indicis proprius, arising in common with a distally placed portion, sent tendons to the index, middle and ring fingers. *c*, An example of an extensor indicis brevis manus (a short muscle arising in the hand), which was associated with an anomalous extensor indicis proprius. *d* and *e*, Bifid varieties of the same muscle. *f*, A short manual muscle to the index finger, comparable to one portion of the typical extensor digitorum brevis on the dorsum of the foot.

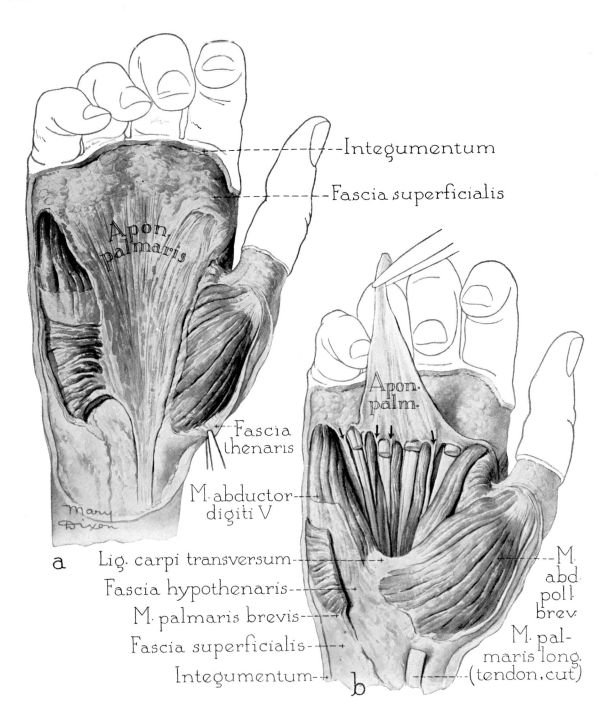

Integumentum

Fascia superficialis

Apon. palmaris

Fascia thenaris

M. abductor digiti V

Lig. carpi transversum

Fascia hypothenaris

M. palmaris brevis

Fascia superficialis

Integumentum

a

Apon. palm.

M. abd poll. brev.

M. palmaris long. (tendon, cut)

b

Palmar aponeurosis and midpalmar compartment.

  a, The integument and the greater part of the superficial fascia have been removed from the palm and the thenar and hypothenar eminences; in the fascia is lodged the palmaris brevis muscle. The deep fascia has been partially removed from the muscles of the thumb and the little finger; it is intact over the middle of the palm, where, receiving the tendon of the palmaris longus muscle, it becomes the palmar aponeurosis.

  b, The strata on the eminences are illustrated (including part of the palmaris brevis), from the skin to the musculature. Over the palm the aponeurotic continuation of the deep fascia (palmar aponeurosis) has been freed and turned distalward; from its deep aspect strong septa (at arrows) are sent into the depths of the palm to form longitudinal compartments for the flexor tendons and their associated lumbrical muscles.

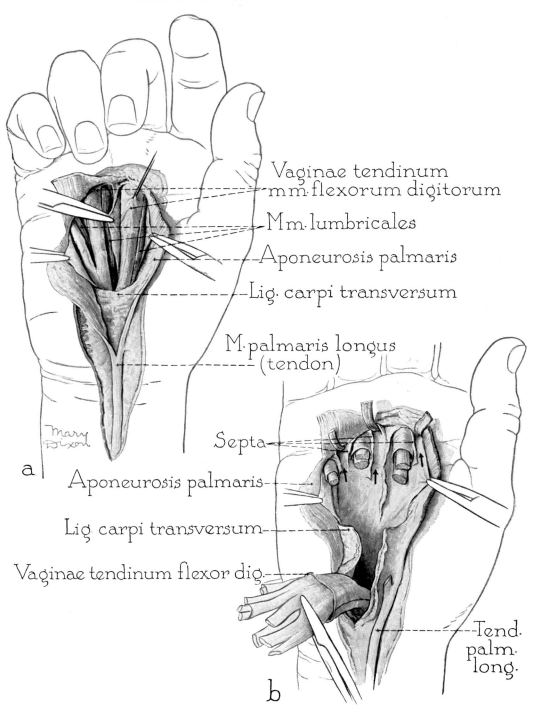

Vaginae tendinum
m.m. flexorum digitorum

Mm. lumbricales

Aponeurosis palmaris

Lig. carpi transversum

M. palmaris longus
(tendon)

Septa

Aponeurosis palmaris

Lig. carpi transversum

Vaginae tendinum flexor dig.

Tend. palm. long.

a

b

Midpalmar compartment.

a, In a second specimen the components of the palmar sheath are separately dissected; the external aponeurotic layer is drawn aside, the internal fascial layer similarly opened and retracted. Within the latter are exposed the lumbricals and flexor tendons with their sheaths (the sheath for the middle finger lifted by thread). The vessels and nerves have been removed.

b, The flexor tendons and their synovial sheaths are here transected; their cut ends appear distally within separate phalangeal sheaths, proximally within a common ulnar sheath; the latter is lifted through a cut transverse carpal ligament. Within the midpalmar compartment the fascial floor is now fully exposed. Septa are deficient proximally so that the midpalmar compartment is a single space; distally septa extend from floor to roof, forming the walls of the canals for the flexor tendons and for the lumbrical muscles (at arrows). The transverse carpal ligament has been cut to show the proximal extent of the space.

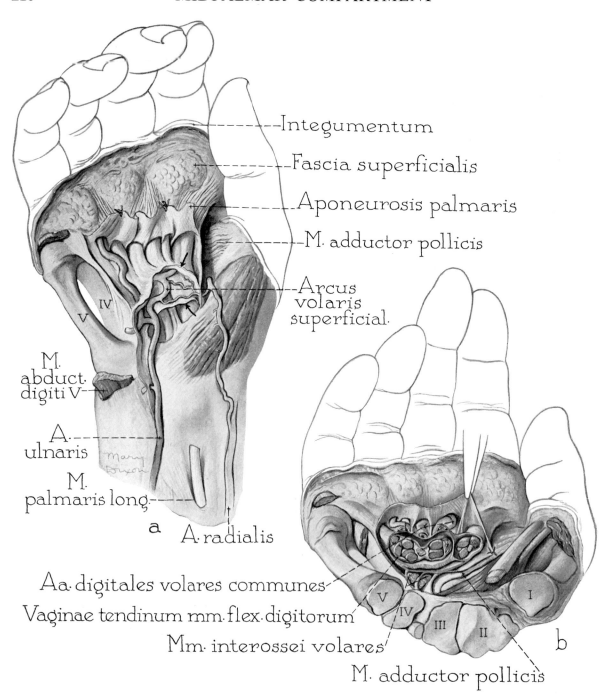

Integumentum

Fascia superficialis

Aponeurosis palmaris

M. adductor pollicis

Arcus
volaris
superficial.

M.
abduct.
digiti V

A.
ulnaris

M.
palmaris long.

a   A. radialis

Aa. digitales volares communes

Vaginae tendinum mm. flex. digitorum

Mm. interossei volares

M. adductor pollicis

b

Structure and contents of the midpalmar compartment.

a, Distally the successive strata are shown to the level of the palmar aponeurosis. Over the middle of the palm the aponeurosis has been cut and turned forward (attached by septal extensions) to expose the inner fascial sheath; the latter is divided along the course of the superficial volar arch to show the manner in which its layers (at arrows) enclose the superficial volar arch. Its deeper layer is the roof for the midpalmar compartment in which are placed the synovial sheaths and lumbrical muscles. Medially, by removal of the thenar and interosseous muscles, is shown the attachment of the aponeurotic layer to the fourth metacarpal bone.

b, The hand has been disarticulated at the carpometacarpal joints (numbered), and viewed from the antebrachial aspect. The midpalmar sheath has been transected at a point distal to the position of the joints; then the aponeurotic outer layer has been lifted away to demonstrate the septal connections, the vessels within the fascial inner layer, the tendons within the synovial sheaths, the interosseous muscles beneath the floor of the aponeurotic sheath, and the oblique septal attachments to the metacarpal bones.

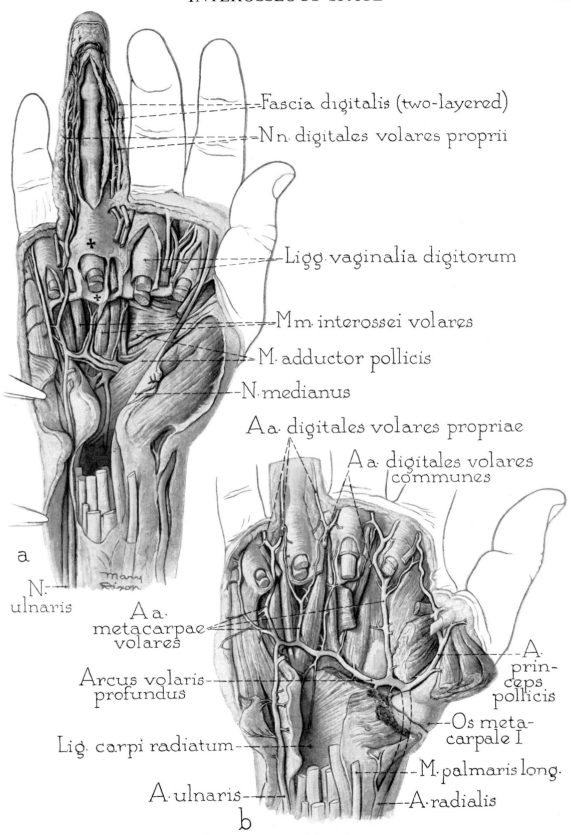

Fascia digitalis (two-layered)

Nn. digitales volares proprii

Ligg. vaginalia digitorum

Mm. interossei volares

M. adductor pollicis

N. medianus

Aa. digitales volares propriae

Aa. digitales volares communes

a

N. ulnaris

Aa. metacarpae volares

Arcus volaris profundus

Lig. carpi radiatum

A. ulnaris

b

A. princeps pollicis

Os metacarpale I

M. palmaris long.

A. radialis

Deep structures of the palm.

a, Deep to the fascial floor course the deep volar arch, its metacarpal branches and the venae comites. The synovial sheath of each pair of flexor tendons is strengthened by a vaginal ligament (at +). *b*, Fascial floor of midpalmar space is removed to expose course of the metacarpal arteries and communications with the common volar digital arteries.

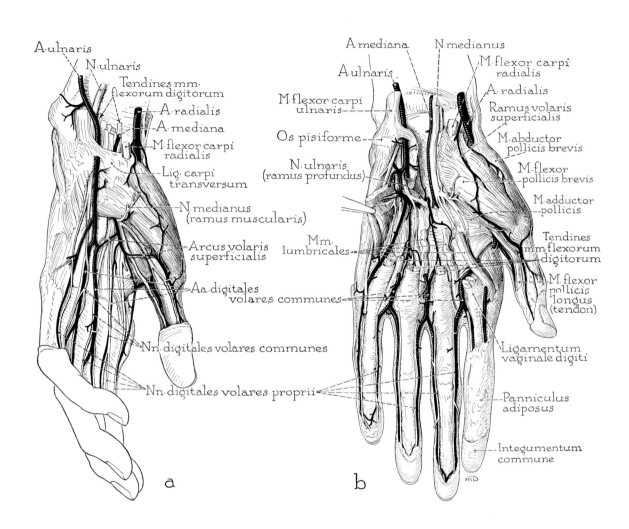

Arteries and nerves of the hand.

a, The structures in the palm, and on the thenar and hypothenar eminences; viewed from the medial side. *b,* The same structures in palmar view.

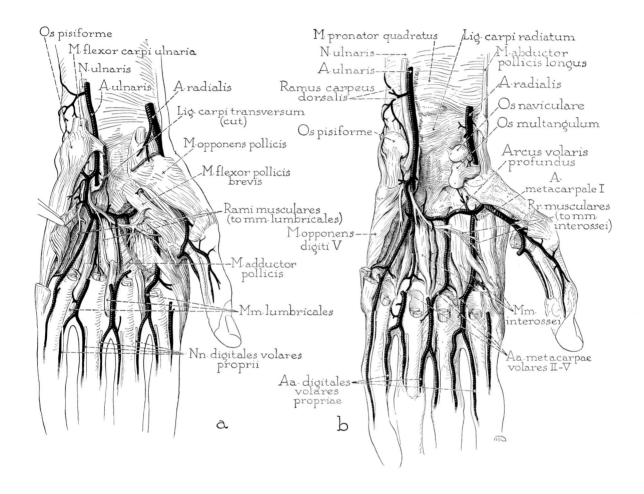

Os pisiforme
M.flexor carpi ulnaria
N.ulnaris
A.ulnaris
A.radialis
Lig.carpi transversum (cut)
M.opponens pollicis
M.flexor pollicis brevis
Rami musculares (to mm.lumbricales)
M.adductor pollicis
Mm.lumbricales
Nn.digitales volares proprii

M.pronator quadratus
N.ulnaris
A.ulnaris
Ramus carpeus dorsalis
Os pisiforme
M.opponens digiti V
Aa.digitales volares propriae

Lig.carpi radiatum
M.abductor pollicis longus
A.radialis
Os naviculare
Os multangulum
Arcus volaris profundus
A.metacarpale I
Rr.musculares (to mm.interossei)
Mm.interossei
Aa.metacarpae volares II–V

a   b

Arteries and nerves of the hand; dissection continued.

a, By dissection of the adductor muscle of the thumb, the deep palmar arterial arch and the deep branch of the ulnar nerve are shown in their course across the palm to the radial side.

b, The ulnar segment of the arterial arch is revealed by removal of the short flexor muscle of the thumb.

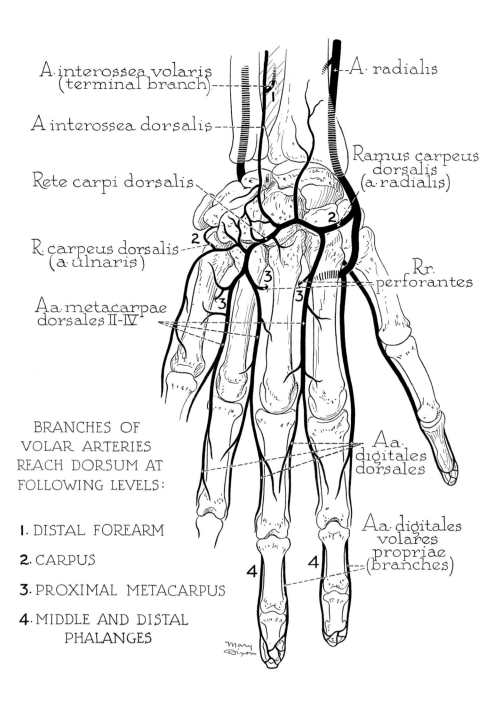

A. interossea volaris
(terminal branch)

A. interossea dorsalis

Rete carpi dorsalis

R. carpeus dorsalis
(a. ulnaris)

Aa. metacarpae
dorsales II-IV

A. radialis

Ramus carpeus
dorsalis
(a. radialis)

Rr.
perforantes

Aa.
digitales
dorsales

Aa. digitales
volares
propriae
(branches)

BRANCHES OF
VOLAR ARTERIES
REACH DORSUM AT
FOLLOWING LEVELS:

1. DISTAL FOREARM

2. CARPUS

3. PROXIMAL METACARPUS

4. MIDDLE AND DISTAL
   PHALANGES

Mary
Dixon

Arteries of the dorsum of the hand; diagrammatic.

The levels at which the arteries of volar antebrachial and palmar positions send branches to the dorsal surface of the hand are listed and numbered.

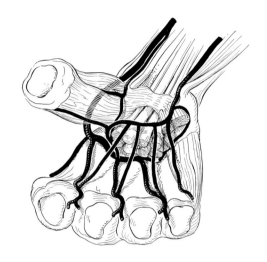

RADIAL ARTERY AFTER SENDING BRANCH
TO JOIN SUPERFICIAL ARCIFORM
CONTINUATION OF ULNAR,
PASSES DORSAL TO FIRST METACARPAL BONE;
THEN, IN CROSSING PALM IN ARCIFORM COURSE
UNDER TENDONS OF DIGITAL FLEXORS
IT GIVES OFF INTERDIGITAL BRANCHES
AND ENDS BY ANASTOMOSING
WITH DEEP BRANCH OF ULNAR.

ULNAR ARTERY DESCENDS
ON VOLAR ASPECT OF CARPUS;
SUPERFICIAL BRANCH CONTINUING IN
ARCIFORM COURSE OVER FLEXOR TENDONS
GIVES OFF RAMI WHICH
MEET CORRESPONDING BRANCHES OF RADIAL
AT CLEFTS BETWEEN FINGERS;
DEEP BRANCH ANASTOMOSES WITH ULNAR.

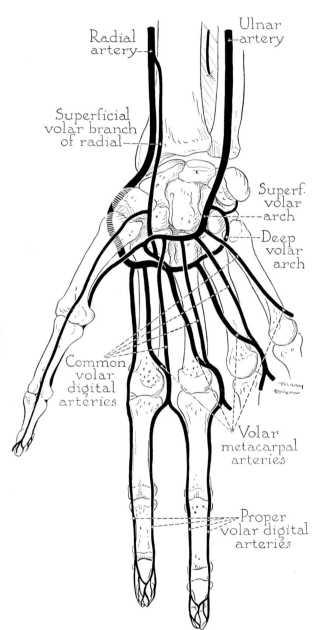

Arteries of the hand; shown diagrammatically.

The palmar continuations of the antebrachial arteries contribute to the formation of the arterial arches at supratendinous and infratendinous levels. Branches derived from the arches join to form common vessels near the metacarpophalangeal joints.

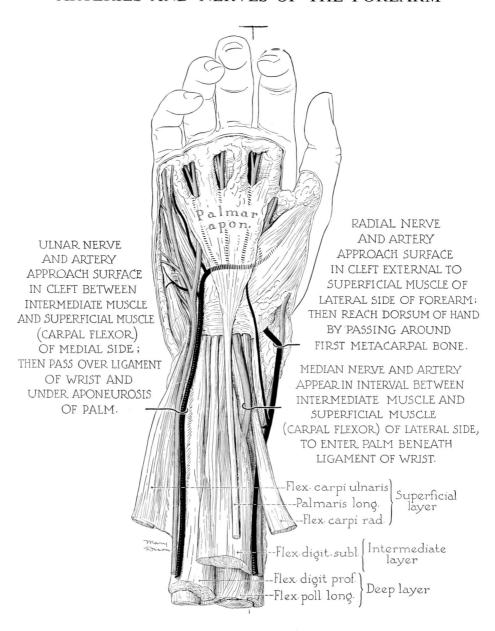

ULNAR NERVE
AND ARTERY
APPROACH SURFACE
IN CLEFT BETWEEN
INTERMEDIATE MUSCLE
AND SUPERFICIAL MUSCLE
(CARPAL FLEXOR)
OF MEDIAL SIDE;
THEN PASS OVER LIGAMENT
OF WRIST AND
UNDER APONEUROSIS
OF PALM.

RADIAL NERVE
AND ARTERY
APPROACH SURFACE
IN CLEFT EXTERNAL TO
SUPERFICIAL MUSCLE OF
LATERAL SIDE OF FOREARM;
THEN REACH DORSUM OF HAND
BY PASSING AROUND
FIRST METACARPAL BONE.

MEDIAN NERVE AND ARTERY
APPEAR IN INTERVAL BETWEEN
INTERMEDIATE MUSCLE AND
SUPERFICIAL MUSCLE
(CARPAL FLEXOR) OF LATERAL SIDE,
TO ENTER PALM BENEATH
LIGAMENT OF WRIST.

palmar apon.

Flex. carpi ulnaris
Palmaris long. } Superficial layer
Flex. carpi rad.

Flex. digit. subl. { Intermediate layer

Flex. digit prof.
Flex. poll. long. } Deep layer

Course and relations of the arteries and nerves in the distal portion of the forearm
and on the volar (palmar) surface of the hand.

mens of this type, the proper volar arteries are derived equally from the radial and ulnar arteries, without communication across the middle line of the hand. *h*, Here the ulnar artery is the chief contributor to the set of digital vessels, supplying 3½ digits, that is, toward the thumb, to include the ulnar aspect of the index finger. *i*, The median artery reaches the hand to furnish digital arteries (compare with *d* and *e*), but without anastomosing the radial and ulnar arteries. Inclining toward the radial side of the hand, the median artery gives off a branch to the thumb. *j*, The deviation of the 3 source-vessels toward the radial side of the hand is of lesser degree than in the preceding type; the branches of the common volar digital artery derived from the median artery pass only to the facing aspects of the index and middle fingers, the radial and ulnar arteries caring for the areas marginal thereto.

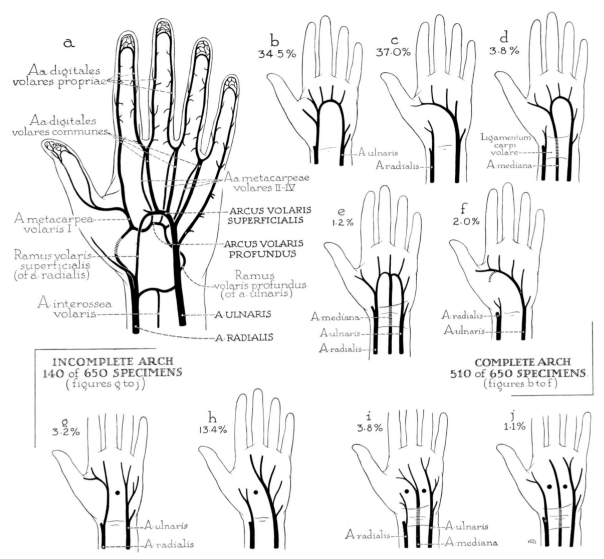

ARCUS VOLARIS SUPERFICIALIS, 650 SPECIMENS

Superficial volar arch.

Types of superficial volar arterial arch (*b* to *j*) encountered in 650 dissections of the hand, together with the "textbook normal" (*a*). Shown schematically, with the percentage occurrence of each of the 9 types. Variations (*b* to *f*) encountered in 510 specimens in which the arch was complete; patterns (*g* to *j*) found in the 140 hands in which the arch was incomplete—in the areas indicated by marker. *a*, The standard, and regularly pictured, pattern of superficial arterial arch with its branches at metacarpal and phalangeal levels. *b*, The complete radio-ulnar communication present in slightly more than one-third of the total number of extremities studied. *c*, A transpalmar arciform continuation of the ulnar artery with a full complement of common volar digital branches. This type occurs more frequently (37 per cent of cases) than the traditional or "standard" type. *d*, An arciform arrangment to which the contributors are ulnar and median arteries—the median artery replacing the radial of the type shown in *a* and *b*. The ulnomedian type initiates the series of patterns whose frequencies of occurrence show a sharp decline from the commonest varieties, namely those depicted in *b* and *c*. *e*, An arch to which the 3 arteries contribute. Here a median communication is sent to the center of the arch formed by anastomosis of the radial and ulnar arteries. *f*, In this type a transpalmar continuation of the ulnar artery (compare with *c*) receives a midpalmar contribution from the deep palmar arterial arch, not from the radial artery itself. In the remaining specimens, 140 out of a total of 650 (1.5 per cent), the superficial arterial arch is incomplete, the area of interruption indicated in each diagram by a black dot. *g*, In speci-

(*Legend is continued at bottom of page 216.*)

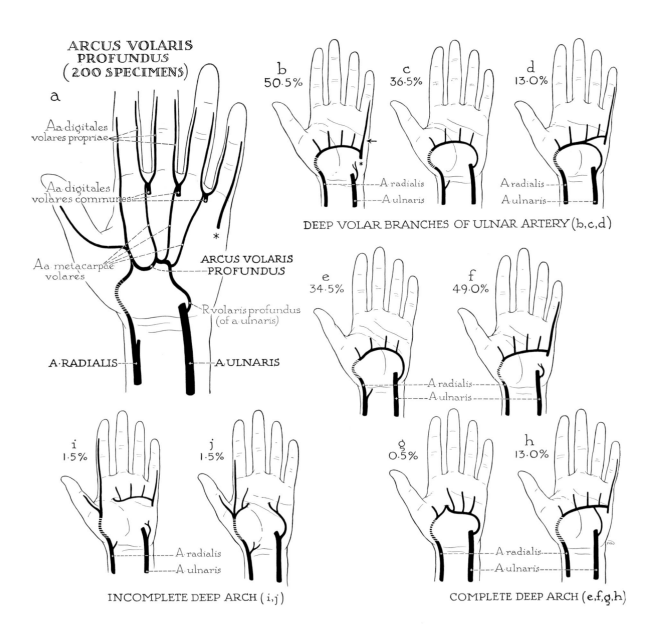

Deep volar arch. Variations in constituency of the deep volar arch,
in comparison with the typical patterns of radioulnar communication.

a, The "standard" pattern of deep volar arch. *b* to *d*, The arrangements dependent upon differences in
ulnar supply. *e* to *h*, The subgroups of patterns in which the deep palmar arterial arch is complete. *i* and *j*,
Derivatives of the incomplete arch. Four types of complete deep arch were found (*a* to *h*) and 2 varieties of
incomplete arch (*i* and *j*).

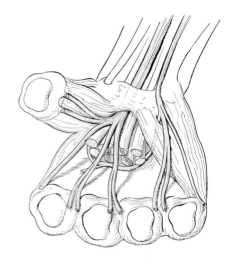

MEDIAN NERVE
AFTER ENTERING PALM
UNDER LIGAMENT OF WRIST
DIVIDES TO SEND
CUTANEOUS BRANCHES TO 3½ DIGITS
BEGINNING WITH THUMB
AND MOTOR BRANCHES TO
SUPERFICIAL THENAR MUSCLES

ULNAR NERVE
ENTERING PALM BY PASSING
OVER LIGAMENT OF WRIST
DIVIDES TO SEND
CUTANEOUS BRANCHES TO 1½ DIGITS,
ANASTOMOTIC BRANCHES
(OVER AND UNDER TENDONS)
TO MEDIAN AND MOTOR BRANCHES
(CHIEFLY DEEP)
TO HYPOTHENAR, INTERMETACARPAL,
DEEP THENAR, ETC., MUSCLES.

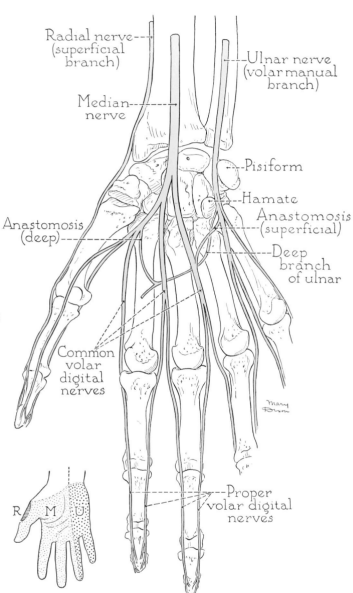

Radial, medial, and ulnar nerves.

Pattern of cutaneous distribution on the palm of the hand.

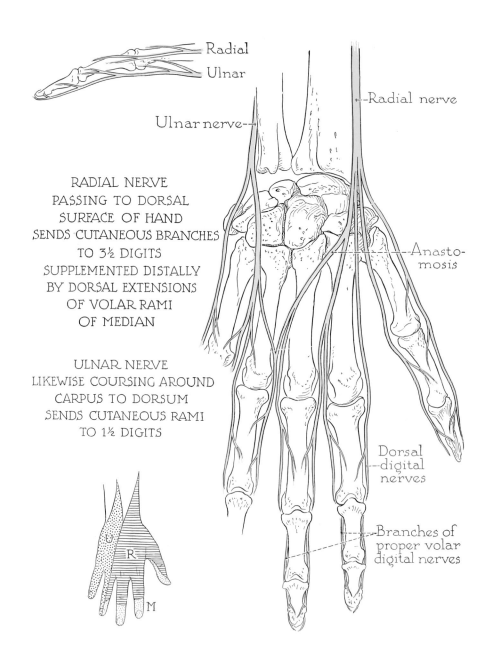

Radial

Ulnar

Radial nerve

Ulnar nerve

RADIAL NERVE
PASSING TO DORSAL
SURFACE OF HAND
SENDS CUTANEOUS BRANCHES
TO 3½ DIGITS
SUPPLEMENTED DISTALLY
BY DORSAL EXTENSIONS
OF VOLAR RAMI
OF MEDIAN

ULNAR NERVE
LIKEWISE COURSING AROUND
CARPUS TO DORSUM
SENDS CUTANEOUS RAMI
TO 1½ DIGITS

Anasto-
mosis

Dorsal
digital
nerves

Branches of
proper volar
digital nerves

Radial, ulnar and median nerves.

Pattern of cutaneous distribution on the dorsum of the hand.

Section Five

THE BACK AND THORAX

VERTEBRAE; TYPICAL AND ATYPICAL.. 223–225

SKELETON... 226

ARTICULATIONS, LIGAMENTS... 227

MUSCLES OF THE BACK: FOUR STAGES IN DISSECTION......................... 228–231

MUSCLES OF THE BACK: EIGHT STAGES IN DISSECTION....................... 232–239

MUSCLES OF THE CHEST AND AXILLA: FOUR STAGES IN DISSECTION............. 240–244

DIAPHRAGM.. 245

THORACIC WALL; INTERNAL ASPECT....................................... 246

PECTORAL MUSCLES: THREE STAGES IN DISSECTION......................... 247–250

THORACIC VISCERA: THREE STAGES IN DISSECTION......................... 251–253

MAMMARY ARTERIES.. 254–255

INTERCOSTAL VESSELS AND NERVES....................................... 256

INTERCOSTAL ARTERIES... 257

THYMUS; TYPES.. 258

THYMIC AND THYROID BLOOD SUPPLY..................................... 259–260

SUBCLAVIAN ARTERY; RETROESOPHAGEAL.................................. 261

AORTIC ARCH; TYPES OF BRANCHING...................................... 262–263

AORTIC ARCH; VARIATION IN BRANCHING.................................. 264

LUNGS.. 265

ACCESSORY PULMONARY LOBE.. 266

LUNGS; TRACHEOBRONCHIAL BRANCHING.................................. 267

PULMONARY HILUS... 268–269

BRONCHIAL ARTERIES; TYPES.. 270

PERICARDIUM, HEART, AND GREAT VESSELS: FOUR STAGES IN DISSECTION.......... 271–274

PERICARDIUM AND HEART; INTERNAL ANATOMY............................. 275–278

RIGHT ATRIUM; VARIATIONS... 279

CORONARY ARTERIES... 280

ESOPHAGEAL ARTERIES... 281–282

(Continued)

VEINS OF THE TRUNK.. 283–285

POSTERIOR ABDOMINAL VESSELS AND NERVES................................ 286–287

THORACIC SYMPATHETIC TRUNK... 288

AZYGOS VEINS; TYPES... 289–291

POSTERIOR MEDIASTINAL STRUCTURES: TWO STAGES IN DISSECTION............. 292–293

SPINAL CORD; SECTIONS, THREE LEVELS.................................... 294

SPINAL CORD; VERTEBRAL LEVELS OF TERMINATION.......................... 295–296

SPINAL CORD; SEGMENTAL ALIGNMENT WITH VERTEBRAE....................... 297

TYPICAL SPINAL NERVE.. 298

SPINAL CORD, NERVES, AND MENINGES.................................... 299

FIELDS OF CUTANEOUS SUPPLY... 300–303

INNERVATION OF MUSCLES, TABULATION................................... 304–305

SYMPATHETIC TRUNK AND GANGLIA OF THE THORAX.......................... 306–307

CRANIOCAUDAL AUTONOMIC CONNECTIONS................................... 308

THORACOLUMBAR AUTONOMIC CONNECTIONS................................. 309

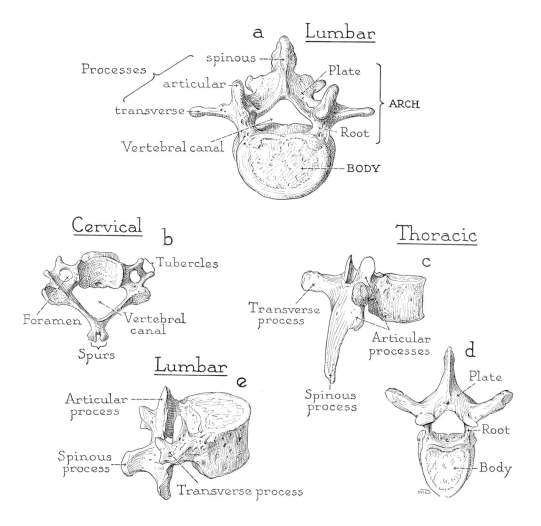

a **Lumbar**

Processes
- spinous
- articular
- transverse

Plate
ARCH
Root

Vertebral canal

BODY

Cervical b

Tubercles

Foramen

Vertebral canal

Spurs

Thoracic c

Transverse process

Articular processes

Spinous process

Lumbar e

Articular process

Spinous process

Transverse process

d

Plate

Root

Body

Typical vertebrae. Description on page 225.

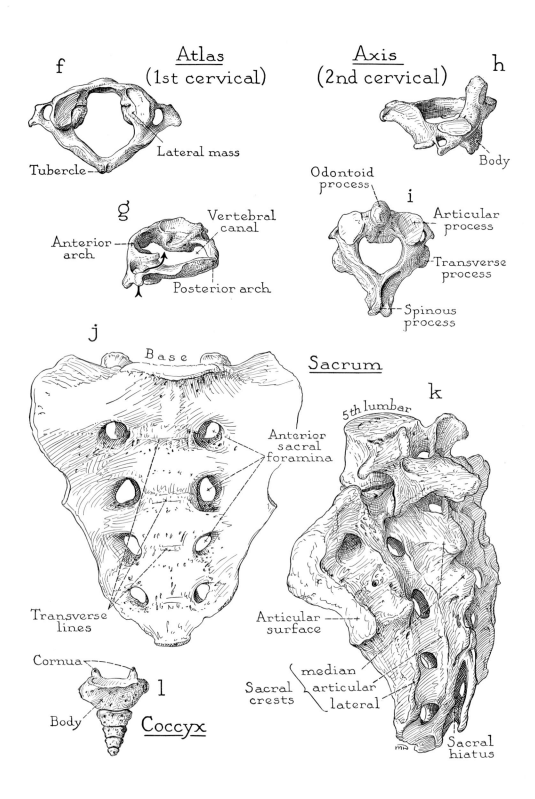

Atypical vertebrae. Description on page 225.

Vertebrae, typical and atypical.

Of the thirty-three skeletal units in the vertebral column, twenty-four remain movable, while nine become fixed through fusion. Of the nine fused elements, the sacrum contains five, the coccyx four. These represent the caudal portion of the vertebral column. At the opposite, or cranial, end of the column, less profound alteration occurs, to modify the first and second cervical vertebrae, atlas and axis (or epitropheus), respectively.

A typical vertebra (a) is composed of two main portions, namely, a body (centrum) and an arch (arcus). The arch consists of two pedicles (roots, radices), and a pair of plates (laminae). The space enclosed by the body and the arch is the vertebral canal. The arch supports seven processes, four articular, two transverse, and one spinous.

The vertebral bodies increase progressively in size from cervical to lumbar regions. Thus, in a typical cervical vertebra the body is relatively small (b); the corresponding part is larger in a thoracic vertebra (c), larger still in a lumbar (a and e). The bodies of the sacral vertebrae are fused (j and k); in the coccyx they are rudimentary (l).

Considering next the several features of the arch, it may be noted that the root of a typical cervical vertebra is short and is directed lateralward (b). The root of the second cervical vertebra is similar (i); that of the first is incorporated into the lateral mass (f). The root of a thoracic vertebra is compressed from side to side. The root of a lumbar vertebra is short, and is directed backward. In the sacrum the roots are not distinguishable (k); in the coccyx they are wanting (l).

The plates of a typical cervical vertebra are long and thin (b), as they are also in the second cervical (i). Those of the first cervical form a slender arch (f). The plates are short and strong in the lumbar vertebrae (a and d), fused in the sacrum (k) and lacking entirely in the coccyx (l).

In a typical cervical vertebra the articular processes approach the horizontal plane; in the thoracic region they stand vertically and frontally. In the lumbar vertebrae their surfaces lie in sagittal plane. On the dorsum of the sacrum the processes are fused to form the articular crest on each side; they are absent in the coccyx.

The transverse processes of a typical cervical vertebra are tuberculate, perforate, short, and laterally directed (b). In a typical thoracic vertebra the transverse processes are faceted, long and thick and backward directed (c); on a lumbar vertebra they are long and slender, and horizontal (e). On the sacrum the transverse processes are atrophic, being represented by the inconspicuous lateral crests (k).

On the coccyx only the first piece bears a transverse process, and then only in very rudimentary form (l).

The spinous process of a typical cervical vertebra is short and bifid (b); on the first cervical it is suppressed, being a mere tubercle on the posterior arch (f). The spinous process of a thoracic vertebra is elongate and sloping, or even vertical (c). In the lumbar region the spinous process is thick and broad, quadrilateral and horizontal (e). On the sacrum the several processes become fused to form the median crest (k). Since no portion of the arch persists on any of the coccygeal segments, the spinous processes are wanting.

The vertebral canal of the first cervical vertebra is large and quintagonal (f). At middle cervical level the canal is wide and triangular in outline (b); in a thoracic vertebra it is small and circular (d). In a lumbar vertebra the canal is also narrow, but again assumes a triangular outline (a). On the last piece of the sacrum the canal is incomplete behind, at the sacral hiatus (k); on the coccyx it is deficient on the sides as well as behind.

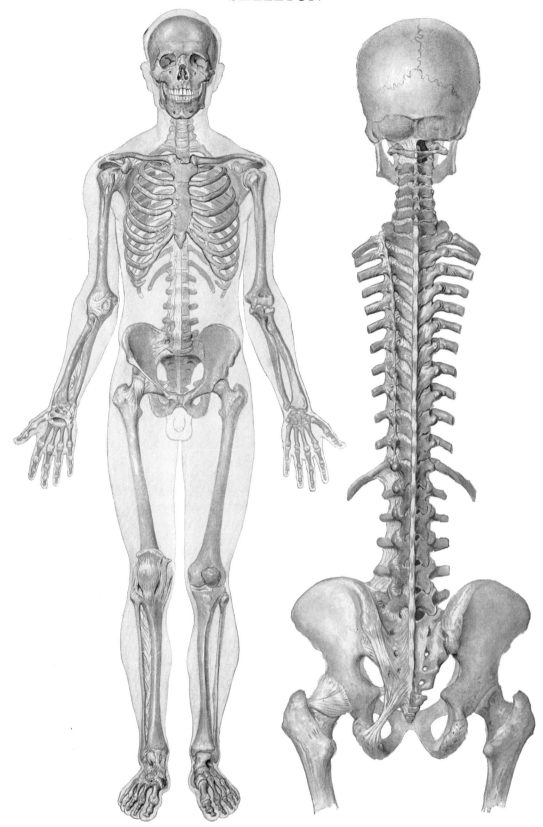

Skeleton, view from the front and from behind.

In both figures certain of the ligaments of the trunk and extremities are shown.

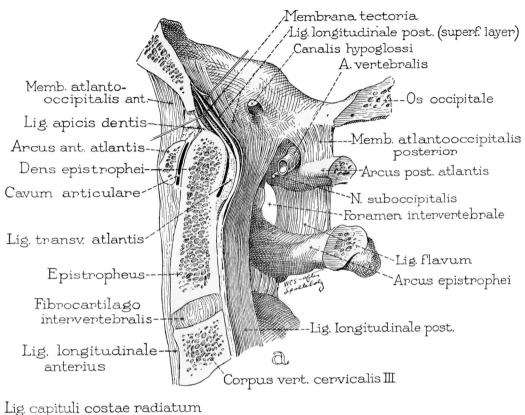

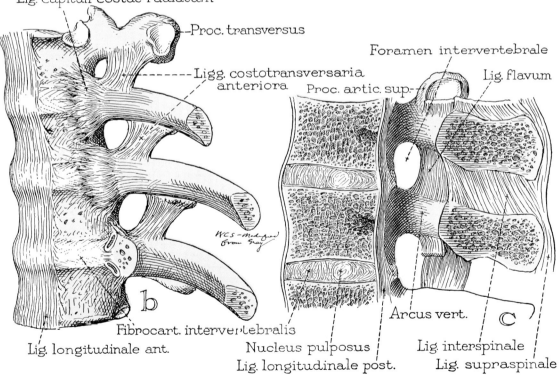

Ligaments of the vertebral column.

a, At the atlanto-occipital joint; hemisection. *b*, Thoracic region. *c*, Lumbar region; hemisection.

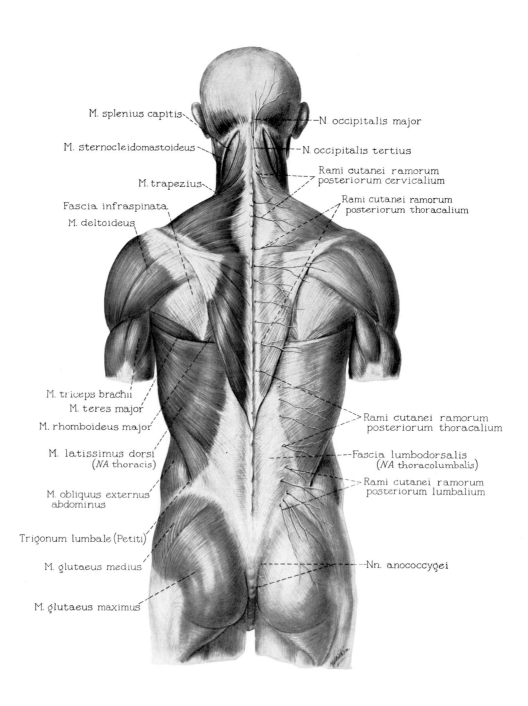

Muscles of the head and trunk; first layer.

(From Warren: Handbook of Anatomy, Harvard University Press.)

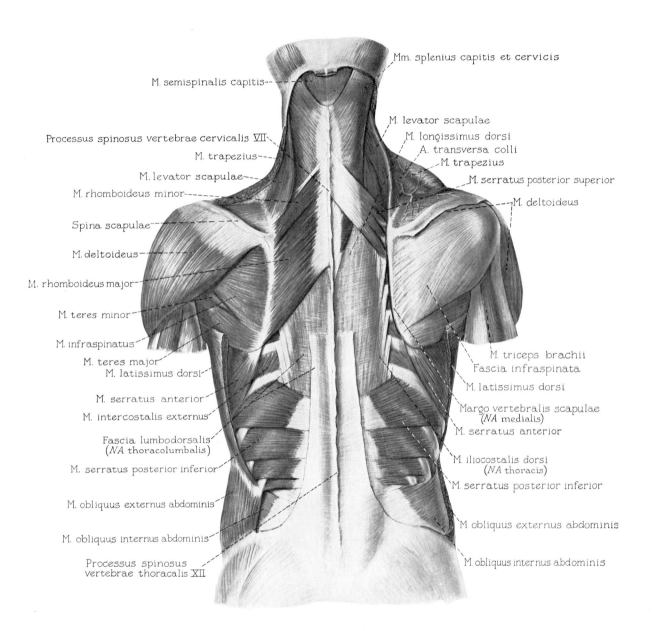

Mm. splenius capitis et cervicis

M. semispinalis capitis

M. levator scapulae
M. longissimus dorsi
A. transversa colli
M. trapezius

Processus spinosus vertebrae cervicalis VII
M. trapezius
M. levator scapulae
M. rhomboideus minor

M. serratus posterior superior

M. deltoideus

Spina scapulae

M. deltoideus

M. rhomboideus major

M. teres minor

M. infraspinatus

M. triceps brachii
Fascia infraspinata

M. teres major
M. latissimus dorsi

M. latissimus dorsi

M. serratus anterior
M. intercostalis externus

Margo vertebralis scapulae
(*NA* medialis)
M. serratus anterior

Fascia lumbodorsalis
(*NA* thoracolumbalis)

M. iliocostalis dorsi
(*NA* thoracis)

M. serratus posterior inferior

M. serratus posterior inferior

M. obliquus externus abdominis

M. obliquus externus abdominis

M. obliquus internus abdominis

M. obliquus internus abdominis

Processus spinosus
vertebrae thoracalis XII

Muscles of the head and trunk; second layer.

The external oblique muscle of the anterolateral abdominal wall has been cut away on the right side; the trapezius has been cut away on the left, turned forward on the right. The subjacent levator scapulae is turned outward. (From Warren: Handbook of Anatomy, Harvard University Press.)

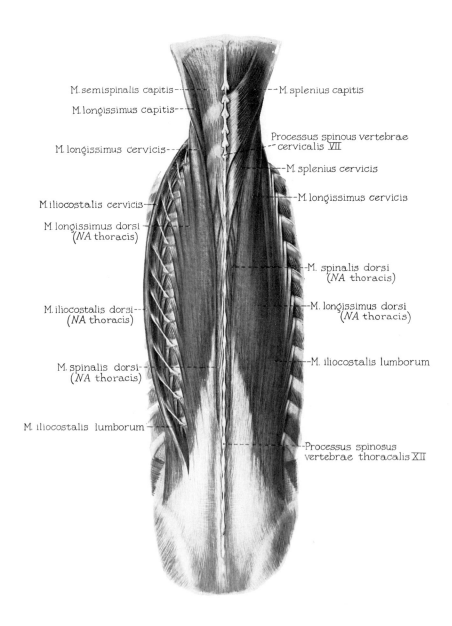

M. semispinalis capitis

M. longissimus capitis

M. longissimus cervicis

M. iliocostalis cervicis

M. longissimus dorsi
(*NA* thoracis)

M. iliocostalis dorsi
(*NA* thoracis)

M. spinalis dorsi
(*NA* thoracis)

M. iliocostalis lumborum

M. splenius capitis

Processus spinous vertebrae
cervicalis VII

M. splenius cervicis

M. longissimus cervicis

M. spinalis dorsi
(*NA* thoracis)

M. longissimus dorsi
(*NA* thoracis)

M. iliocostalis lumborum

Processus spinosus
vertebrae thoracalis XII

Muscles of the trunk; third layer.

The lateral constituents of the muscular column are turned outward on the left.
(From Warren: Handbook of Anatomy, Harvard University Press.)

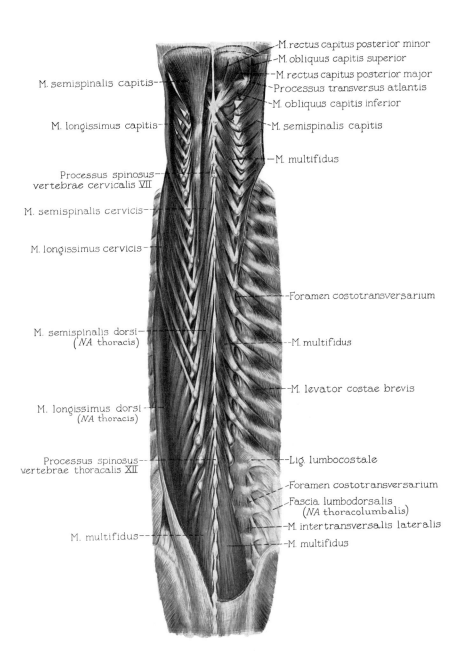

Muscles of the trunk; fourth layer.

The divisions of the longissimus are turned outward on the left side. The capital segment of the semi-spinalis has been cut away on the right. (From Warren: Handbook of Anatomy, Harvard University Press.)

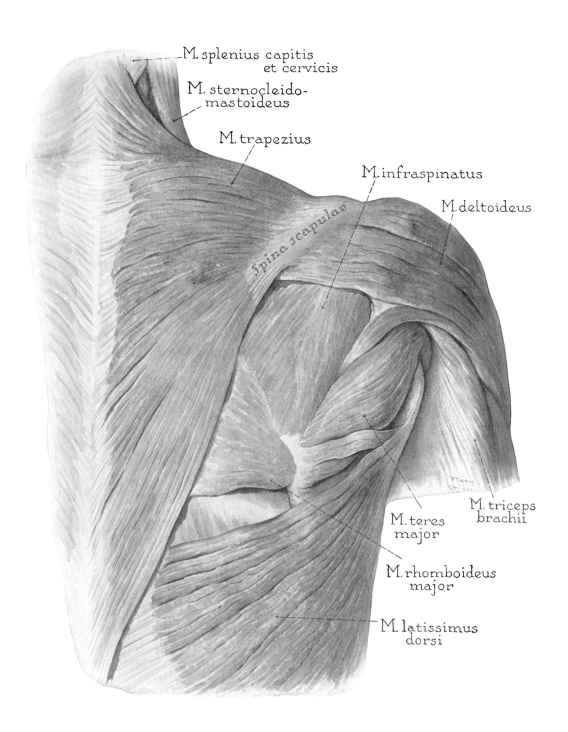

M. splenius capitis
et cervicis

M. sternocleido-
mastoideus

M. trapezius

M. infraspinatus

M. deltoideus

Spina scapulae

M. triceps
brachii

M. teres
major

M. rhomboideus
major

M. latissimus
dorsi

Muscles of the back, neck and shoulder.

First layer of muscles of the back. The following seven figures carry the dissection to successively deeper levels, terminating with the musculature of the suboccipital space.

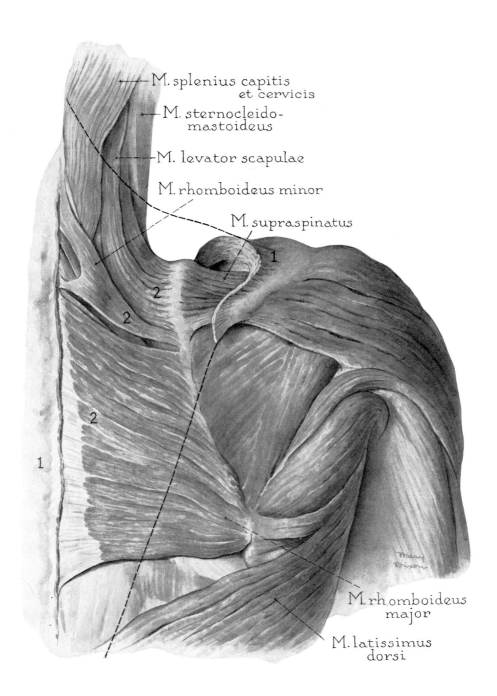

M. splenius capitis
et cervicis

M. sternocleido-
mastoideus

M. levator scapulae

M. rhomboideus minor

M. supraspinatus

M. rhomboideus
major

M. latissimus
dorsi

Muscles of the back; second layer.

The trapezius muscle has been removed (cut ends at 1, original extent indicated by broken lines); the latissimus dorsi remains intact. The muscles of the second stratum are now exposed; these indicated by 2 are the levator scapulae, the rhomboideus major, and the rhomboideus minor.

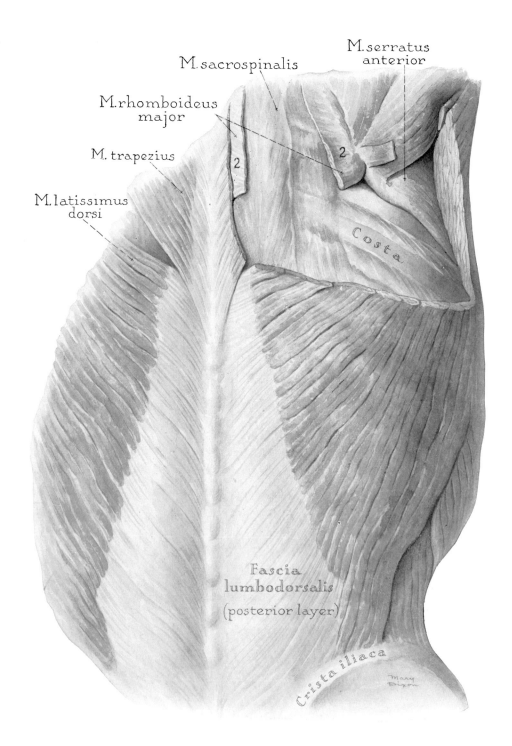

M. sacrospinalis

M. serratus anterior

M. rhomboideus major

M. trapezius

M. latissimus dorsi

2

2

Costa

Fascia lumbodorsalis (posterior layer)

Crista iliaca

Muscles of the back; first and second layers.

The trapezius muscle has been removed; a triangular segment has been cut from the cranial portion of the latissimus dorsi. The rhomboideus major (at 2), one of the three constituents of second layer of flat muscles of the back, has been removed in its lower half to expose the column of long muscles.

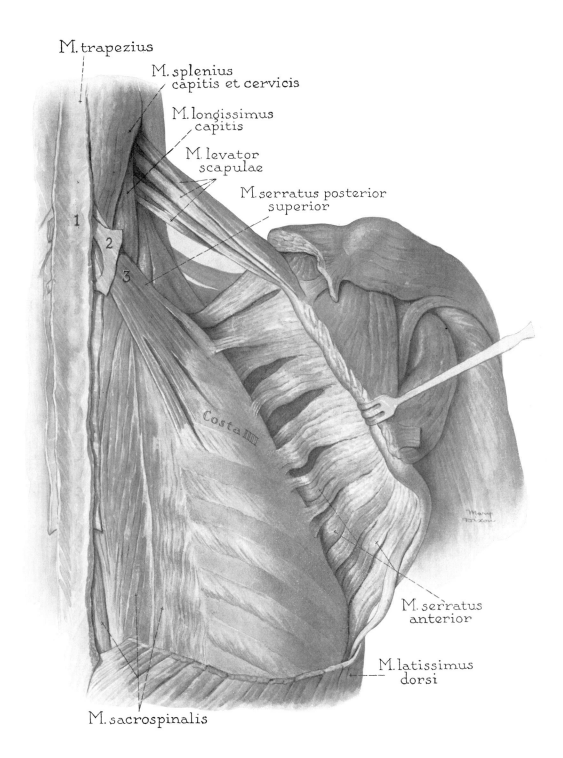

M. trapezius

M. splenius
capitis et cervicis

M. longissimus
capitis

M. levator
scapulae

M. serratus posterior
superior

Costa III

M. serratus
anterior

M. latissimus
dorsi

M. sacrospinalis

Muscles of the back; third stratum.

The rhomboids have been cut; thus freed, the shoulder has been drawn outward and forward, the levator scapulae serving as a pedicle. The serratus posterior superior muscle (at 3) is brought into view.

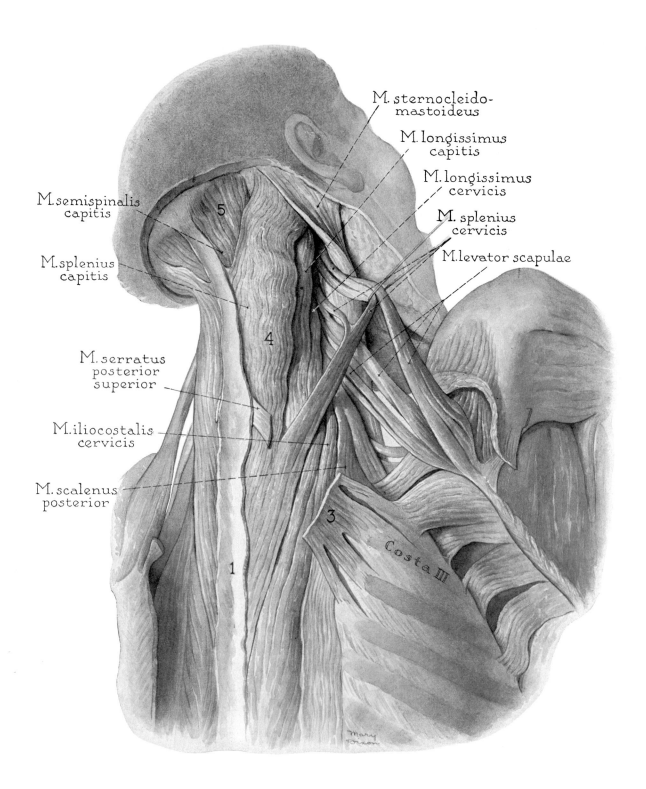

M. sternocleido-
mastoideus

M. longissimus
capitis

M. longissimus
cervicis

M. splenius
cervicis

M. levator scapulae

M. semispinalis
capitis

M. splenius
capitis

M. serratus
posterior
superior

M. iliocostalis
cervicis

M. scalenus
posterior

Costa III

Muscles of the back and of the neck; fourth and fifth layers.

The midportion of the serratus posterior superior muscle (at 3) has been excised to expose the cervical and capital parts of splenius (4); these muscles, as shown, are cranial continuations of the sacrospinalis (NA, erector spinae). The semispinalis capitis (5) lies next beneath the splenius.

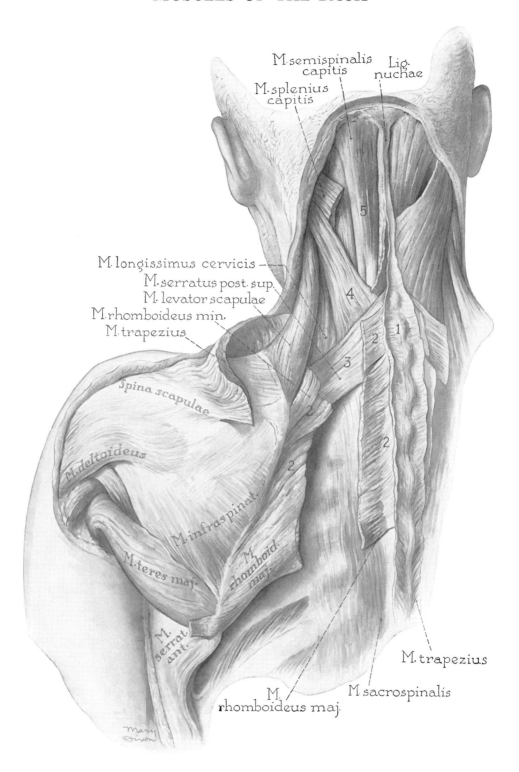

Muscles of the back and dorsum of the neck; fourth and fifth layers.

On the left a portion of the splenius capitis (at 4) has been removed, in order to expose the underlying semispinalis capitis (5); on the right side the corresponding muscle remains intact.

The muscles of the shoulder, from which the investing fascia has not yet been removed, are pictured in the section on the upper extremity (NA, superior member).

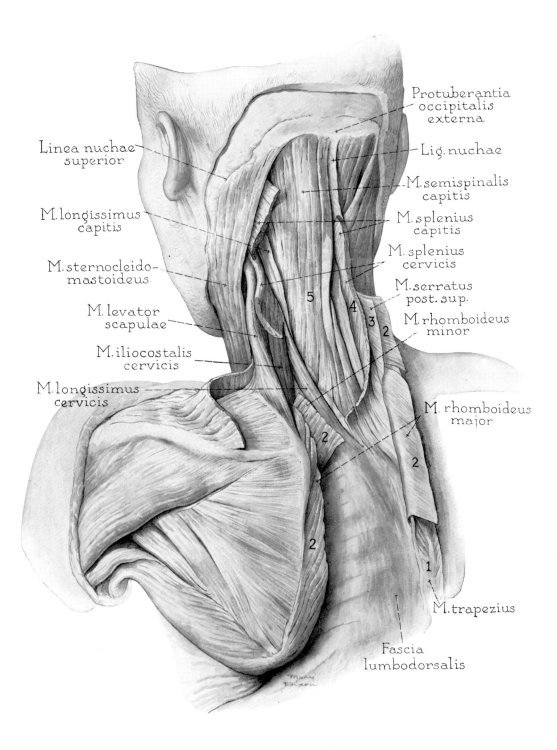

Linea nuchae superior

Protuberantia occipitalis externa

Lig. nuchae

M. longissimus capitis

M. semispinalis capitis

M. sternocleido-mastoideus

M. splenius capitis

M. levator scapulae

M. splenius cervicis

M. iliocostalis cervicis

M. serratus post. sup.

M. longissimus cervicis

M. rhomboideus minor

M. rhomboideus major

M. trapezius

Fascia lumbodorsalis

Musculature of the back and dorsum of the neck; dissection continued.

The splenius cervicis has been cut and the ends reflected, in order to complete the demonstration of muscular strata. The layers are numbered to correspond with the serial enumeration in the preceding stages of the dissection.

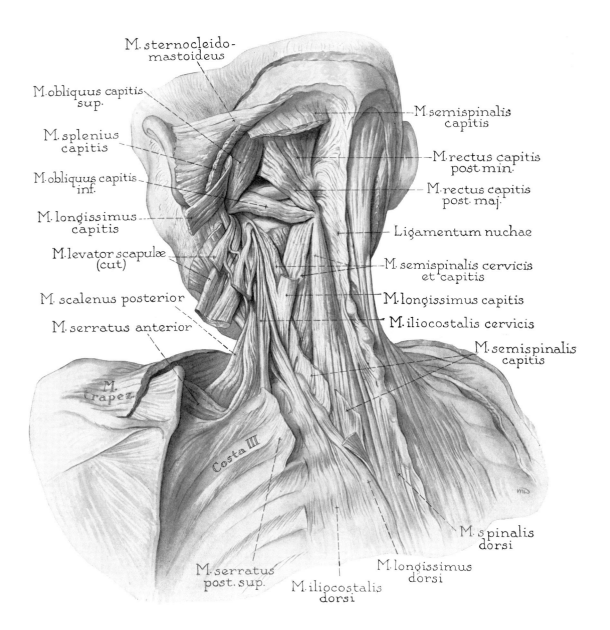

M. sternocleido-
mastoideus

M. obliquus capitis
sup.

M. splenius
capitis

M. obliquus capitis
inf.

M. longissimus
capitis

M. levator scapulæ
(cut)

M. scalenus posterior

M. serratus anterior

M.
trapez.

Costa III

M. semispinalis
capitis

M. rectus capitis
post. min.

M. rectus capitis
post. maj.

Ligamentum nuchae

M. semispinalis cervicis
et capitis

M. longissimus capitis

M. iliocostalis cervicis

M. semispinalis
capitis

M. spinalis
dorsi

M. longissimus
dorsi

M. serratus
post. sup.

M. iliocostalis
dorsi

Muscles of the dorsum of the neck; dissection concluded.

On the left side the semispinalis capitis muscle has been removed. In this way the oblique and the straight capital muscles are exposed in the suboccipital space. Medially they are attached to the atlas and axis, near the ligamentum nuchae in the midline of the neck. The cervical elements of the semispinalis column, together with the recti and the obliqui, make up a radiating set of muscular bands.

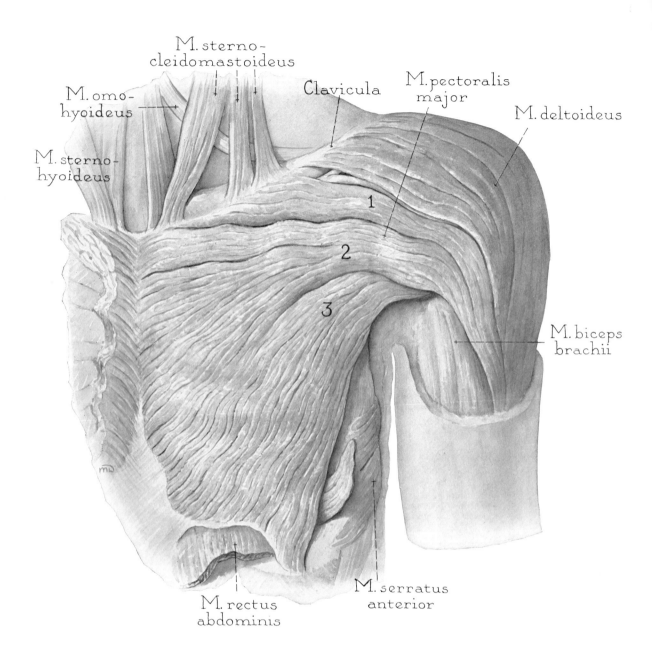

Muscles of the chest; pectoralis major muscle.

The pectoralis major takes origin in three main portions, as follows: from the clavicle (at 1); from the sternoclavicular joint and the sternum (at 2); from the sternum and the sheath of the rectus muscle (at 3). The three portions are separated by clefts. Lesser slips of costal origin (not exposed) are implanted into the deep surface of the muscle. The portion (at 1) which arises from the clavicle narrows as it approaches the humerus. The sternal part (at 2) blends with the preceding as the insertion is approached. The third, or sterno-vaginal, portion (at 3) passes beneath the other two, forming a second leaf of humeral insertion. In coursing toward the humerus, the cranial division passes somewhat downward from its origin, as well as lateralward; the caudal division inclines upward; the intermediate portion is, at least in part, transverse. The portions converge as would the blades of a fan.

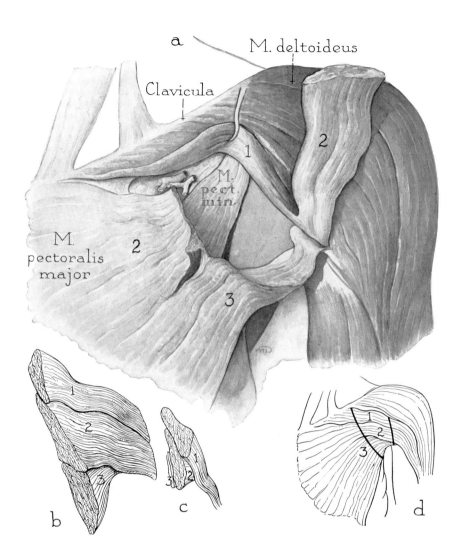

Muscles of the chest: pectoralis major and pectoralis minor muscles.

The middle segment (at 2) of the pectoralis major has been reflected to expose the structures beneath, namely, the pectoralis minor, the costocoracoid membrane, and the thoracoacromial vessels. The upper piece (at 1), here retracted toward the clavicle, forms the inferior boundary of the deltopectoral cleft through which the cephalic vein reaches the axilla; its lower border overlaps the second piece of the same muscle. The second piece, as it approaches the axilla, covers progressively more of the third piece (at 3). The first and second parts fuse at their insertions, being entirely separate near their origins. The second and third portions are continuous in their medial half, but separate as they approach the humerus. The distal half of the pectoralis minor is seen in the opening in the pectoralis major.

b, Pectoralis major; divisions as marked in *d*.

c, Pectoralis major; segment near the insertion. Showing the imbricated arrangement near the humeral insertion.

d, Pectoralis major. Showing the lines of section in the two preceding figures, and the three major subdivisions of the muscle. Semidiagrammatic.

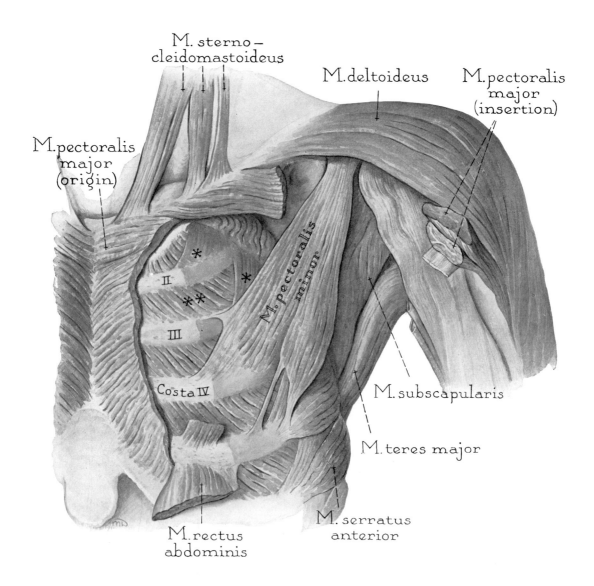

Muscles of the chest: pectoralis minor and related muscles.

The pectoralis major has been removed, except for the portions that constitute its attachments. The pectoralis minor is revealed throughout its entire extent. The following areas and structures are exposed: the thorax, in the area of junction of the ribs and costal cartilages; the attachment of the rectus muscle to the fifth rib, and a costal slip of the pectoralis major (pointing upward from the superior surface of the same rib); the intercostales (external at * and internal at **), after removal of the external intercostal membrane; several digitations of the serratus anterior; the subscapularis muscle, on the anterior surface, and the teres major on the lateral border of the scapula; the coracobrachialis and biceps brachii muscles on the medial aspect of the humerus.

The origin of the pectoralis minor is aponeurotic, by means of slips from the third, fourth, and fifth ribs; it is inserted into the coracoid process of the scapula.

The pectoralis major, pectoralis minor, and subclavius muscles together bound the axillary space anteriorly. With removal of the pectoralis major muscle, the other muscular boundaries are exposed. Medially are situated the external and internal intercostals, and the serratus anterior; posteriorly placed are the subscapularis, the teres major, and the latissimus dorsi; on the lateral wall are the coracobrachialis and biceps brachii.

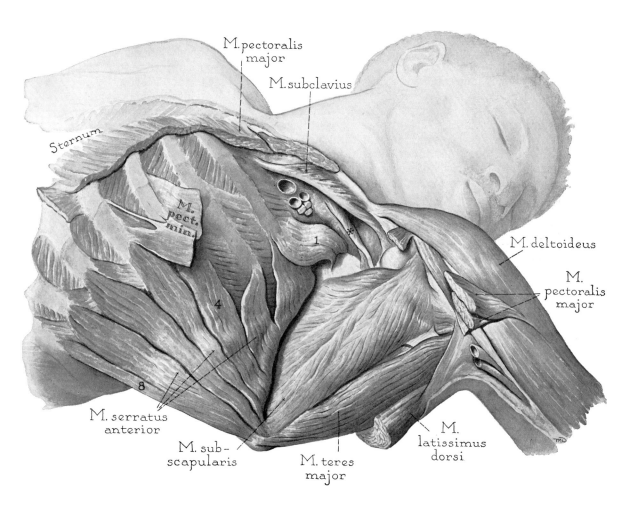

Pectoral, thoracic, and associated muscles shown in relation to the axillary space.
Viewed from the side and from below. (See full description on page 244.)

The following structures have been removed: the pectoralis minor, except at its extremities; the pectoralis major, cut proximally at its sternal and clavicular origin and distally at the humeral insertion; the latissimus dorsi, except at insertion. The axillary vessels and the brachial plexus appear proximally and only as cut ends, where they enter the axilla beneath the clavicle and upon the first rib; distally, their brachial continuations enter the sulcus situated dorsal to the coracobrachialis muscle. In order to show fully the various structures enumerated and described above, the arm is abducted. With the axillary space opened widely from the front, the serratus anterior is seen in full surface view, from origin to insertion; the posterior wall, formed by the subscapular structures, is also brought into favorable exposure. The bilaminar tendon of insertion of the pectoralis major is shown as it enters the cleft between the deltoid and the biceps brachii muscles. The latissimus dorsi appears near its brachial attachment.

The fibers of the subclavius arise in penniform manner, a feature which is especially striking when, by traction, the muscle is drawn downward away from the clavicle. Just inferior to the medial extremity of the origin a tendon appears on the inferior margin of the muscle, and into it the fibers are implanted; the last of these finally terminate near the medial end of the muscle. Behind the muscle lie the subclavian vessels and the brachial plexus.

The structure of the serratus anterior muscles is such that it is subdivided into three sets of digitations. The first part (at 1) takes origin by digitations from the first and second ribs, and from a fibrous arch uniting these two attachments. The second part arises by three digitations from the second through the fourth ribs (ending at 4). The third part is the longest piece. It consists of four digitations from the fifth through the eighth ribs (ending at 8). The digitations are separated by clefts.

The origin of the subscapularis takes place in the form of fiber bundles from the costal surface of the scapula. It is divided into parts which, although continuous at their margins, suggest a series of muscles placed side by side.

The origin and the pectoral part (at *) of the omohyoideus muscle are seen. The muscle arises from the superior margin of the scapula, near the superior transverse ligament. In the area of dissection the muscle courses medially, to ascend, behind the clavicle, into the posterior triangle of the neck.

The clavicular portion of the deltoid is in view; its anterior margin faces the reader. This margin borders the cleft in which lay the cephalic vein.

The muscles described above form the boundaries of the axilla. The axillary space, between the upper part of the side of the thorax and the proximal part of the arm, assumes the form of a four-sided pyramid when the arm is abducted. The apex reaches the coracoid process of the scapula; the base lies between the free edges of the muscles of chest and shoulder. The anterior wall is formed by the following three muscles: the pectoralis major (as it passes from the sternum and clavicle to the humerus), the pectoralis minor (as it courses from the ribs to the coracoid process of the scapula), and the subclavius (as the muscle is lodged against the inferior surface of the clavicle). The posterior wall is also made up of three muscles: the subscapularis (as it occupies the fossa on the costal surface of the scapula); the latissimus dorsi (as it narrows, en route from the vertebral column to the humerus); the teres major (on the axillary, or inferolateral, border of the scapula). On the medial wall, in addition to parts of the upper five ribs, are situated the intercostales and the serratus anterior. The lateral wall is formed by the coracobrachialis and biceps brachii muscles.

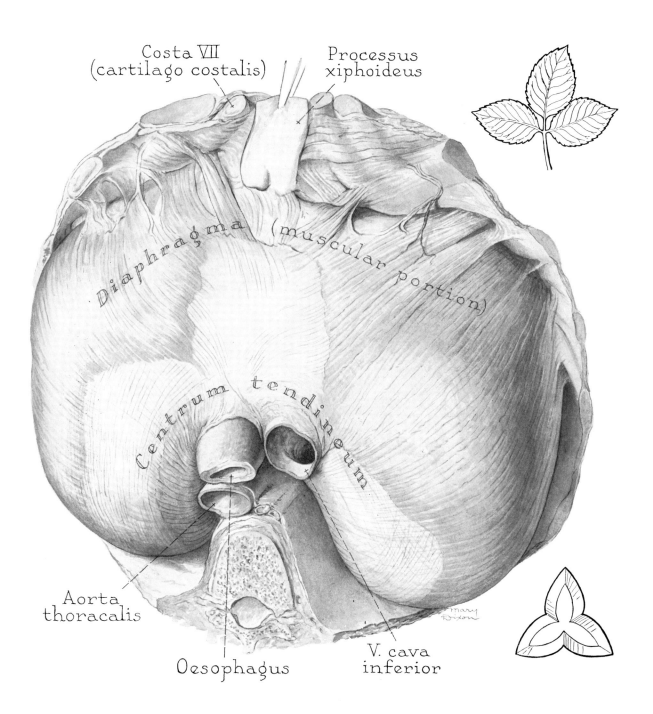

Costa VII
(cartilago costalis)

Processus
xiphoideus

Diaphragma (muscular portion)

Centrum tendineum

Aorta
thoracalis

Oesophagus

V. cava
inferior

Respiratory diaphragm; thoracic aspect.

Anteriorly the transected ribs and xiphoid process of the sternum have been drawn peripheralward, in order to show the muscular slips of costal origin. The trilobate, or trefoil, form of the central tendon is demonstrated (compare insets).

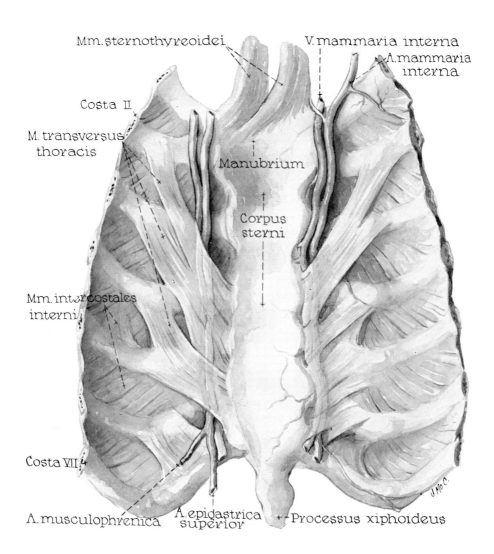

Mm. sternothyreoidei   V. mammaria interna
A. mammaria interna

Costa II

M. transversus
thoracis

Manubrium

Corpus
sterni

Mm. intercostales
interni

Costa VII

A. musculophrenica   A. epigastrica   Processus xiphoideus
superior

Anterior thoracic wall, from within.

The sternothyroid muscles (of the infrahyoid group) are shown cut at their sternal attachments. The internal intercostal and the transverse muscles are shown. In their parasternal course the internal mammary (NA, internal thoracic) artery and vein pass between the transverse thoracic muscle and the costal cartilages of the ribs.

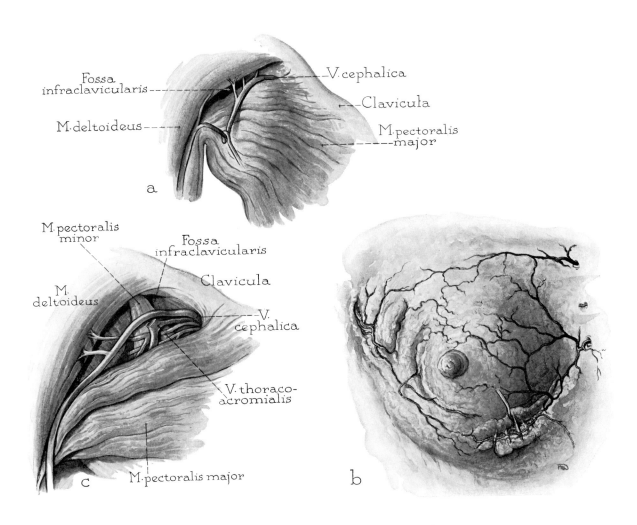

Pectoral region in two selected specimens, showing a small deltopectoral triangle in a female (*a*),
the mammary anatomy of the same individual (*b*), and an unusually large triangular
interval in a male (*c*); the specimen is pictured on pages 248 and 249.

For the exposure of the mammary arteries, the dissection was carried only to subcutaneous level except
on the superolateral and inferomedial margins of the gland, where the vessels were traced to slightly deeper
level in the fat-laden tissue. The mammary rami in this specimen arose from the axillary artery laterally
(reader's left) and from the perforating branches of the internal mammary (NA, internal thoracic) artery
medially (reader's right). The vessels from axillary source passed around the inferolateral margin of the
pectoralis major muscle in the form of a pedicle; those of parasternal origin were segmentally arranged
branches that pierced the intercostal muscles. None of the arteries reached the breast through the deltopectoral triangle.

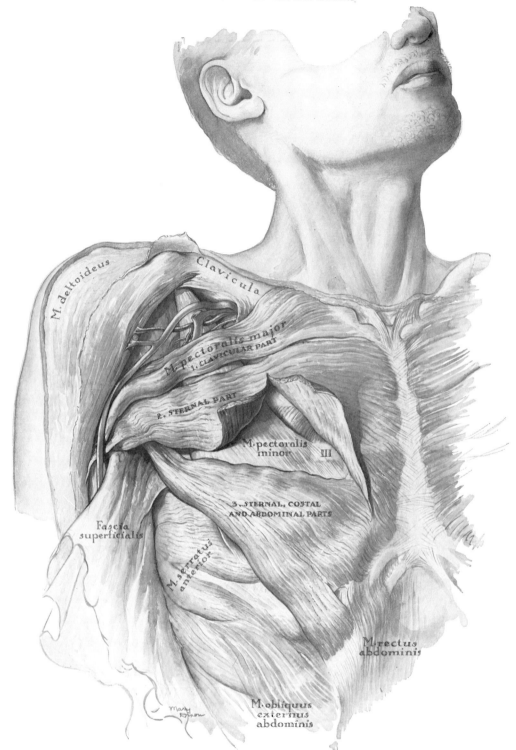

Pectoral region; showing musculature, the related intermuscular spaces and the contained blood vessels.

The investing fascial layer, removed from the pectoral muscles and the adjacent portions of the abdominal and thoracic regions, remains on part of the deltoideus. The deltoideus has been drawn lateralward, the pectoralis major somewhat inferiorly, in order to expose more fully the structures visible in the infraclavicular fossa through the already large deltopectoral triangle. In this way the following are shown: the upper fourth of the pectoralis minor (at its scapular insertion); the fascia that still covers the coracobrachialis and short head of the biceps brachii; the cephalic and thoracoacromial veins (with their deltoid and pectoral tributaries) en route to the axillary and subclavian veins. The middle band of the pectoralis major has been cut across, the edges retracted in order to reveal the pectoralis minor in part of its costal origin.

In this specimen the deltopectoral triangle is unusual in width, while the pectoralis major is exceptional in being divisible into three distinct segments: claviculosternal, broad sternal, and sternoabdominal.

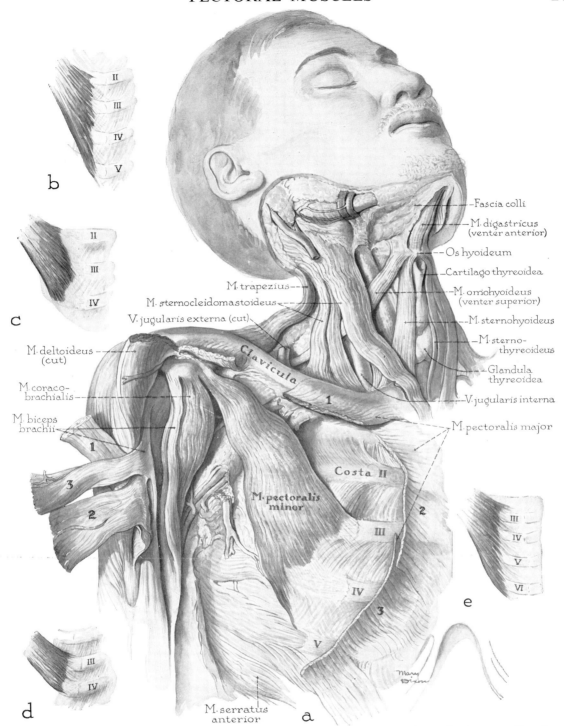

Pectoral and related regions, continued. Deeper dissection of the specimen shown in the preceding figure, together with examples of variation in the extent of origin of the pectoralis minor.

a, Dissection carried to ventral axillary level and, in the neck, to the level of the muscles that bound the cervical triangles. The pectoralis major muscle has been cut along its curving origin; the bands of insertion (1, 2, and 3) have been cut and retracted in order to expose the coracoid process of the scapula, from which arise the short head of the biceps brachii and the coracobrachialis, and into which the pectoralis minor inserts. In the second intercostal space, both intercostal muscles are seen; in the third, only the internal is in view, since the external intercostal is concealed by the pectoralis minor; in the third and fourth spaces, the fascia is still intact as it forms the anterior intercostal membrane. In the axilla the cords and nerves of the brachial plexus, together with the axillary vessels, are partially removed from their sheath of combined adventitia and fascia. The lateral thoracic vessels are seen as they rest upon, and supply, the serratus anterior muscle.

b to *e*, Types of origin of the pectoralis minor: from the second to the fifth ribs; from the second, third, and fourth; from the third and fourth ribs; and from the third to the sixth.

The pectoralis minor originates through tendinous lips that spring from the cranial borders of the ribs. Medially they blend with the anterior intercostal aponeurosis; laterally, with the fibers and investing fascia of the external intercostal muscles, and fleshy slips derived from the outer surfaces of the ribs. They are attached to the ribs near the costochondral junction.

In a series of 1000 specimens, the pectoralis minor muscle originated from the second to the fifth ribs in 337 thoracic halves; then, in the order of decreasing frequency, from third to fifth ribs in 344 instances; from second to fourth ribs, 193 times; and from the third and fourth ribs in 67 thoracic halves—totalling 941 out of 1000 specimens. The small remainder was covered under 8 categories.

Since the pectoralis minor is a lesser associate of the closely related pectoralis major muscle, occasional absence of the pectoralis minor might be expected, but this did not occur. However, in the same laboratory, dissection revealed that other muscles were lacking as follows: the palmaris longus ("subsidiary" to the other members of the flexor-pronator group of volar antebrachial muscles), absent in 12.74 per cent of specimens (281 out of 2205); the pyramidalis (related to the much larger rectus muscle), missing in 17.67 per cent of body-halves (76 in 430); the plantaris (related to the bulky gastrocnemius and soleus), lacking in 6.46 per cent of lower extremities (100 cases out of 1545). In more than 5000 specimens dissected by students in the author's laboratory, neither pectoral muscle has ever been absent. In 2000 lower extremities examined for the relation of the muscle to the ischiadic (sciatic) nerve, the piriformis has always been present. Here its absence might be expected because this small external rotator of the thigh is a member of an exceptionally strong gluteal set.

ATTACHMENT OF THE PECTORALIS MINOR MUSCLE ORIGINS
ARRANGED IN THE ORDER OF DECREASING FREQUENCY

ORIGIN								OCCURRENCE	
Ribs								Number	Per cent
1	2	3	4					10	1.0
1	2	3	4	5				6	0.6
1	2	3	4	5	6			4	0.4
	2	3						1	0.1
	2	3	4				(figure c)	193	19.3
	2	3	4	5			(figure b)	337	33.7
	2	3	4	5	6			11	1.1
	2	3	4	5	6	7		2	0.2
		3						1	0.1
		3	4				(figure d)	67	6.7
		3	4	5			(figure a)	344	34.4
		3	4	5	6		(figure e)	15	1.5
			4	5				7	0.7
			4	5	6			2	0.2
								1000	100.0

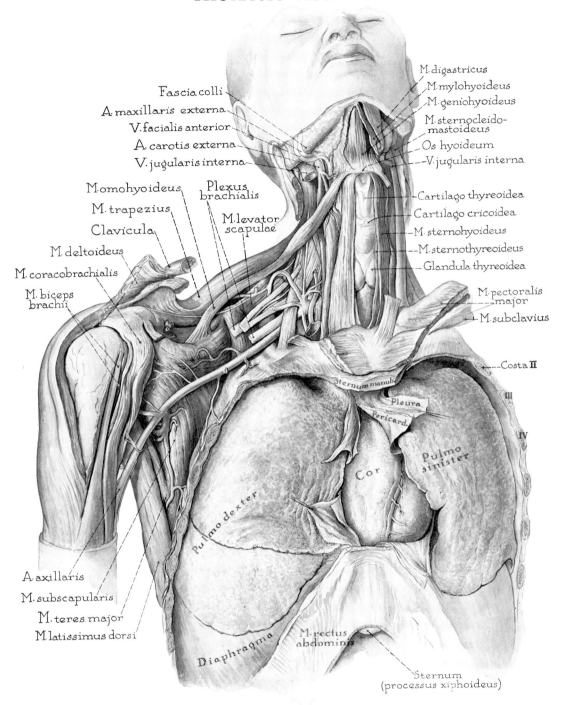

Fascia colli

A. maxillaris externa

V. facialis anterior

A. carotis externa

V. jugularis interna

M. omohyoideus

M. trapezius

Clavicula

M. deltoideus

M. coracobrachialis

M. biceps brachii

Plexus brachialis

M. levator scapulae

M. digastricus

M. mylohyoideus

M. geniohyoideus

M. sternocleido- mastoideus

Os hyoideum

V. jugularis interna

Cartilago thyreoidea

Cartilago cricoidea

M. sternohyoideus

M. sternothyreoideus

Glandula thyreoidea

M. pectoralis major

M. subclavius

Costa II

Sternum manub.

Pleura

Pericard.

Pulmo sinister

III

IV

Cor

Pulmo dexter

A. axillaris

M. subscapularis

M. teres major

M. latissimus dorsi

Diaphragma

M. rectus abdominis

Sternum (processus xiphoideus)

Anatomy of the neck, axilla, and thoracic cavity.

In the cervical region the dissection has been carried to the level of the suprahyoid and infrahyoid muscu-lature; the superficial fascia remains only along the inferior border of the mandible. Part of the mylohyoid muscle has been removed in order to expose the subjacent geniohyoid. On each side of the neck the deep cervical fascia and the sternocleidomastoid muscle have been removed to reveal the blood vessels that were contained within the carotid sheath; both the common carotid artery and the internal jugular vein are intact on the specimen's left, whereas the vein has been removed on the right.

By cutting away the medial half of the clavicle and the subclavius muscle, and by removing the pectoralis major and pectoralis minor muscles, the shoulder has been freed. The arm is abducted to reveal the muscles that constitute the medial, posterior, and lateral boundaries of the axillary space, as well as the contained axillary artery and its chief branches. The brachial plexus is shown in its relation to the scalene muscles and to the subclavian artery. The front of the thoracic cage has been removed in order to expose the lungs, the heart in the opened pericardial sac, and the respiratory diaphragm.

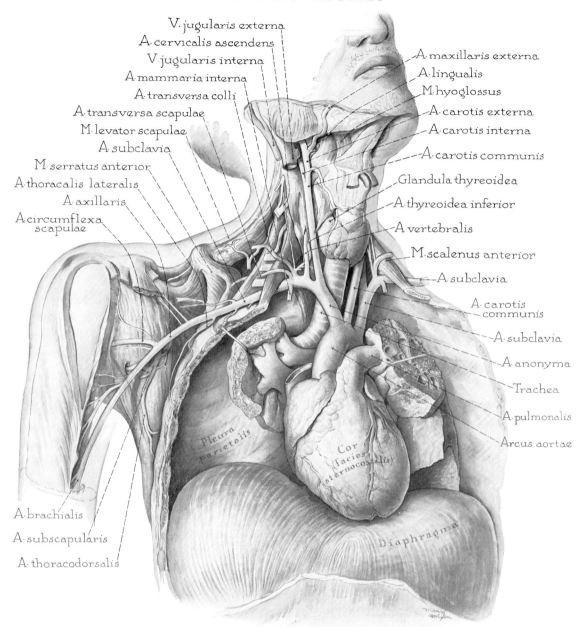

V. jugularis externa
A. cervicalis ascendens
V. jugularis interna
A. mammaria interna
A. transversa colli
A. transversa scapulae
M. levator scapulae
A. subclavia
M. serratus anterior
A. thoracalis lateralis
A. axillaris
A. circumflexa scapulae

A. maxillaris externa
A. lingualis
M. hyoglossus
A. carotis externa
A. carotis interna
A. carotis communis
Glandula thyreoidea
A. thyreoidea inferior
A. vertebralis
M. scalenus anterior
A. subclavia
A. carotis communis
A. subclavia
A. anonyma
Trachea
A. pulmonalis
Arcus aortae

Pleura parietalis
Cor (facies sternocostalis)
Diaphragma

A. brachialis
A. subscapularis
A. thoracodorsalis

Anatomy of the neck, axilla, and thoracic cavity, continued.

The manubrium of the sternum has been removed, as well as the sternal half of the first ribs and the infra-hyoid muscles. In the thorax, much of the pulmonary tissue has been dissected away. The part that remains to hold the pulmonary vessels has been drawn lateralward in order to reveal more clearly the relationships of the structures that constitute the hilus in each half of the middle mediastinum. The pleura and pericardium have been removed; the superior vena cava and its tributaries have been excised, but the aortic arch and its branches remain intact.

In this way the dissection emphasizes the pattern of arterial supply to the head, neck, shoulder, and arm. The external carotid artery sends the external maxillary artery upward to the face, and the superior thyroid artery down to the gland. The internal carotid artery is shown as it ascends beneath the mandible on the way to the cranial cavity, where it joins the vertebral artery to vascularize the brain. The vertebral artery, as the first branch of the subclavian, enters the transverse foramen of the third vertebra. Next, distally, the thyro-cervical trunk gives rise to vessels that ascend in the neck, pass backward to the musculature of the shoulder, and medially to the thyroid gland, trachea, and esophagus. From the axillary continuation of the subclavian artery, branches go to musculature, fascia, and integument of the shoulder, the back, the lateral wall of the thorax, and the proximal portion of the arm. The axillary artery continues into the arm as the brachial.

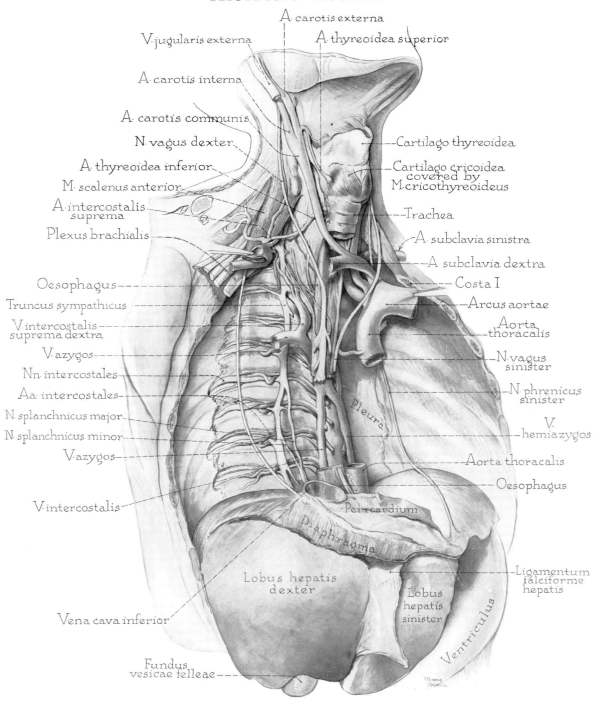

A carotis externa

V jugularis externa — A thyreoidea superior

A carotis interna

A carotis communis

N vagus dexter — Cartilago thyreoidea

A thyreoidea inferior — Cartilago cricoidea covered by M cricothyreoideus

M scalenus anterior

A intercostalis suprema — Trachea

Plexus brachialis — A subclavia sinistra

— A subclavia dextra

Oesophagus — Costa I

Truncus sympathicus — Arcus aortae

V intercostalis suprema dextra — Aorta thoracalis

V azygos — N vagus sinister

Nn intercostales — N phrenicus sinister

Aa intercostales

N splanchnicus major — V hemiazygos

N splanchnicus minor — Aorta thoracalis

V azygos — Oesophagus

Pleura

V intercostalis — Pericardium

Diaphragma

Ligamentum falciforme hepatis

Lobus hepatis dexter — Lobus hepatis sinister

Ventriculus

Vena cava inferior

Fundus vesicae felleae

Structures in the prevertebral region of the neck, in the posterior mediastinum, and in the upper abdomen. Dissection concluded.

In the neck the dissection has been carried to the level of the esophagus and trachea (the latter transected below the level of the third ring). The thoracic cage has been removed along the midaxillary line.

In the thorax, the heart and lungs have been removed, the aorta excised except for, above, the portion that gives rise to the great vessels and, below, the part near the hiatus in the diaphragm. The arch, thus freed, has been retracted to expose the esophagus and related arteries, veins, and nerves. On the specimen's right half and in the prevertebral region the following structures are shown: the azygos vein, with the hemiazygos tributary on the left and the highest intercostal vein on the right; the segmentally arranged intercostal nerves and vessels (the arteries appearing as open channels medially where they have been cut from the excised segment of the thoracic aorta); the sympathetic trunk with the derived splanchnic nerves. On the specimen's left half the parietal pleura is intact; on the right it has been removed. The phrenic nerves are shown in their cervical and thoracic descent into the diaphragm; the vagus nerves are shown converging upon the esophagus. The pericardium has been cut down to its phrenic attachment; the inferior caval vein, the thoracic aorta, and the esophagus remain where they approach their hiatuses in the diaphragm. The ventral portion of the diaphragm has been cut away to show the liver, the latter's falciform ligament, and the stomach.

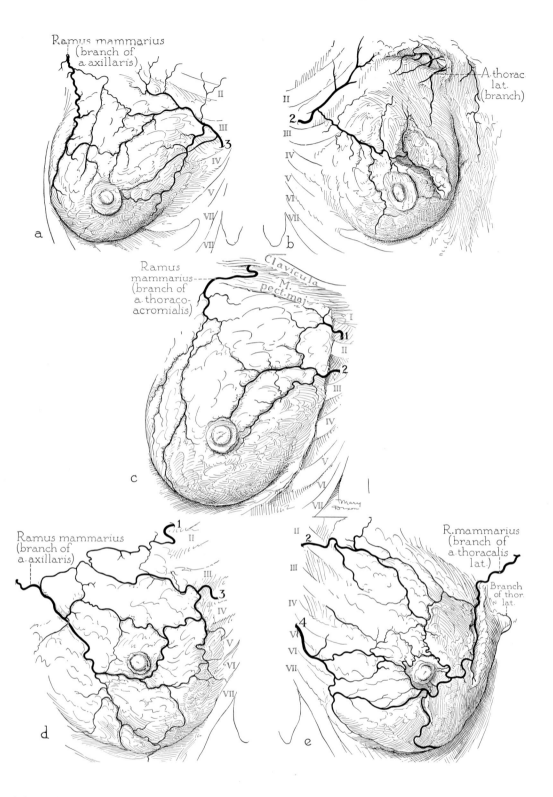

Arterial supply of the mammary gland. Variations in the source and anastomotic pattern of the vessels.

a and *b*, Both glands of a specimen; *c*, gland of the right side of a second specimen; *d* and *e*, both glands of a third specimen. In addition to supply from the medial aspect, vessels of superior (pectoral) and lateral (axillary) sources are shown.

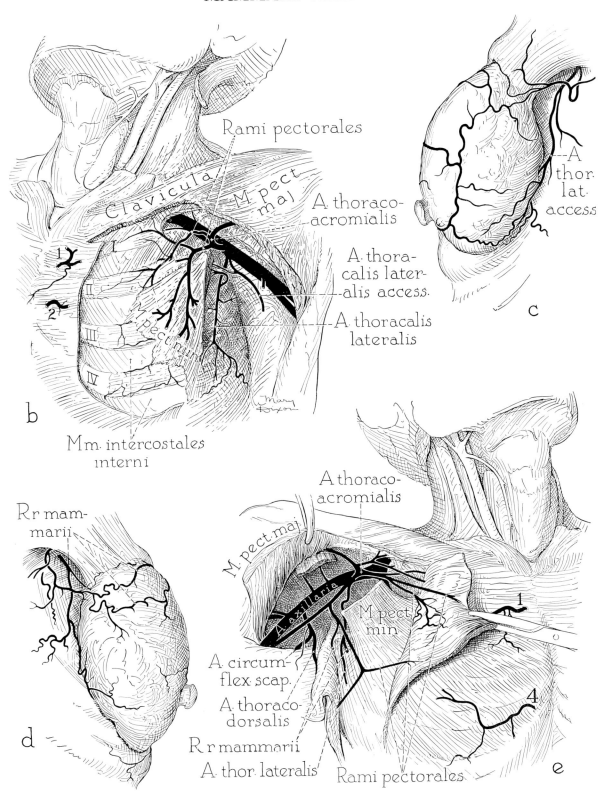

Arterial supply of the mammary gland.

Regarding arteries that attain the gland from the lateral and superior aspects, it may be stated the vessels from the former source descend as a pedicle, leaving the axillary space by passing around the free border of the pectoralis major muscle; those from the superior position perforate the pectoralis major.

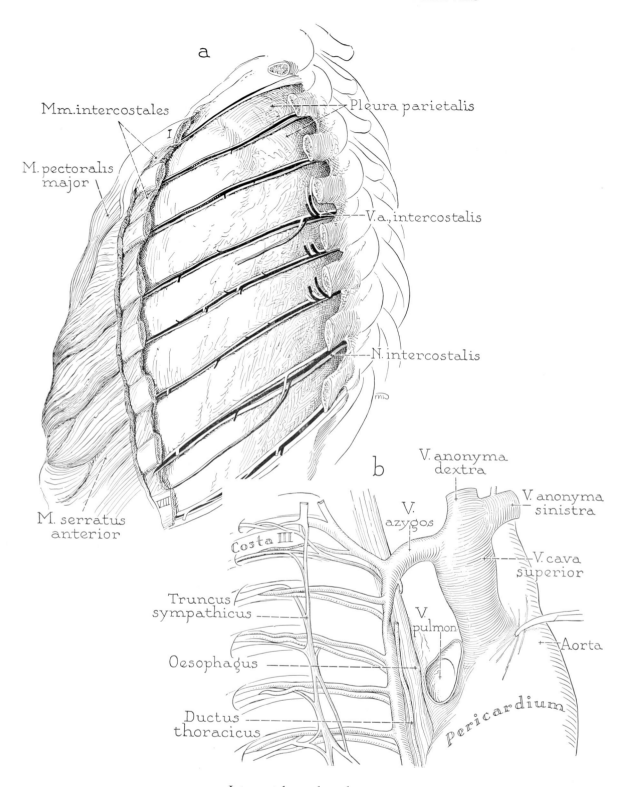

a

Mm. intercostales

Pleura parietalis

M. pectoralis major

V. a., intercostalis

N. intercostalis

M. serratus anterior

b

V. anonyma dextra

V. anonyma sinistra

V. azygos

V. cava superior

Costa III

V. pulmon

Truncus sympathicus

Oesophagus

Aorta

Ductus thoracicus

Pericardium

Intercostal vessels and nerves.

a, Lateral view of the arteries, veins, and nerves of intercostal position, shown by removal of the ribs and intercostal muscles. *b*, Anterolateral view of the upper intercostal veins of the right side and the azygos vein of which they are tributaries. The innominate (NA, brachiocephalic) veins have been transected near the point of their junction to form the superior caval vein.

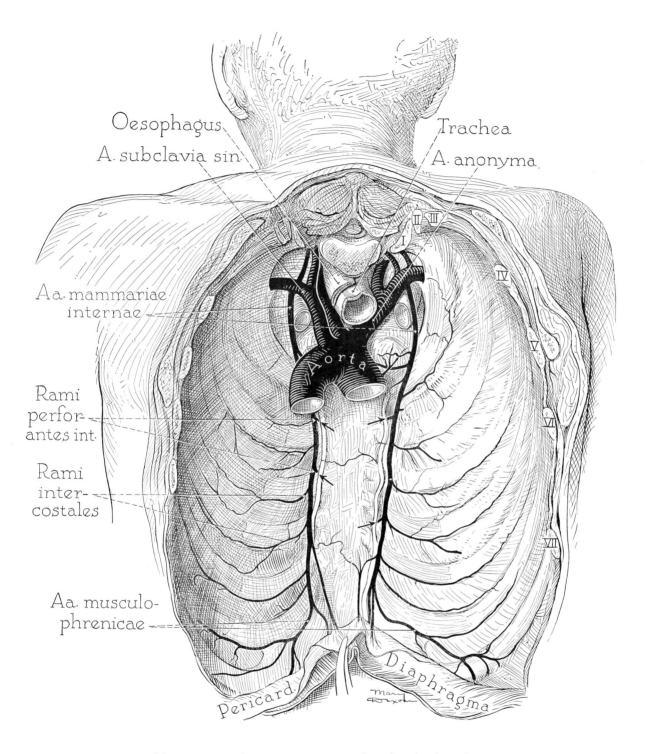

Mammary arteries; source, course and perforating branches.

  The anterior thoracic wall is viewed from within. After arising from the inferior border of the subclavian artery, each internal mammary (NA, thoracic) artery descends vertically in parasternal course. Near the diaphragm each artery divides into a superior epigastric and musculophrenic portions. In descent, both intercostal and perforating branches (latter indicated by arrows) arise segmentally from the internal mammary. The perforating rami of the first through the fourth intercostal spaces are commonly the largest in the female (see preceding figures).

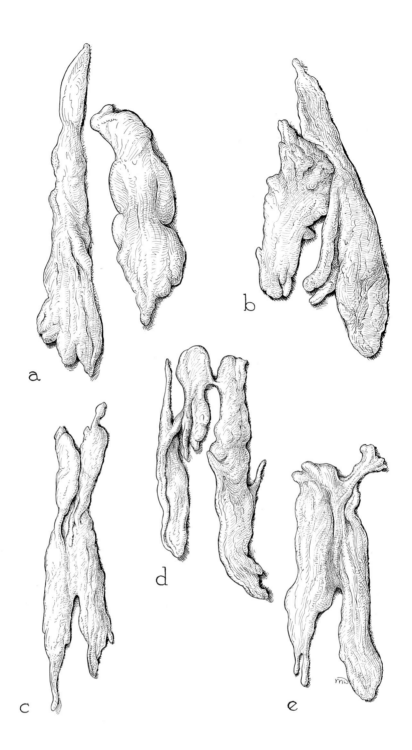

Excised specimens of adult thymus, selected to demonstrate variations in form and dimensions.
Approximately ⅔ natural size.

Usually the lobes differ in size and shape; they may be wholly separate (*a*), fused (*c* to *e*), or merely contiguous (*b*). In most instances they come to a tapering extremity cranially; namely, in the neck, near the thyroid gland.

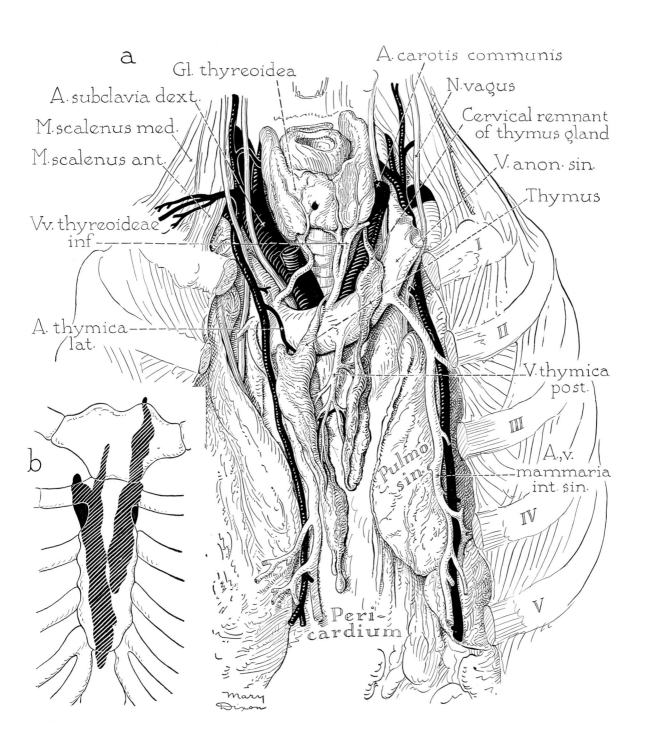

a

Gl. thyreoidea

A. carotis communis

A. subclavia dext.

N. vagus

M. scalenus med.

Cervical remnant of thymus gland

M. scalenus ant.

V. anon. sin.

Thymus

Vv. thyreoideae inf.

I

A. thymica lat.

II

V. thymica post.

III

A, v. mammaria int. sin.

Pulmo sin.

IV

b

V

Peri- cardium

Mary Dixon

Blood supply of the thyroid gland and the thymus in the adult.

a, In the neck the dissection is carried to tracheal level by removal, with the sternum and clavicle, of all of the infrahyoid muscles. In the thorax the dissection exposes the space and contents of the anterior medi- astinum. On the specimen's left half the thymic and internal mammary (NA, internal thoracic) veins are shown as they terminate in the innominate (NA, brachiocephalic).

b, Form and position of the thymus, in relation to the thoracic cage.

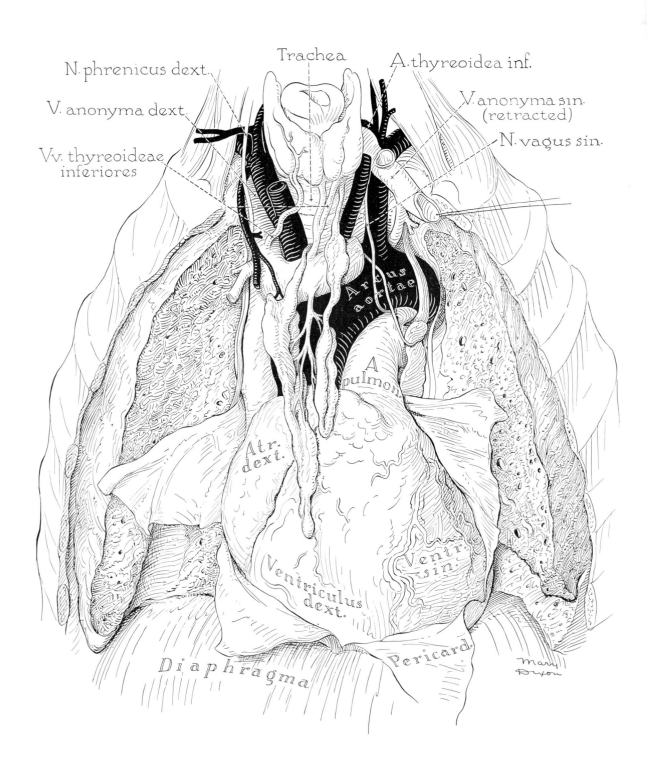

Blood supply of the thyroid gland and thymus. Deeper dissection of the same specimen.

The thoracic cage has been more widely cut away; the lungs have been similarly cut; a portion of the left innominate vein (NA, brachiocephalic) has been excised to expose the area of aortic source of the subclavian artery (from which is derived the inferior thyroid artery). That portion of the innominate vein remains into which empty tributaries from the thyroid gland and the thymus.

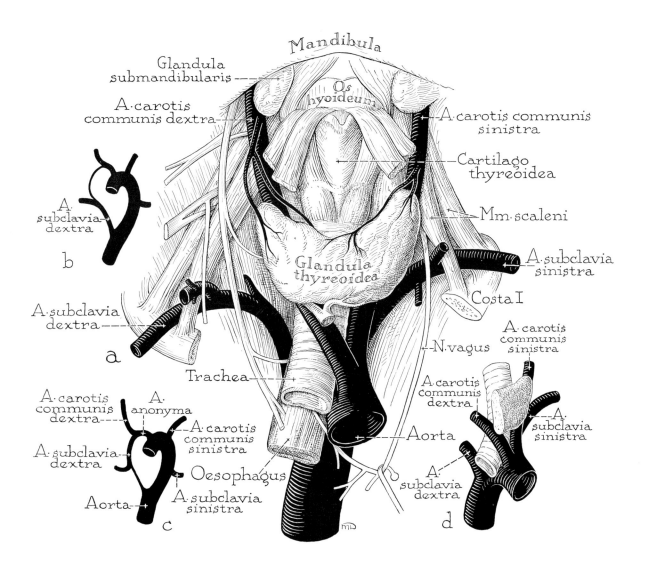

Retroesophageal right subclavian artery. Drawings from a laboratory specimen, accompanied by schematic figures to demonstrate embryological changes that account for the anomalous branching.

a, Deep cervical and thoracic structures, showing the relation of the anomalous artery to the trachea and the esophagus; *b*, developmental establishment of a right subclavian artery as the last branch of the aortic arch; owing to subsequent disappearance of the thin segment between the common carotid and subclavian arteries of the right side, an innominate stem will be absent; *c*, embryonic establishment of the usual pattern of branching of the aortic arch, as a result of disappearance of the short caudal segment of the right aortic arch; the cranial segment thereof will become the right subclavian branch of an innominate artery; *d*, a portion of the specimen shown in the main illustration; excision of the right lobe of the thyroid gland reveals the relation of the carotid and subclavian arteries, and the intervening portion of the aortic arch to the trachea.

ARCUS AORTAE
TYPES OF BRANCHING, 1000 SPECIMENS

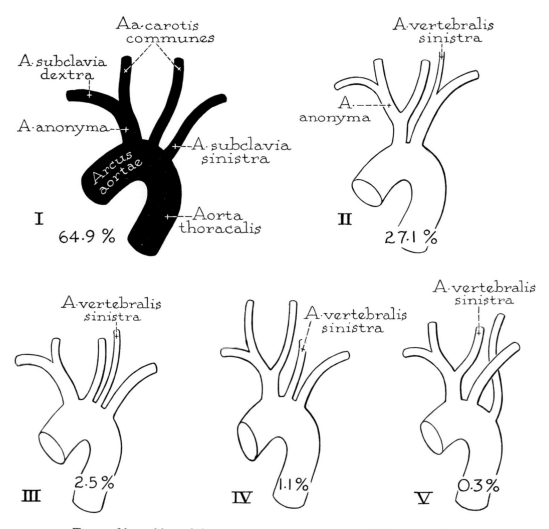

Types of branching of the aortic arch encountered in 1000 adult cadavers.

I, The arrangement regarded as "normal" for man is actually encountered more frequently than all other types combined. In specimens of this variety, 3 branches leave the arch in the following succession, from the specimen's right to left: innominate (with right common carotid and right subclavian as derivatives); left common carotid; left subclavian. II, An arrangement distinguished by reduction in the number of stems to 2, both common carotid arteries arising from the innominate. III, Here the distinguishing feature is increase, not reduction, in the number of derived branches. The left vertebral artery (usually arising from the subclavian) is the additional vessel. IV, Differing from the preceding variety, the feature is replacement, the left vertebral artery (not the left common carotid, as in Type I) being the second stem in right-to-left succession. Both common carotid arteries arise from a common stem, as they do in examples of Type II. V, In this departure from the anatomic norm, the left vertebral artery arises from the innominate, and the order of the left common carotid and left subclavian arteries is reversed. VI to VIII (facing page), Three patterns similar in respect to the position of origin of the right subclavian artery; the latter vessel arises as the last branch of the aortic arch, reaching the right upper extremity by passing dorsal to the esophagus. In respect to the origin of the other branches, the types differ. IX, A bi-innominate sequence, in which paired vessels (in turn having matching main branches) are the only derivatives of the aortic arch. X and XI, In both these varieties the left vertebral artery arises from an aortic trunk from which the left subclavian is also derived. However, in Type X a regular innominate artery is present (as in Type I), whereas in Type XI the "innominate" (with

(*Legend is continued on the facing page.*)

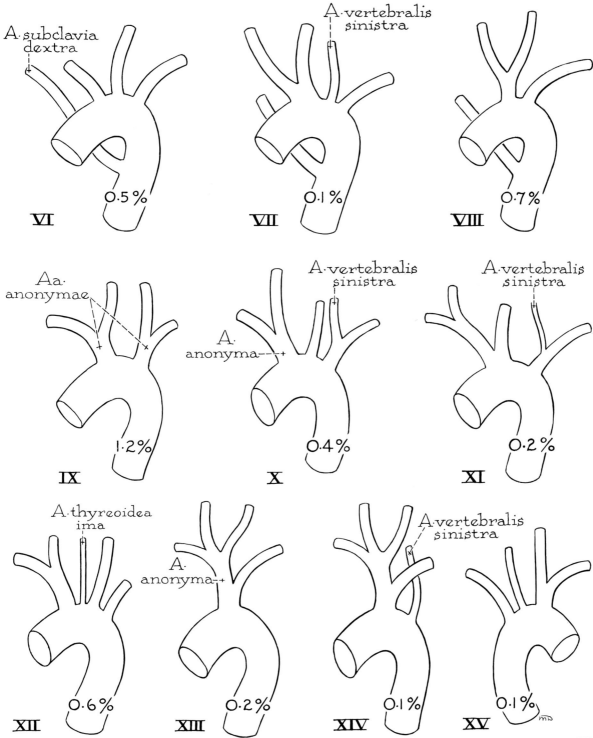

regular branches) arises from an aortic trunk shared with the common carotid. XII, Here, as in Type III, an extra vessel arises from the arch between the innominate and the left subclavian, but the added derivative is the *a. thyreoidea ima* instead of the *a. vertebralis*. XIII, Unification is the distinguishing feature of this departure from the typical scheme of branching; the usual branches (see Type I) take origin from the aortic arch through a single trunk as an intermediary vessel. XIV, An infrequent variety with all branches derived from a common stem (as in Type XIII) with the exception of the left vertebral, which arises from the arch to the right of the common stem. XV, In this rare variety, in which the arch passes in a reversed direction from heart to thoracic aorta, the branches maintain a normal succession in relation to the body itself; however, their position on the aortic arch itself is as a mirror-image of the "standard" scheme of derivation.

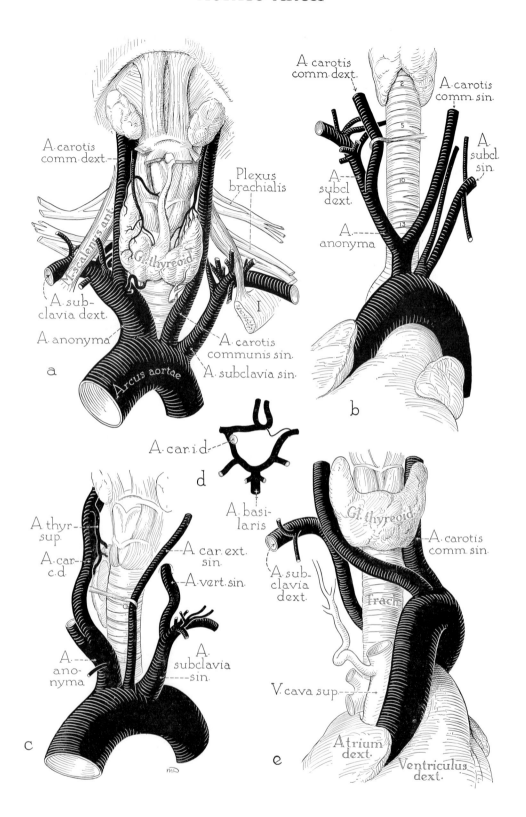

Branches of the aortic arch. Variation in the pattern of origin.

a, Regular schema; *b*, left common carotid from the innominate; *c*, absence of left internal carotid artery; *d*, form of the arterial circle (of Willis) in the same specimen; *e*, retroesophageal right subclavian artery.

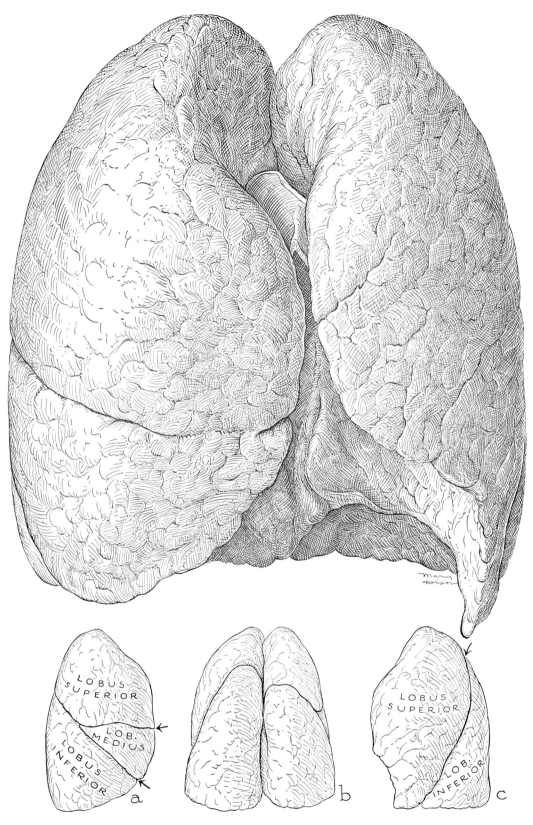

Lungs; from an inflated, unfixed specimen (prepared by Elmer Hagens, M.D.).

a to *c*, Views of the same specimens from the right, from behind, and from the left, respectively.

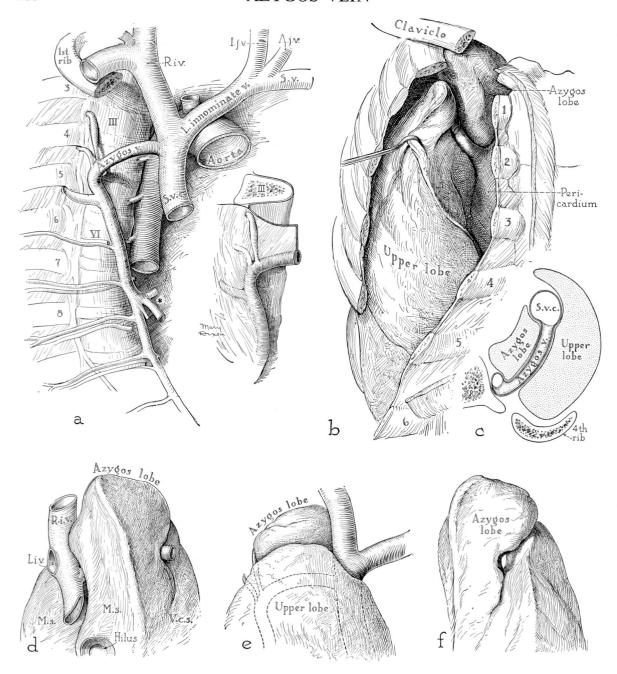

Accessory pulmonary lobe and the azygos vein.

a, Posterior thoracic structures, seen in anterolateral view; showing the azygos vein, the associated great vessels, and (at *) the transverse connection between the azygos and hemiazygos veins. *b*, Contents of the right pleural cavity; upper pulmonary lobe is retracted to expose the accessory lobe and the anomalous azygos vein. *Inset:* The anomalous azygos vein with part of its reflection of the parietal pleura. *c*, Transverse section through the right lung and related structures at the level of the loop of the anomalous azygos vein. *d* to *f*, Upper portion of the right lung, showing the pulmonary relations of the anomalous azygos vein and its connections; three aspects.

Incidence of anomalous lobe, in the author's laboratory, 0.4 per cent (8 cases in 2000 specimens).

Abbreviations: R.i.v., L.i.v., I.j.v., A.j.v., S.v., S.v.c.; right innominate vein (NA, brachiocephalic), left innominate vein, internal jugular vein, anterior jugular vein, subclavian vein, and superior vena cava, respectively; M.s., mediastinal surface; V.c.s., vertebrocostal surface.

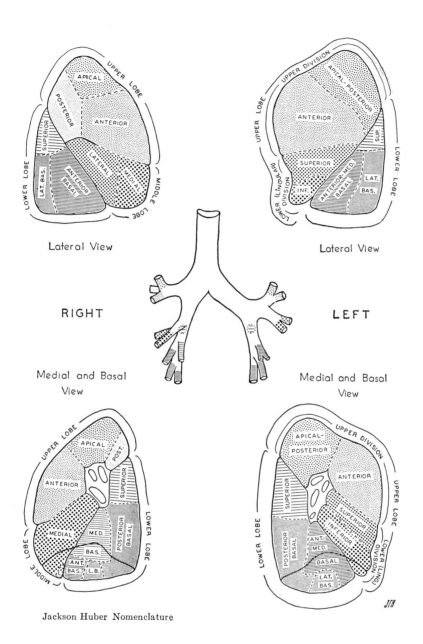

Tracheobronchial branching correlated with the subdivisions of the lungs;
shown in the form of pulmonary charts.

Each bronchial branch is named on the basis of the portion of the lung to which it is distributed; the pulmonary subdivisions are marked by designs corresponding with those used in bronchial diagram. (From Jackson and Huber: Diseases of the Chest.)

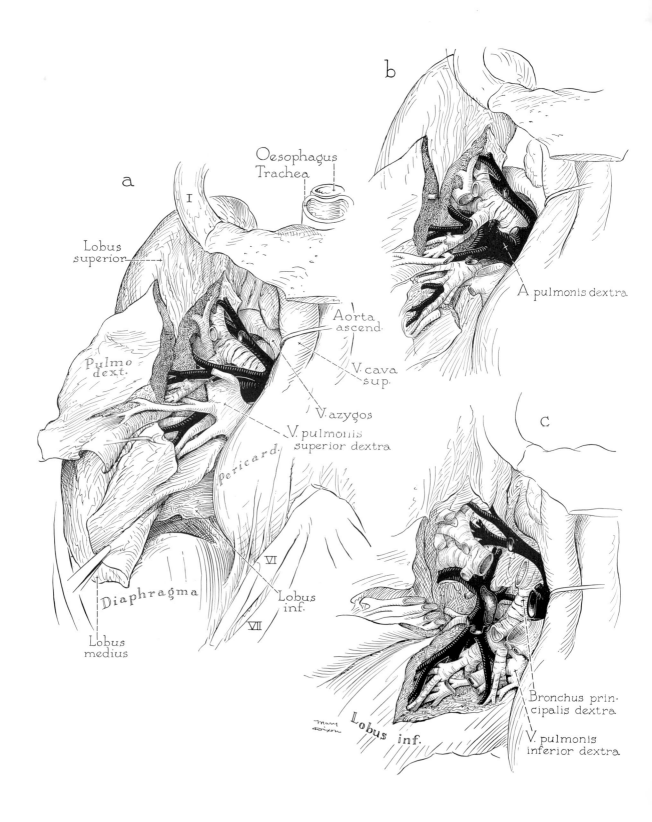

Structures of the hilus of the right lung.

a to *c*, Dissections at successively deeper levels.

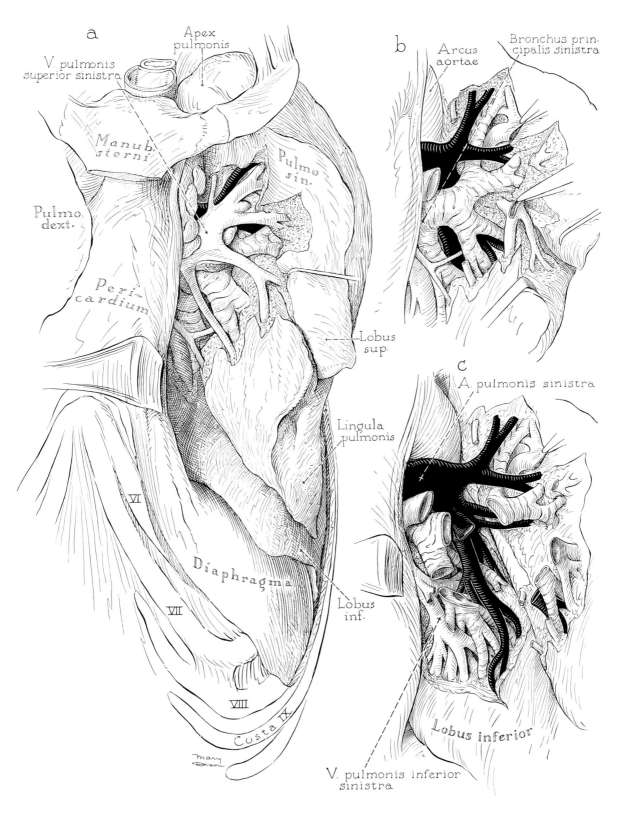

Structures of the hilus of the left lung; same specimen.

a to *c*, The constituents exposed at successively deeper levels.

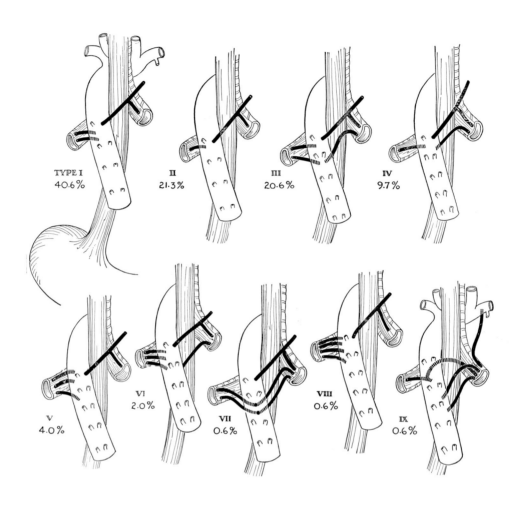

Bronchial arteries; types in 300 specimens, shown schematically. Dorsal views.

The classification is based upon origin, number and course of the vessels.

Type I (40.6 per cent) is described as "normal" in standard textbooks. In these specimens, one right and two left bronchial arteries are present. In every case there is at least one bronchial artery to each lung, and this simplest vascular scheme occurs next in order of frequency as Type II (21.3 per cent). The third major group, Type III, is characterized by bilateral duplication of the arteries (20.6 per cent of cases). These three types comprise approximately 82.7 per cent of the arterial patterns in all cadavers studied.

In 14 cases (Type IV; 9.7 per cent) the pattern is the reverse of Type I, with one artery to the left and two to the right lung. The arteries to the left lung are increased to 3, with a single vessel persisting on the right side in 6 cases (Type V; 4.0 per cent). A maximum number of 5 arteries is encountered in 6 cases (4.0 per cent). Of these, 3 specimens possess 3 left and 2 right arteries (Type VI; 2 per cent), and a single case demonstrates the reversed scheme (Type VII; 0.6 per cent). The remaining 2 examples have four arteries to one lung and a solitary vessel to the opposite organ. The quadruple pattern is found on the left in Type VIII (0.6 per cent), on the right in Type IX (0.6 per cent).

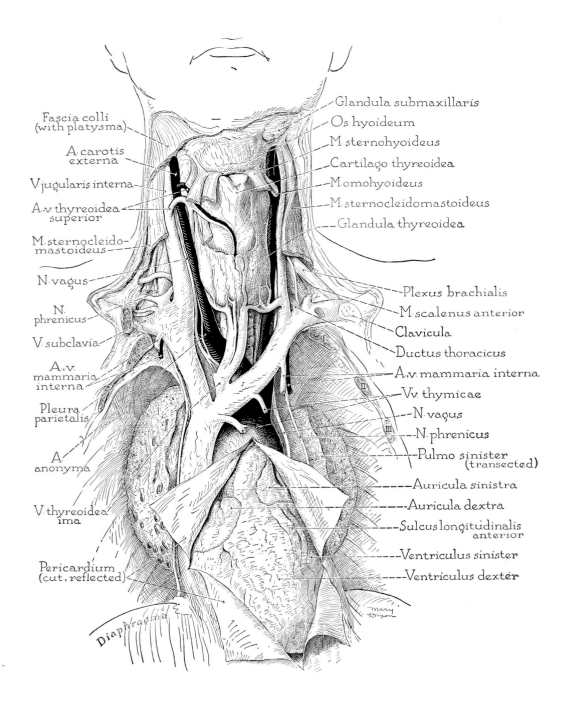

Thoracic and cervical anatomy of a male specimen, especially in relation to the
pericardium and the vascular structures invested thereby.

The sternocleidomastoid muscles have been cut and turned aside. The infrahyoid muscles have been
transected, leaving short ends at their thyroid and hyoid extremities. In this way the following have been
exposed; thyroid cartilage and hyoid bone; jugular veins and carotid arteries; brachial plexus and scalene
musculature; trachea; phrenic and vagus nerves; thoracic duct. The clavicles have been removed in their
sternal portions, as have also the sternum and the sternal portions of the ribs. Within the thoracic cavity the
lungs have been transected near each hilus. The pericardial sac has been opened to expose the heart and the
ascending segment of the aorta. The thymus has been removed, but its veins of drainage have been retained.

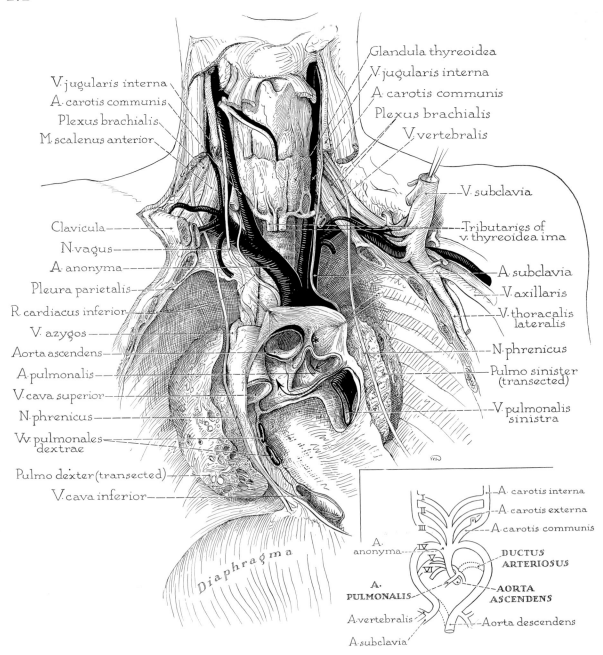

The relation of the serous layer of the pericardium to the aorta, to the branches of the latter's arch and to the pulmonary artery, shown by deeper dissection of the same specimen; and the origin of the ductus arteriosus and other derivatives of the vascular arches.

Major relationships are demonstrated by cutting along the line at which the parietal layer of the pericardium becomes continuous with the epicardium. It is shown that in this particular specimen, unlike certain others in the present series, no pericardial cul-de-sac is prolonged upon the ligamentum arteriosum; however, a shallow bay, marked by a star, came within 2 mm. of the inferior (pulmonary) extremity of the ligament. Additionally, by excision of the heart and reflection of the transected innominate (NA, brachiocephalic) veins, the following attendant features are demonstrated: the relation of the epicardium to the caval and pulmonary veins, and to the aorta and pulmonary artery; the deep relations of the aortic arch and of the latter's branches in the neck. The crest between rami of the pulmonary artery is indicated by a short, straight arrow. A long, sinuous arrow passes through the transverse sinus.

The transformation of the aortic arches (numbered I to VI) in the human embryo, are shown schematically, in ventral view, with the vessels spread to the same plane (after Arey).

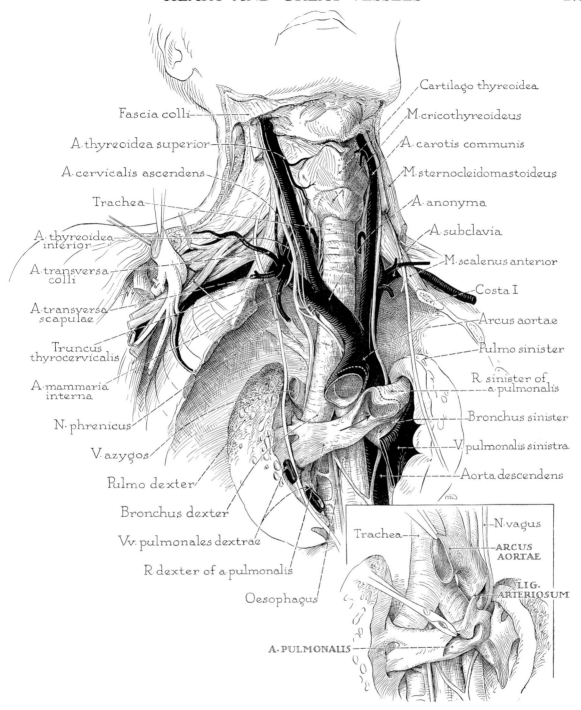

Fascia colli

A. thyreoidea superior

A. cervicalis ascendens

Trachea

A. thyreoidea inferior

A. transversa colli

A. transversa scapulae

Truncus thyrocervicalis

A. mammaria interna

N. phrenicus

V. azygos

Pulmo dexter

Bronchus dexter

Vv. pulmonales dextrae

R. dexter of a. pulmonalis

Oesophagus

Cartilago thyreoidea

M. cricothyreoideus

A. carotis communis

M. sternocleidomastoideus

A. anonyma

A. subclavia

M. scalenus anterior

Costa I

Arcus aortae

Pulmo sinister

R. sinister of a. pulmonalis

Bronchus sinister

V. pulmonalis sinistra

Aorta descendens

Trachea

N. vagus

ARCUS AORTAE

LIG. ARTERIOSUM

A. PULMONALIS

Arterial ligament, with its pulmonary and aortic connections, and the structures situated in the region of the ligament at middle and posterior mediastinal levels, shown by carrying the dissection in the same specimen to still deeper level; and the connections of the ligament.

The above-named anatomical structures are exposed by removal of the remaining portion of the serous layer of pericardium (lines of reflection dotted) and of the connective tissue related to the aorta and pulmonary vessels, trachea, bronchi, and esophagus. The thyroid gland has been removed in order to reveal the branches of the subclavian artery, and of the vagus and phrenic nerves. The azygos vein, transected at the point of entry into the superior vena cava, appears at a more caudal level on the lateral margin of the esophagus. In the axilla the stump of the subclavian vein has been retracted, exposing the corresponding artery and the related elements of the brachial plexus (suprascapular nerve drawn upward, median nerve downward).

The form, angular course, and attachments of the ligament are demonstrated by elevating the transected aortic arch and by drawing the pulmonary artery downward.

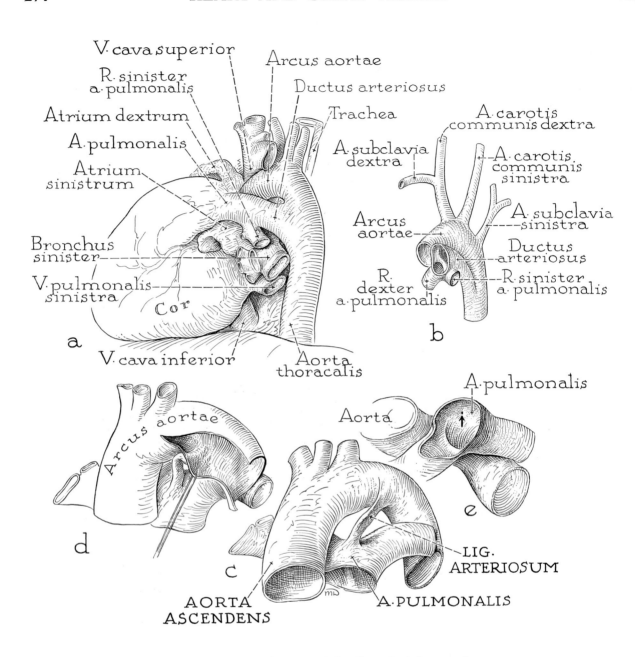

Arterial duct and ligament; infantile and adult examples.

a, The arterial duct (ductus arteriosus), pulmonary artery, aorta, and related structures in an infant 6 days old; specimen viewed from the left. The trachea and the bronchi have been transected, the lungs removed; the great veins have been cut near their terminations, and the arteries derived from the aortic arch have been transected.

b, The arterial duct, the pulmonary artery, the aorta, and the branches of the latter's arch in a 6-month fetus.

c to *e*. The arterial ligament (ligamentum arteriosum) in an adult male (past middle age), shown in relation to the point of bifurcation of the pulmonary artery and to the ventral wall of the aortic arch. *c*, The specimen viewed from the front, to demonstrate the form and continuities of the ligament. *d*, The same specimen, with the aorta opened from the ventral aspect, revealing the smoothness of the internal wall of the aorta in the area of attachment of the ligament. *e*, The specimen viewed from below, showing the pin-point orifice (at arrow) of the arterial ligament on the anterosuperior wall of the pulmonary artery, where the latter divides into its right and left rami.

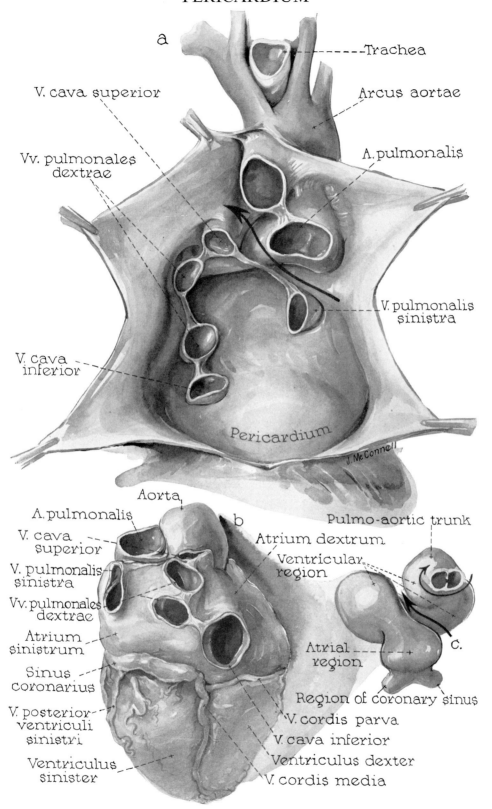

Pericardial sac, with vessels which enter or leave it; excised adult and embryonic hearts.

a, The interior of the pericardial cavity; the heart has been removed following transection of the vessels. *b*, Dorsal surface of the heart. *c*, Embryonic heart, with the site of the transverse sinus indicated by arrow (as in *a*).

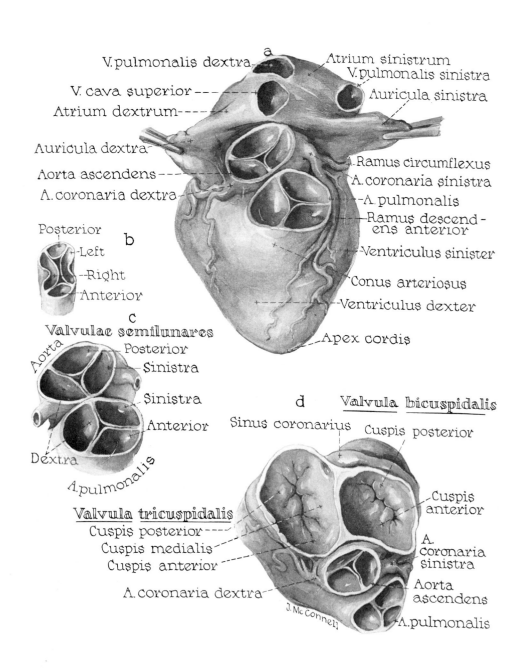

V. pulmonalis dextra
Atrium sinistrum
V. pulmonalis sinistra
V. cava superior
Atrium dextrum
Auricula sinistra
Auricula dextra
Aorta ascendens
A. coronaria dextra
Ramus circumflexus
A. coronaria sinistra
A. pulmonalis
Ramus descendens anterior
Ventriculus sinister
Conus arteriosus
Ventriculus dexter
Apex cordis

b
Posterior
Left
Right
Anterior

c
Valvulae semilunares
Aorta
Posterior
Sinistra
Sinistra
Anterior
Dextra
A. pulmonalis

d   Valvula bicuspidalis
Sinus coronarius
Cuspis posterior
Cuspis anterior
A. coronaria sinistra
Aorta ascendens
A. pulmonalis

Valvula tricuspidalis
Cuspis posterior
Cuspis medialis
Cuspis anterior
A. coronaria dextra

J. McConnell

Heart: bicuspid and tricuspid valves.

a, The heart seen from above and in front; the aorta and pulmonary artery have been transected close to the attachments of the valves. b and c, The semilunar valves of the embryo and of the adult, respectively; recording the manner in which elongate right and left cusps become divided into aortic and pulmonary portions. d, The atrioventricular valves, seen from the superior aspect, after removal of the atria.

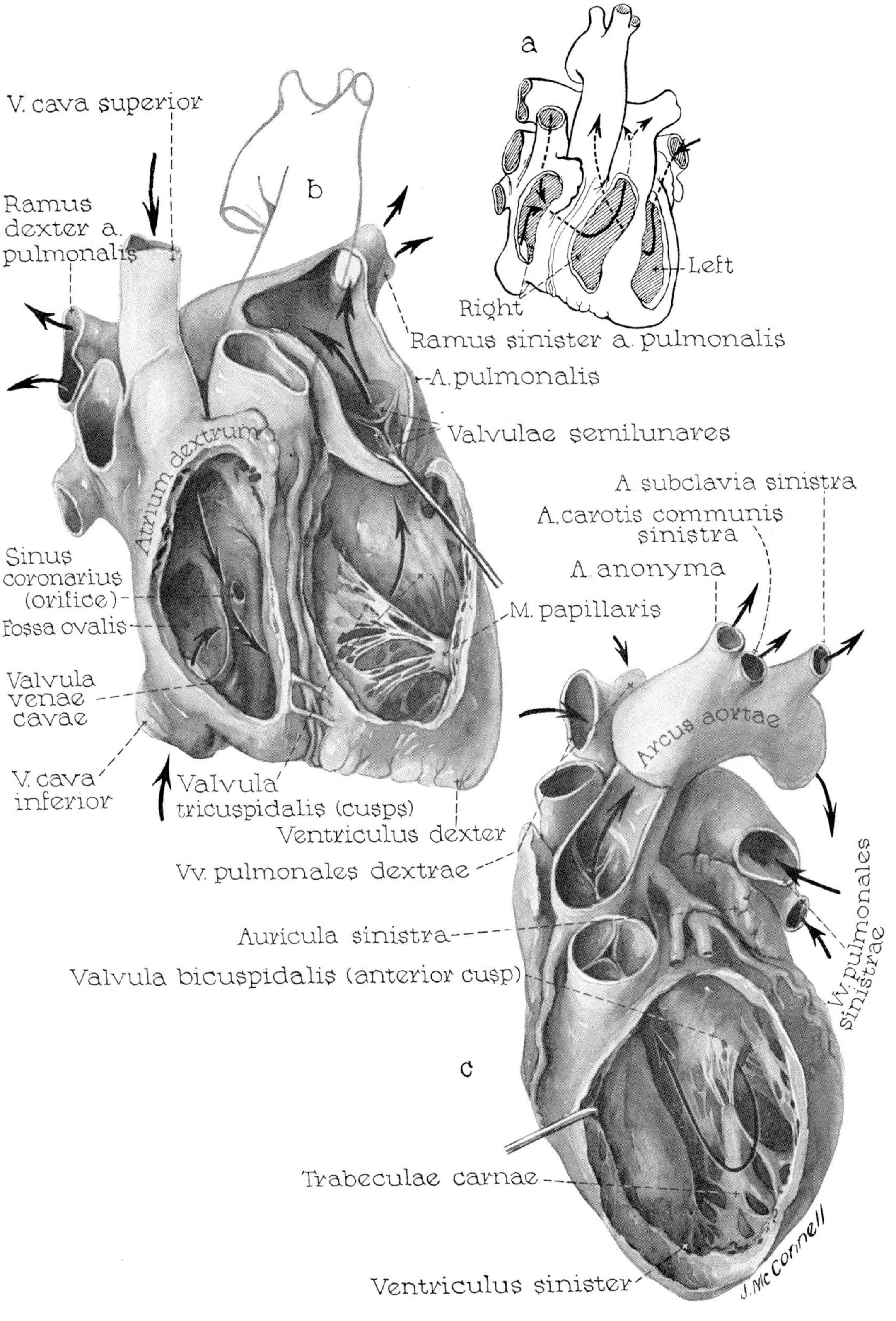

V. cava superior

Ramus
dexter a.
pulmonalis

b

a

Right

Left

Ramus sinister a. pulmonalis

A. pulmonalis

Valvulae semilunares

Atrium dextrum

A. subclavia sinistra

A. carotis communis
sinistra

A. anonyma

M. papillaris

Arcus aortae

Sinus
coronarius
(orifice)

Fossa ovalis

Valvula
venae
cavae

V. cava
inferior

Valvula
tricuspidalis (cusps)

Ventriculus dexter

Vv. pulmonales dextrae

Auricula sinistra

Valvula bicuspidalis (anterior cusp)

Vv. pulmonales sinistrae

c

Trabeculae carnae

J. McConnell

Ventriculus sinister

Heart: internal structure of the atria and ventricles.

a, The course of the blood through the chambers of the heart. Schematic. *b*, The arterial "side" of the heart; direction of flow indicated by arrows. *c*, The venous "side" of the heart; course of vascular flow recorded by arrows.

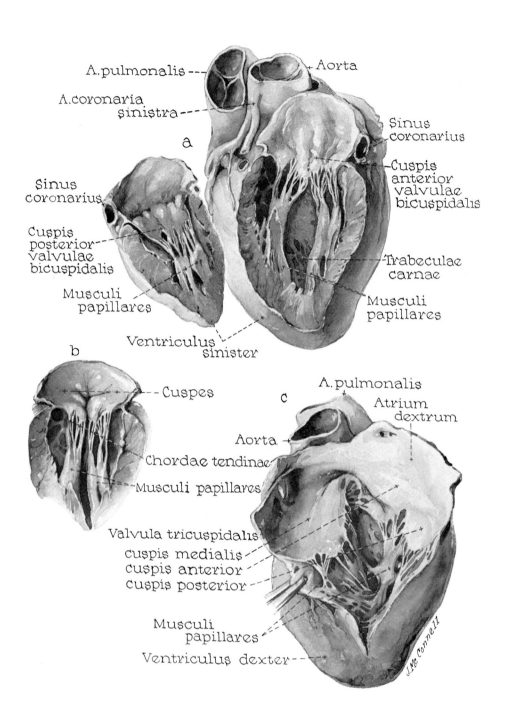

A.pulmonalis -- Aorta

A.coronaria sinistra ---

a

Sinus coronarius

Cuspis anterior valvulae bicuspidalis

Sinus coronarius

Cuspis posterior valvulae bicuspidalis

Trabeculae carnae

Musculi papillares

Musculi papillares

Ventriculus sinister

b

Cuspes

c

A.pulmonalis

Atrium dextrum

Aorta

Chordae tendinae

Musculi papillares

Valvula tricuspidalis
cuspis medialis
cuspis anterior
cuspis posterior

Musculi papillares

Ventriculus dexter

J.M.Connell

Heart: valves, their papillary muscles and related muscular trabeculae.

a and *b*, The bicuspid valves. *c*, The tricuspid valves.

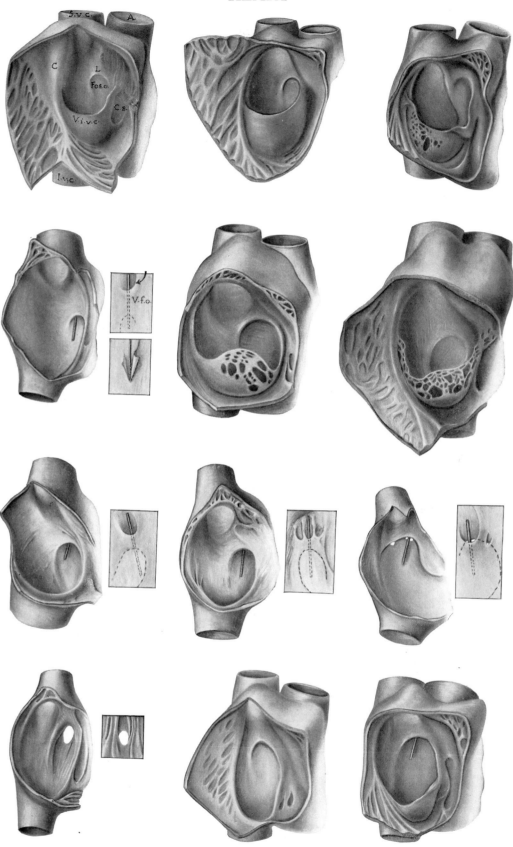

Right atrium of the heart.

Variations in form of the valve of the inferior vena cava and of the interatrial foramen. Insets: portions of interatrial wall, from the right atrium (foramen probed).

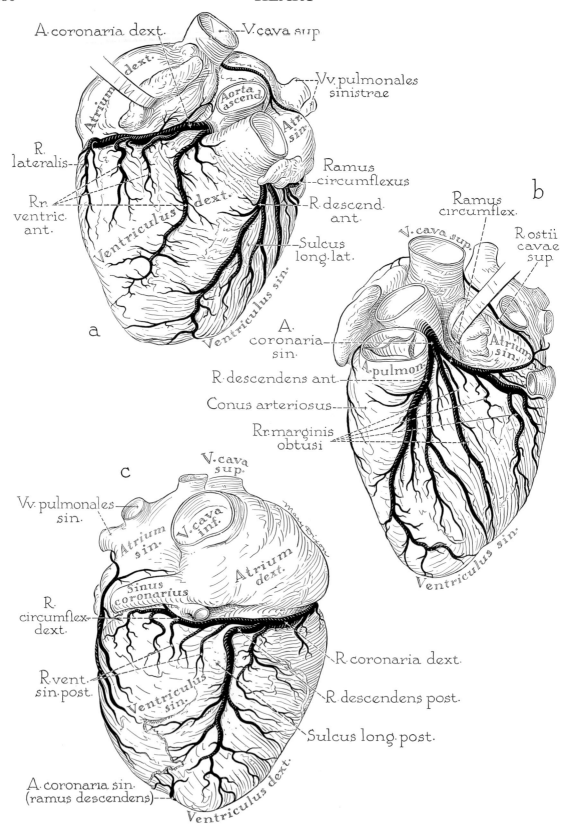

Coronary arteries.

a, Heart, anterior view. *b* and *c*, Same specimen, lateral views (from the left and the right, respectively).

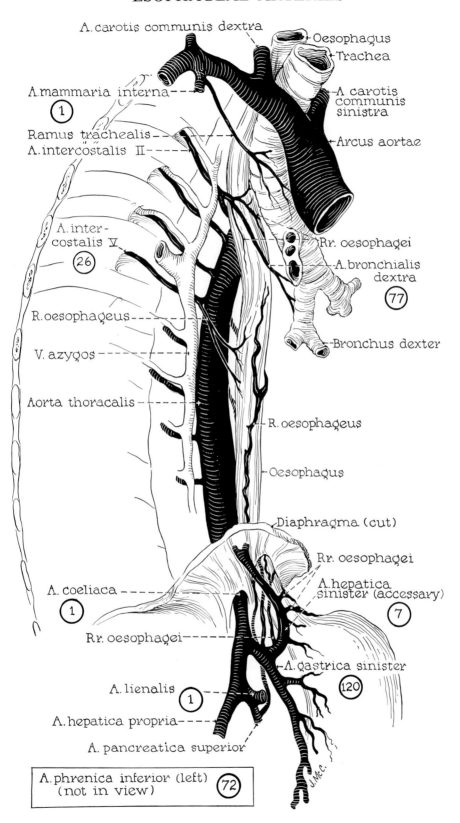

A. carotis communis dextra
Oesophagus
Trachea
A. mammaria interna
A. carotis communis sinistra
(1)
Ramus trachealis
A. intercostalis II
Arcus aortae
A. inter-costalis V
(26)
Rr. oesophagei
A. bronchialis dextra
(77)
R. oesophageus
Bronchus dexter
V. azygos
Aorta thoracalis
R. oesophageus
Oesophagus
Diaphragma (cut)
Rr. oesophagei
A. coeliaca
A. hepatica sinister (accessary)
(1)
(7)
Rr. oesophagei
A. gastrica sinister
A. lienalis
(120)
(1)
A. hepatica propria
A. pancreatica superior
A. phrenica inferior (left) (72) (not in view)

Esophageal and bronchial arteries; diagrammatic.

The encircled numbers near the labeled vessel record the frequency of origin of esophageal rami from the particular vessel in 125 specimens.

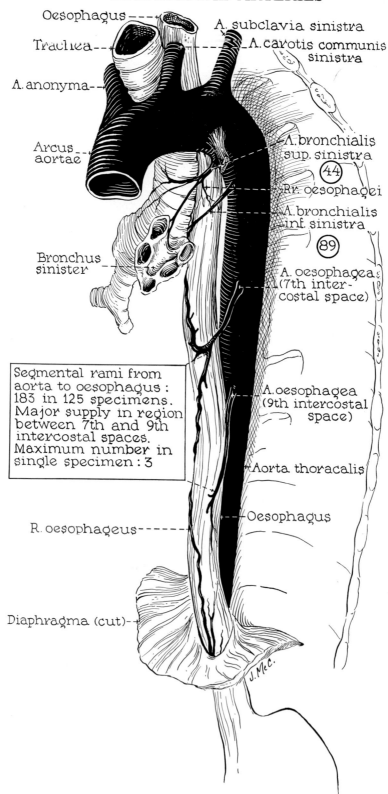

Oesophagus

Trachea

A. subclavia sinistra

A. carotis communis sinistra

A. anonyma

A. bronchialis sup. sinistra

(44)

Arcus aortae

Rr. oesophagei

A. bronchialis inf. sinistra

(89)

Bronchus sinister

A. oesophagea (7th inter-costal space)

Segmental rami from aorta to oesophagus: 183 in 125 specimens. Major supply in region between 7th and 9th intercostal spaces. Maximum number in single specimen: 3

A. oesophagea (9th intercostal space)

Aorta thoracalis

Oesophagus

R. oesophageus

Diaphragma (cut)

J. McC.

Thoracic sources of esophageal arteries; diagrammatic.

The encircled numbers represent the frequency with which esophageal rami arose from the particular bronchial artery in 125 dissections. Ascending branches of esophageal arteries from abdominal level and descending branches of the segmental esophageal arteries of thoracic level are also shown.

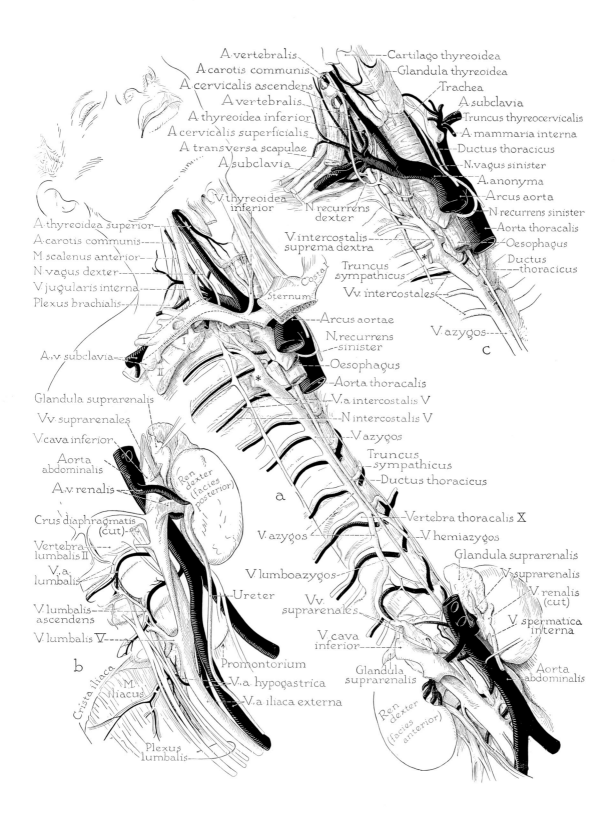

Veins of the trunk and certain of the visceral tributaries. Right side of specimen; anterolateral view. Detailed description on page 285.

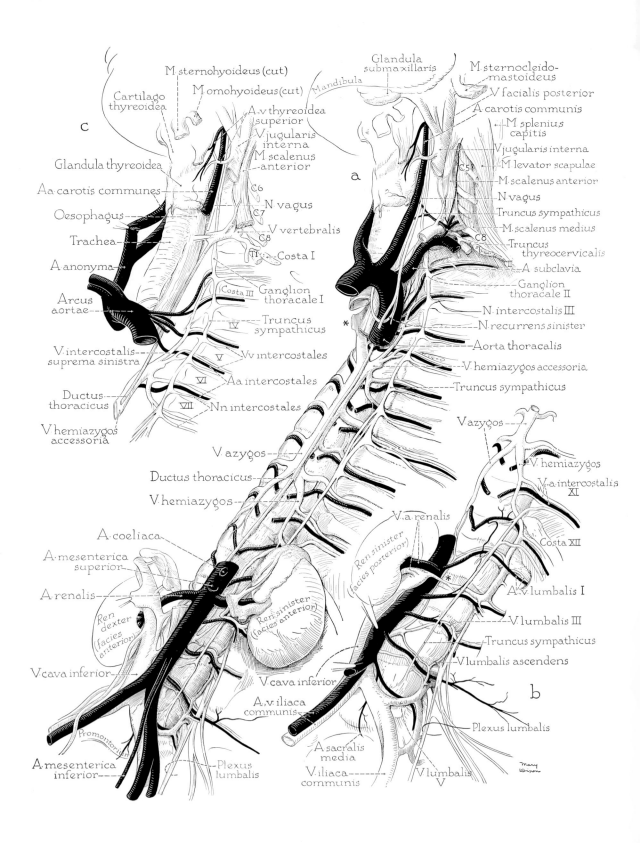

Veins of the trunk and certain of their visceral tributaries. Left side of specimen; anterolateral view. Detailed description on page 285.

Veins of the trunk: right side.

a, On the right side the clavicle and a portion of the sternum have been removed; the sternocleido-mastoid and lower segments of the infrahyoid muscles have been excised; the dissection has been carried to the level of the trachea, thyroid gland, vascular contents of the carotid sheath, subclavian vessels, the scalene muscles, and the brachial plexus.

In the thoracic division the dissection has been carried to vertebral level, thus exposing the contents of the posterior mediastinum (chiefly, the veins of the azygos system, the sympathetic trunk, and the thoracic duct). In the superior mediastinum the following structures remain: aortic arch, trachea, esophagus, and vagus nerves; the superior vena cava at the point of confluence of the innominate (NA, brachiocephalic) veins. The azygos vein has been transected (at *).

In the abdominal region the dissection has been carried to subserous level. The portions of the digestive tube have been removed, the abdominal aorta with its lumbar and renal branches retained, the prevertebral tributaries of the lumbar and ascending lumbar veins exposed, together with the inferior vena cava—for which the parietal and visceral veins are tributaries.

b, The right kidney and suprarenal gland have been drawn to the opposite side of the body to show how visceral and parietal tributaries reach the inferior vena cava, and the relationship of the segmentally arranged lumbar veins (of generally transverse course) to the ascending lumbar vein.

c, To demonstrate the interrelationship of deep structures at and near the superior aperture of the thoracic cavity, the following parts were removed: ribs, with the costal segment of the scalenus anterior muscle; the innominate veins and their tributaries (jugular, subclavian, and thyroid); the portions of the longus colli muscle that overlie the transverse processes of the sixth and seventh cervical vertebrae (in order to expose the vertebral artery); the clavicle and piece of the sternum of the specimen's left side (to show the termination of the thoracic duct).

Veins of the trunk: left side.

a, On the left side a more complete exposure is afforded than in the corresponding figure of the right side (sternum and first rib have been removed). The following deep structures are shown: the vagus nerve and its recurrent branch; the cervical sympathetic chain; the superior and inferior thyroid arteries; rami con-tributory to the brachial plexus; tracheal and bronchial rami of the inferior thyroid artery; thoracic duct.

In the thorax and abdomen the intercostal and lumbar tributaries of the azygos system are exposed, together with related arteries and nerves, and the ganglionated sympathetic trunk.

In the abdominal region the kidney and suprarenal gland appear, together with their vessels of supply. Several lumbar veins are shown, as well as the ascending lumbar vein; through the latter, as an intermediary, they communicate with the left common iliac vein.

b, The left kidney, with the suprarenal gland, has been rolled to the opposite side of the trunk on its vascular pedicle; the abdominal aorta has been retracted in order to expose components of the prevertebral plexus of veins. At second lumbar level the visceral (renal) and parietal (ascending lumbar) veins are brought into communication (at *). The left common iliac artery has been excised in order to exhibit more fully the tributaries of the corresponding vein.

c, The aortic arch has been drawn downward and to the right, to demonstrate its intercostal and related branches. The stump of the left subclavian vein has been lifted, showing the termination therein of the thoracic duct. In this way, too, the cervicothoracic segment of the sympathetic chain is revealed. The left subclavian artery has been removed from the dissection.

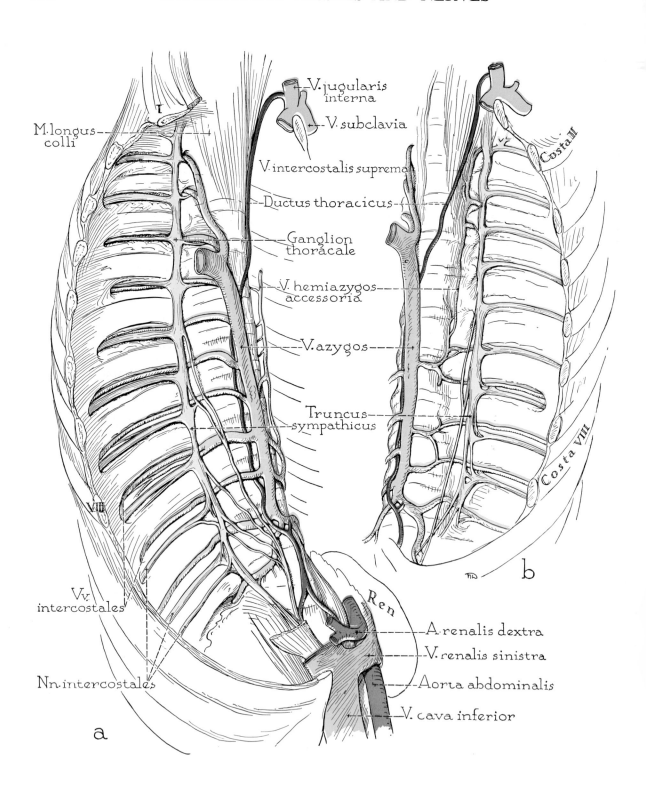

Intercostal vessels and nerves; azygos system of veins, thoracic duct, and sympathetic trunk.

a, The azygos vein and its intercostal tributaries; the ganglionated sympathetic chain and the intercostal nerves; the thoracic duct, in its course from the abdomen to the neck, where the channel terminates in the internal jugular vein. *b*, The hemiazygos vein and related structures.

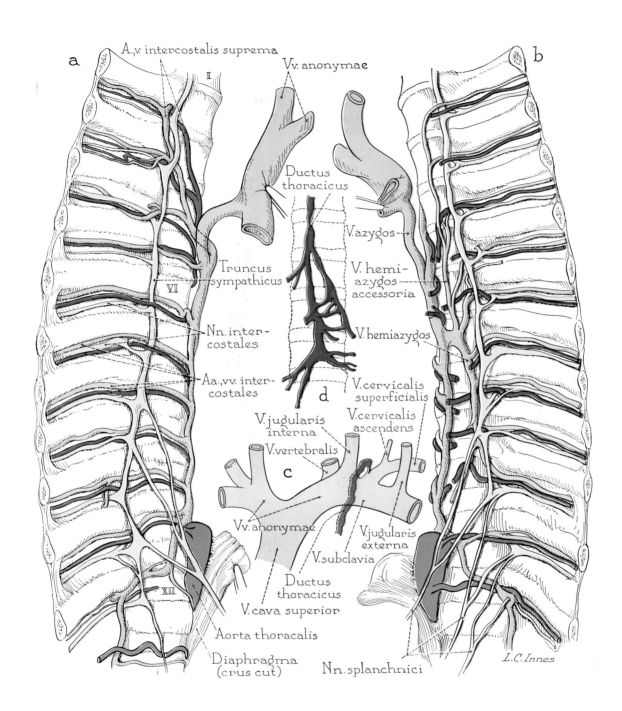

Posterior thoracic structures.

Intercostal vessels and nerves, azygos system of veins, thoracic duct, and sympathetic trunk.
a and *b*, Structures viewed from the right and left sides, respectively. *c*, The termination of the thoracic duct. *d*, The origin of the thoracic duct at lumbar level (see also pages 426 and 427).

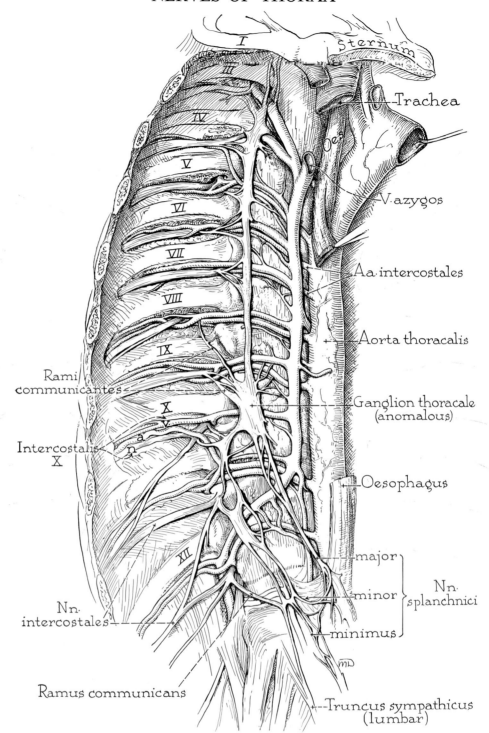

Thoracic division of the sympathetic trunk, and related posterior mediastinal and intercostal structures.

In this case the large ganglionic swelling represents a fusion of the ganglia of several thoracic segments.

There is no true sympathetic trunk. The *rami communicantes*, instead of joining a nerve in the usual location of the sympathetic chain, at the level of the necks of the ribs, pass ventrally to join a nerve trunk. This trunk occupies the usual site of the first branch of the great splanchnic nerve. The greatly elongated communicating rami levels converge in the large ganglionic mass, which lies at the level of the tenth thoracic vertebral body. There is a small accessory ganglion just caudal to the larger ganglion and adjacent to the head of the eleventh rib. A definite lesser splanchnic nerve is wanting; however, there is a least splanchnic nerve. The origin of the lumbar sympathetic chain follows the usual pattern.

The tenth intercostal artery, instead of having a separate origin from the aorta, arises as a branch of the eleventh intercostal artery, passing forward over the head of the eleventh rib. The azygos vein is of normal configuration, as are the remaining intercostal arteries; but the eighth intercostal vein takes an anomalous turn about the eighth intercostal nerve.

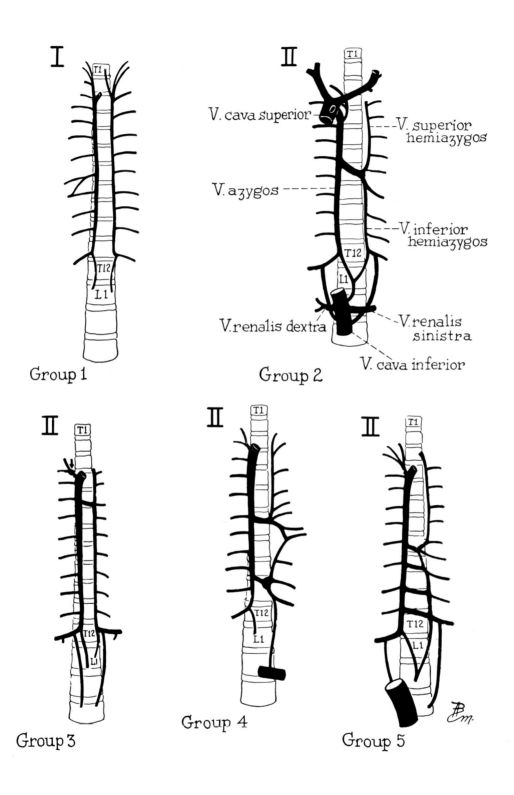

Azygos system of veins. Types encountered in 100 consecutive specimens. Detailed description on page 291.

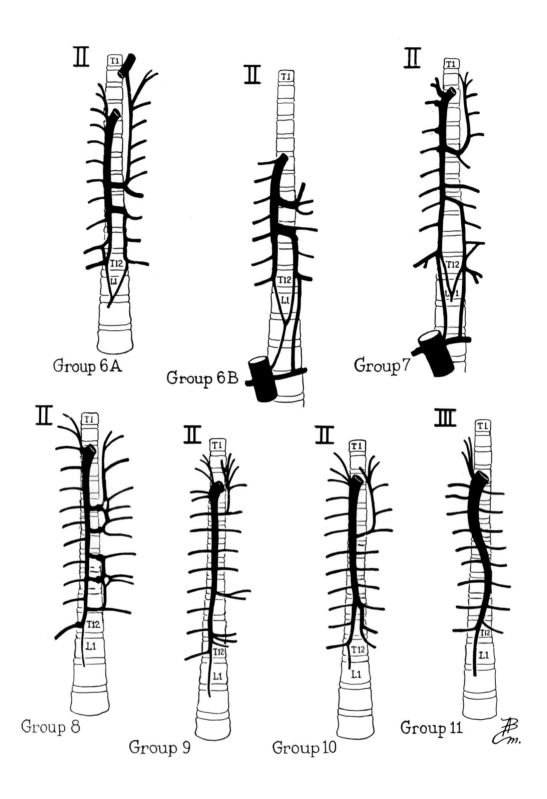

Azygos system of veins. Types, continued. Detailed description on page 291.

The patterns of the azygos system of veins fall into 3 main types. One variety, the primitive and embryological form, consisted of 2 separate, parallel vessels lying along the lateral anterior border of the vertebral column in the posterior mediastinum. The second type (which comprised the major portion of all specimens) consisted of a series of gradations from a pattern having a single communication between the azygos and hemiazygos systems to multiple retroaortic communications. In the third variety, a single azygos vein occupied the midline of the anterior surface of the thoracic vertebrae.

Type I, Group 1 consists of 2 completely separate, parallel ascending veins: the azygos on the right, and the inferior and superior azygos on the left in continuity, draining from the left lumbar vein to the left innominate. The left intercostals were the only tributaries to the vessel. This pattern occurred in 1 per cent of subjects.

In Type II the variations show a progressive approach to Type III. Groups 1 and 11 make up Types I and III, respectively. They represent the extremes of the 100 anatomical patterns. Only one example of each was found in all the dissections.

Type II consists of Groups 2 to 10, which make 98 per cent of the total. The specimens in Groups 2 to 5 are characterized by the presence of 2 ascending veins running parallel without any vertical break; they receive an increasing number of midline horizontal connections (retroaortic anastomoses) as they approach Group 5. These connections occur most frequently at the eighth vertebral level and gradually lessen in frequency as the upper and lower extremes are reached.

In the remaining groups of Type II, 6 to 10, the trunk of the left side is broken, the horizontal connections reduced in number.

(Illustrations reproduced with the permission of Surgery, Gynecology and Obstetrics.)

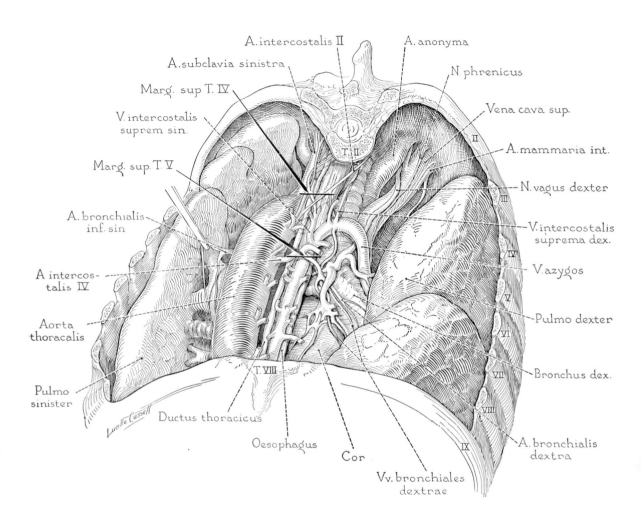

Structures in the posterior mediastinum, especially the arteries of supply to the bronchi.

The aorta and the azygos vein are intact; the intercostal branches of the aorta and the intercostal tributaries of the azygos vein have been transected. The bronchial arteries have been freed from the left and right bronchi. For topographical purposes, the levels of the superior margins of the fourth and fifth thoracic vertebrae are indicated.

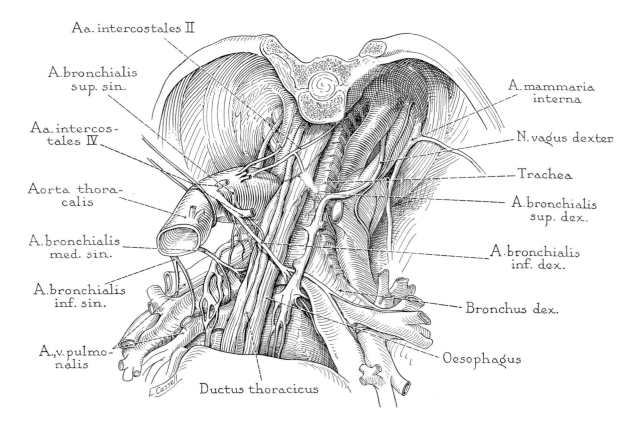

Aa. intercostales II

A.bronchialis sup. sin.

Aa. intercostales IV

Aorta thoracalis

A.bronchialis med. sin.

A.bronchialis inf. sin.

A.,v. pulmonalis

L.Cassell

Ductus thoracicus

A. mammaria interna

N. vagus dexter

Trachea

A.bronchialis sup. dex.

A. bronchialis inf. dex.

Bronchus dex.

Oesophagus

Structures in the posterior mediastinum; deeper dissection of the same specimen.

The thoracic aorta has been transected and drawn to the left side; the azygos vein has been removed. By these means it is demonstrated that the bronchial arteries arise in series with the aortic intercostal. The bronchial arteries follow the bronchi in their inferolateral descent.

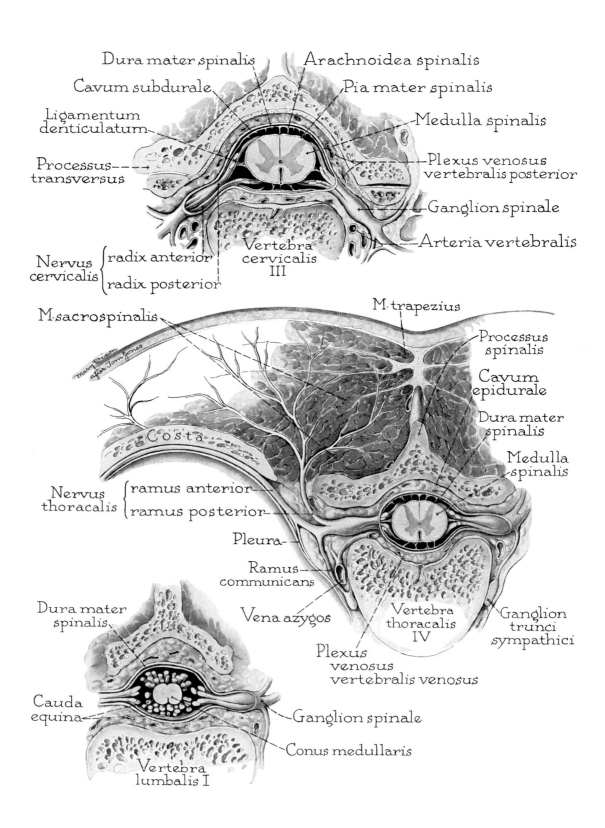

Transverse sections through the spinal cord at cervical, thoracic, and lumbar levels.

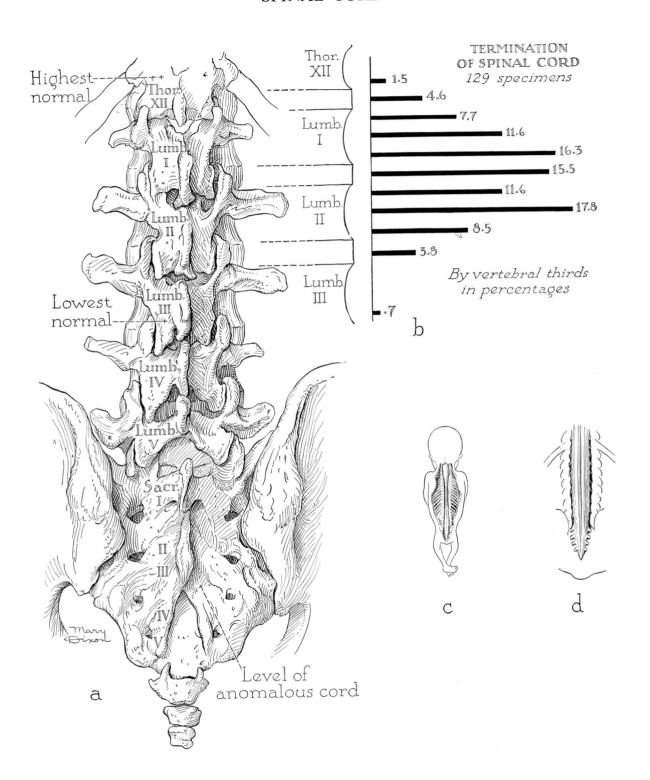

Vertebral level of termination of the spinal cord. Variation in the adult; fetal position.

a, Posterior aspect of the lumbosacral vertebral column in an adult. *b*, Graph, recording point of termination of the spinal cord in 129 specimens. *c*, Posterior aspect of the spinal cord, exposed by laminectomy, in a fetus of two and a half months. *d*, Lumbosacral area of the same specimen. The spinal cord occupies the entire length of the vertebral canal.

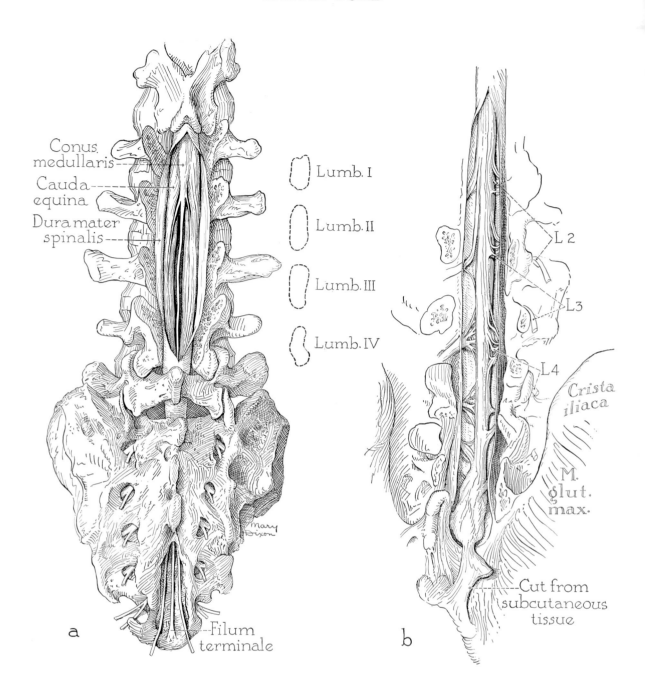

Vertebral level of termination of the spinal cord. Normal and anomalous position.

a, Posterior aspect of a normal spinal cord in an adult, exposed by laminectomy. The spinal cord proper ends opposite the first lumbar vertebra, while the terminal filament is prolonged to a coccygeal attachment. To the right of the figure the positions of the spinous processes are recorded by horizontal projection; each is caudal to the level of the corresponding vertebral body.

b, Posterior view of an anomalous spinal cord in an adult. The cord, ending in a bulbous mass, reaches the level of the third sacral piece; a distal tag (cut), passing through a hiatus at the usual site of the middle sacral crest, becomes continuous with subcutaneous tissue.

With the exception of this single specimen in a series of 129 adults, the point of termination of the spinal cord ranged from the lower third of the twelfth thoracic vertebra to the middle third of the third lumbar. In 95 per cent of the cases the spinal cord terminated within the territory of the upper two lumbar vertebrae.

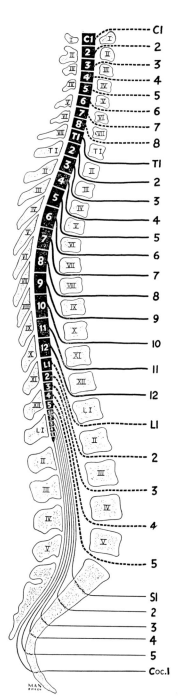

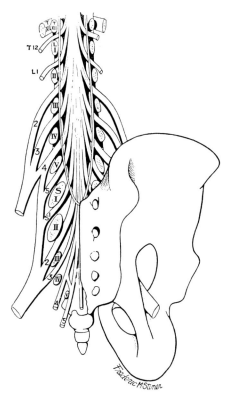

Left. Alignment of spinal segments with vertebrae.

The bodies and spinous processes are indicated by Roman numerals, the spinal segments and their roots by Arabic. The cervical roots cranial to the level of C8 emerge from the vertebral canal through intervertebral foramina above their respective vertebral bodies. The others issue caudal to these bodies, and with an increasing interval as the coccygeal nerve is approached: T1 through the length of one vertebra; L1, two and a half; S1, seven and a half; Coc 1, through the length of ten.

Right. Relation of the roots of the cauda equina to vertebrae.

The pedicles of vertebrae are indicated by Roman numerals, the spinal nerves by Arabic. Before extending through an intervertebral foramen a given root passes close to the next higher intervertebral disc. Landmarks of the pelvis as they pertain to the vertebral column and spinal roots also are indicated. (From Haymaker and Woodhall: Peripheral Nerve Injuries. 1956.)

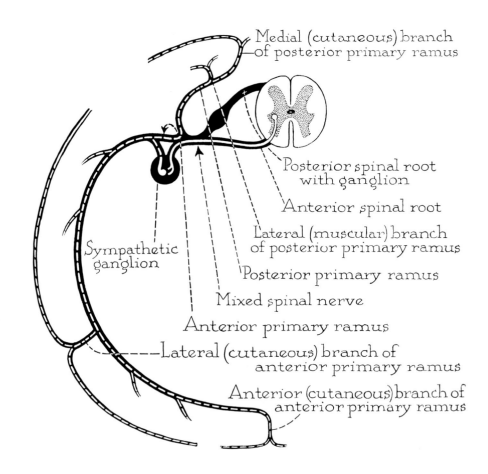

Medial (cutaneous) branch
of posterior primary ramus

Posterior spinal root
with ganglion

Anterior spinal root

Lateral (muscular) branch
of posterior primary ramus

Posterior primary ramus

Mixed spinal nerve

Anterior primary ramus

Lateral (cutaneous) branch of
anterior primary ramus

Anterior (cutaneous) branch of
anterior primary ramus

Sympathetic
ganglion

Typical spinal nerve; root-sources, branches, and cutaneous rami, shown schematically.

An anterior and posterior nerve root attach each nerve to the spinal cord. The anterior (ventral) nerve roots, which are purely motor, emerge in series from the anterior column of gray matter. The posterior (dorsal) nerve roots, which are purely sensory, enter the cord in series on its posterolateral aspect. On each posterior root is a ganglion, the cells of which give origin to central and peripheral fibers. Within or near the intervertebral foramen each pair of nerve roots unite to form a spinal nerve, which then contains both motor and sensory fibers. Each nerve divides into posterior and anterior primary rami. From the anterior ramus are derived lateral and anterior branches. Just distal to the point of division each typical spinal nerve sends communications to a sympathetic ganglion.

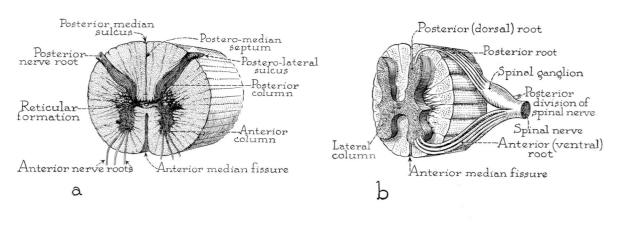

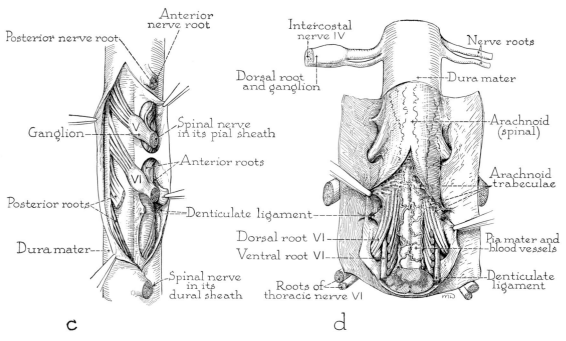

Spinal cord, nerve roots, and meninges.

a, Transverse section through the cord, showing columns, roots, and sulci.

b, A segment of the cord, schematized. The grey columns are carried beyond the level of the section; the origin of each root is shown, as well as the manner in which the anterior and posterior roots join to form a spinal nerve.

c, The membranes of the spinal cord and the mode of origin of the nerves.

d, The membranes and the spaces enclosed between them.

Adapted from familiar sources: *a* and *b* from Gray; *c* from Cunningham; *d* from Mettler.

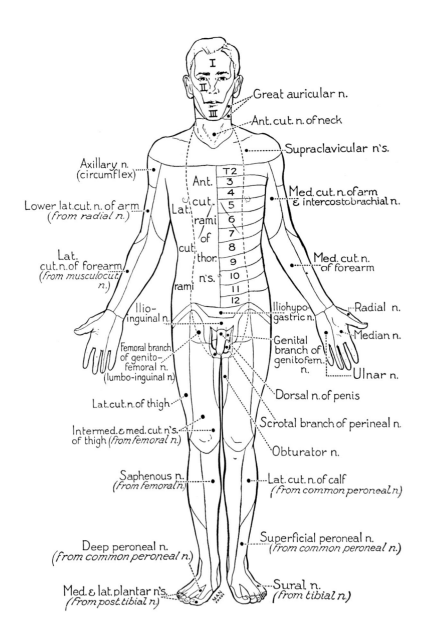

Cutaneous fields of peripheral nerves from the anterior aspect.

The numbers on the left side of the trunk refer to the intercostal nerves. On the right side are shown the cutaneous fields of the lateral and medial branches of the anterior primary rami. The asterisk just beneath the scrotum is in the field of the posterior cutaneous nerve of the thigh. (From Haymaker and Woodhall: Peripheral Nerve Injuries 1956.)

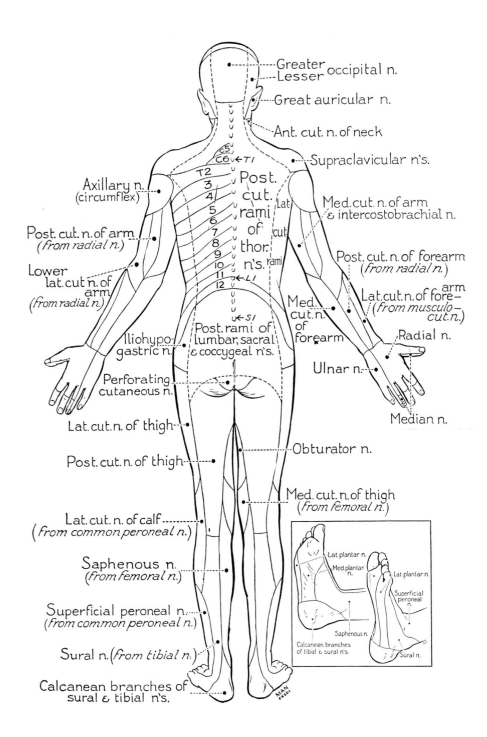

Cutaneous fields of peripheral nerves from the posterior aspect.

The boundaries of cutaneous supply of the posterior primary rami are indicated by broken lines. The designation, *Post. cut. rami of thor. n's.*, refers to the cutaneous branches of the posterior primary rami; *Lat. cut. rami* indicates the distribution from the lateral branches of the anterior primary rami. For purposes of orientation the spinous processes of the first thoracic (T1), the first lumbar (L1), and the first sacral (S1) vertebrae are indicated by arrows. (From Haymaker and Woodhall: Peripheral Nerve Injuries. 1956.)

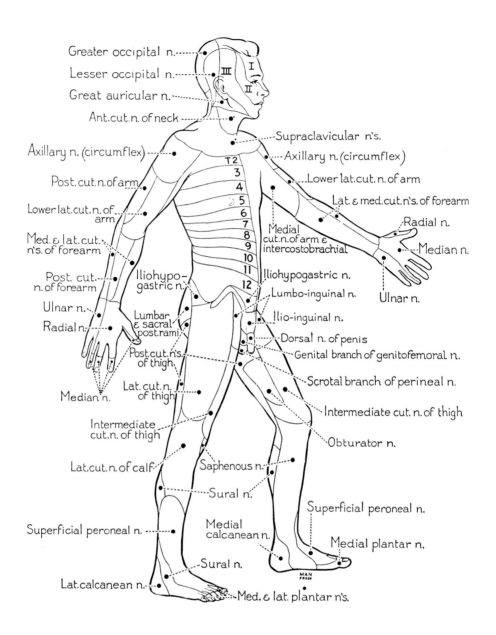

Greater occipital n.

Lesser occipital n.

Great auricular n.

Ant.cut.n. of neck

Axillary n. (circumflex)

Post. cut.n. of arm

Lower lat.cut.n. of arm

Med. & lat.cut. n's. of forearm

Post. cut. n. of forearm

Ulnar n.

Radial n.

Iliohypo-gastric n.

Lumbar & sacral post.rami

Median n.

Post.cut.n's. of thigh

Lat.cut.n. of thigh

Intermediate cut.n. of thigh

Lat.cut.n. of calf

Superficial peroneal n.

Lat.calcanean n.

III I
II

T2
3
4
5
6
7
8
9
10
11
12

Supraclavicular n's.

Axillary n. (circumflex)

Lower lat.cut.n. of arm

Lat. & med.cut.n's. of forearm

Radial n.

Median n.

Medial cut.n.of arm & intercostobrachial

Iliohypogastric n.

Ulnar n.

Lumbo-inguinal n.

Ilio-inguinal n.

Dorsal n. of penis

Genital branch of genitofemoral n.

Scrotal branch of perineal n.

Intermediate cut. n. of thigh

Obturator n.

Saphenous n.

Sural n.

Superficial peroneal n.

Medial plantar n.

Medial calcanean n.

Sural n.

Med. & lat. plantar n's.

MAN FRED

Cutaneous fields of peripheral nerves from the lateral aspect.

The face and anterior half of the head are innervated by the three divisions of the trigeminal: I, ophthalmic; II, maxillary; III, mandibular. The fields of the intercostal nerves are indicated by numerals. The unlabeled cutaneous field between great and second toe is supplied by the deep peroneal nerve. (From Haymaker and Woodhall: Peripheral Nerve Injuries. 1956.)

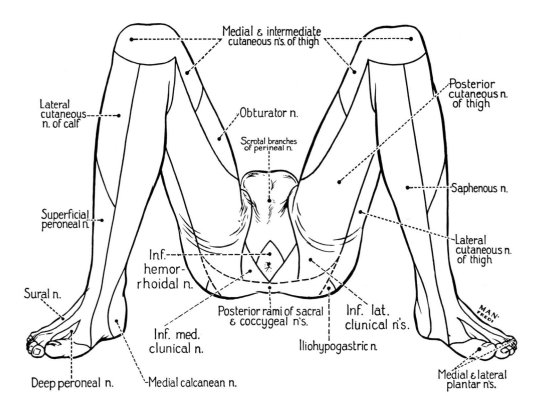

Peripheral nerve fields of the perineum and limbs. (From Haymaker and Woodhall: Peripheral Nerve Injuries. 1956.)

SPINAL SEGMENTS

	C1	C2	C3	C4	C5	C6	C7	C8	T1
Sternomastoid*									
Trapezius*									
Levator scapulae									
Teres minor									
Supraspinatus									
Rhomboids									
Infraspinatus									
Deltoid									
Teres major									
Biceps									
Brachialis									
Serratus anterior									
Subscapularis									
Pectoralis major									
Pectoralis minor									
Coraco-brachialis									
Latissimus dorsi									
Anconeus									
Triceps									

SPINAL SEGMENTS

	C5	C6	C7	C8	T1
Brachioradialis					
Supinator					
Pronator teres					
Ext. carpi radial. longus & brevis					
Flexor carpi ulnaris					
Flexor carpi radialis					
Ext. digitorum					
Ext. carpi ulnaris					
Ext. indicis					
Ext. digiti 5					
Ext. pollic. longus					
Ext. pollic. brevis					
Abductor pollicis longus					
Palmaris longus					
Pronator quadratus					
Flexor digitorum sublimis					
Flexor digitorum profundus					
Flexor pollicis longus					
Opponens pollicis					
Abduct. pollic. brevis					
Flexor pollicis brevis					
Palmaris brevis					
Adductor pollicis					
Flexor digiti 5					
Abductor digiti 5					
Opponens digiti 5					
Interossei					
Lumbricals					

Tabulation recording the segmental innervation of the muscles of the neck, shoulder, arm, forearm, and hand.

The asterisks indicate an additional supply from the accessory nerve. A line bisecting a segment indicates that the muscle receives minor innervation from that segment. (From Haymaker and Woodhall: Peripheral Nerve Injuries. 1956.)

SPINAL SEGMENTS

Upper table (L4–S2), leg and foot muscles:

Tibialis anterior, Popliteus, Plantaris, Peroneus tertius, Extensor digitorum longus, Abductor hallucis, Flexor digitorum brevis, Flexor hallucis brevis, Extensor hallucis brevis, Flexor digitorum longus, Peroneus longus, Peroneus brevis, Tibialis posterior, Flexor hallucis longus, Extensor hallucis longus, Soleus, Gastrocnemius, Extensor digitorum brevis, Flexor digitorum accessorius, Adductor hallucis, Abductor digiti quinti, Flexor digiti quinti brevis, Interossei, Lumbricals

Lower table (L1–S2), hip and thigh muscles:

Iliopsoas, Gracilis, Sartorius, Pectineus, Adductor longus, Adductor brevis, Adductor minimus, Quadriceps femoris, Adductor magnus, Obturator externus, Tensor fasciae latae, Gluteus medius, Gluteus minimus, Quadratus femoris, Gemelli, Semitendinosus, Semimembranosus, Piriformis, Obturator internus, Biceps femoris, Gluteus maximus

Tabulation recording the segmental innervation of the muscles of the hip, thigh, leg, and foot. (From Haymaker and Woodhall: Peripheral Nerve Injuries. 1956.)

A line bisecting a segment indicates that the muscle receives minor innervation from that segment.

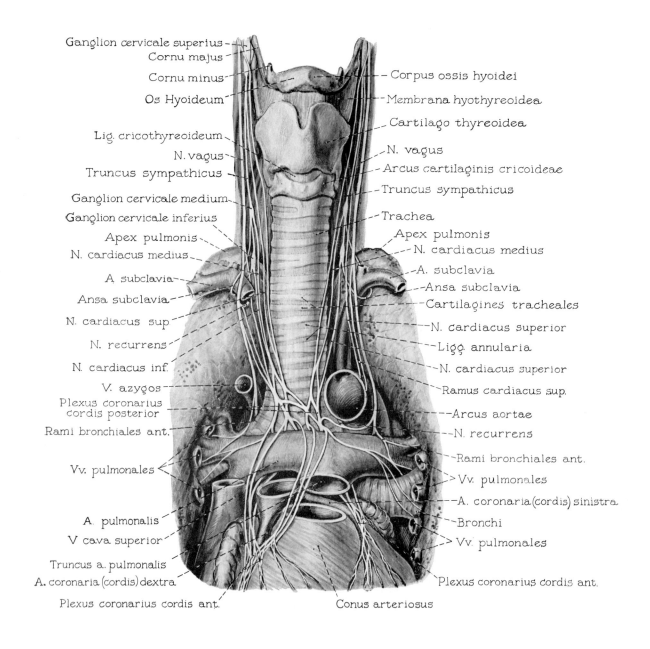

Ganglion cervicale superius
Cornu majus
Cornu minus
Os Hyoideum
Lig. cricothyreoideum
N. vagus
Truncus sympathicus
Ganglion cervicale medium
Ganglion cervicale inferius
Apex pulmonis
N. cardiacus medius
A. subclavia
Ansa subclavia
N. cardiacus sup
N. recurrens
N. cardiacus inf.
V. azygos
Plexus coronarius cordis posterior
Rami bronchiales ant.
Vv. pulmonales
A. pulmonalis
V cava superior
Truncus a. pulmonalis
A. coronaria (cordis) dextra
Plexus coronarius cordis ant.

Corpus ossis hyoidei
Membrana hyothyreoidea
Cartilago thyreoidea
N. vagus
Arcus cartilaginis cricoideae
Truncus sympathicus
Trachea
Apex pulmonis
N. cardiacus medius
A. subclavia
Ansa subclavia
Cartilagines tracheales
N. cardiacus superior
Ligg. annularia
N. cardiacus superior
Ramus cardiacus sup.
Arcus aortae
N. recurrens
Rami bronchiales ant.
Vv. pulmonales
A. coronaria (cordis) sinistra
Bronchi
Vv. pulmonales
Plexus coronarius cordis ant.

Conus arteriosus

Autonomic nerves and related structures of the neck and thorax.

Emphasizing the source, course, and coronary termination of the cardiac nerves.
(From Warren: Handbook of Anatomy, Harvard University Press.)

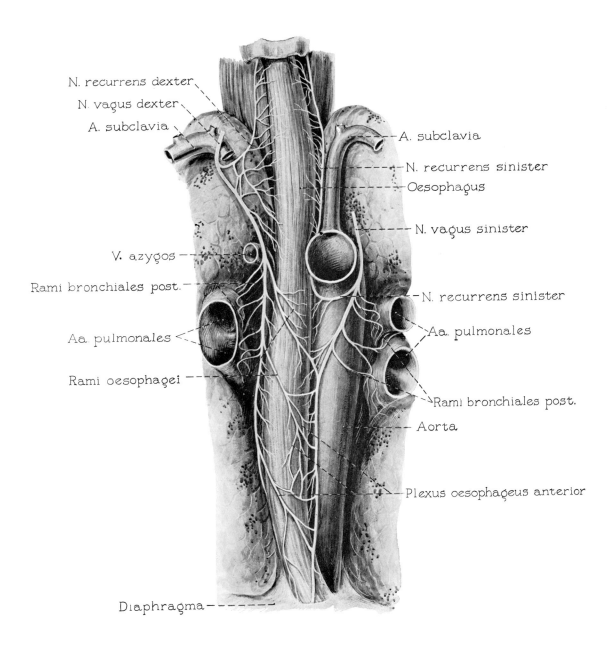

N. recurrens dexter

N. vagus dexter

A. subclavia

A. subclavia

N. recurrens sinister

Oesophagus

N. vagus sinister

V. azygos

Rami bronchiales post.

N. recurrens sinister

Aa. pulmonales

Aa. pulmonales

Rami oesophagei

Rami bronchiales post.

Aorta

Plexus oesophageus anterior

Diaphragma

Vagus nerves, with their rami to the bronchi and esophagus.
(From Warren: Handbook of Anatomy, Harvard University Press.)

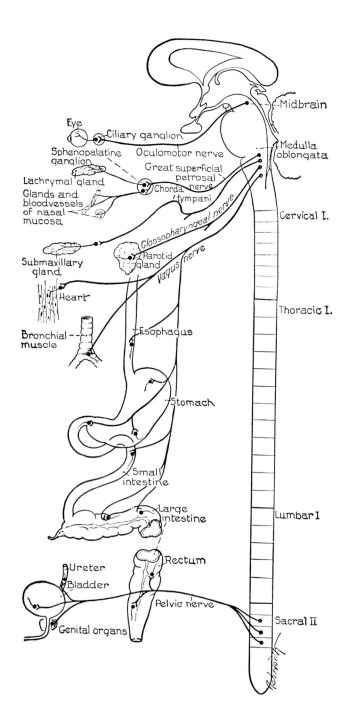

Craniosacral autonomic connections; schematic. (Larsell: Anatomy of the Nervous System.
Appleton-Century-Crofts, Inc.)

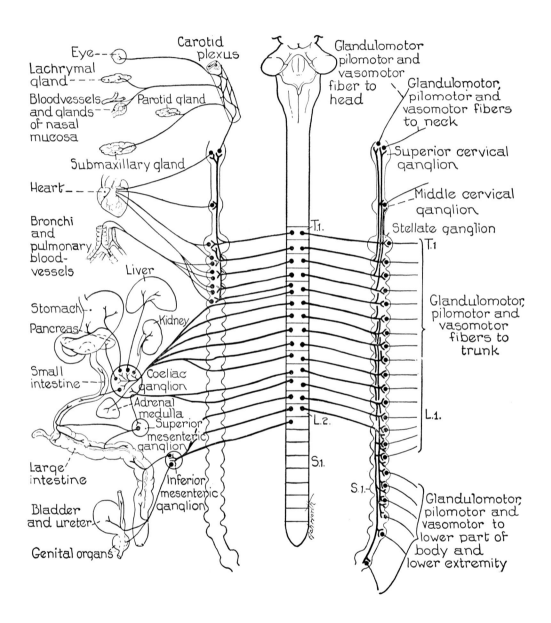

Thoracolumbar autonomic connections; schematic. Showing those to the internal viscera and the head on the left side, and those to the periphery on the right side. (Larsell: Anatomy of the Nervous System. Appleton-Century-Crofts, Inc.)

Section Six

THE ABDOMEN

MUSCLES OF THE ABDOMEN: SEVEN STAGES IN DISSECTION........................ 313–319

MUSCLES OF THE ABDOMEN AND THORAX...................................... 320

PERITONEUM AND VISCERA *in situ*.. 321

ABDOMINAL MUSCLES; SEMISCHEMATIC....................................... 322

RECTUS ABDOMINIS MUSCLE AND SHEATH.................................... 323–325

NERVES OF THE ABDOMINAL WALL... 326–327

APONEUROTIC CONTINUITIES, ABDOMEN TO THIGH: SIX STAGES IN DISSECTION...... 328–331

INGUINAL REGION OF THE FEMALE: SIX STAGES IN DISSECTION.................... 332–333

SPERMATIC CORD AND INGUINAL CANAL: FOUR STAGES IN DISSECTION............. 334

PYRAMIDALIS MUSCLE; TYPES.. 335

ABDOMINAL MUSCLES; TYPES OF LAYERING: FIVE EXAMPLES..................... 336–339

INGUINAL LAYERS; VARIATIONS IN EXTENT: RECORDS, SHOWN SCHEMATICALLY...... 340

ABDOMINAL WALL FROM WITHIN: FIVE STAGES IN DISSECTION.................... 341–343

UMBILICAL REGION; EMBRYONIC AND ADULT.................................. 344

ABDOMINAL WALL... 345

INGUINAL LAYERS IN HERNIATION.. 346–352

DEVELOPMENT OF THE MESENTERIES.. 353–356

PERITONEAL CAVITY... 357–358

ABDOMINAL VISCERA AND THEIR BLOOD SUPPLY: SIX STAGES IN DISSECTION........ 359–365

ABDOMINAL VISCERA, MESENTERIES, AND BLOOD VESSELS: SIX STAGES IN DISSECTION.. 366–372

SYMPATHETIC PLEXUSES OF THE ABDOMEN................................... 373–374

ABDOMINAL VISCERA; VARIATIONS IN POSITION.............................. 375

STOMACH; VARIATIONS IN FORM: NINETEEN SELECTED EXAMPLES................. 376

LIVER; VARIATIONS IN FORM: SEVENTEEN EXAMPLES.......................... 377

LIVER AND GALLBLADDER... 378–382

STOMACH.. 383

DUODENUM, PANCREAS, AND GALLBLADDER................................... 384

DUODENUM; VARIATION IN FORM AND POSITION: EIGHT SELECTED EXAMPLES........ 385

SPLEEN... 386

CECUM AND VERMIFORM PROCESS; VARIATIONS: TWELVE SELECTED EXAMPLES........ 387–389

311

(Continued)

CECUM AND ASCENDING COLON; VARIATIONS IN ATTACHMENT: EIGHTEEN SELECTED EXAMPLES, SHOWN SCHEMATICALLY... 390

CECUM... 391

ARTERIES OF THE STOMACH, LIVER, AND GALLBLADDER......................... 392

CYSTIC ARTERY; VARIATIONS: TWELVE EXAMPLES, SHOWN SCHEMATICALLY........ 393

HEPATIC PEDICLE; VARIATIONS: TEN SELECTED EXAMPLES...................... 394–395

GALLBLADDER; VARIATIONS: FOURTEEN SELECTED EXAMPLES.................... 396

GASTRIC, DUODENAL, AND PANCREATIC ARTERIES............................. 397–399

INTESTINAL ARTERIES.. 400–401

CECAL AND COLIC ARTERIES... 402–403

SUPERIOR MESENTERIC ARTERY; VARIATIONS: TEN EXAMPLES, SHOWN SCHEMATICALLY. 404–405

APPENDICEAL ARTERIES; VARIATIONS: NINE EXAMPLES, SHOWN SCHEMATICALLY.... 406

INFERIOR MESENTERIC ARTERY; VARIATIONS: SEVEN TYPES, SHOWN SCHEMATICALLY.. 407

KIDNEY AND URETER.. 408

GENITOURINARY TRACT.. 409

SUPRARENAL AND RENAL ARTERIES.. 410

INFERIOR PHRENIC ARTERY; VARIATIONS: EIGHT SELECTED TYPES.............. 411

RENAL FORM, POSITION, AND BLOOD SUPPLY; VARIATIONS: TWENTY SELECTED EXAMPLES... 412–417

RELATIONS OF THE KIDNEYS... 418

VERTEBRAL LEVELS OF THE KIDNEYS; VARIATIONS: TABULATION, 194 SPECIMENS...... 419

RENAL VEINS AND THEIR COMMUNICATIONS................................ 420–421

LUMBAR AND RELATED VEINS.. 422–423

INFERIOR VENA CAVA; VARIATIONS....................................... 424

INFERIOR PHRENIC AND LUMBAR ARTERIES................................. 425

THORACIC DUCT AND CISTERNA CHYLI; VARIATIONS: TWELVE SELECTED EXAMPLES... 426–427

LUMBAR PLEXUS.. 428

LUMBOSACRAL PLEXUS.. 429

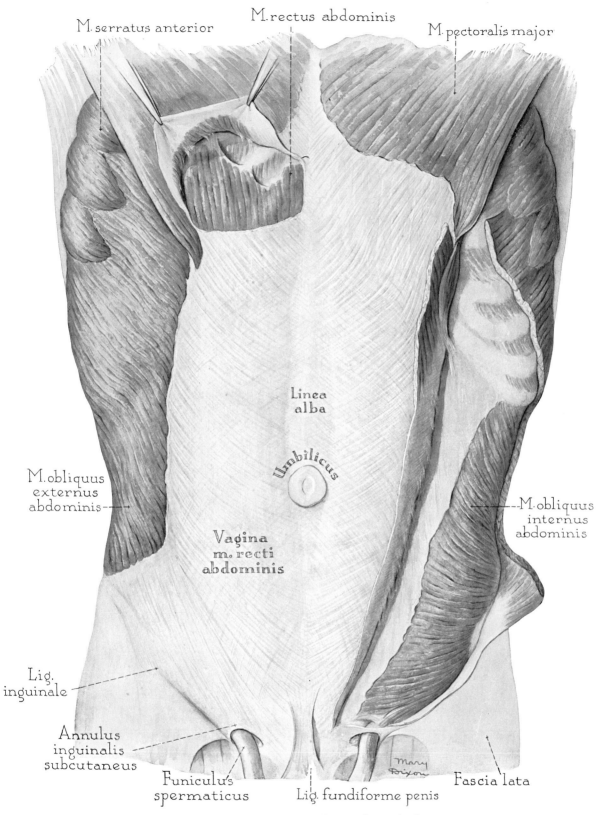

M. serratus anterior

M. rectus abdominis

M. pectoralis major

Linea alba

Umbilicus

M. obliquus externus abdominis

M. obliquus internus abdominis

Vagina m. recti abdominis

Lig. inguinale

Annulus inguinalis subcutaneus

Funiculus spermaticus

Lig. fundiforme penis

Fascia lata

Anterolateral abdominal musculature; from the front.

On the reader's left the external oblique is intact; on the right it has been reflected to expose the internal oblique muscle. The deep investing fascia has been removed from both muscles. Rectus sheath has been opened superiorly.

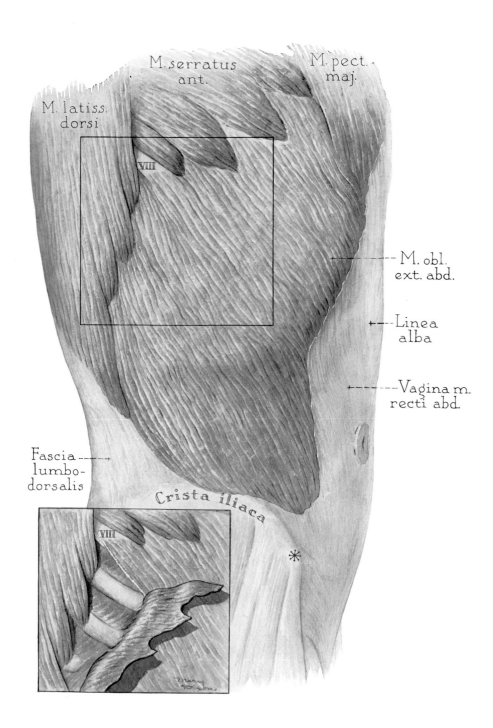

Abdominal musculature; first layer, from the side.

Showing the form and extent of the external oblique muscle and of the rectus sheath. The eighth rib is seen (at VIII); the anterior superior spine of the ilium is marked by *. Inset: The external oblique has been reflected along the line of the digitations, which interdigitate with those of the latissimus dorsi muscle. The area represented in the inset is outlined in the main figure.

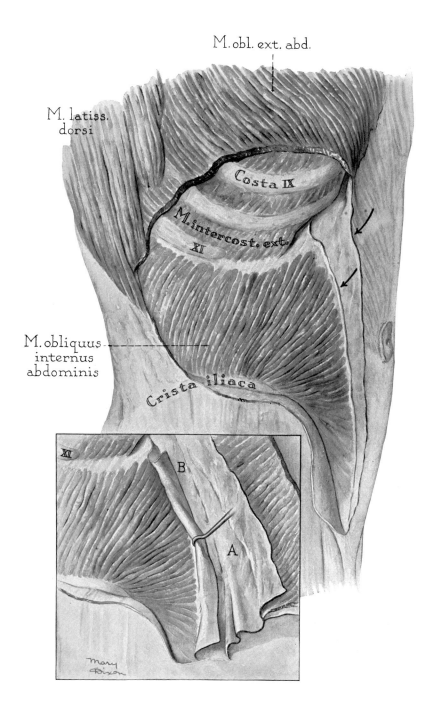

Second layer of anterolateral abdominal musculature.

The external oblique has been largely removed to expose the subjacent internal oblique. Upper arrow points to the line along which the aponeurosis of the external oblique fuses medially with that of the internal oblique; lower arrow indicates the line along which the internal oblique becomes aponeurotic (up to which the outer investing fascia has been removed). Inset: The internal oblique and the external oblique (reflected forward). A indicates the aponeurosis of the latter; B marks that of the former muscle. The apposed fascial layers of the two strata have been freed from their respective muscles.

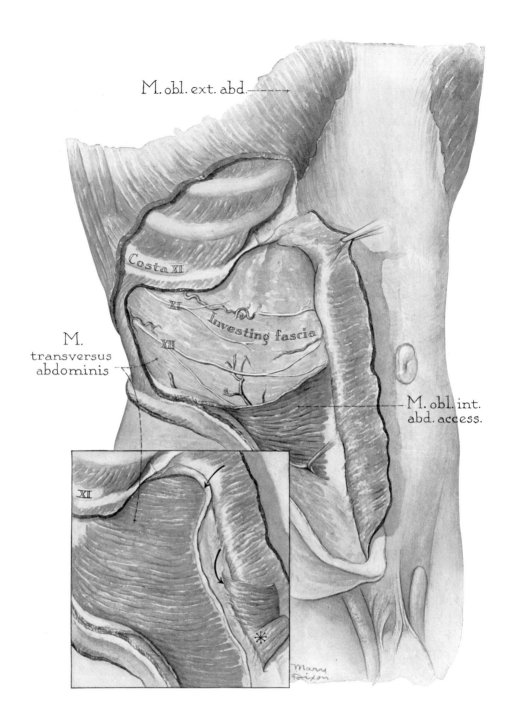

Third layer of anterolateral abdominal musculature.

Showing the accessory muscle and the outer investing fascia of the transverse abdominal muscle. The eleventh and twelfth intercostal nerves (labelled XI and XII) have been freed from the fascia, as have also (unlabelled) intercostal arteries and upward-directed branches of the deep circumflex artery. Inset: The accessory internal oblique muscle (at *) has been reflected along the line (at lower arrow) of its continuity with the aponeurosis of the transverse abdominal muscle; the fascia has been removed from the transverse abdominal to the point (at upper arrow) at which fleshy fibers give way to aponeurosis.

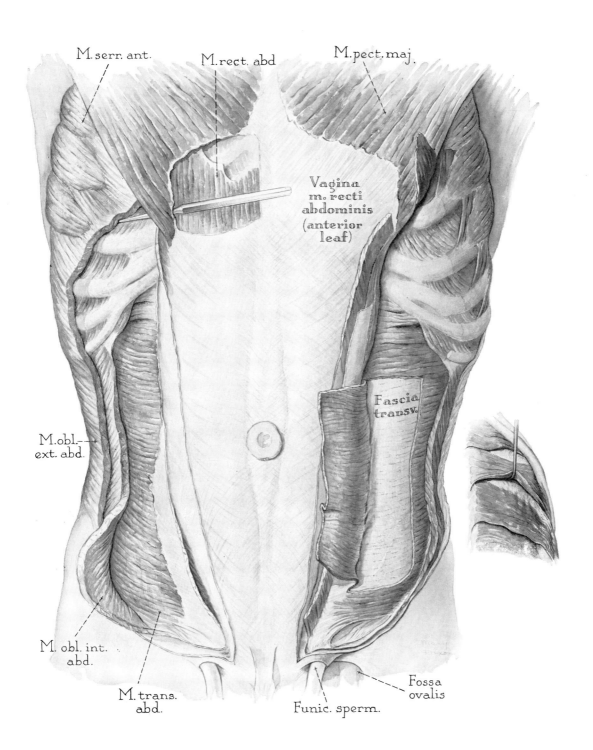

Third layer of lateral abdominal musculature.

On reader's right the transverse abdominal muscle has been reflected to expose internal investing (transversalis) fascia. On left, anterior leaf of rectus sheath on one side has been partially removed. Inset: Costal slips of origin of transverse abdominal muscle.

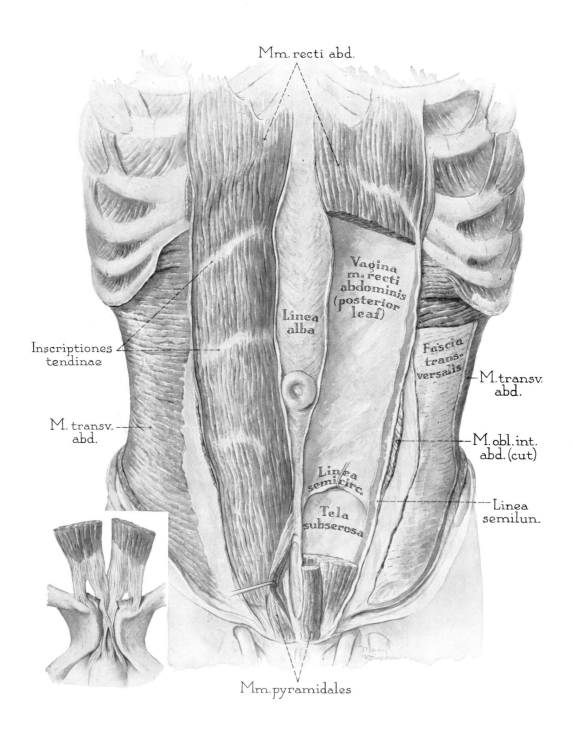

Mm. recti abd.

Inscriptiones
tendinae

M. transv.
abd.

Linea
alba

Vagina
m. recti
abdominis
(posterior
leaf)

Fascia
trans-
versalis

M. transv.
abd.

M. obl. int.
abd. (cut)

Linea
semicirc.

Tela
subserosa

Linea
semilun.

Mm. pyramidales

Anterior and lateral abdominal muscles.

The transversus abdominis muscle (left) and the transversalis fascia (right) are more fully exposed. The rectus sheath has been opened on each side. On the reader's left the rectus muscle is intact; on the right it has been largely removed to expose the posterior leaf of the sheath. Inset: Pubic attachments of the recti (pyramidal muscles cut).

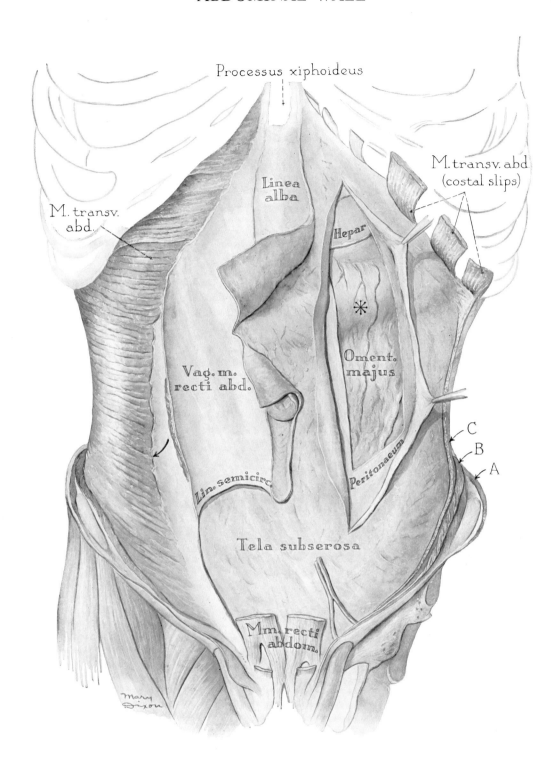

Deep abdominal layers and the abdominal contents.

The subserous layer is exposed on the reader's right half of the abdomen, on the left side in the area caudal to the semicircular line of the rectus sheath and, in the midline, under the transected linea alba. The subserous and serous layers have been incised vertically to expose the liver and greater omentum. The transverse colon (at *) lies beneath the omentum. A, External oblique muscle; B, internal oblique; C, transverse abdominal; arrow indicates the margin of the latter's aponeurosis.

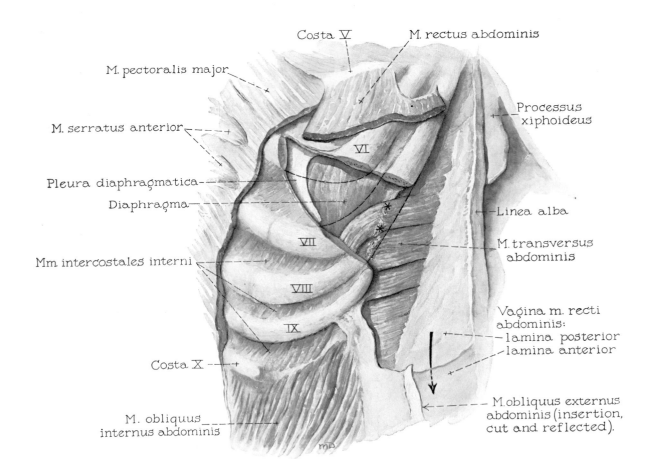

Costa V — M. rectus abdominis

M. pectoralis major

M. serratus anterior

Pleura diaphragmatica

Diaphragma

Mm. intercostales interni

Costa X

M. obliquus internus abdominis

Processus xiphoideus

Linea alba

M. transversus abdominis

Vagina m. recti abdominis:
—lamina posterior
—lamina anterior

M. obliquus externus abdominis (insertion, cut and reflected).

VI

VII

VIII

IX

mD

Muscles at the costal margin.

The outermost stratum of musculature consists of the pectoralis major, serratus anterior, and external oblique. This composite layer, together with the rectus abdominis, has been removed to expose the lower ribs, the intercostal muscles, and the internal oblique. Cutting away segments of sixth, seventh, and eighth ribs reveals the diaphragm, its pleural investment, and the costal attachments of the transverse abdominal muscles (line of fusion indicated by **). The posterior and anterior laminae of the rectus sheath are demonstrated by cutting away the cranial part of the latter layer. The arrow enters the sheath, from which the muscle has been removed.

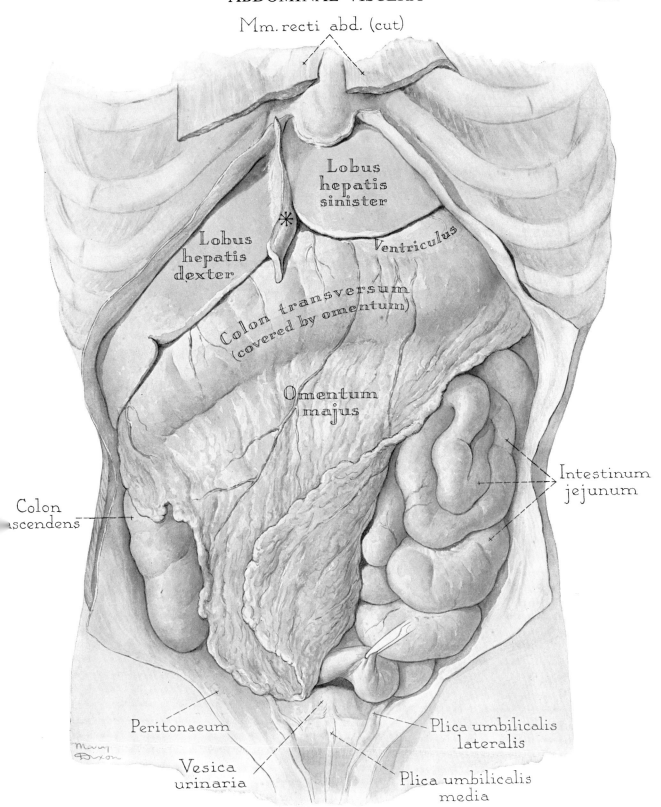

Mm. recti abd. (cut)

Lobus hepatis sinister

Lobus hepatis dexter

Ventriculus

*

Colon transversum (covered by omentum)

Omentum majus

Intestinum jejunum

Colon ascendens

Peritonaeum

Vesica urinaria

Plica umbilicalis lateralis

Plica umbilicalis media

Abdominal viscera, *in situ.*

The greater omentum is turned medialward to reveal the coils of jejunum; the falciform ligament (at *) has been cut from its parietal attachment.

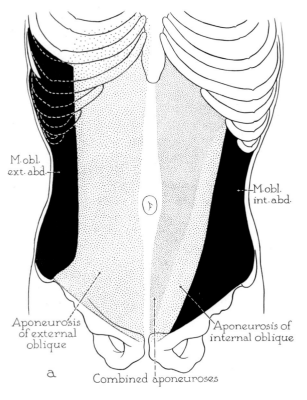

M.obl.
ext. abd.

M.obl.
int.abd.

Aponeurosis
of external
oblique

Aponeurosis of
internal oblique

a

Combined aponeuroses

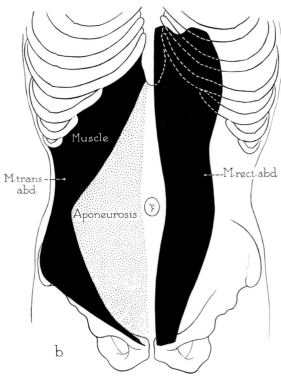

Muscle

M.trans.
abd.

M.rect.abd.

Aponeurosis

b

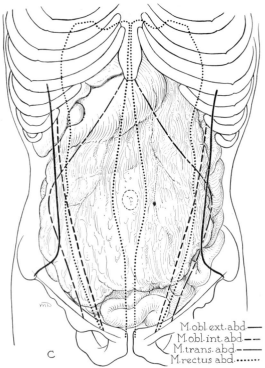

M.obl.ext.abd.——
M.obl.int.abd.---
M.trans.abd.-·-·
M.rectus abd.·······

c

Anterolateral muscles and aponeuroses of the abdominal wall, and their relation to the subjacent abdominal contents. Semidiagrammatic. Prepared from dissections illustrated in the preceding figures.

In *a* and *b* the muscles are shown in black; the aponeurotic areas are stippled. In *c* the margins of the muscles are indicated by lines (see key).

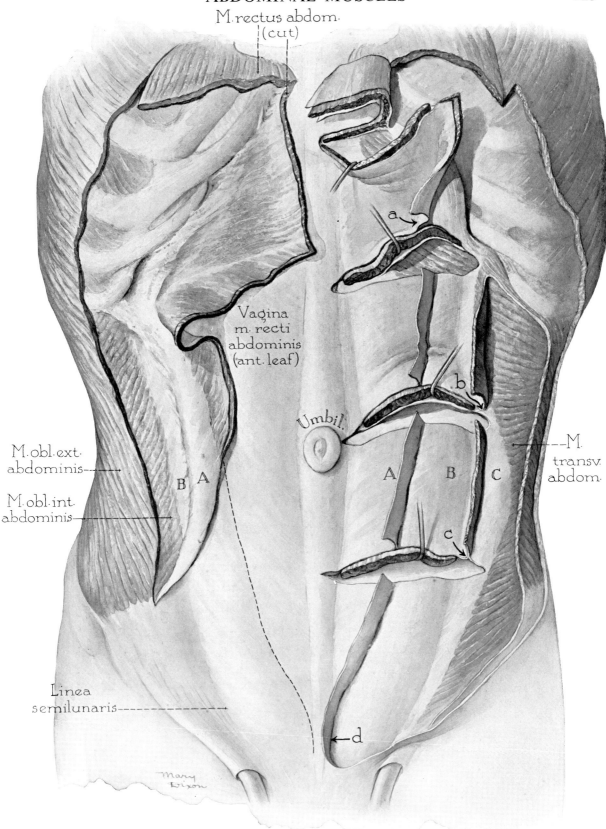

Abdominal muscles and the rectus sheath.

The rectus sheath and the contained muscle have been transected to demonstrate the lines of fusion, at *a* to *d*, of the aponeuroses of the three contributing layers: *A*, external oblique; *B*, internal oblique; *C*, transverse abdominal.

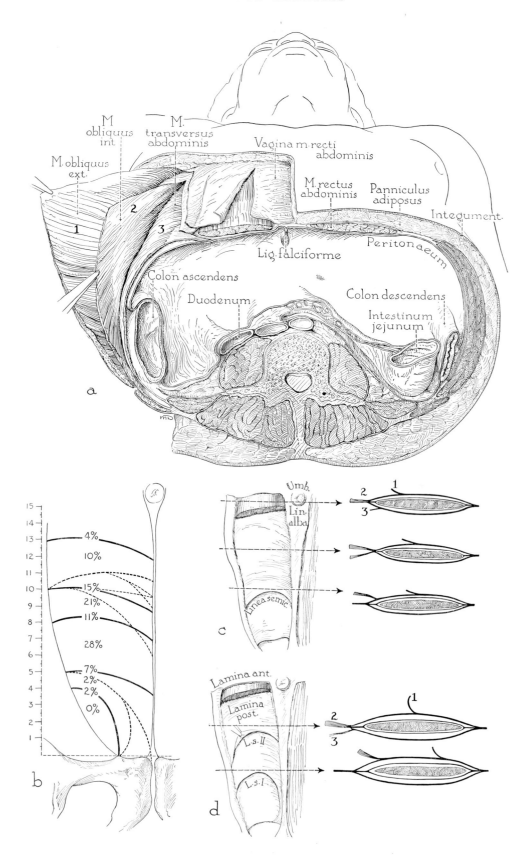

M. obliquus ext.

M. obliquus int.

M. transversus abdominis

Vagina m. recti abdominis

M. rectus abdominis

Panniculus adiposus

Integument.

Peritonaeum

Lig. falciforme

Colon ascendens

Duodenum

Colon descendens

Intestinum jejunum

a

b

15
14
13 — 4%
12 — 10%
11
10 — 15%
9 — 21%
8 — 11%
7
6 — 28%
5
4 — 7%
3 — 2%
2 — 2%
1 — 0%

Umb.
Lin. alba

Linea semic.

c

Lamina ant.

Lamina post.

L.s. II

L.s. I

d

See opposite page for description.

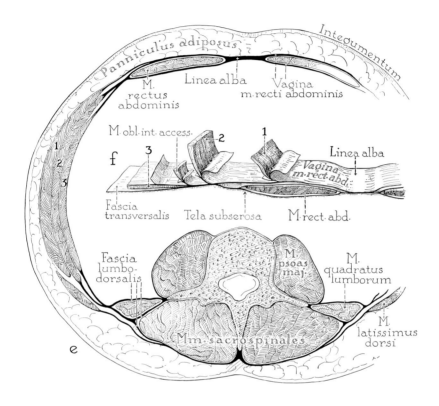

Rectus muscle and the rectus sheath, with variations of the latter.

a, Abdominal muscles, as seen in a transverse section above the level of the umbilicus.

b, Variation in location of the linea semicircularis, in a large series of specimens. Height in centimeters and percentage occurrence are indicated.

c and d, Variation in constituency of the posterior wall of the rectus sheath. Anterior views and transverse sections. In d, primary and secondary lineae are present.

e and f, Constitution of the rectus sheath and fascial relations of the contributory aponeuroses. Layers are numbered correspondingly. The fascial investments have been freed and turned away from the muscles.

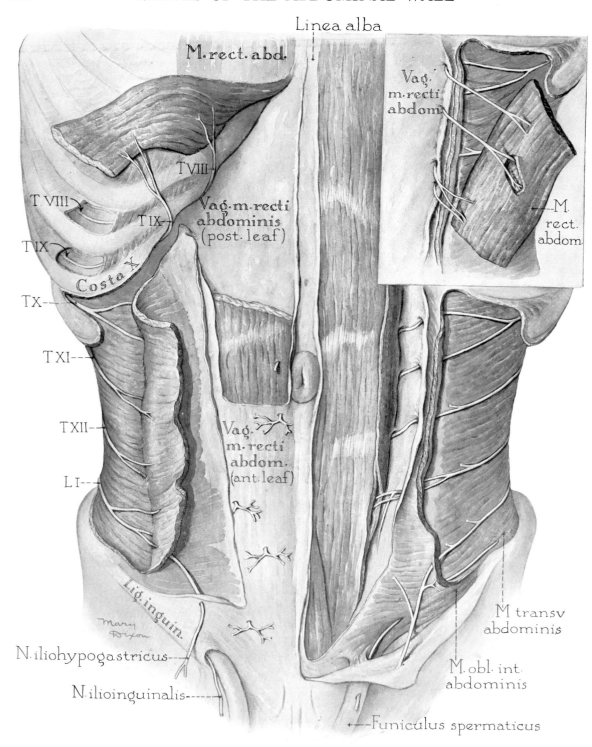

Nerves of the abdominal wall.

On the left the internal oblique has been reflected medialward; on the right it has been largely cut away. On the left, the cranial third of the rectus muscle is reflected; on the right the lateral margin of the muscle is turned inward. Typically, the anterior rami of the thoracic nerves course forward, with inclination downward, between the intermediate and deep strata of abdominal musculature. They pierce the rectus sheath to attain the deep aspect of the rectus muscle. Then, after innervating the muscle as they pass through its substance, the nerves become subcutaneous by emerging through openings in the anterior leaf of the sheath. Inset: By freeing a segment of the rectus muscle, and lifting it out of the sheath, the hiatuses for transmission of the thoracic nerves are shown.

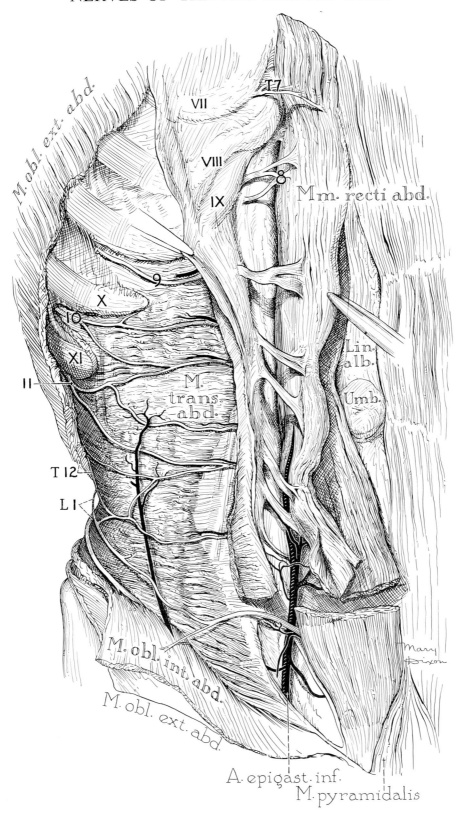

Abdominal wall, showing the abdominal plexus of the thoracic nerves.

The nerves are exposed by removal of the external and internal oblique muscles and by reflection of the rectus muscle. The seventh through the twelfth thoracic nerves, and the first lumbar, are shown.

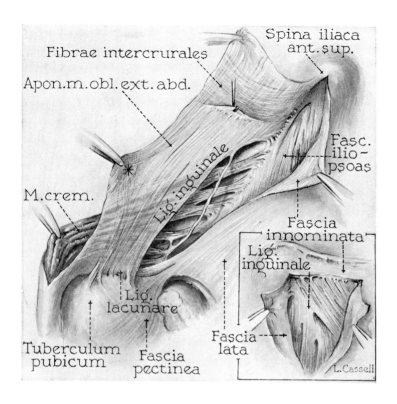

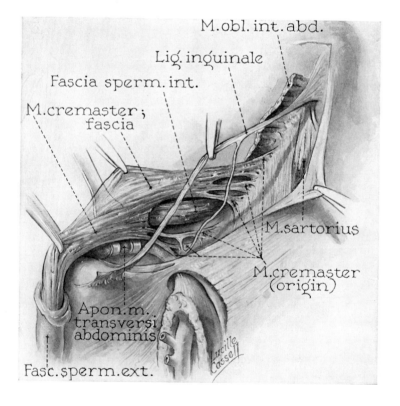

See opposite page for description.

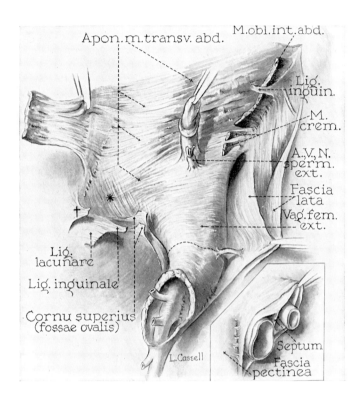

Aponeurotic and fascial continuities in the abdomen, pelvis, and thigh.

In the figure at the upper left, the deep fascia on the outer surface of the external oblique aponeurosis, with contained intercrural fibers, has been removed except in an area near the iliac spine. Cremaster fascicles arise from the iliopsoas fascia and the latter's medial continuation, the deep layer of the fascia lata. The inguinal ligament is attached to the iliopsoas fascia. Inset: The deep fascia over the inguinal ligament, near the anterior superior iliac spine, has been drawn aside to demonstrate the continuity of the fascia lata with the innominate fascia (opposite half of body).

In the figure at the lower left, the external spermatic fascia has been rolled downward on the spermatic cord, exposing the cremaster layer. The origin of the cremaster muscle from the iliopsoas fascia is demonstrated; the cremaster layer is stretched to show its musculofascial character. A retractor, passed deep to the cord and the cremaster, elevates the transversus abdominis aponeurosis; the latter is continuous with the femoral sheath.

In the above figure the proximal stump of the spermatic cord has been elevated to show the external appearance of the abdominal inguinal ring; the internal spermatic fascia has been rolled backward, leaving the constituents of the cord in their preperitoneal connective tissue (grasped by the forceps). The inguinal ligament remains as medial (†) and lateral stumps. The superior cornu of the fossa ovalis has been cut, only the stumps of its attachment remaining. The expansion of the rectus tendon passes to the pecten of the pubis (at *). In the inset the sheath and its contents have been transected.

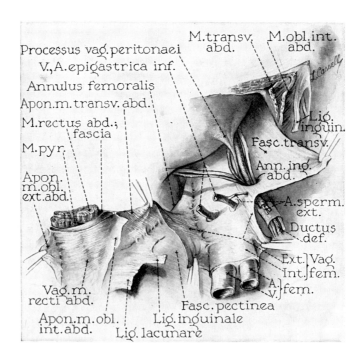

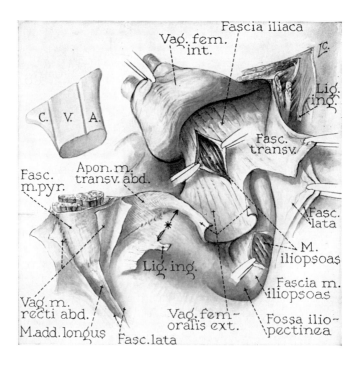

See opposite page for description.

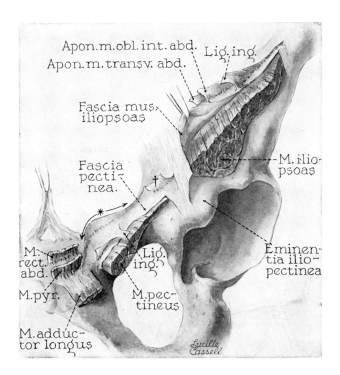

Aponeurotic and fascial continuities in the abdomen, pelvis and thigh.
Dissection continued and completed.

In the figure at the upper left, the femoral sheath has been transected and opened longitudinally to demonstrate the femoral continuation of the preperitoneal tissue. The transversus abdominis has been incised by the same cut, the lateral flap turned outward to reveal the form of the abdominal inguinal ring as seen from within. The constituents of the cord have been segregated.

In the figure at the lower left, the femoral vessels, with their covering of preperitoneal tissue, have been elevated. The iliopsoas fascia has been incised both above and below the origin of the posterior component of the sheath to demonstrate that the latter is a subsidiary slip of the former. The rectus sheath has been incised to show the underlying anterior lamina of the rectus fascia as it divides to enclose the pyramidalis muscle. The arrows (at *) indicate the distance between the lacunar ligament and the medial margin of the femoral ring. Inset: Clay cast of the space enclosed by the femoral sheath (C., canal; V., vein; A., artery).

In the figure above, the abdominal layers have been trimmed to their bony attachments. The arrows (at *) indicate the pubic attachment of the tranversus abdominis and internal oblique aponeuroses (including the insertion, into the pecten, of the inguinal falx). The adminiculum of the linea alba is lifted. At † the origin of the posterior component of the femoral sheath remains as a tag. The iliopsoas fascia has been cut and lifted to show the muscle, the layers attaching to the fascia lifted as successive leaves.

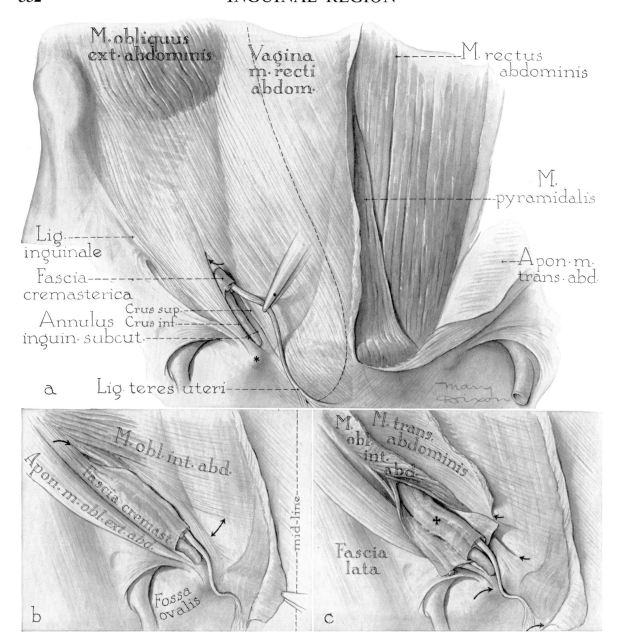

Inguinal layers in the female.

a, The round ligament, subcutaneous inguinal ring, and related structures. The superficial fascia and the external layer of investing (innominate) fascia have been removed to expose the aponeurosis of the external oblique muscle (right side); at the apex of the aponeurotic cleft (at arrow) the internal layer of investing fascia rests upon cremasteric fascia. The relation of the seam of fusion of the external and internal oblique aponeuroses to the margins of the rectus and pyramidalis muscles is indicated by dotted lines on the specimen's right; the muscles themselves are exposed on the left. The inferior crus is attached to the pubic tubercle (at *).

b, Cremasteric layer, shown by reflecting the external oblique aponeurosis. The internal oblique and its cremasteric derivative have been transected where they pass through the outlet of the canal; within the substance of the fascial tube is imbedded the ilioinguinal nerve. The arrow at the left marks the point of divergence of parietal and funicular fibers. The arrow at the right points to the margins of an area of fascia bounded by aponeurosis. A hernia adiposa projects beyond the cut end of the tube.

c, Internal spermatic fascia. The internal oblique has been cut and reflected, the cremasteric tube opened to expose the fascial prolongation (at +) derived from the transversus abdominis. The upper arrows mark the margins of the fascial (thinned) area in the internal oblique; the lower arrows indicate the points of attachment of the crura of the external oblique aponeurosis.

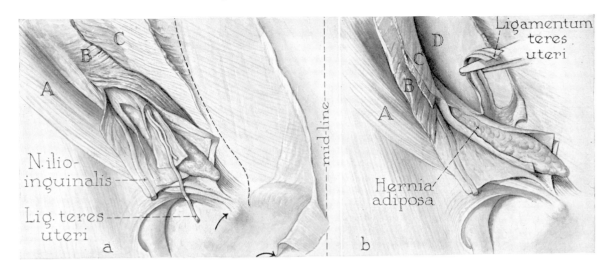

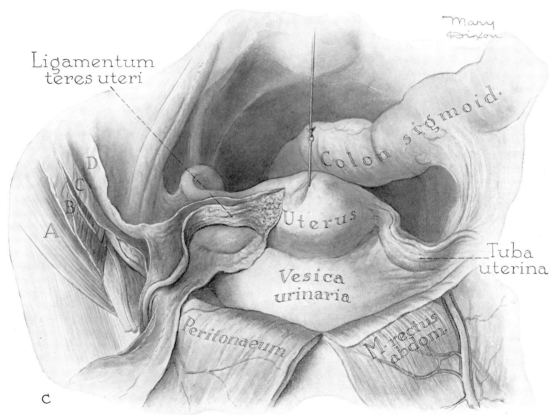

Inguinal region (continued) and pelvic cavity in the female.

a, Layers covering the round ligament (and hernia adiposa) in the inguinal canal. The internal oblique has been reflected to expose the transversus; the former's funicular prolongation has been opened to show the covering contributed to the round ligament by the transversalis fascia. The external oblique is turned medialward along the seam of fusion with the internal oblique; the latter's seam of fusion with the transversus is indicated by a dotted line.

b, Round ligament and hernia adiposa at the peritoneal level. The transversus abdominis muscle and aponeurosis are turned aside, the transversalis fascia being freed from the deep aspect of the muscle near the point of reflection upon the ligament. The ligament, with its fascial tube opened, is elevated by forceps. A to D, in succession indicate: A, external oblique; B, internal oblique; C, transversus abdominis; D, peritoneum.

c, Round ligament seen in anterosuperior view of the pelvis. The peritoneum has been incised and turned aside along the course of the ligament (specimen's right side).

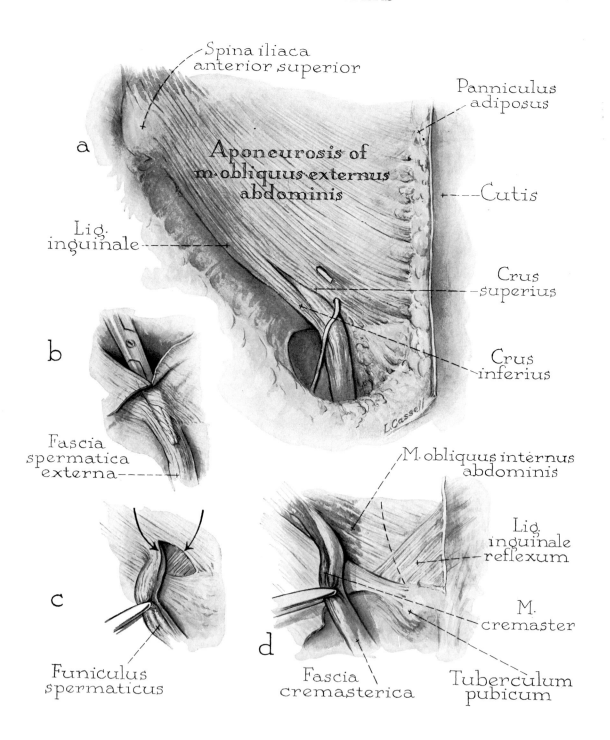

Spina iliaca
anterior superior

Panniculus
adiposus

a

Aponeurosis of
m·obliquus externus
abdominis

Cutis

Lig.
inguinale

Crus
superius

b

Crus
inferius

Fascia
spermatica
externa

M. obliquus internus
abdominis

Lig.
inguinale
reflexum

c

M.
cremaster

d

Funiculus
spermaticus

Fascia
cremasterica

Tuberculum
pubicum

L.Cassell

Investments of the spermatic cord.

a, The cleft in the external oblique, bounded by the crura of the aponeurosis.

b, The outermost coat of the spermatic cord is demonstrated by passing an instrument deep to the layer.

c, The external spermatic fascia has been cut (the margins indicated by arrows) and the spermatic cord retracted; in this way a "ring" is produced at this medial extremity of the aponeurotic fault.

d, At the next deeper level the cremasteric muscle and its fascia contribute an investment to the cord. A large, reflected inguinal ligament is present; the lateral margin of the rectus abdominis muscle is indicated by a broken line.

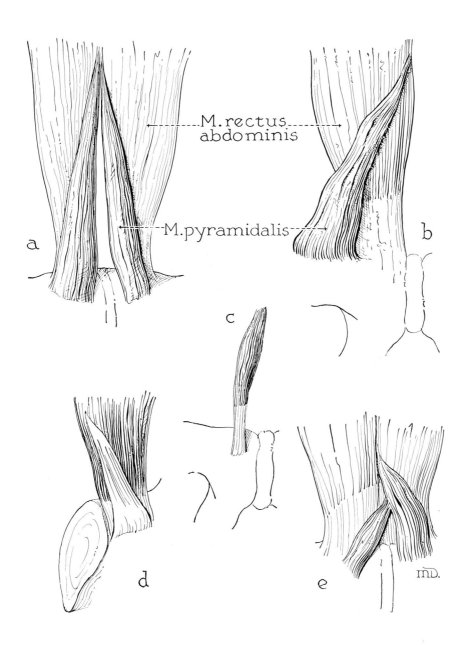

Pyramidalis muscle. Variation in form and size.

a, Typical form. *b*, Laterally placed pubic origin. *c*, Muscle, ribbon-like. *d*, Small muscle of unusual form. *e*, Muscle crossing midline to opposite side.

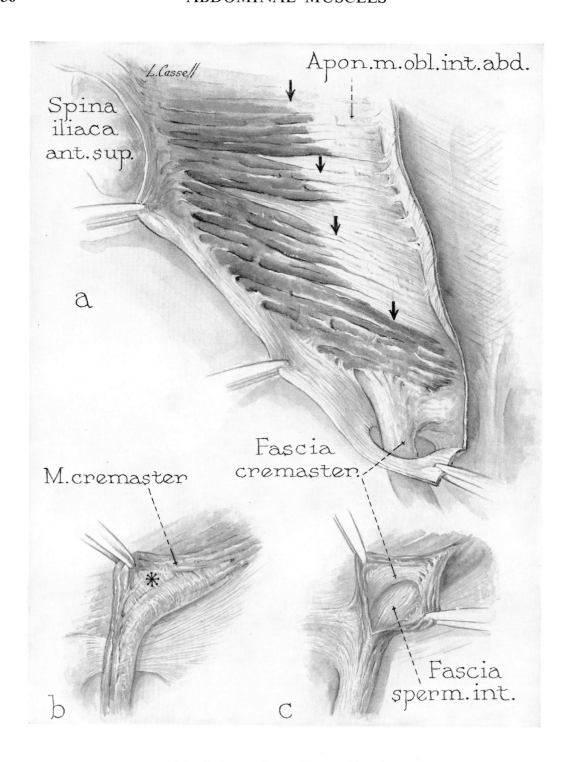

Abdominal musculature. Types of layering.

a, Inguinal part of a prominently banded internal oblique muscle. The bands of the internal oblique are indicated by arrows.

b, The internal oblique muscle sends but few fascicles downward upon the cord, the remainder of the cremasteric investment being fascial (marked by *).

c, The cremasteric fascia has been incised and the margins have been drawn aside to expose the internal spermatic fascial layer of the cord, in the same specimen.

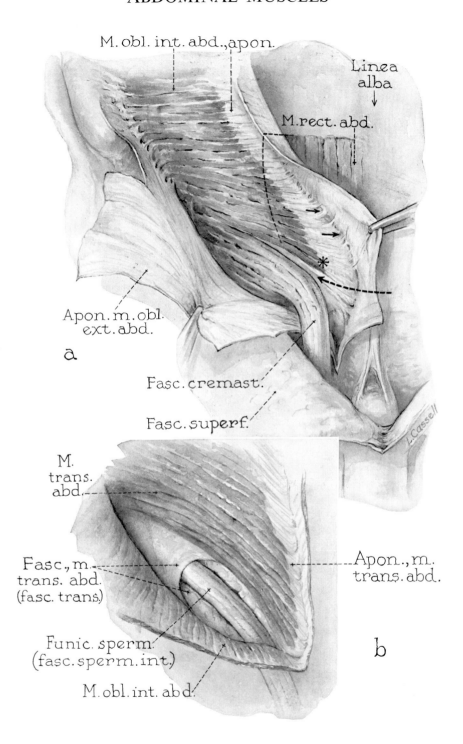

Abdominal musculature. Types of layering.

a, Common type of internal oblique. The internal oblique muscle, its aponeurosis, and the cremasteric fibers are shown. A small cleft, apparent when the cord is drawn downward, sets off an "aponeurotic inguinal falx" (above arrow at *). The line of junction of the aponeuroses of the oblique muscles lies well to the medial side of the lateral border of the rectus muscle (the latter at dotted line).

b, A rare condition in which the muscle fibers of the transversus abdominis (ending in an arching border) left exposed the transversalis fascia. The latter is a thick aponeurotic layer in the lateral two-fifths of the area, a thin one in the medial three-fifths.

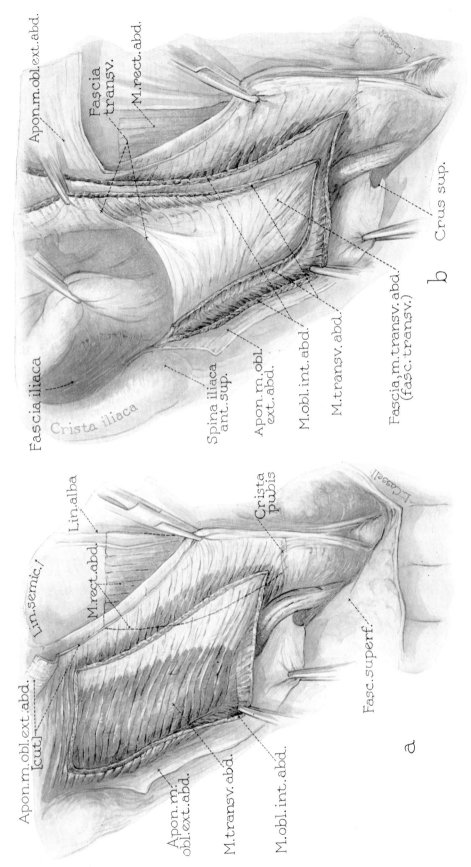

Abdominal musculature. Types of layering.

a, Common type of transversus abdominis. The internal oblique muscle has been drawn aside and the muscle fibers of the transversus abdominis muscle removed to expose the fascia (transversalis fascia) on the deep aspect of the latter. The fascia has been freed to the level of the iliac spine; superior to that level it has been left attached to the muscle and turned medially therewith. The layer is continuous with the iliac fascia, the latter exposed by drawing aside the peritoneal sac.

b, The external and internal oblique muscles have been drawn aside and the muscle fibers of the transversus abdominis muscle removed to expose the underlying transversus abdominis muscle.

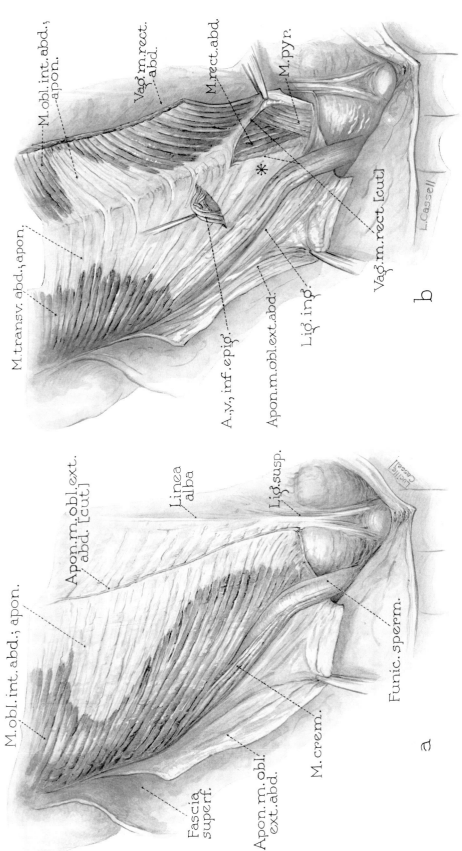

Abdominal musculature. Types of layering.

a, The aponeurosis of the internal oblique muscle is wider than in the specimen pictured in the preceding figure, being more than a broad stripe between muscle fibers and line of continuity with the external oblique.

b, Similarly, the aponeurosis of the transversus is unusually broad; it occupies all of the inguinohypogastric area except a small portion near the iliac origin. Area at * is that at which a direct inguinal hernia would protrude.

M. OBLIQUUS EXTERNUS ABDOMINIS
Superolateral extent of fault
in aponeurosis

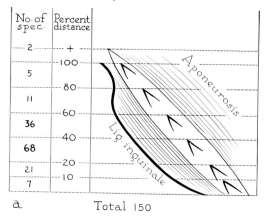

No. of spec.	Percent distance		
2	+		
5	100		
11	80		
36	60		
68	40		
21	20		
7	10		

a   Total 150

M. TRANSVERSUS ABDOMINIS
Inferior extent (at inferomedial angle)

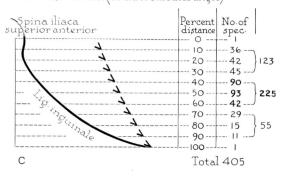

Spina iliaca superior anterior

Percent distance	No. of spec.	
0	1	
10	36	
20	42	123
30	45	
40	90	
50	93	225
60	42	
70	29	
80	15	55
90	11	
100	1	

c   Total 405

M. OBLIQUUS INTERNUS ABDOMINIS
Inferior extent (at inferomedial angle)

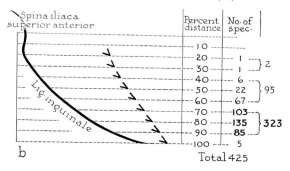

Spina iliaca superior anterior

Percent distance	No. of spec.	
10		
20	1	2
30	1	
40	6	
50	22	95
60	67	
70	103	
80	135	323
90	85	
100	5	

b   Total 425

Variations in the inguinal portion of each of the anterolateral abdominal muscles; shown schematically. The figures recorded are for both sides combined although only the right side is diagrammed.

a, In approximately 70 per cent of specimens (104 of 150) the superolateral extent of the intercrural fault in the aponeurosis of the external oblique layer lay caudal to the transverse level of the anterior superior spine of the ilium and that of the pubic symphysis. *b*, In 76 per cent of specimens (323 of 425) the muscle fibers of the internal oblique layer descended into the caudal third of the area bounded by the skeletal landmarks named in the preceding description of the external oblique layer. Beyond the caudal border of the fleshy portion, the layer was represented by fascia. *c*, Muscle fascicles terminated at a more cranial level in the case of the transverse abdominal layer than in the case of the internal oblique; in 53 per cent of specimens (225 of 405) the area into which muscle fibers of the former layer descended was situated near the middle third of the area between the anterior superior spine of the ilium and the symphysis of the pubis.

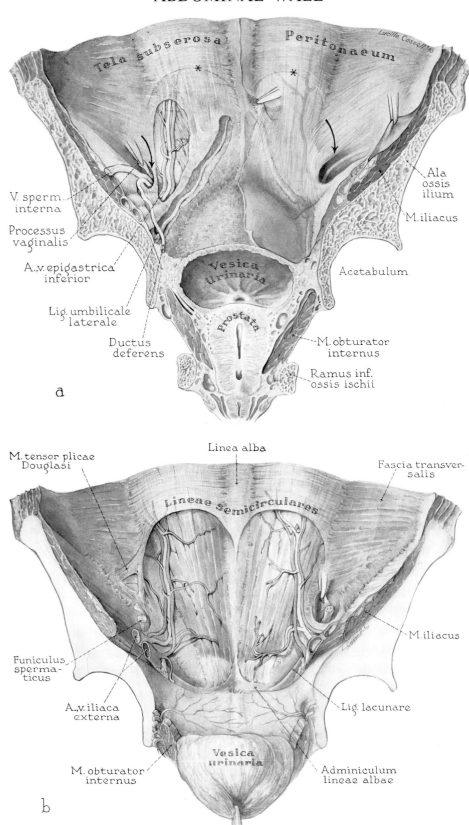

Internal aspect of the anterior abdominal wall. See following page for description.

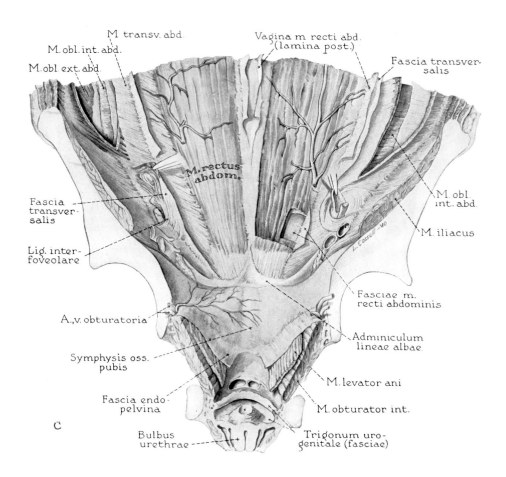

M transv. abd

M. obl. int. abd.

M. obl. ext. abd.

Vagina m recti abd.
(lamina post.)

Fascia transver-
salis

M. rectus
abdom.

Fascia
transver-
salis

Lig. inter-
foveolare

M. obl.
int. abd.

M. iliacus

A.,v. obturatoria

Fasciae m.
recti abdominis

Adminiculum
lineae albae.

Symphysis oss.
pubis

M. levator ani

Fascia endo-
pelvina

M. obturator int.

Bulbus
urethrae

Trigonum uro-
genitale (fasciae)

C

Internal aspect of the anterior abdominal wall.

In *a*, peritoneum and preperitoneal connective are shown. The pelvis has been coronally sectioned. On the right the peritoneum is intact; on the left the peritoneum has been removed to expose the preperitoneal layer in which lie the middle and lateral umbilical ligaments. The preperitoneal layer has been removed only along the course of the inferior epigastric artery and turned outward. Through it (right side) are visible rectus muscle, inferior epigastric artery, linea semicircularis. The iliac fascia of the greater pelvis has been freed from the muscles, as has, likewise, the thin preperitoneal layer from the muscle-fascia; the layers are also shown in relation to the external iliac vessels. The peritoneum remains on the right half of the superior surface of the urinary bladder; on the left the combined preperitoneal and endopelvic fascial layers are exposed. Arrows point to abdominal inguinal rings.

In *b* the preperitoneal tissue has been removed, the transversalis fascia and iliopsoas fascia exposed. The urinary bladder has been drawn backward to expose the pubic part of the bony pelvis, the obturator vessels, and the pubic branches of the obturator arteries.

In *c*, the transversus abdominis muscle and aponeurosis are shown. The transversalis fascia has been removed from both sides. On the right side, additionally, the transversus abdominis muscle has been partly cut away, exposing the internal oblique. At the lateral border of the right rectus muscle a window has been cut to expose the layer of rectus fascia which passes in front of the muscle. The transversus has been cut on the left side; additionally, the internal oblique is cut away in a V-shaped piece near the anterior superior spine, showing the muscular part of the external oblique, and the investing fascial layers on the abdominal aspect of each of the muscles. The iliopsoas muscles have been removed from the iliac fossae except near the inguinal ligament. The transected external iliac vessels rest upon the iliopsoas of each side. The bladder and prostate (with large plexiform veins) have been excised to show the important bony structures in the anterior part of the pelvis.

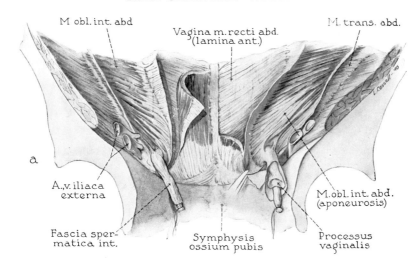

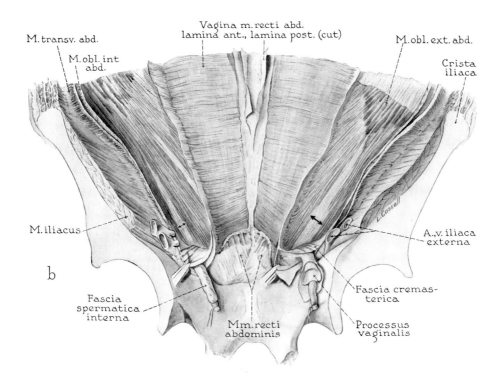

Internal surface of the anterior abdominal wall; dissection concluded.

In *a*, on the right side the transversalis fascia and transversus abdominis (and aponeurosis) remain at the marginal attachments only, and upon the sac; the internal oblique is, therefore, almost entirely exposed. For purposes of comparison, on the left side the exposure is similar. On the right side a small hernial sac was present.

In *b*, the internal oblique has been almost entirely removed to expose virtually the full extent of the external oblique aponeurosis; the rectus and pyramidalis muscles have been excised to show the anterior layer of the rectus sheath; the transversalis and rectus fascia have been removed except at the attachment along the pubic crest (remaining here only as a tag). The internal spermatic fascia is present as a constituent of the hernial sac. The transversus abdominis muscle appears merely as a narrow strip, along the inferior attachment. The funicular part of the internal oblique is chiefly fascial; only a few fascicles appear in the layer. By these means are demonstrated the triangular cleft in the external aponeurosis of each side (margins indicated by arrows), the thin fascial layer which crosses the space in the aponeurosis and the thick anterior component of the rectus sheath.

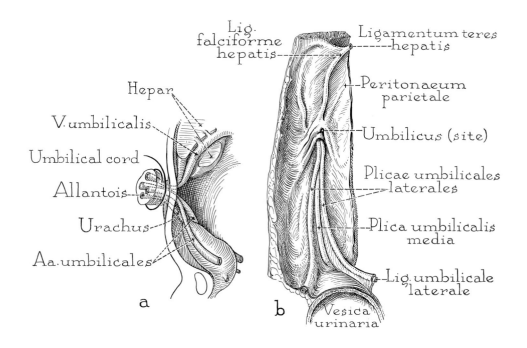

Umbilical region in the embryo and in the adult.

a, Umbilical and related structures in the human embryo; sagittal view of a reconstruction. As a constituent of the placental circulation, the umbilical vein passes through the umbilical cord to the navel, and thence in the free edge of the falciform ligament to a fossa on the inferior surface of the liver. The umbilical arteries ascend from pelvic source, passing forward and upward to the anterior abdominal wall. Reaching the navel, the arteries occupy the umbilical cord with the corresponding vein and the urachus, the latter structure being an elongate tube continuous with the apex of the urinary bladder. In the umbilical cord the urachus becomes continuous, in turn, with the allantoic stalk.

b, Adult ligamentous remnants of the umbilical blood vessels and of the urachus, and the serous folds caused by their presence on the internal aspect of the anterior abdominal wall. The obliterated umbilical vein occupies a fold of peritoneum, the falciform ligament of the liver, which, arising from the upper part of the anterior abdominal wall, runs to the umbilical incisura of the liver. Below the level of the umbilicus the urachus, persisting as a ligamentous strand, lifts the peritoneum in the median plane to produce a middle umbilical fold. Over the umbilical arteries the peritoneum projects, to each side of the midline, as a lateral umbilical fold. These *plicae*, together with lesser serous elevations over the functional inferior epigastric vessels, form boundaries of *foveae* on the internal aspect of the wall, as illustrated on page 348. (After Cullen.)

In the specimen illustrated on page 346 not only is the anatomy of the inguinal and scrotal walls depicted, but also the position and form of a patent *processus vaginalis peritonaei;* when occupied by a mobile portion of the digestive tube, the vaginal process becomes the innermost of the several hernial coverings derived from the inguinal parietes.

The constituent layers will be described in the order in which they would be encountered by a hernia.

Peritoneum. Regularly, not the slightest peritoneal protrusion, or even small foveate depression, occurs at the site of the abdominal inguinal ring. In exceptional cases, like the one illustrated, the serous sac, once occupied by a hernial mass, readily dilates the surrounding fascial, or musculofascial, tubes, derived from the inguinal layers.

Preperitoneal connective tissue. Over the serous sac the preperitoneal (retroperitoneal or subserous) layer is thin yet usually dissectable as a complete stratum. In some specimens, however, the stratum is so slight in bulk that it constitutes nothing more than a cleavage plane between internal spermatic fascia and peritoneum.

Transverse abdominal muscle. The transversus stratum, like the external oblique and internal oblique, is trilaminar in character. Often the muscle fibers of the transversus layer do not extend as far inferiorly as the abdominal inguinal ring, nor do heavy aponeurotic bands occupy this distal zone. The area of herniation, then, is mainly fascial. Here, where heavier tissue ends, the two layers of investing fascia fuse, to become a single stratum distal to the abdominal ring. The internal, stronger, contributing layer is termed the transversalis fascia; the external, weaker element possesses no special name, and is commonly disregarded in standard accounts. Together, on the cord, these layers form the internal spermatic fascia.

Internal oblique muscle. The internal oblique layer is also trilaminar in character, being composed of a musculoaponeurotic portion covered on the outer and inner surfaces by fascia. Together, the lamellae form the cremasteric fascial layer, in which scattered muscle fibers are commonly present.

Just as investing fasciae bridge across the intercrural fault in the external oblique (see hereinafter), so also the comparable fasciae of the internal oblique stratum extend across the interfascicular spaces, and remain to represent the whole layer in instances in which muscle fibers are wanting. The funicular part of the layer is, therefore, chiefly fascial as it constitutes the dilated and saccular covering for the hernial contents.

External oblique aponeurosis. The inguinal part of the external oblique layer is an aponeurotic continuation of the more proximal, muscular, portion of the stratum. It is invested on both surfaces by fascia, the external one of which is the fascia innominata.

As the fibers which make up the inguinal ligament pass to an attachment upon the pubic tubercle, they depart from the neighboring aponeurotic bands which descend, as the superior crus, to an insertion at the pubic symphysis. Between these diverging columns a triangular intercrural cleft exists, the apex of which may reach the muscular part of the external oblique layer at the level of the anterior superior iliac spine (see page 340). Only the external and internal investing fasciae bridge the intercolumnar, aponeurotic, gap; in this gap the two fascial layers are applied to each other back-to-back.

At the medial extremity of the triangular cleft, and just cranial to the pubic tubercle, the spermatic cord passes beyond the plane of the parietal layers and receives its investment of fascia. There the two fascial lamellae fuse to form the thin external spermatic fascia, in which a varying number of intercrural fibers occur.

In its course through the inguinal wall the spermatic cord carries downward an investment from each of the three layers. Each of the strata which invest the spermatic cord reflects in general the character of the source layer on the inguinal wall. The contribution from the external oblique (the external spermatic fascia) is entirely fascial; it consists of the conjoined fasciae which invest the external oblique aponeurosis. The layer derived from the internal oblique (the cremasteric layer) is carried downward, not from the definite margins of an aponeurotic fault or cleft, but rather from a layer which regularly contains muscle fascicles in its inguinal portion. Since the fascicles displaced to cover the spermatic cord are few and attenuate, the cremasteric coat is predominantly fascial. The portion of the transversus layer (the internal spermatic fascia) which contributes to the set of funicular coats, and, therefore, to the hernial coverings, is that part which is situated between the arching transversus musculature superiorly and the transversalis fascia inferiorly. The layer represents a fusion of the thin outer lamina of investing fascia and the thicker inner one, the latter being the transversalis fascia. The preperitoneal connective tissue is usually a definite layer on the inguinal wall, but it is variable in character on the hernial sac. The peritoneal sac retains its serous character. Being innermost, it is accompanied by the ductus deferens, the internal spermatic artery and vein, lymphatic vessels, and autonomic nerve fibers.

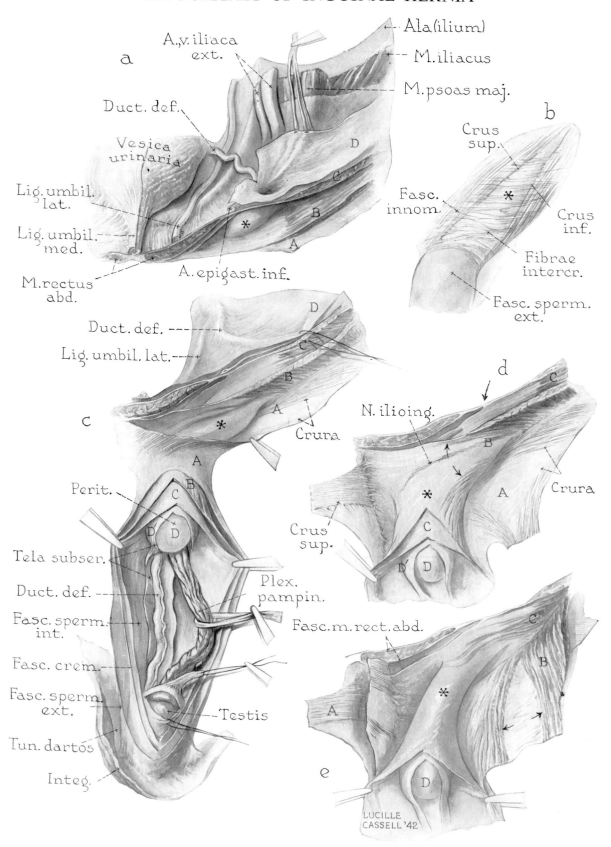

a

A.,v. iliaca ext.

Ala (ilium)

M. iliacus

M. psoas maj.

Duct. def.

Vesica urinaria

Lig. umbil. lat.

Lig. umbil. med.

M. rectus abd.

A. epigast. inf.

b

Crus sup.

Fasc. innom.

Crus inf.

Fibrae intercr.

Fasc. sperm. ext.

Duct. def.

Lig. umbil. lat.

c

Crura

d

N. ilioing.

Crura

Crus sup.

Perit.

Tela subser.

Duct. def.

Fasc. sperm. int.

Fasc. crem.

Fasc. sperm. ext.

Tun. dartos

Integ.

Plex. pampin.

Testis

Fasc. m. rect. abd.

e

LUCILLE CASSELL '42

Inguinal region. See facing page for description.

a to *e*, Dissections of inguinal and funicular layers in a specimen with bilateral indirect inguinal hernia (left half of specimen illustrated). A indicates external oblique; B, internal oblique; C, transversus abdominis; D′, retroperitoneal tissue; D, peritoneum.

The hernial mass has been removed from the serous sac. For these successive dissections the specimen was transected above the iliac alae, and the abdominal wall sectioned transversely. The skin and superficial fasciae were removed, the external oblique layer separated from the internal oblique. This separation was continued where the layers became funicular about the spermatic cord. The peritoneum and preperitoneal layer were then freed from the internal aspect of the transversus layer. This line of separation was carried into the tube of the internal spermatic fascia.

a, The peritoneal aspect of the inguinal wall viewed from above and behind. The genitofemoral nerve is held by forceps. By removing the peritoneum (D) in the area around the abdominal inguinal ring, the oblique course and relations of the inguinal canal (*) are demonstrated. *b*, The area of the subcutaneous inguinal ring, seen from the outside. The dilated processus vaginalis (at *) is here covered superficially by the external spermatic fascia (derived from the innominate fascia of the external oblique layer), in which are lodged the intercrural fibers. The fault in the aponeurosis of the external oblique is triangular, and is bounded by columns (superior and inferior crura). *c*, The external oblique and internal oblique layers have been drawn forward; the dissection has been carried to the level of the testis, and the layers of the spermatic cord have been incised successively to expose the constituents of the cord and their investments. The retroperitoneal layer forms a definite sheath for the internal spermatic artery, pampiniform plexus, and ductus deferens (sheath opened to show the contents).

Each of the parietal layers that clothe the spermatic cord retains the general character of the source layer of the inguinal region. The funicular derivative of external oblique (external spermatic fascia) is completely fascial; it is composed of the conjoined fascial laminae, which invest the external oblique aponeurosis. The layers become fused at or near the subcutaneous inguinal ring. The layer derived from the internal oblique (the cremaster) contains only scattered muscle fascicles; like the covering received from the external oblique, the cremasteric coat is predominantly fascial. The portion of the transversus layer (internal spermatic fascia) which contributes to the set of funicular coats (and, therefore, to the hernial coverings) is the portion that is situated between the arching transversus musculature superiorly and the iliopsoas fascia inferiorly. The layer represents a fusion of the thin outer lamina of investing fascia and the thicker inner one, the transversalis fascia. The subserous stratum is usually a definite layer on the inguinal wall; however, it may vary in character in the hernial sac. On the inguinal parietes and within the pelvis, it houses the iliac vessels with their branches and tributaries, and the lymphatic glands and vessels. On the cord the vessels and nerves that are lodged within this prolongation of the retroperitoneal tissue are rarely of dissectable size. The peritoneal sac (processus vaginalis) lies innermost; in indirect herniation it contains the displaced portion of intestine or omentum.

d, The external oblique layer has been incised vertically and then turned aside to expose the broad, funnel-like, portion of the internal oblique stratum (indicated at *). The upper arrow indicates the point at which the transversalis fascia sends off a lamella to invest the rectus muscle. The smaller arrows point to margins of the muscular portion of the internal oblique; the lower fibers are prolonged upon the cord as cremasteric muscle fibers. Except where they are present, the cremasteric layer is completely fascial. In the reflected portion of the external oblique the aponeurotic crura and the intercrural fascia (at A) are evident. *e*, The transversus stratum is shown by incising and reflecting the overlying portion of the internal oblique layer. By continuing the incision into the scrotum the internal spermatic fascia (at *) is exposed. Distally the latter envelope has been opened to show the retroperitoneal connective tissue and the peritoneal (serous) sac (D). The margins of the fascial portion of the internal oblique layer (B) are indicated by arrows (compare *d*).

In its course through the abdominal wall the spermatic cord carries about it, in funicular manner, strata which are prolonged from the parietal layers. On its external surface the transversus layer becomes tubular about the spermatic cord in the plane of the abdominal wall, the tube resembling a curved pipe emerging from a flat surface. The internal oblique stratum does not invest the cord tightly at its proximal end, but surrounds the cord as a broad infundibuliform investment. There is no reduplication to form an "intermediate inguinal ring"; therefore the mouth of the funnel is usually over twice the size of the abdominal inguinal ring. After acquiring its cremasteric coat, somewhat below the level of pubic tubercle and inguinal ligament, the cord passes forward beyond the plane of the external oblique layer, carrying with it the external spermatic fascia in tubular form.

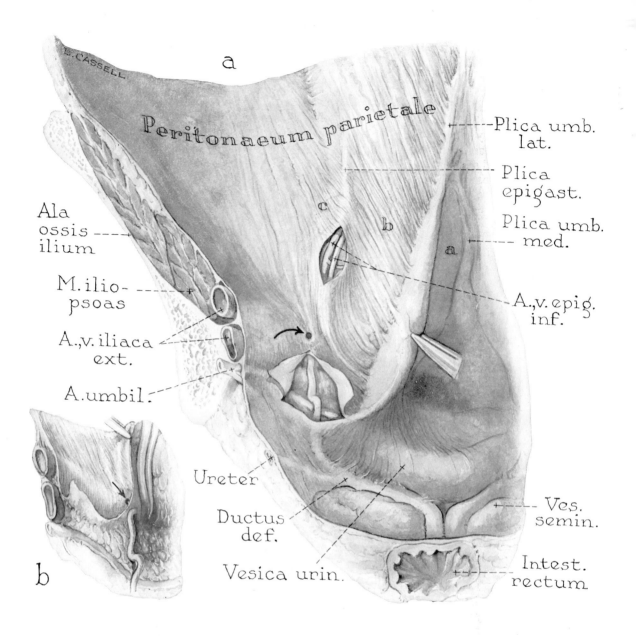

a, Dissection of the internal surface of the left half of the anterior abdominal wall, below umbilical level, with peritoneal folds, foveae, processus vaginalis (at arrow) and important subperitoneal structures.

The specimen was sectioned coronally through the ala of the ilium just dorsal to the tuberosity of the ischium, then cut in paramedian plane to the right of the midline. The peritoneum is intact except where locally slit and turned aside to expose the inferior epigastric artery and vein and the ductus deferens as the latter crosses the umbilical artery and the external iliac vessels en route to the abdominal inguinal ring. The peritoneal fossae are lettered: a, supravesical; b, medial inguinal; c, lateral inguinal. The arrow points to the abdominal orifice of the vaginal process of the peritoneum. The lateral umbilical fold has been elevated to demonstrate the depth of the medial inguinal fovea. (Compare page 344.)

b, Further exposure of the structures near the abdominal inguinal ring. The peritoneum has been reflected to expose the epigastric vessels and the umbilical artery which passes deep to the ductus deferens. As shown, the peritoneal process lies medial to the duct and to the inferior epigastric vessels, and superior to the femoral artery. The retroperitoneal (subserous) layer is exposed medial to the epigastric vessels and inferior to the external iliac vessels. The abdominal orifice of the processus vaginalis is indicated by an arrow. This is the site of the abdominal ring of the inguinal canal, present in the subjacent transversalis fascia.

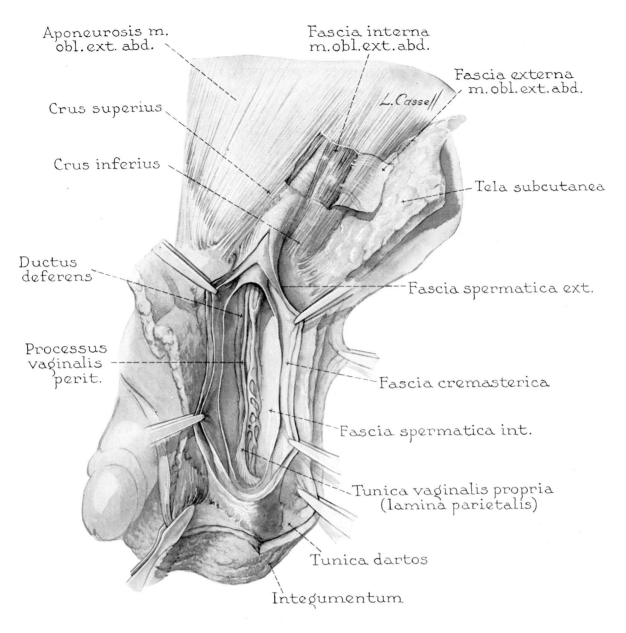

Aponeurosis m. obl.ext. abd.

Fascia interna m.obl.ext.abd.

Fascia externa m.obl.ext.abd.

L. Cassell

Crus superius

Crus inferius

Tela subcutanea

Ductus deferens

Fascia spermatica ext.

Processus vaginalis perit.

Fascia cremasterica

Fascia spermatica int.

Tunica vaginalis propria (lamina parietalis)

Tunica dartos

Integumentum

The external parietal layer and the funicular continuations of the
several inguinal layers (same specimen as in preceding figure).
Left inguinal region from the exterior.

In the inguinal region the external oblique is exposed by reflection of the superficial fascia. In a quadrangular area over the superior portion of the intercrural fault, the external investing (innominate) fascia is reflected in order to demonstrate the corresponding internal investing fascia; the two thin fascial layers, conjoined, form the external spermatic fascia. In the scrotal area the external spermatic fascia and the other two funicular coats (cremasteric and internal spermatic fasciae) have been incised and turned aside to show the processus vaginalis and the constituents of the spermatic cord (duct and vessels). The funicular part of the vaginal process, although minute, is an uninterrupted diverticulum from the abdominal orifice of the inguinal canal through the length of the canal, into the scrotum and to the testis. The process widens distally to become the tunica vaginalis propria of the testis. An indirect inguinal hernia would occupy, and progressively dilate, this vaginal process of the parietal peritoneum. The retroperitoneal stratum, because of its areolar character, is not removable as a distinct layer. In the inguinal region the superficial fascia contains a heavy deposit of fat; in the scrotum the dartos muscle replaces fat.

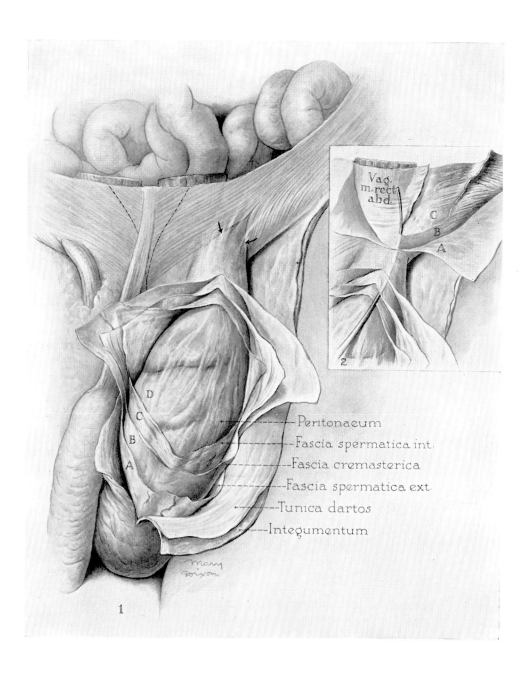

Inguinal and scrotal layers of a large indirect inguinal hernia.

1, The skin and superficial fascia have been reflected to expose the outer layer of investing fascia (innominate fascia) of the external oblique aponeurosis; on the scrotum, the parietal layers have been incised and reflected in serial succession; only the subserous layer is not separately dissectible. The crura of the subcutaneous inguinal ring (at arrows) are spread apart by the herniating mass. *2,* The 3 inguinal strata from which the scrotal layers are derived. A probe is placed between the cremaster and the internal spermatic fascia. Lettering in both figures corresponds to that on page 346.

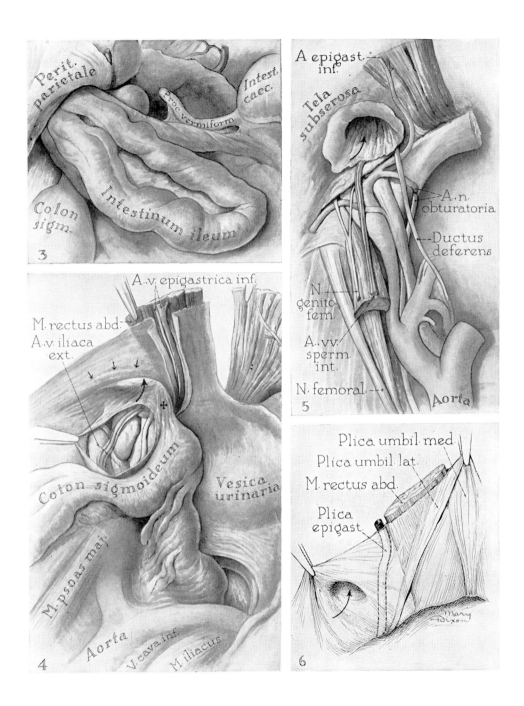

Contents of the hernial sac. Same specimen as preceding.

3, The ileum, cecum, and sigmoid colon in relation to the hernial orifice, as seen from above and left.

4, Peritoneal structures, including the hernial orifice. The jejunoileum has been retracted; the colon remains undisturbed. The peritoneum has been locally removed to show the inferior epigastric and external iliac vessels. Arrows indicate the line along which the subjacent transversus becomes fascial.

5, The retroperitoneal structures related to the hernial area, shown in the hemisected pelvis by removal of the peritoneum (except that of the hernial sac), and of the subperitoneal tissue of the pelvis.

6, Early hernial sac (at arrow) and related structures, in another specimen.

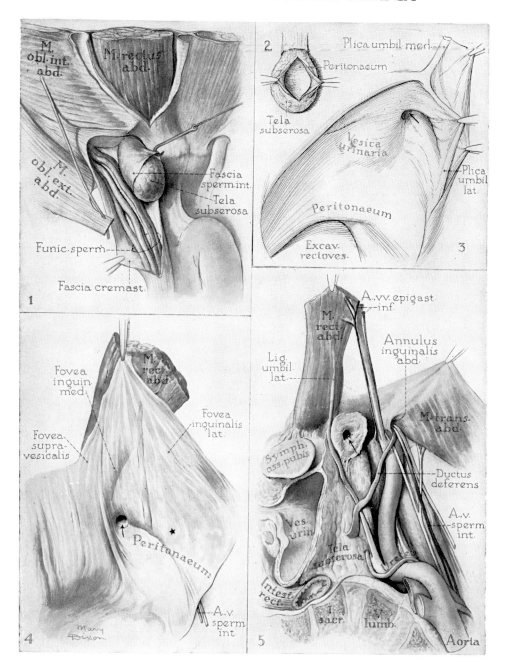

Direct (diverticular) inguinal hernia in male specimens.

1, The cremaster, internal spermatic fascia, and spermatic cord in relation to the hernial protrusion. *2,* The hernial sac opened. *3,* The orifice in relation to the peritoneal elevations.

4 and *5,* Hernial anatomy in a second specimen. *4,* Hernial orifice and peritoneal foveae. *5,* Related retroperitoneal structures in the hemisected pelvis.

In *1* the internal spermatic fascia covers the proximal part of the lipomatous enlargement in the preperitoneal layer. The external oblique aponeurosis has been reflected, the aponeuroticofascial part of the internal oblique incised obliquely, and the lower flap of cremasteric layer is then retracted. In *2* the opened peritoneal process is shown within the lipomatous lobule of the preperitoneal layer. In *5* the peritoneum has been removed except in a small area around the orifice of the sac. Arrows point to peritoneal diverticula of direct hernias. In *c* the site of the subjacent abdominal inguinal ring is indicated by a star.

STOMACH, OMENTA

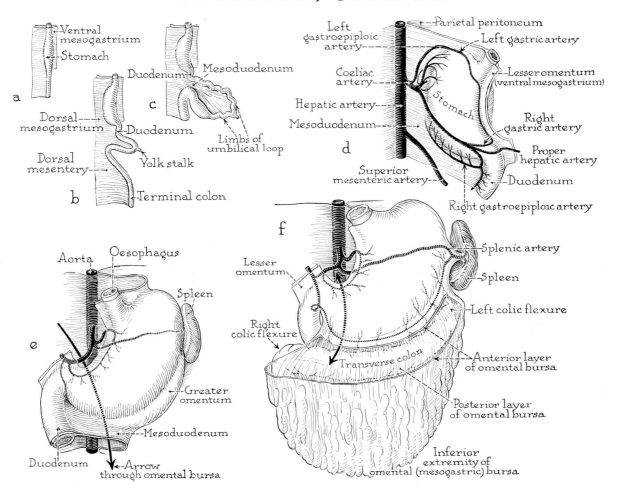

Development of the stomach and omenta.

a, The early tubular form of the stomach, and the primordial condition of the ventral mesogastrium and the dorsal mesogastrium; at the cut margins, in front and behind, these mesenterial supports would be continuous with the parietal peritoneum.

b and *c,* Stages in the development of the mesenterial supports of the small and large intestines.

d, Further development of the stomach; the ventral mesogastrium has become subdivided by the presence of the liver (not shown), into a lesser omentum and a falciform ligament.

e, The stomach, in undergoing torsion, encloses a bursa (through which the arrow passes); the dorsal mesogastrium, prolonged downward, becomes the greater omentum.

f, The space of the bursa, further enlarged, is opened to demonstrate the modified mesenterial layers that form its boundaries. (Adapted from Callander.)

STOMACH, SPLEEN, INTESTINES

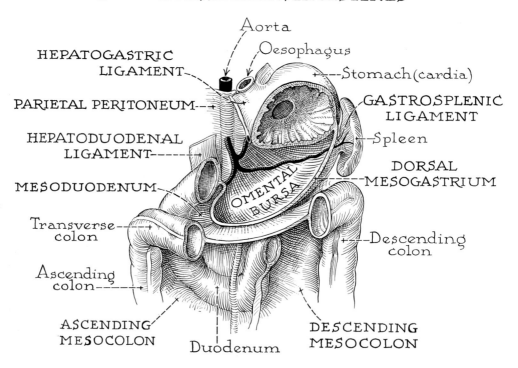

Development of the mesenterial supports of the upper abdominal viscera.

The primitive dorsal mesogastrium has become divided locally by the growth of the spleen between its constituent layers. The lesser omentum now has two regional subdivisions: the cranial division passes between the stomach (*gaster*) and the liver (*hepar*), while the other joins the duodenum and the liver. (Adapted from Callander.)

DUODENUM

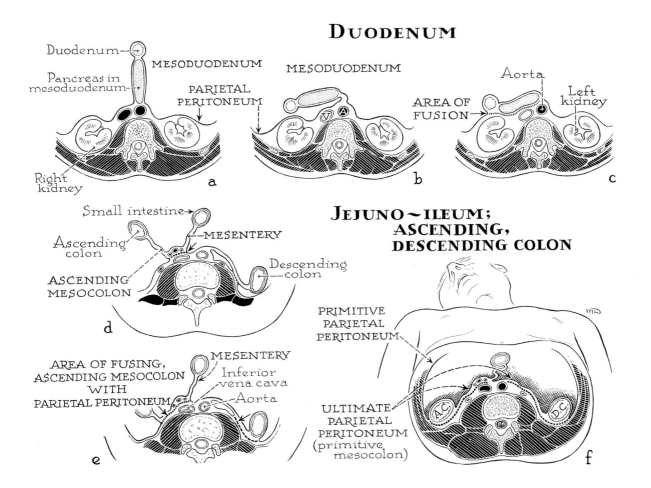

Development of the mesenterial supports of parts of the small intestine.

a, b, and *c,* Three successive stages in the process by which the duodenum and its mesentery, carried from sagittal to coronal position, become fixed to the dorsal body wall (area of fusion indicated in *c* by dotted line). In this way the duodenum becomes a retroperitoneal structure.

d and *e,* Demonstrating the manner in which the mesentery of the small intestine and the mesenterial supports of the large intestine become fixed to the peritoneum of the dorsal body. Primary fusion occurs at the point (*d*) where the intestinal and colic arteries are contained within the primitive mesentery.

f, As the final stage in this process, fusion spreads in both directions from the area of original fixation. As a result, the mesentery of the jejunoileum is shortened, and the ascending and descending segments of the large intestine attain a retroperitoneal position. (Adapted from Callander.)

STOMACH, SPLEEN, PANCREAS

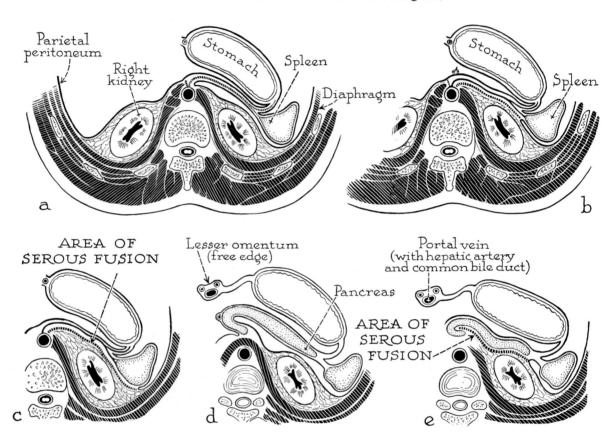

Development of the gastric, splenic, and pancreatic divisions of the primitive dorsal mesentery.

a, *b*, and *c*, Demonstrating the three major steps in the course of which the dorsal mesentery of the stomach, now containing the spleen, becomes shortened in its dorsal segment by fusion with the parietal peritoneum.

d and *e*, Similar fixation of the primitive dorsal mesentery of the stomach in the part that contains the pancreas. The mesoduodenum is thereby lost, and the splenic segment of the original mesentery is shortened. (Adapted from Callander.)

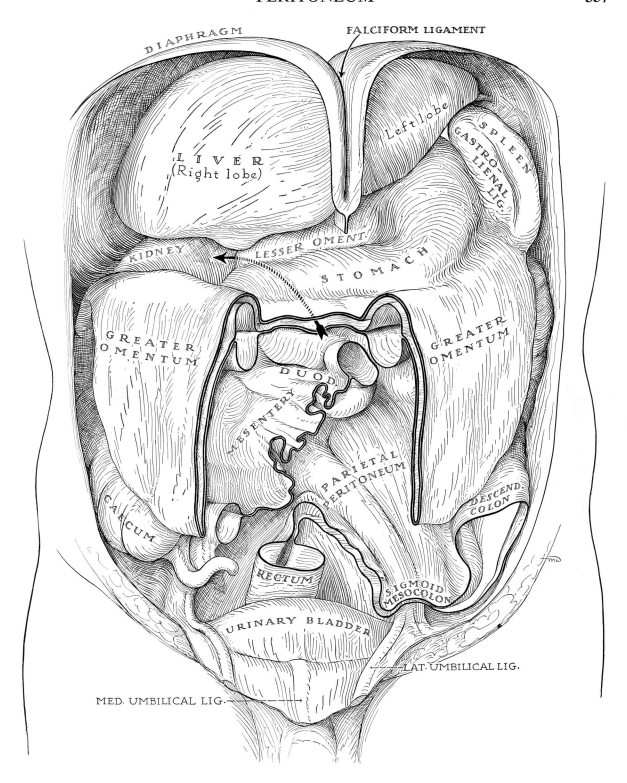

Anterior view of the opened peritoneal cavity; from a life-sized wax model.

The organs are represented by the spaces which they occupied. Portions of the greater omentum and the transverse colon have been cut away to reveal subjacent structures; the mesentery of the jejunoileum and the sigmoid mesocolon have been cut close to their parietal attachments. The arrow passes upward in the omental bursa, through the epiploic foramen.

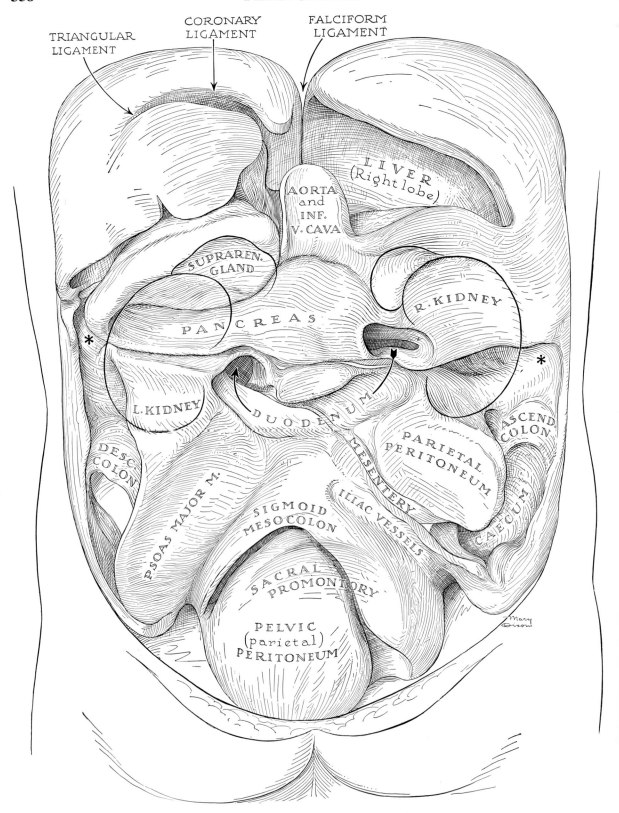

TRIANGULAR LIGAMENT

CORONARY LIGAMENT

FALCIFORM LIGAMENT

LIVER (Right lobe)

AORTA and INF. V. CAVA

SUPRAREN. GLAND

R. KIDNEY

PANCREAS

L. KIDNEY

DUODENUM

ASCEND. COLON

DESC. COLON

PARIETAL PERITONEUM

PSOAS MAJOR M.

SIGMOID MESOCOLON

MESENTERY

ILIAC VESSELS

CAECUM

SACRAL PROMONTORY

PELVIC (parietal) PERITONEUM

Posterior view of the same model.

The positions held by the organs are shown as excavations, and the lines of origin of the mesenteries as parallel (bilaminar) reflections of the parietal layer of peritoneum. The sites of the colic flexures are indicated by asterisks, and the retroperitoneal course of the duodenum by arrow.

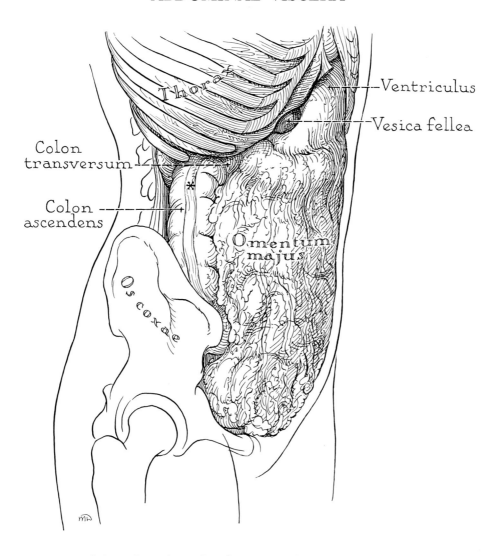

Contents of the main peritoneal cavity, seen as the greater omentum lies *in situ*.

The following portions of the digestive tube and of the accessory organs are partially in view: stomach, liver and gallbladder, ascending colon, and transverse colon.

The anterosuperior surface of the stomach appears below the costal margin. Above the stomach the superior surface and anterior margin of the liver are exposed; the fundus of the gallbladder appears in a notch on the anterior margin of the liver. The greater omentum, draped from the greater curvature of the stomach, descends apron-like to the pelvis. Along the right margin of the omentum a portion of the ascending colon is exposed (taenia libera marked by *); likewise, on the left side, the omentum fails to obscure all of the descending portion of colon. The transverse colon, which crosses the cavity just inferior to the stomach, is usually apparent on the right half of the body at the hepatic flexure; on the left half, since the splenic flexure is deeply situated, the transverse colon is regularly out of view. The coils of small intestine (jejunoileum) are obscured by the greater omentum.

In the next six figures the following anatomic features are illustrated: in the first, the coils of small intestine, the ascending and transverse portions of the large intestine, and the blood vessels which supply these divisions of the abdominal part of the digestive tube; in the second, the remaining portions of the large intestine, with the blood vessels of the descending colon; in the third, the liver, spleen, and stomach, with the arteries of supply to the greater curvature; in the fourth, the same organs, together with the transverse colon and the arteries and ducts in the hepatogastric and hepatoduodenal ligaments; in the fifth, chiefly the various visceral arteries, shown in relation to the parietal peritoneum and to mesenterial supports of the abdominal organs. In the sixth plate of figures are pictured the vessels of visceral arterial supply and of venous drainage; both the segments exposed in the preceding figures and those covered by peritoneum are shown.

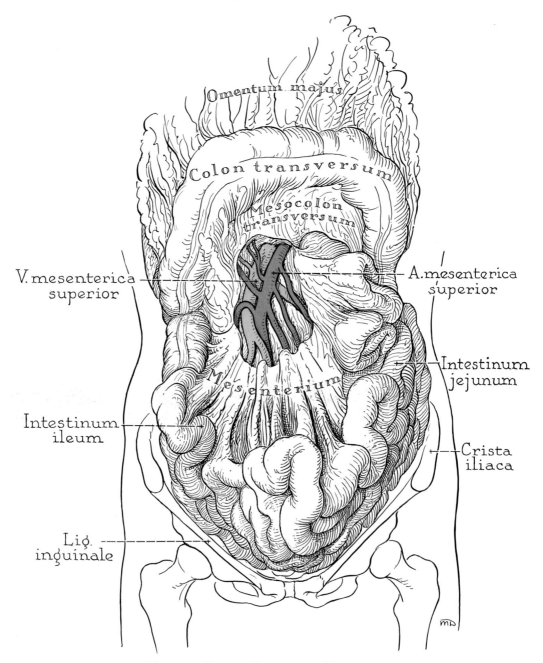

Viscera and supporting mesenterial structures.

The mesentery is revealed by lifting the greater omentum, the transverse colon, and mesocolon; blood vessels exposed by removal of a plaque of the anterior lamella of the mesentery of the jejunoileum.

The greater omentum splits to enclose the transverse colon, becoming, thereby, the latter's serous coat. Joining again, the lamellae form the transverse mesocolon; this mesentery of the transverse colon passes to a horizontal attachment on the posterior abdominal wall, there becoming continuous with the parietal peritoneum. The coils of intestine (jejunum and ileum) are now fully exposed, as is likewise the mesentery; however, the duodenal portion of the small intestine is concealed beneath the proximal coils of the ileum. The superior mesenteric vessels course side by side; the artery gives off intestinal branches (seen coursing toward the specimen's left), and colic branches (toward the right); tributaries, corresponding to the arteries, return blood to the superior mesenteric vein. As the intestinal arteries spread outward, in radiating fashion, to the jejunum and ileum, they are lodged between layers of the mesentery; on the other hand, colic arteries to the ascending colon lie behind the peritoneum. Comparable vessels to the transverse colon are likewise retroperitoneal in position as they leave the superior mesenteric artery; however, in their distal reaches they course between the layers of the transverse mesocolon.

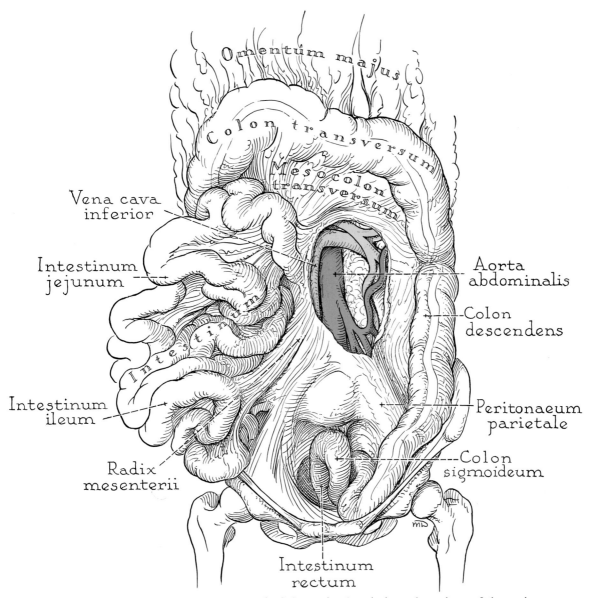

Abdominal parts of the alimentary tract and of the parietal and visceral portions of the peritoneum.

The mesocolon and parietal peritoneum are revealed by moving the coils of small intestines to the specimen's right side; inferior mesenteric and related arteries and veins are exposed by removing a plaque of the parietal peritoneum in the area to the left of the great vessels.

The first, or duodenal, portion of the small intestine (here concealed) becomes continuous with the jejunal division; the latter passes into the ileal portion without morphological line of distinction. Both, unlike the duodenum, are attached to the posterior abdominal wall by an extensive fold of peritoneum, termed the mesentery. The line of parietal fixation, or root, is directed downward and to the right. The root begins at the duodenojejunal junction and ends at the ileocecal junction. The ascending colon (here covered by the coils of intestine) passes upward, to attain the under surface of the liver; the colon then turns sharply forward and to the left, forming the right colic, or hepatic, flexure. Through all or the greater part of its length, the ascending colon is held in contact with the posterior abdominal wall, peritoneum covering its sides and anterior surface. The transverse portion of the colon passes across the upper portion of the abdominal cavity. In its transverse course, the colon possesses a mesenterial support, the transverse mesocolon. The descending colon is in contact with the posterior abdominal wall, that is, partially invested by peritoneum; the sigmoid colon, on the other hand, possesses a mesenterial support, the sigmoid mesocolon. The rectum, which lacks a mesorectum, is, in the proximal part of its descent through the true pelvis, covered in front and on the sides by peritoneum; in the distal portion, it is so invested in front only.

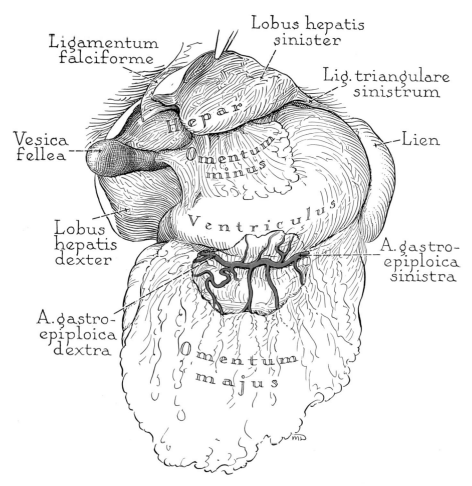

Upper abdominal viscera, their mesenterial (omental) supports, and the peritoneal relations
of certain of the gastric vessels.

As the peritoneum passes from the anterior abdominal wall and the diaphragm to the liver, it is reflected around a fibrous cord, the round ligament (obliterated umbilical vein), to form a triangular fold, the falciform ligament. Therefrom, the peritoneum is carried lateralward, toward the right and left, forming on each side a coronary ligament; each coronary ligament, in turn, terminates as a triangular ligament. After investing the liver (here elevated), the layers of peritoneum meet again back to back, at the portal area of the liver; then, in the form of a bilaminar support, the peritoneum descends to the lesser curvature of the stomach and the duodenum as the lesser omentum (divisible, then, into hepatoduodenal and hepatogastric portions, which are termed ligaments). The lesser omentum ends in a free edge on the right (see succeeding figure); it forms part of the anterior wall of the lesser division of the peritoneal cavity, the omental bursa. Splitting to invest the stomach, the layers join again to form the greater omentum. This broad mesenterial apron descends into the pelvis, then ascends to attain the transverse colon (see preceding figure), for which it forms a serous coat. Along the cardiac end of the greater curvature of the stomach, just beneath the diaphragm, the layers of the greater omentum similarly separate to enclose the spleen; joining again, they pass backward to the diaphragm. These subdivisions of the omentum are, respectively, the gastrolienal and phrenicolienal ligaments. Traced downward, the greater omentum reaches the pelvis; then, turning backward upon itself, it passes cranialward to the transverse colon (see preceding and following figures); because of its attachments to the stomach and the colon, the omentum has been termed the gastrocolic ligament. After surrounding the transverse colon, the mesenterial support becomes the transverse mesocolon. It passes upward and backward, to become continuous with the parietal peritoneum at the horizontal level of the pancreas. The stomach, the transverse colon, the omenta, and the transverse mesocolon are thus the chief anterior and posterior boundaries of the omental bursa (opened in following figure).

The arteries of supply to the greater curvature of the stomach and the corresponding veins (not shown) are lodged between the lamellae of the greater omentum; similarly, those to the lesser curvature are situated between the layers of the lesser omentum (see following figures).

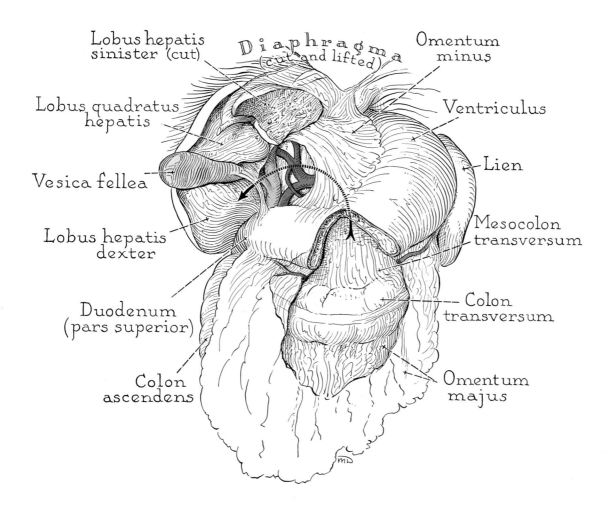

Lobus hepatis sinister (cut)

Diaphragma (cut and lifted)

Omentum minus

Lobus quadratus hepatis

Ventriculus

Vesica fellea

Lien

Lobus hepatis dexter

Mesocolon transversum

Duodenum (pars superior)

Colon transversum

Colon ascendens

Omentum majus

Mesenterial supports of the stomach and transverse mesocolon,
structures contained within the omenta, and the space bounded by the latter.

A part of the anterior lamella (one layer) of the lesser omentum has been cut away, together with an adjacent segment of the stomach. The arrow passes from the omental bursa, or lesser peritoneal sac, into the greater, or main, cavity; in so doing, it emerges through the epiploic foramen, behind the free edge of the lesser omentum.

As is now rendered evident, through removal of a portion of the anterior leaf of the two-layered lesser omentum, the arteries of supply to stomach and duodenum, the excretory ducts of the liver, together with the associated veins (here removed), are lodged between the constituent serous layers of the omentum. In descending from the portal area of the liver to the lesser curvature of the stomach and the corresponding margin of the proximal segment of the duodenum, the omentum thus serves as a route for arteries of hepatic and gastroduodenal supply, for the portal vein and its gastric tributaries, and for the hepatic, cystic, and common bile ducts. Similarly, along the greater curvature of the stomach, between the layers of the greater omentum, course vessels for additional gastric supply.

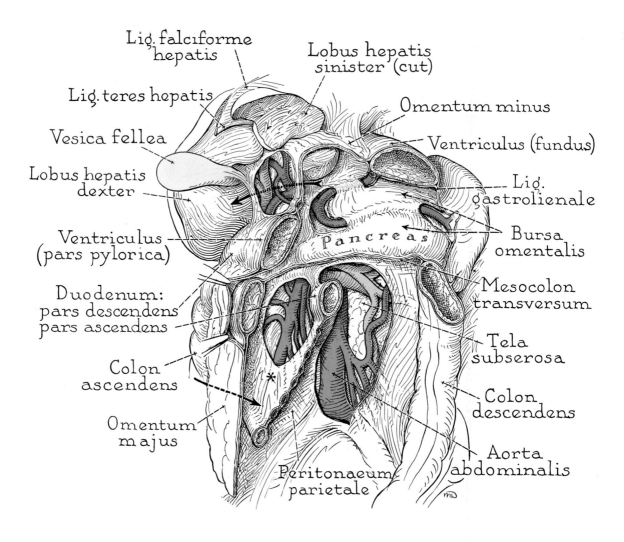

Course of peritoneum as it covers the posterior abdominal wall,
and is reflected from parietal position to form mesenterial supports for,
or to cover, portions of the digestive tube and the latter's accessory organs.

The body of the stomach, the left lobe of the liver, the transverse colon, and all but the proximal (duo-denal) and distal (cecal) portions of the jejunoileum have been cut away. With the organs the following peri-toneal structures have been removed: the lesser omentum, except its superior (hepatic) portion; all but the right marginal part of the greater omentum; the mesentery of the small intestine, except along the line of its parietal attachment, or root; a plaque of the anterior lamella of the lesser omentum (to expose the hepatic artery and its branches, and the neighboring ducts). A portion of the anterior lamella of mesentery of the small intestine has been similarly dissected to show the superior mesenteric artery and its intestinal and colic branches. On the dorsal body wall, within the omental bursa and the greater peritoneal cavity, areas of parietal peritoneum have been removed to show, above, the retroperitoneal branches of the celiac artery, and, below, the similar position of the aorta and its branches, and certain tributaries of the inferior vena cava and the portal vein.

In respect to peritoneal relations, the following features are demonstrated: investment of the stomach, through splitting of the lesser omentum; fusion of the opposing layers of the greater omentum; covering of the transverse colon, through division of the greater omentum; attachment, at pancreatic level, of the transverse mesocolon; concealment of the small intestine and its mesentery (at *) by the greater omentum (behind which the lower arrow passes); covering (without free mesentery) of the descending colon; boundaries of the lesser peritoneal sac, and the latter's communication with the greater peritoneal cavity at the epiploic foramen (at upper arrow).

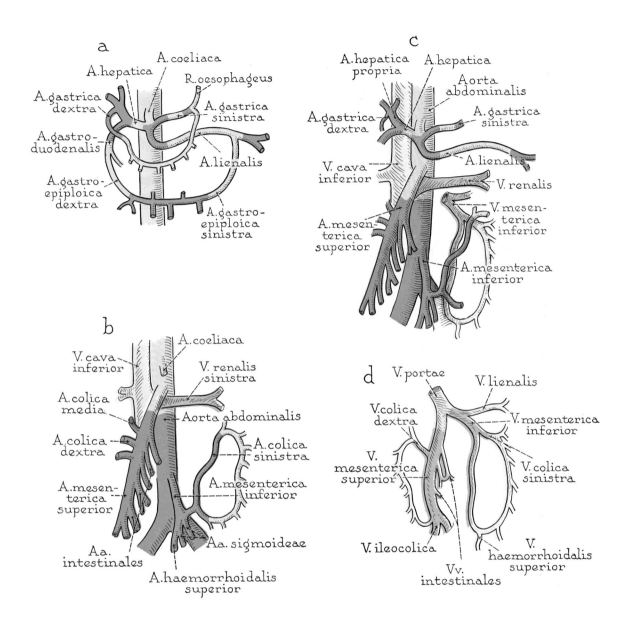

Blood vessels of the abdominal organs; diagrammatic.

Deeply colored portions of the arteries and veins are exposed in the dissections pictured in the preceding figures; lightly tinted segments therein are covered by parietal peritoneum or invested by mesenteric supports.

a, Aorta, celiac artery, and branches of the latter. *b,* Aorta, superior and inferior mesenteric arteries, and inferior vena cava. *c,* Aorta and its arteries of visceral supply, inferior vena cava, and mesenteric tributaries of the portal vein. *d,* Portal vein and its tributaries.

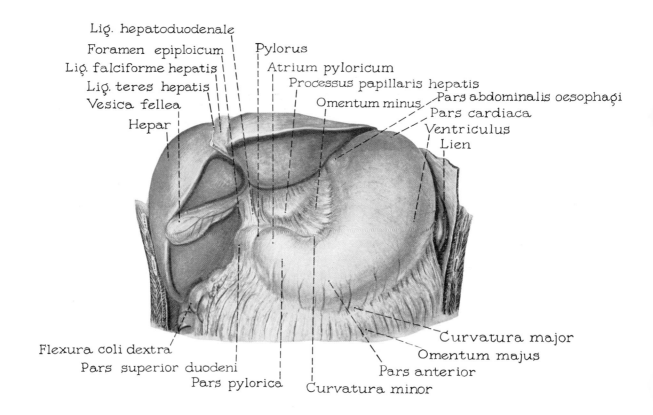

Upper abdominal viscera in anterior view.

The stomach is *in situ*, the liver elevated. The peritoneum is intact. (From Warren: Handbook of Anatomy, Harvard University Press.)

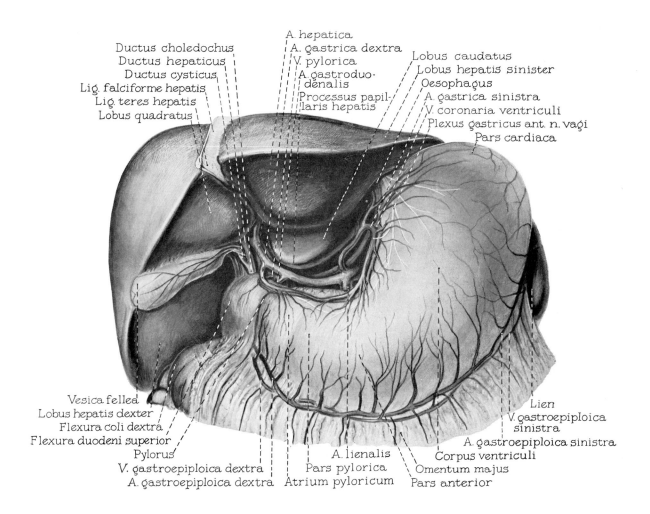

Ductus choledochus
Ductus hepaticus
Ductus cysticus
Lig. falciforme hepatis
Lig. teres hepatis
Lobus quadratus

A. hepatica
A. gastrica dextra
V. pylorica
A. gastroduo-
denalis
Processus papil-
laris hepatis

Lobus caudatus
Lobus hepatis sinister
Oesophagus
A. gastrica sinistra
V. coronaria ventriculi
Plexus gastricus ant. n. vagi
Pars cardiaca

Vesica fellea
Lobus hepatis dexter
Flexura coli dextra
Flexura duodeni superior
Pylorus
V. gastroepiploica dextra
A. gastroepiploica dextra

A. lienalis
Pars pylorica
Atrium pyloricum

Lien
V. gastroepiploica sinistra
A. gastroepiploica sinistra
Corpus ventriculi
Omentum majus
Pars anterior

Blood vessels of the stomach and liver.

The lesser omentum has been removed to expose the arteries and veins in the lesser omentum as they course along the lesser curvature of the stomach and ascend to the portal area of the liver. Along the greater curvature the vessels are shown as they supply the stomach and send branches in the opposite direction to the greater omentum. (From Warren: Handbook of Anatomy, Harvard University Press.)

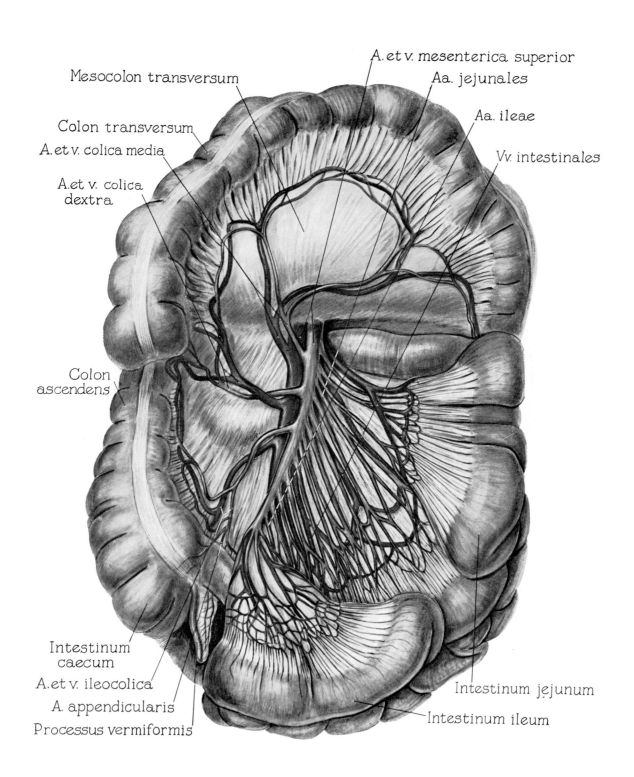

Blood supply of the intestines.

The transverse colon is lifted to show the patterns of distribution of the intestinal and colic branches of the superior mesenteric artery, and the accompanying venous tributaries to the portal vein. (From Warren: Handbook of Anatomy, Harvard University Press.)

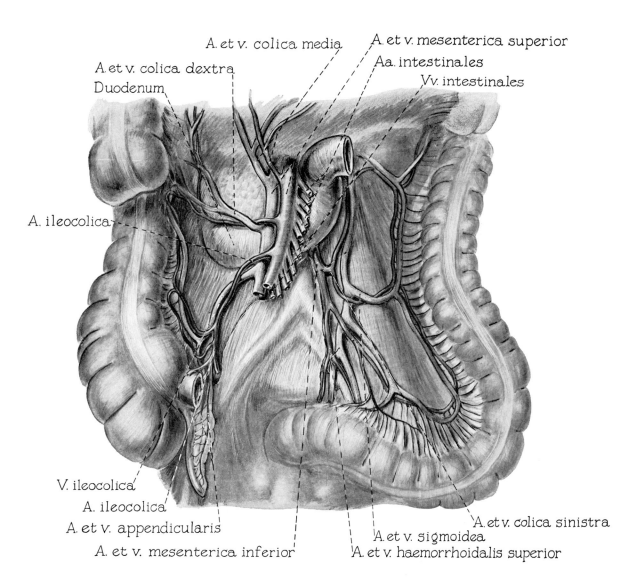

Blood supply to the large intestine.

The jejunal and ileal divisions of the small intestine have been removed in order to expose the arterial branches of the inferior mesenteric and the corresponding veins of colic drainage. (From Warren: Handbook of Anatomy, Harvard University Press.)

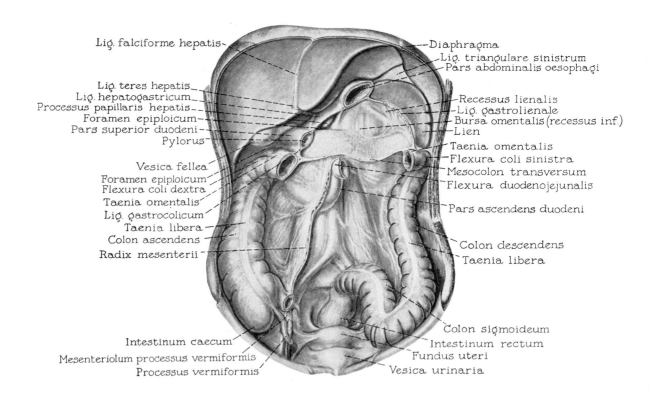

Greater and lesser peritoneal cavities.

The lesser cavity (omental bursa) is revealed by removal of the stomach. In clockwise direction from the caudal boundary the following mesenterial supports have been cut: transverse mesocolon; gastrocolic ligament; lesser omentum; gastrolienal ligament. In the region of the greater peritoneal cavity, the transverse colon has been removed by sectioning at its two flexures; the jejunoileum has been excised, the mesentery cut along its root of continuity with the parietal peritoneum. (From Warren: Handbook of Anatomy, Harvard University Press.)

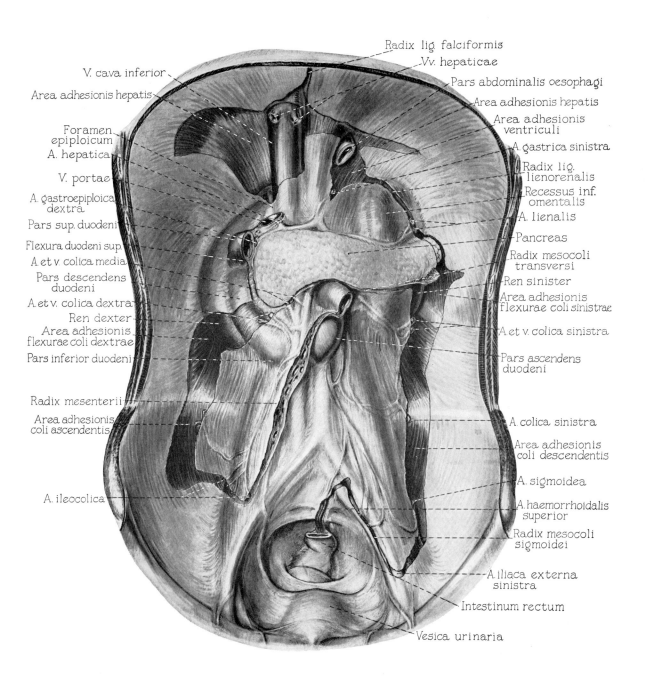

Lines of visceral reflection of the peritoneum.

The denuded areas on the diaphragm and the posterior abdominal wall are those on which the mesenterial supports and serous investments of the viscera are derived from the parietal peritoneum (full description on the following page). (From Warren: Handbook of Anatomy. Harvard University Press)

As the parietal peritoneum (which lines the abdominal and pelvic cavities) is carried outward (ventrally) to cover the organs as a visceral layer, it extends between the body-wall and viscera in a series of mesenterial supports for the organs (stomach, jejunum, ileum, transverse colon, and sigmoid mesocolon). Other parts of the digestive tube and glandular outgrowths therefrom are fixed to the dorsal body-wall. Although the serous layer covers them to give a partial investment, they lie in a predominantly retroperitoneal position. Examples of retroperitoneal structures are the duodenum, the pancreas, the ascending and descending portions of the colon, and the rectum.

From the diaphragm and from the uppermost part of the posterior abdominal wall, the peritoneum extends downward and forward, to enclose the liver and its round liagment. Over the round ligament it forms the falciform ligament; over the liver it is reflected as the right and left coronary ligaments and their narrower marginal portions, the right and left triangular ligaments. The bare area is an exposed, subserous field bounded by the four ligaments just named. From the middle of the left coronary ligament the peritoneal reflection is deflected to the left and constitutes the phrenicolienal (diaphragmatico-splenic) ligament—so termed because it passes from the diaphragm to the spleen, the latter viscus subdividing the primordial dorsal mesentery of the stomach. The gastrolienal (gastrosplenic) ligament passes from the spleen to the stomach (as the second part of the original dorsal mesentery of the stomach, or dorsal mesogastrium). At its inferior (caudal) extremity the gastrolienal ligament meets the transverse mesocolon.

In reference to the proximal portion of the digestive tube, it must be pointed out that the stomach possesses no direct attachment to the diaphragm or to the abdominal wall; superiorly its lesser omentum is attached to the inferior surface of the liver; inferiorly, its greater omentum is interrupted by the transverse colon; on the body's left, the spleen intervenes in a like manner. However, the succeeding segment, the duodenum or first part of the small intestine, is directly related to the posterior parietes; with the adjacent pancreas it is in retroperitoneal position. The jejunum and the ileum, which together constitute the succeeding, coiled portions of the small intestine, are supported by the mesentery; its line of attachment (root, or radix) begins at the duodenojejunal junction, to the left side of the second lumbar vertebra; descending therefrom in oblique course toward the right, it terminates in front of the right sacroiliac articulation. Like the duodenum, part of the cecum and all of the ascending colon have lost their mesenterial supports (through embryonic fusion with the parietal peritoneum); consequently, they are retroperitoneal (bare area). The next (or transverse) segment of the colon, having retained a mesenterial structure, is supported by the transverse mesocolon. This mesentery begins at the right colic (or hepatic) flexure and ends at the left colic (or splenic) flexure of the colon. Its line of attachment marks the inferior (caudal) boundary of the main portion of the omental bursa; the other boundaries are the lines of attachment of the phrenicolienal ligament; laterally, the inferior portions of the coronary ligaments and that of the right triangular ligament. Like the ascending colon, the descending part of the large intestine lacks a mesentery. However, the succeeding (or sigmoid) portion of the colon possesses a mesenterial support, the sigmoid mesocolon, whose S-shaped line of attachment crosses the iliac fossa in the greater pelvis, the pelvic brim, and attains presacral position in the lesser pelvis. The next segment of the large bowel, the rectum, is typically devoid of mesorectal attachment and lies against a bare area in front of the sacrum.

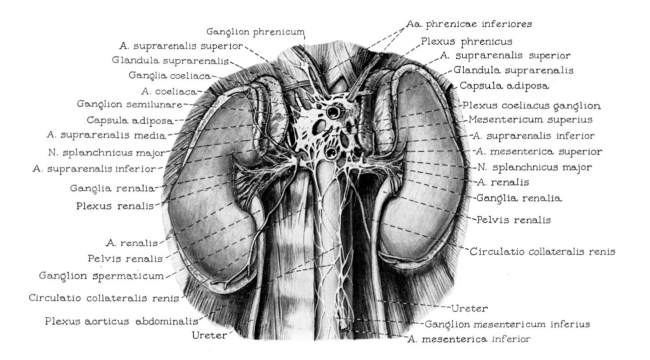

Autonomic nerves of the abdomen.

The celiac, mesenteric, and aortic sympathetic plexuses, with their related ganglia and nerves. (From Warren: Handbook of Anatomy, Harvard University Press.)

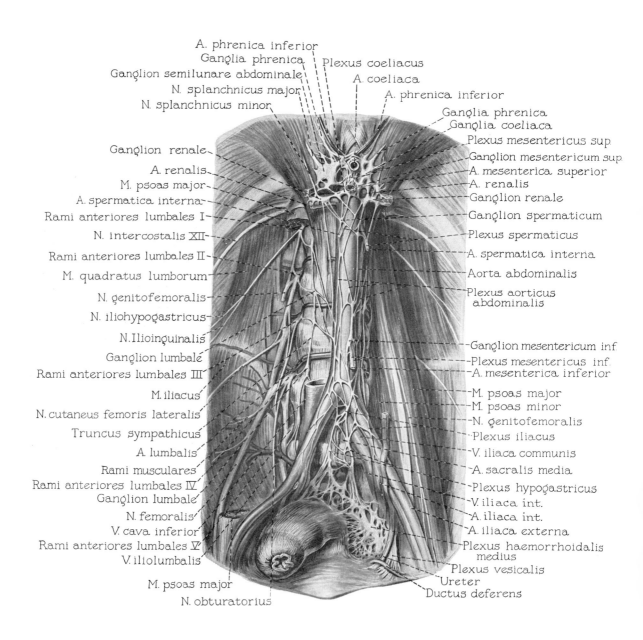

Autonomic nerves of the abdomen and pelvis.

(From Warren: Handbook of Anatomy, Harvard University Press.)

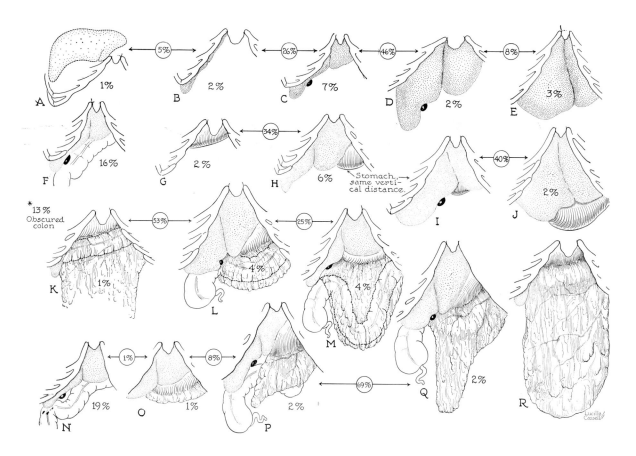

Abdominal viscera. Variations in position in 125 consecutive laboratory specimens.

A to R, Drawings of liver (A to E), stomach (F to J), transverse colon (K to M), and omentum (N to R). Within each set, the examples are arranged in order of increasing distance from xiphisternal articulation. One-sixth natural size.

A percentage placed near or upon a figure indicates the fraction of 125 cases which the illustration represents; a percentage between two figures, encircled, indicates the fraction of the cases that fall between the adjacent figures. *The examples of obscured colon are not represented in the illustrations.

Liver. In 94 per cent of the series of 125 sets of organs, the left lobe of the liver projected below the xiphisternal articulation (infrasternal notch) to an extreme descent of 18.5 cm. In only 6 per cent of the cases was it entirely concealed in anterior view, reaching an extreme height of 2 cm. superior to the notch (A).

Stomach. In 16 per cent of the specimens the stomach was entirely concealed by the liver and the transverse colon (F). It was invariably covered in at least a portion of its anterior aspect by the liver. The greater curvature in 42 per cent of the cases extended below the xiphisternal articulation for a distance of 5 cm. (G) to 13.5 cm. (H and I), and for a distance of 14 cm. to 25 cm. (J) in 42 per cent. The stomach variously occupied the infrasternal notch (G), the subcostal space near the left lobe of the liver (H), the notch between the hepatic lobes (I), and a wider area inferior to the anterior margin (J).

Transverse colon. In 13 per cent of the cases (not illustrated) the transverse colon was not in view inferior to the liver or stomach; in 58 per cent its lower margin extended for a distance of 8 cm. (K) to 21 cm. (L) below the xiphisternal articulation; in 29 per cent, for 21.5 cm. to 33 cm. (M).

Greater omentum. The greater omentum was not in view in 19 per cent of the specimens (N), and appeared as a mere fringe in an additional 2 per cent (O); in 8 per cent it extended 14 cm. to 19.5 cm. (P) below the xiphisternal articulation; in the remaining 71 per cent, from 20 cm. to 36 cm. (Q and R).

The illustrations of the liver (A to E) were selected to show the costal relations of the left lobe, since the right lobe was concealed in 38 per cent of the cases.

In 34 of 120 specimens the cecum was not in view, being covered by the coils of small intestine or by the omentum; in the 86 cases in which it was showing, its inferior margin was situated superior to the anterior superior iliac spine in 42 instances, opposite the spine in 26, and inferior to it in 18 cases.

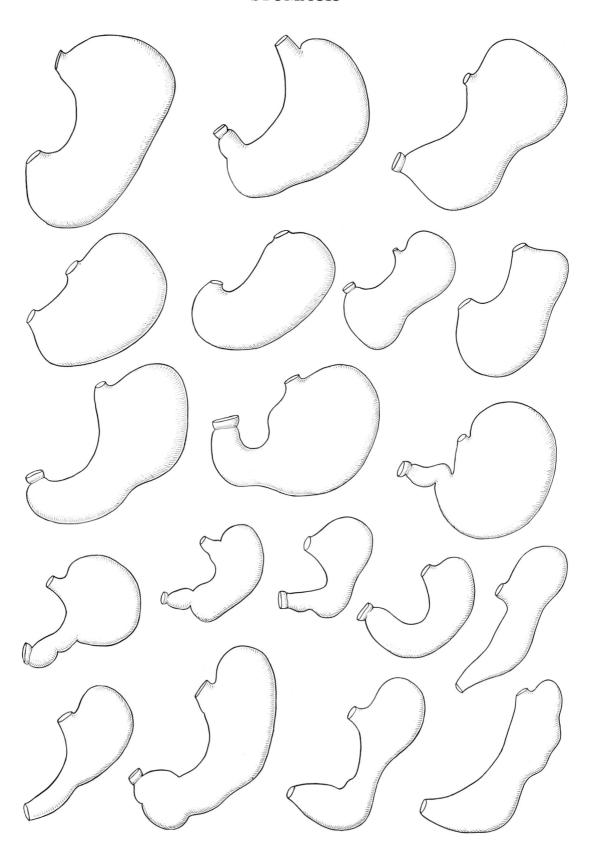

Stomach; variations in form. From laboratory specimens.

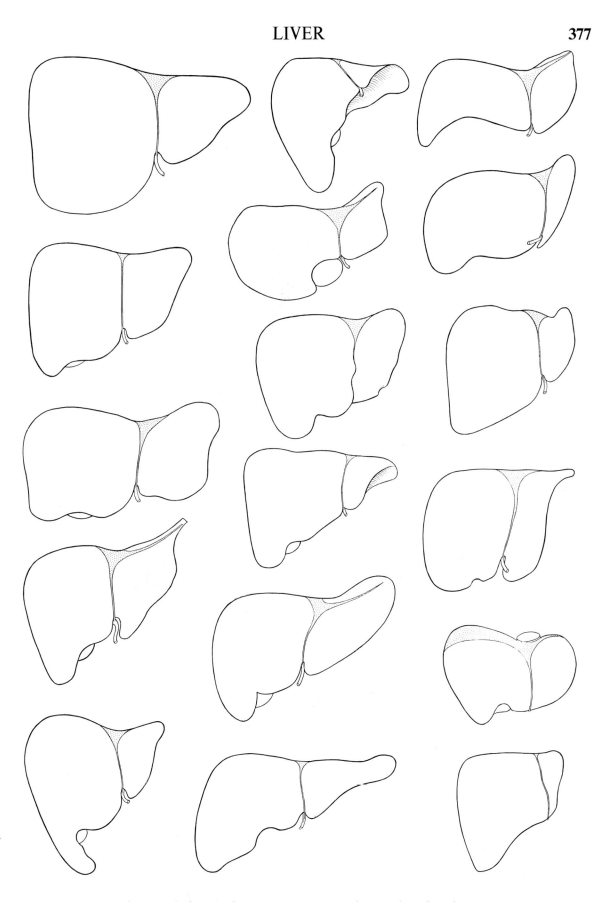

Liver; variations in form. Laboratory specimens. Anterior views.

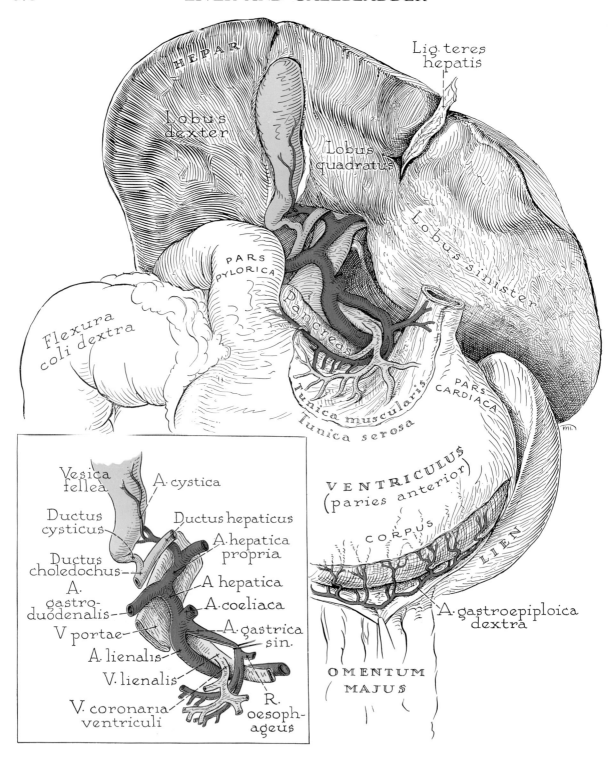

Hepatic and gastric blood vessels, the gallbladder, and the biliary ducts.

In the main figure the structures at the porta of the liver and along the curvatures of the stomach are shown. The liver has been lifted, the celiac artery cut away from the aorta, the esophagus transected and drawn forward; the serous investment of the stomach has been dissected away along the upper and lower borders of the organ; the lesser omentum has been removed. In the auxiliary figure the celiac artery and its branches are shown, together with the portal and splenic veins, and the gallbladder and its ducts.

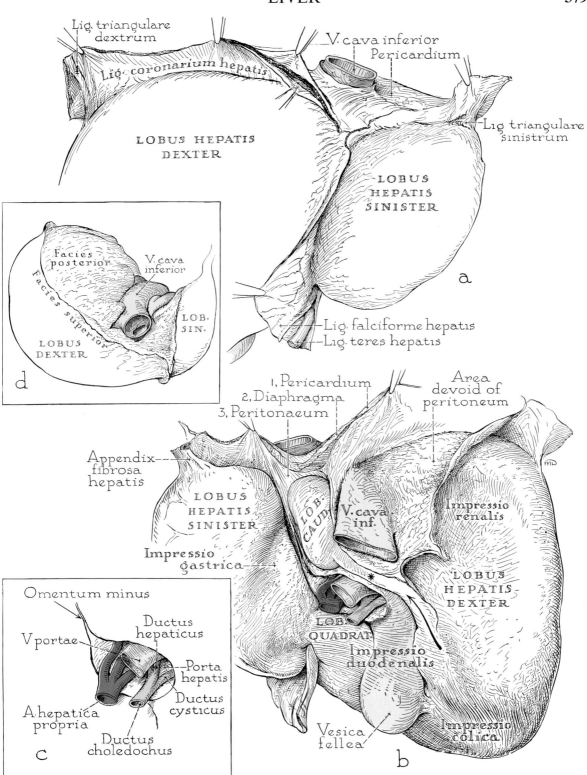

Liver: two excised specimens.

a, *b*, and *c*, Anterior and inferior surfaces of a specimen, and structures at the porta. The arrow in *b* passes into the omental bursa; the latter is roofed by a narrow lobe (at *). *d*, Superior surface of a second specimen.

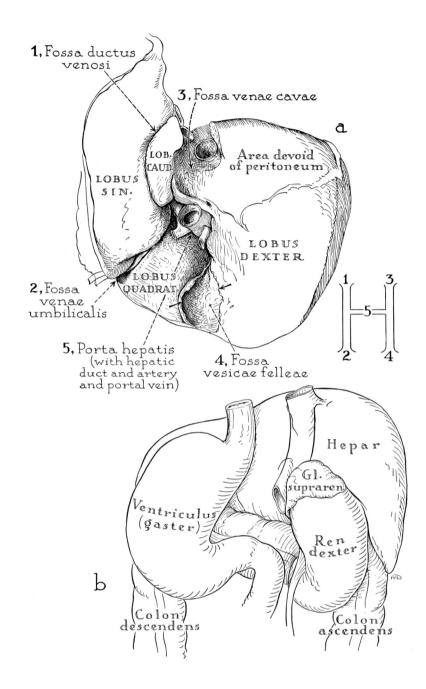

1, Fossa ductus venosi

3, Fossa venae cavae

LOB. CAUD.

LOBUS SIN.

Area devoid of peritoneum

LOBUS DEXTER

2, Fossa venae umbilicalis

LOBUS QUADRAT.

5, Porta hepatis (with hepatic duct and artery and portal vein)

4, Fossa vesicae felleae

a

Hepar

Gl. supraren.

Ventriculus (gaster)

Ren dexter

b

Colon descendens

Colon ascendens

Liver: form, fossae, and visceral relations. Inferior and postero-inferior views.

a, Fossae (1 to 5) for the venous duct, umbilical vein (round ligament), caval vein, gallbladder, and portal triad (artery, vein, and duct). The five fossae are regularly described as possessing, roughly, the form of the capital H (see inset, with arms numbered to correspond to enumeration of the fossae). In *a*, the cut edges of the serous covering of the gallbladder are indicated by arrows.

b, Organs which produce impressions on the inferior surface of the liver. Diagrammatic.

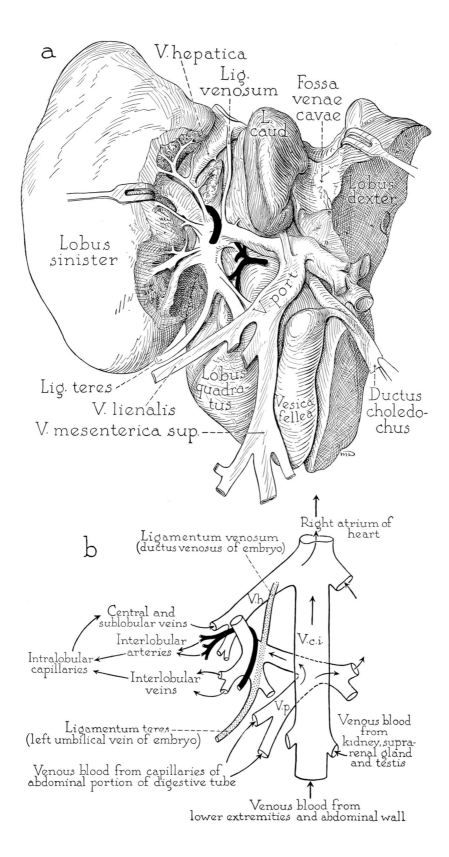

Liver: internal structure; arteries, veins, and ducts. (See following page for description.)

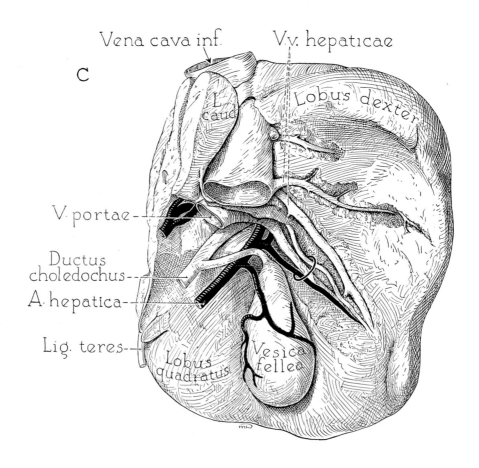

Liver: internal structure; arteries, veins, and ducts.

a, The following structures are shown: the portal vein and its tributaries; the branches of the hepatic artery; the cystic duct and the remains of embryonic vessels (ligamentum teres and ligamentum venosum); and a hepatic vein of the left lobe. The right lobe has been cut away; the hepatic parenchyma of the left lobe has been removed to the level at which appear several functional branches of the portal vein, a hepatic tributary of the inferior vena cava (the latter vessel removed), and the "nonfunctional," yet still patent, remains of the umbilical vein (ligamentum teres) and venous duct (ligamentum venosum).

b, The venous channels shown diagrammatically. The direction of blood flow is indicated by arrows.

c, The hepatic tributaries of the inferior vena cava, the branches of the hepatic artery and the portal vein, shown by local removal of the hepatic parenchyma.

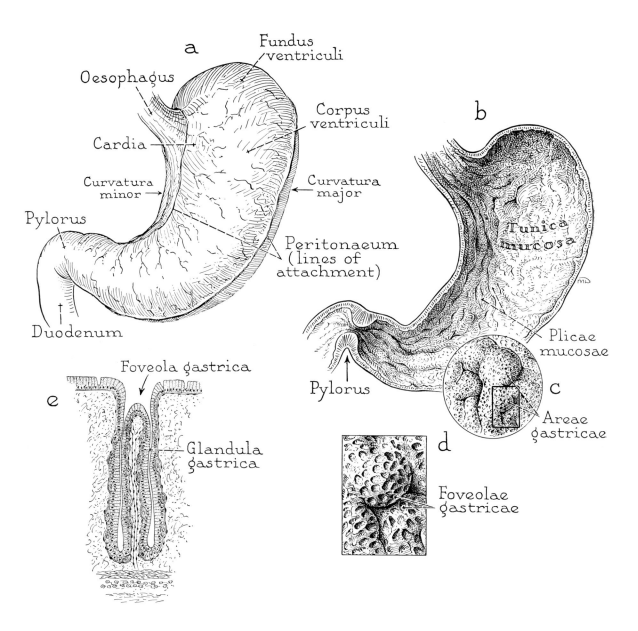

Stomach: external and internal form and mucosal structure.

a, The stomach entire, seen from the front. The lesser and greater omenta have been cut away along the lines of attachment to the borders, or curvatures, of the stomach.

b, The internal form of the stomach, showing the muscosal folds, or plicae.

c and *d,* The macroscopic appearance of the mucosal lining of the stomach; the area outlined in *c* is shown at somewhat higher magnification in *d.*

e, The microscopic structure of the tunica mucosa. The gastric glands descend into the submucosal layer from the foveolae (compare *d*).

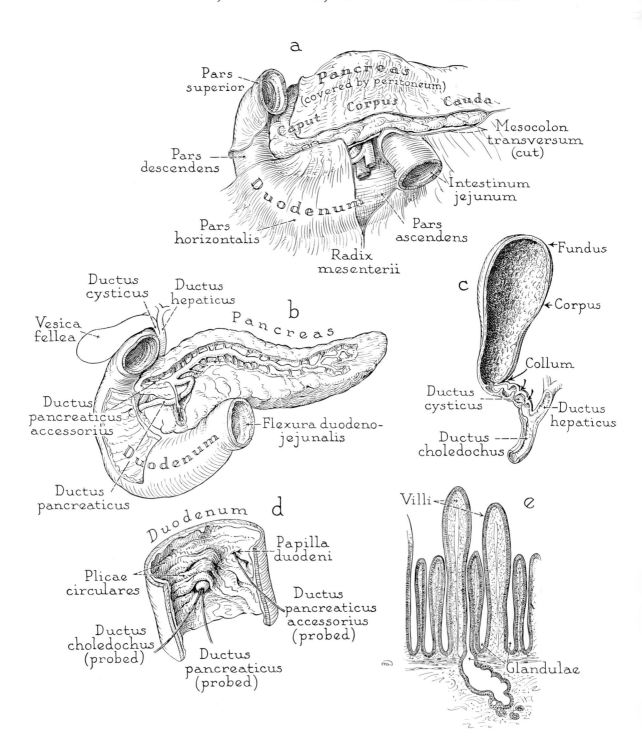

Duodenum, pancreas, and gallbladder.

a, *b*, and *d*, The pancreas and the duodenum. Showing the immediate relations of the organs (visceral, vascular, and peritoneal), the form and course of the pancreatic ducts, and the internal anatomy of the duodenum in the area of entrance of the pancreatic ducts and the common bile duct.

c, The gallbladder and its ducts. The valves in the cystic duct are indicated by the unlabelled arrows.

e, Microscopic appearance of the duodenal glands and villi.

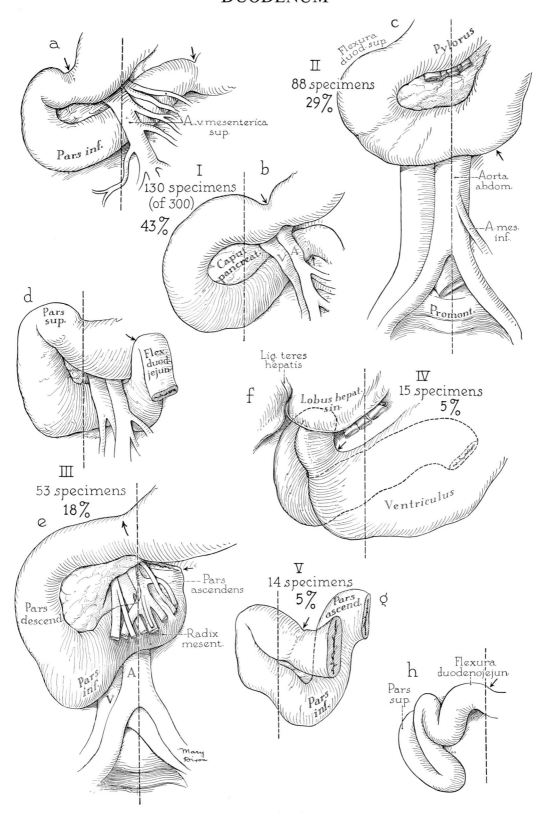

Duodenum; variations in form and positions.

Types are pictured, with record of the percentage occurrence of each in a series of 300 specimens.

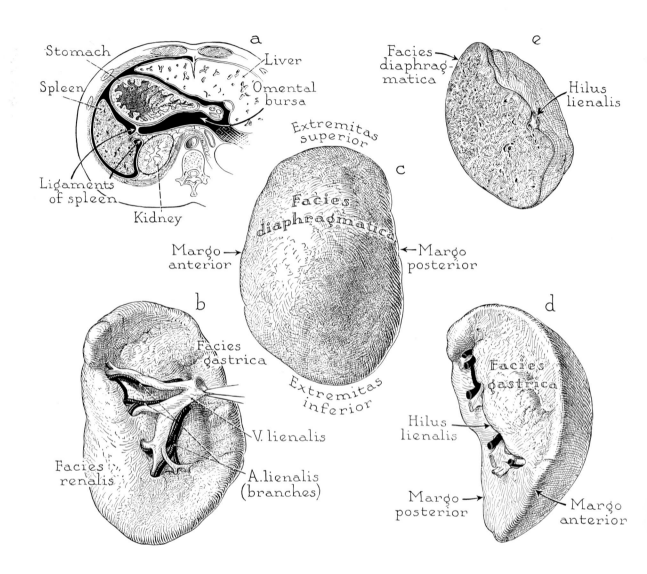

Spleen: relations, external configuration, and internal structure.

a, Relations of the spleen shown by transverse section of the body. Diagrammatic. The labelled arrows at the left point to the phrenicolienal (diaphragmaticosplenic) and gastrolienal (gastrosplenic) ligaments; the arrow at the right passes from the main peritoneal cavity into the omental bursa, or lesser peritoneal cavity. The bursa reaches the hilar area of the spleen.

b, *c*, and *d*, The spleen as seen in medial, lateral, and anterior veins, respectively.

e, The spleen, sectioned transversely at the level of the hilus.

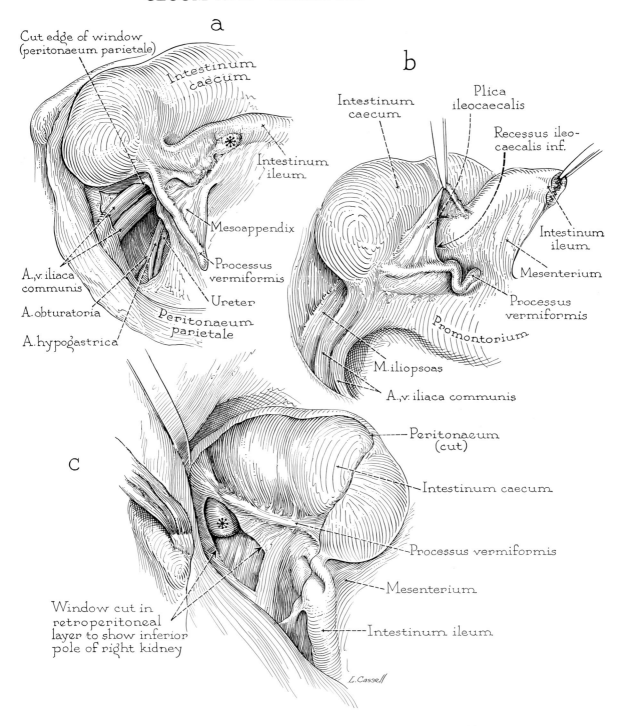

Cecum and vermiform appendix. Variations in form and position.

a, Commonest, or most frequent, form and position. The vermiform appendage crosses the pelvic brim, to rest on the peritoneal lining of the lesser, or true, pelvis. In so doing, the appendix, on deep, or retroperitoneal, level, would be related to the common iliac vessels, the obturator nerve and vessels, and the obturator internus muscle. Fatty lobule marked by *.

b, Vermiform appendix related to an ample ileocecal fold.

c, Vermiform appendix of elongate type, lodged in retrocecal position. The peritoneal layer has been incised and the cecum, thus mobilized, has been drawn medialward. In this way the right kidney is shown (at *) through an opening cut in the retroperitoneal layer.

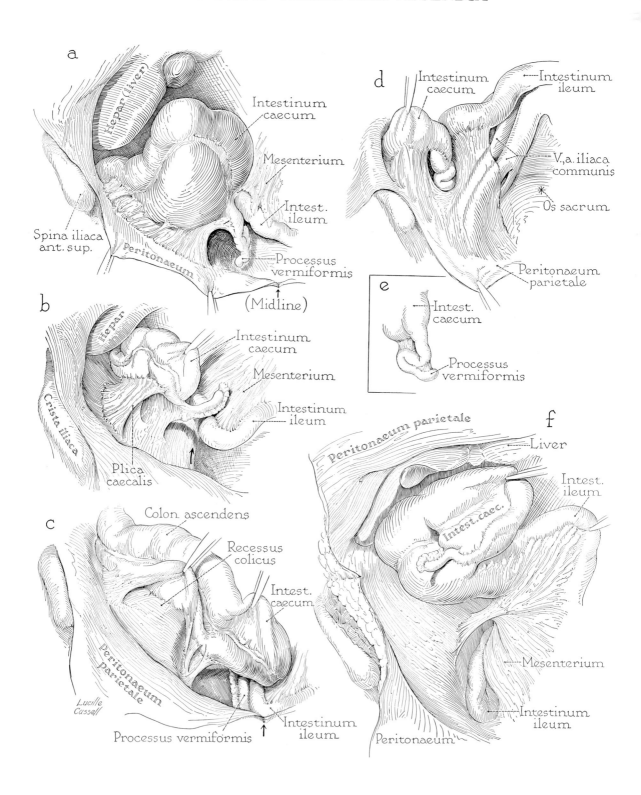

Ascending colon, cecum, and vermiform appendix.
Variations in form, position, and relationships; continued.

In all of the figures the cecum has been lifted in order to reveal the vermiform appendix or to demonstrate a fold (*b*) or a peritoneal fossa (*c*).

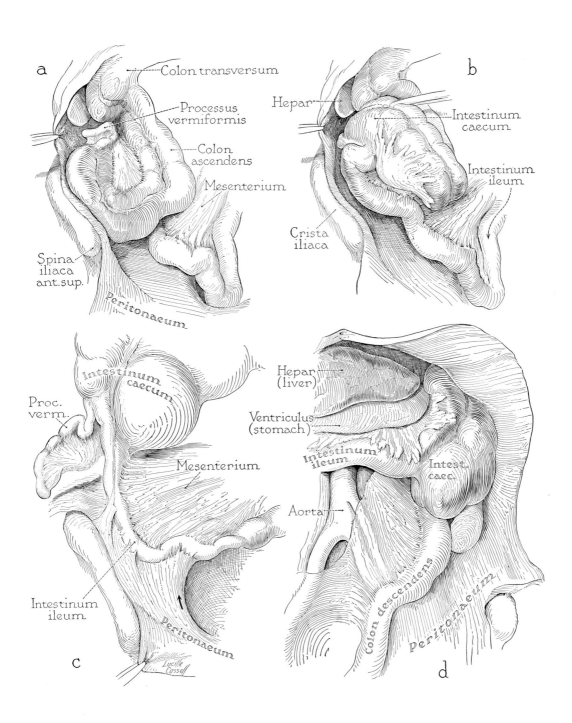

Ascending colon, cecum, and vermiform appendix. Variations; concluded.

a, Cecum situated cranial to a looped ascending colon. *b*, Elongate, redundant type of ascending colon. *c*, Mobile cecum, associated with a contorted vermiform process. *d*, Cecum in a case of situs inversus viscerum.

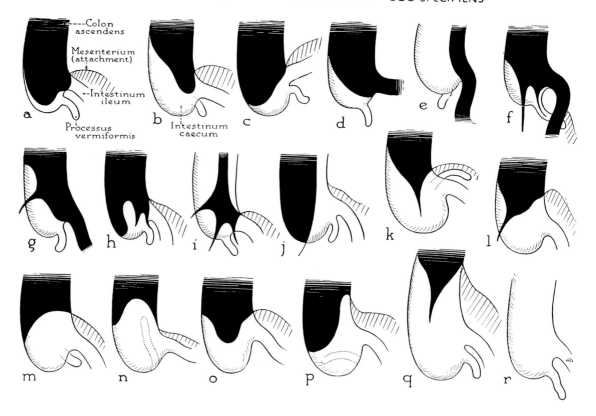

INTESTINUM CAECUM, COLON ASCENDENS
VARIATIONS IN PERITONEAL ATTACHMENT — 300 SPECIMENS

Attachment of the cecum, ascending colon, and ileum to the dorsal body wall
(areas of fixation shown in black).

Variations, shown by representative types in 300 adult specimens. *a*, An instance of almost complete dorsal fixation of the cecum. *b* and *c*, Cases in which the cecum was largely free and in which mobility was increased by the presence of a mesenterial support for the terminal portion of the ileum. Because the line of serous reflection from the cecum to the dorsal body is of even contour, retrocecal recesses are lacking (compare *f* to *i*). *d* and *e*, Specimens in which mobility of the cecum was reduced by fixation of the terminal ileum. *f* to *i*, Examples of occurrence of retrocecal recesses, that is, depressions occurring as offsets from the cecal fossa. *j*, A case in which the cecum and ascending colon were anchored laterally but free medially. *k*, *l*, and *q*, Specimens in which the area of parietal fixation showed as a dart-shaped prolongation carried downward on the ascending colon and the cecum (*k*, *l*) or only on the colon (*q*). *m* to *n*, Cases in which the cecum, the proximal portion of the ascending colon, and the ileum were free of dorsal parietal attachment. In such instances the vermiform appendix is likely to be retrocecal and occasionally longer than normal (as in *n*). *r*, A case of mobile cecum and ascending colon.

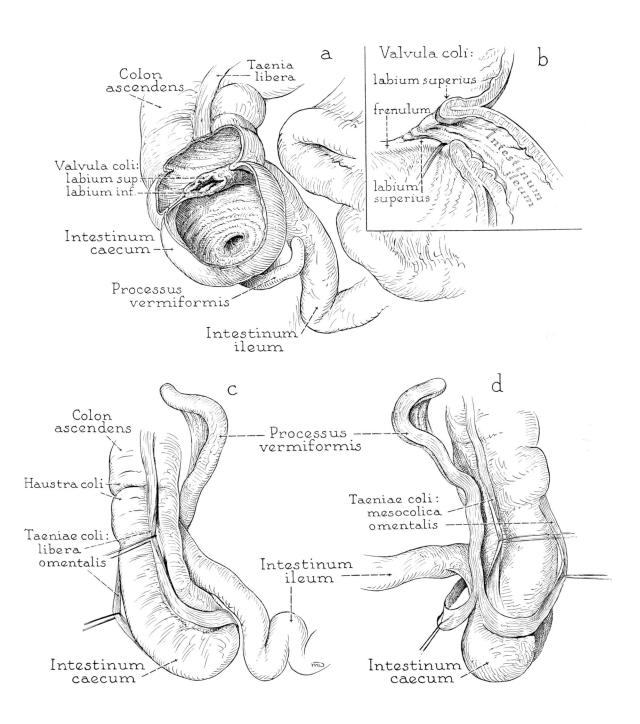

Cecum and vermiform appendix. External form and internal structure.

a, The cecum, opened to show the colic valve and the orifice of the vermiform process (NA, appendix).

b, The colic valve, shown by longitudinal section.

c and *d*, The cecum, ascending colon, and vermiform appendix, from the anterior and posterior aspects respectively. The taeniae have been freed from the colic wall; they converge upon the appendix, the latter being of the elongate, retrocecal type.

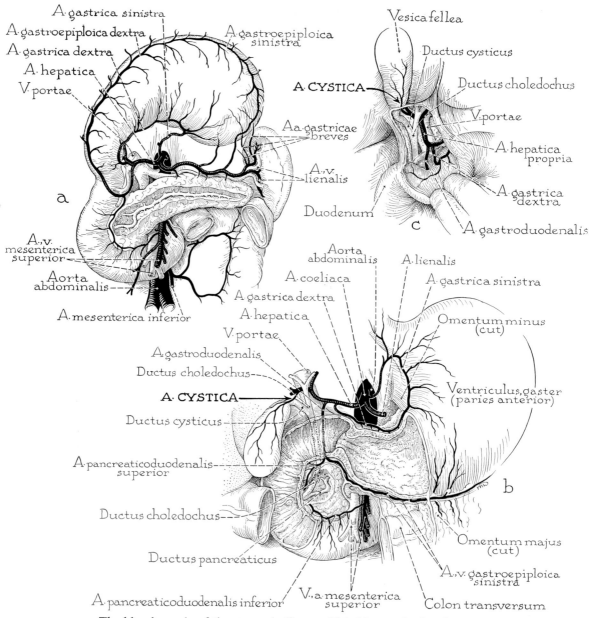

The blood supply of the stomach, liver, gallbladder, and related organs.

a, The branches of the celiac artery, exposed by lifting the stomach upward. The stomach is shown without its omental supports, in order to present more graphically the pattern of triradiate division and subsequent distribution of the celiac branches.

b, The branches of the hepatic division of celiac artery, shown with the stomach restored to natural position. Here the artery to the gallbladder is derived from the right ramus of the hepatic artery proper. This and other types are illustrated on the following page.

c, The relation of the biliary ducts to the blood vessels, as seen upon dissection of the anterior layer of the hepatoduodenal ligament.

(From Jones and Shepard: A Manual of Surgical Anatomy.)

Group III. The third general group comprises specimens in which the immediate source of the cystic artery matches the regular pattern (Group I) but differs from them in the derivation of the parent vessel (*g* and *h*). The parent stem may be the superior mesenteric in each, but the hepatic artery itself may be either an accessory artery or a replacing one.

Group IV. To this category are assigned those specimens in which the cystic artery is "moved" toward the aorta. These vessels have been observed in four types: from the right gastric (*i*); from the hepatic artery near the celiac source (*j*); from the celiac itself (*k*); and from the superior mesenteric (*l*).

ARTERIA CYSTICA
Types of origin, 800 specimens

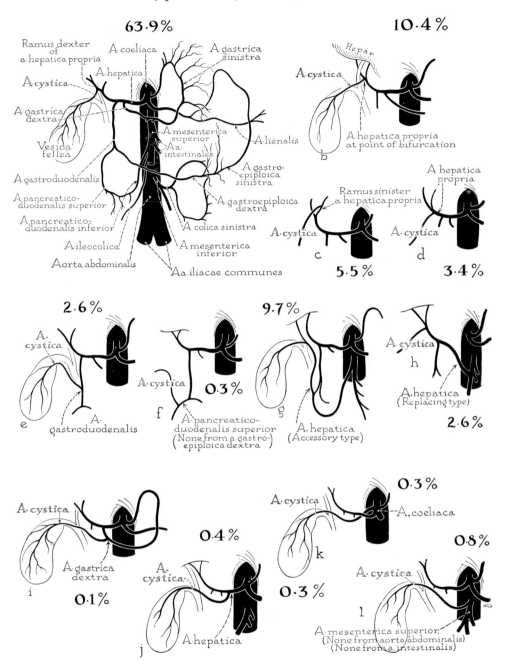

Cystic artery. Variations in origin.

Patterns fall into four major divisions.

Group I. In specimens of the first (and most numerous) category, the cystic artery arises from a ramus of the proper hepatic artery, from the latter at the point of division, or from the same vessel proximal to the point of bifurcation (*a* to *d*). In succession, and in the order of decreasing frequency, these origins are: right ramus of the hepatic proper; the latter vessel at the point of division; the left ramus; and the hepatic proper, proximal to the point of bifurcation.

Group II. In these specimens the cystic artery springs from the downward-directed vessel, the gastroduodenal artery, or the latter's branch, the superior pancreaticoduodenal (*e* and *f*). Origin from the more distant source is far less common than the nearer.

(*This legend is continued at the bottom of page 392, beneath the rule.*)

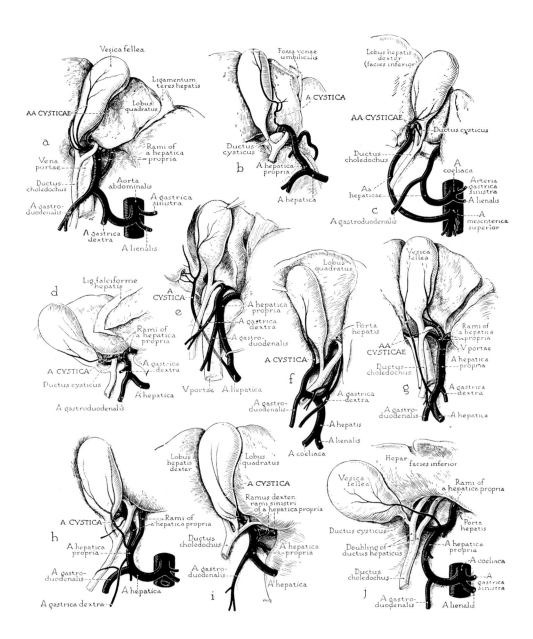

See facing page for description.

Constituents of the hepatic pedicle. Variations encountered in a study of 500 laboratory specimens.

a, The larger of 2 cystic arteries originates from the right ramus of the hepatic artery proper after the latter has passed behind the hepatic duct.

b, The cystic artery in this specimen is a branch of the right ramus of the hepatic artery proper, which crosses in front of the hepatic duct.

c, When the regular hepatic artery is absent, the artery to the left lobe of the liver arises as a branch of the celiac axis. The artery to the right lobe, derived from the superior mesenteric artery, passes obliquely upward and to the right, first posterior to the common bile duct, then to the right of it. Just before entering the right lobe of the liver, it gives origin to a large cystic branch to the hepatic surface of the gallbladder. The artery to the left lobe, derived from the celiac, contributes no cystic branch.

d, The cystic artery, originating from the left ramus of the proper hepatic artery, courses to the right in front of the hepatic duct.

e, An unusually long cystic artery derived from the proximal portion of the hepatic artery. The artery ascends to the right, then passes behind the common bile duct and portal vein. It gives origin to several small twigs to the right hepatic lobe before reaching the gallbladder and the tissues in the fossa.

f, The hepatic artery divides at a point distant from the porta; consequently the rami are exceptionally long. From the right ramus a cystic artery ascends to the gallbladder, and a gastroduodenal descends. From the left ramus, 3 arteries ascend to the left lobe of the liver, and a right gastric descends. Because of these arrangements the blood supply of the stomach is a constituent of the hepatic pedicle.

g, One of a pair of cystic arteries arises low as a branch of the gastroduodenal; it courses upward, then crosses in front of the common bile duct and the portal vein. The second cystic artery is a branch of the left ramus; it turns abruptly to the right and crosses in front of the left hepatic duct, then supplies the left half of the gallbladder and fossa.

h, A rare example of dual cystic arteries, fused distally (at arrow) to form a single terminal trunk, thus contributing to an arterial circle around the hepatic duct.

i, The cystic artery is derived, in the familiar way, from the right ramus of the proper hepatic artery. A large accessory hepatic duct from the right lobe of the liver enters the common bile duct just distal to the fusing point of the cystic and hepatic ducts.

j, The cystic duct enters the right hepatic duct. The cystic artery arises from the division point of the proper hepatic artery; it crosses in front of the right and left hepatic ducts to reach the gallbladder.

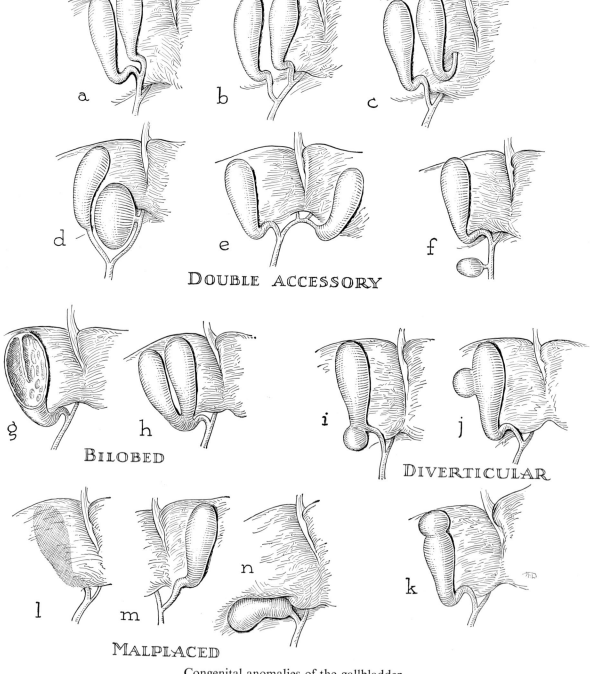

DOUBLE ACCESSORY

BILOBED

DIVERTICULAR

MALPLACED

Congenital anomalies of the gallbladder.

a to *f*, Types of double gallbladder, showing the position of the accessory organ and relationship of the cystic duct. *a*, Regular and accessory gallbladders lodged in a fossa of normal position and possessing a common cystic duct. *b*, A pattern differing from the preceding in the occurrence of separate cystic ducts. *c*, Termination of one of the cystic ducts in the liver. *d*, An accessory gallbladder, with a cystic duct terminating in the common hepatic duct. *e*, An accessory *vesica* situated beneath the left lobe of the liver. *f*, An instance of doubling, in which the accessory gallbladder, situated in the lesser omentum, emptied into the common bile duct. *g* and *h*, Forms of bilobed gallbladder. *g*, Partially separated by an internal septum. *h*, Paired through the fundus and body, but joined at the neck to form a single cystic duct. *i* to *k*, Types of congenital diverticula. *i*, Diverticulum at the neck of the gallbladder. *j*, Cul-de-sac from the body of the organ. *k*, Similar expansion at the fundus. *l* to *n*, Abnormality in position of the gallbladder. *l*, Lodgment within the substance of the liver. *m*, Placement under the left hepatic lobe. *n*, Posterior situation under the right lobe. (Redrawn from Gross: Arch. Surg., *32*:131-62, 1936.)

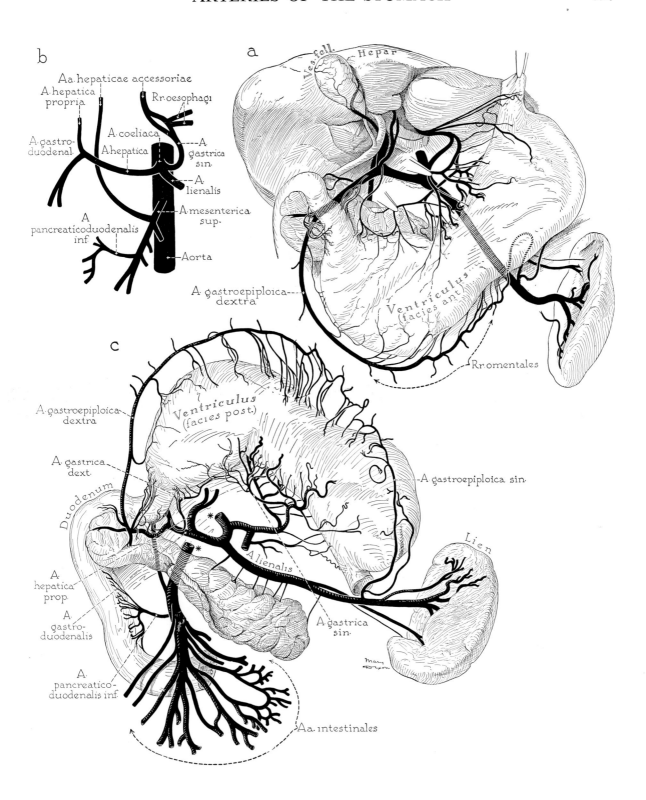

Hepatic, gastric, pancreatic, and splenic arterial supply.

a, The excised organs are seen from the front.

b, The chief arteries shown in the preceding figure. Diagrammatic.

c, The stomach has been lifted, in order to reveal the splenic, pancreatic, and duodenal arteries.

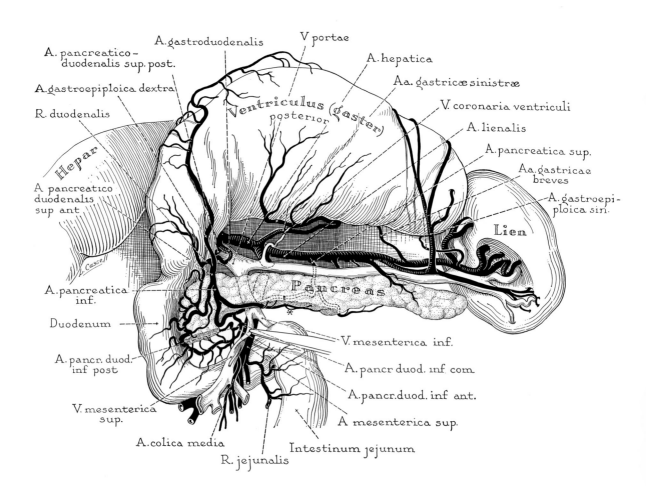

The arteries of supply of the stomach, pancreas, duodenum, and spleen.
The stomach is elevated to show the retrogastric structures.

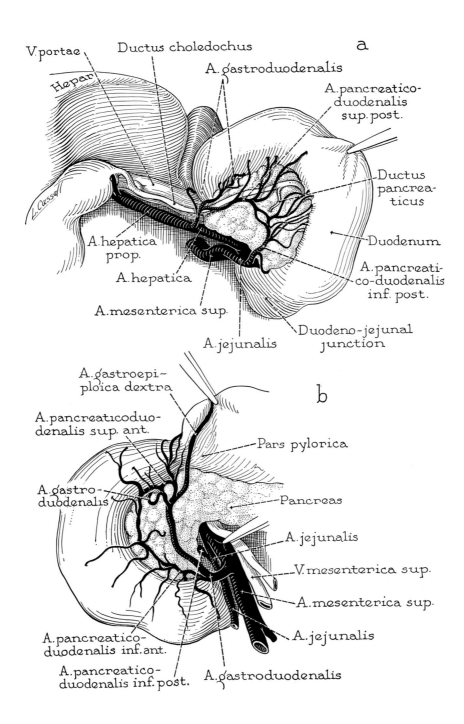

The arteries of supply to the duodenum and to the head of the pancreas.
Same specimen as that shown in the preceding illustration.

a, Arteries of the dorsal aspect of duodenum and head of the pancreas, shown by retraction of the duodenum.

b, Arteries of the ventral aspect of the same organs. The pyloric portion of the stomach has been lifted.

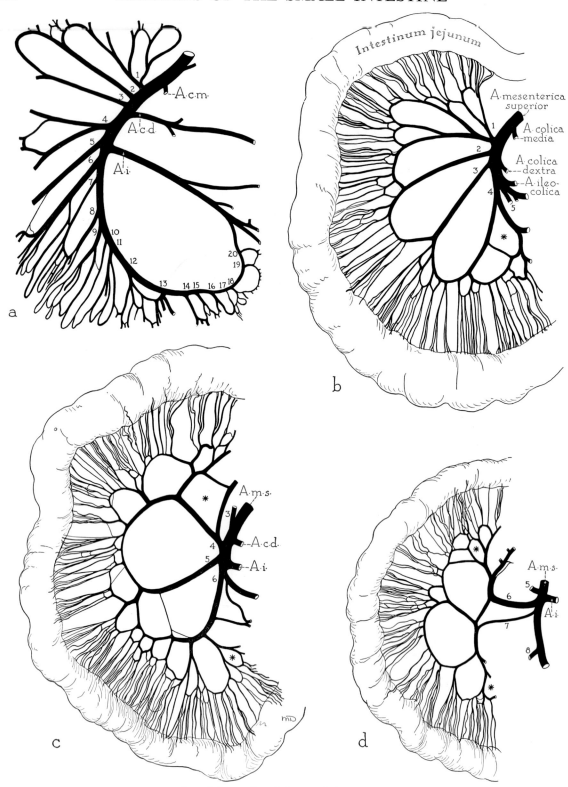

Arterial supply of the small intestine.
Full dissection (with following figure) of a single specimen.

a, Superior mesenteric artery with the intestinal arteries (numbered). *b* to *d*, Successive loops of intestine, showing the pattern of arterial supply. Asterisks mark the same lunette in the distal end of one segment and proximal end of the succeeding one.

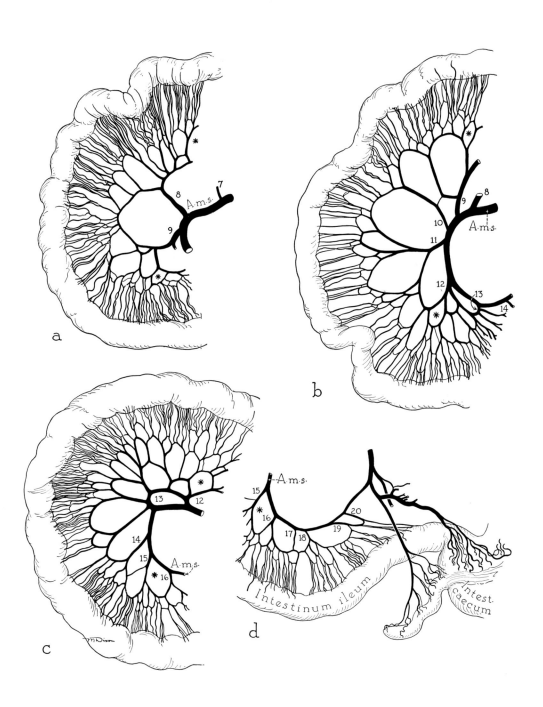

Arterial supply of the small intestine. Completing dissection of the vessels in a single specimen.

a to *d*, Successive loops of small intestine, continuing the series. *d* also demonstrates the vessels of the dorsum of the cecum and of the vermiform process, and the anastomosis between the last intestinal and the ileocolic arteries.

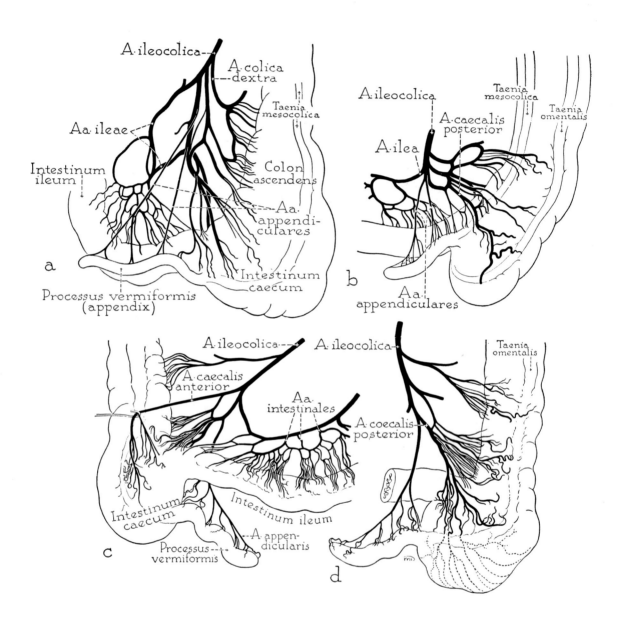

Arterial supply to terminal segment of the ileum, the cecum, and the vermiform appendix.

a, *b*, and *d*, Posterior views. *c*, An anterior view.

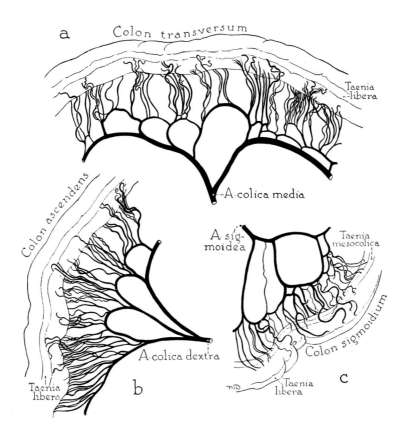

Arterial supply to the large intestine.

a, The transverse colon. *b*, The ascending colon. *c*, The sigmoid colon.

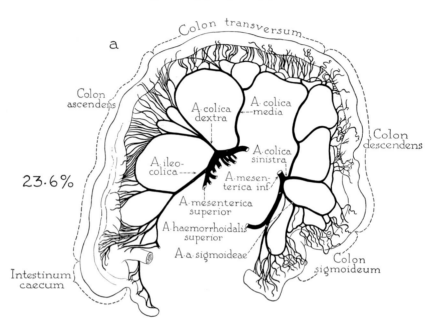

A. MESENTERICA SUPERIOR
TYPES OF BRANCHING, 700 SPECIMENS
Frequent types (81.7%)

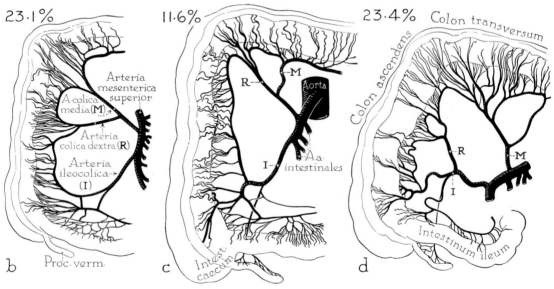

Description on the opposite page.

Infrequent types (18·3%)

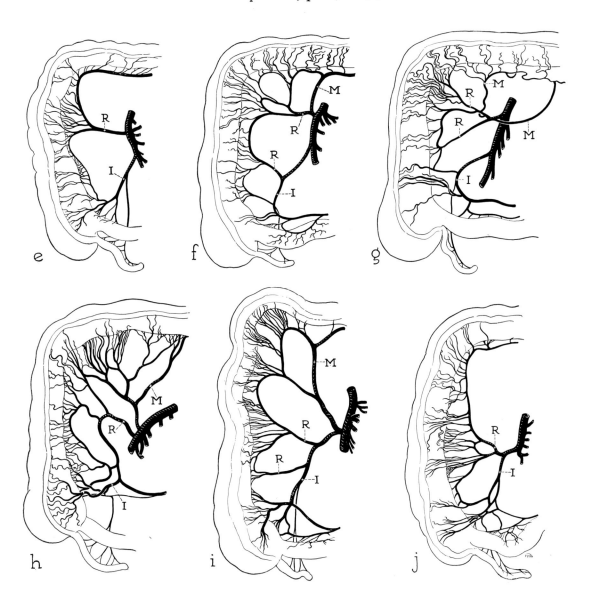

Superior mesenteric artery. Variations.

In approximately 60 per cent of cases, the three regular branches of the superior mesenteric arteries either arose separately (*a*), or the right colic and middle colic originated from a common stem. Often the right colic and ileocolic (*d*) came from a common source-vessel.

Reduction in number of major branches (*e* and *j*), and increase beyond the standard number (*f* to *i*), each infrequent, accounted for the remainder of the specimens.

A·APPENDICULARIS
VARIATIONS IN ORIGIN, 225 SPECIMENS

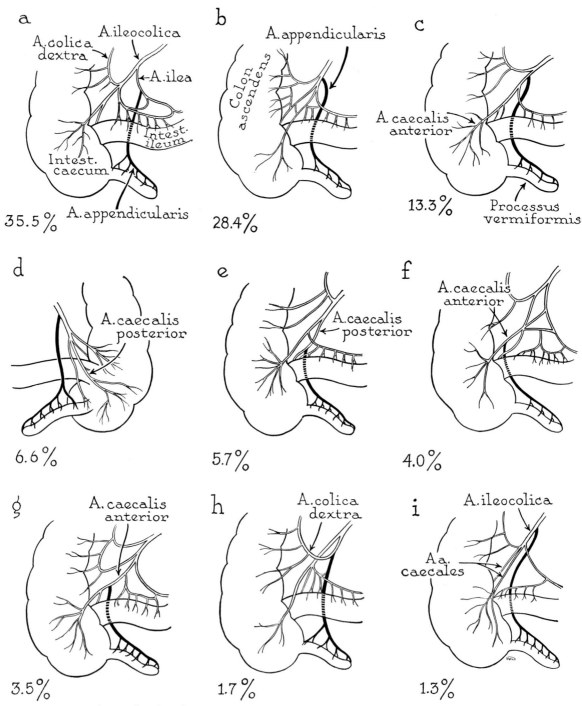

Appendiceal and cecal arteries. Variations encountered in 225 specimens.
The patterns are arranged in the order of decreasing frequency.

to two sigmoidal arteries and to the superior hemorrhoidal. *f*, In examples of this unusual variety, the initial division matches the branching in *a*. However, the dextral division gives origin solely to the superior hemorrhoidal; the sinistral part is the source of the sigmoidal and the left colic arteries.

    g, As in the equally uncommon type *e*, the middle colic artery arises from the inferior mesenteric, but in this case a true middle colic artery is present, derived from a short trunk which is also the source of several sigmoidal arteries. The third division of the inferior mesenteric is the superior hemorrhoidal artery.

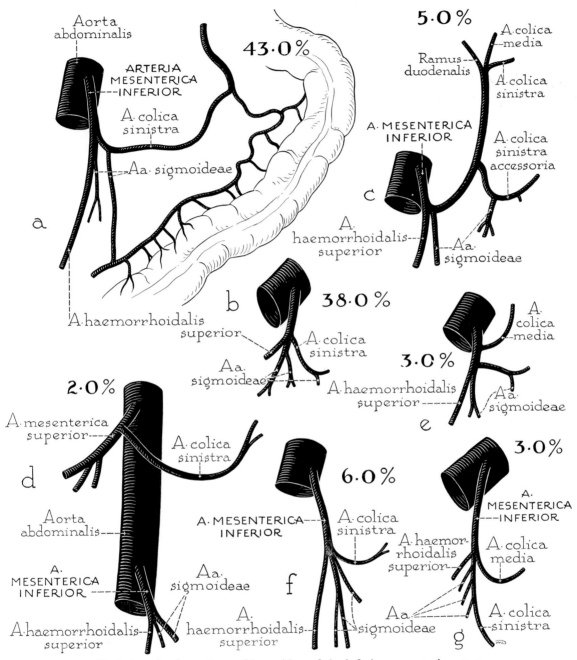

Variations in the pattern of branching of the inferior mesenteric artery.

a, The most common scheme of branching, in which the left colic and a sigmoidal artery arise from a short common trunk of inferior mesenteric origin. *b,* The second most frequent variety; the superior mesenteric artery divides triradially into middle colic and superior hemorrhoidal (NA, *A. rectalis superior*) portions marginally, with a common stem for the sigmoidal rami placed between the other two.

c, The first among the less common types, in which the inferior mesenteric artery divides primarily into two portions. The left division gives rise in succession to the following: a sigmoidal artery; an accessory left colic with a sigmoidal ramus; and an elongate common trunk for left colic and middle colic branches and a duodenal ramus. The superior hemorrhoidal is the dextral division of the inferior mesenteric artery.

d, A rare variety; the left colic artery originates from the superior instead of the inferior mesenteric; the latter artery from the aorta gives rise to the sigmoidal and superior hemorrhoidal arteries.

e, Another uncommon type; in the absence of a true left colic artery, the inferior mesenteric gives origin

(*Legend continued at bottom of page 406.*)

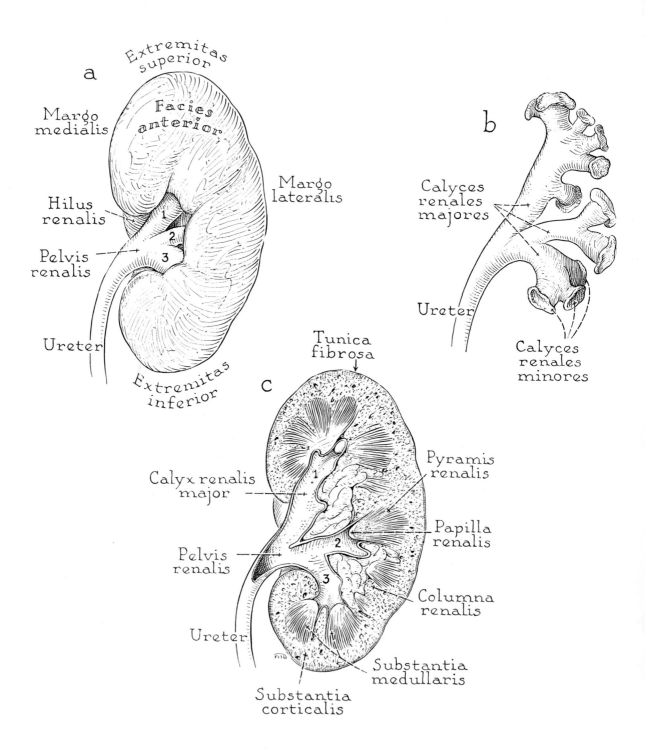

Kidney and ureter; external form and internal structure.

a, The kidney, renal pelvis, and proximal portion of the ureter. Anterior surface.

b, The renal pelvis and calyces.

c, The structure of the kidney, seen in section. The major calyces are numbered to correspond with the enumeration in *a*.

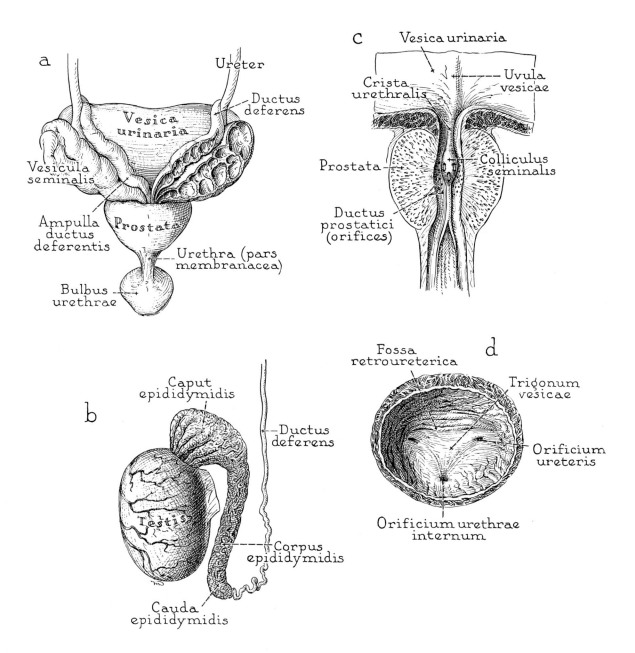

Urinary bladder and urethra, ductus deferens and seminal vesicles, prostate and testis.
External form, internal structure.

a, The urinary bladder, seminal vesicles, ductus deferens, prostate, and urethra. Posterior aspect of dissection. The seminal vesicle and the ampulla of the duct are opened on the right side.

b, Testis and ductus deferens. The structure of the epididymis is shown by removal of connective tissue. The vaginal tunic covers the testis.

c, The trigonal area of the urinary bladder, the prostate, and the urethra. Shown by coronal section through the prostate.

d, The trigonal portion of the urinary bladder.

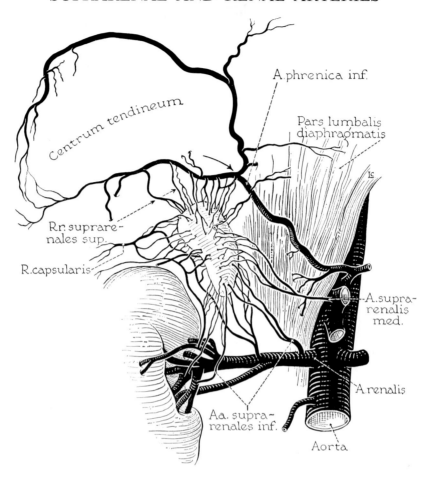

Suprarenal and renal arteries.

Suprarenal branches here arise from the inferior phrenic, the celiac, and the renal arteries, from hilar divisions of the renal and from supernumerary twigs to the parenchyma of the kidney. Regularly the suprarenal branches from the inferior phrenic artery spring from the inferior division of the latter (below the arrow.)

Illustrations in some textbooks of gross anatomy still lead to the belief that only three arteries supply a suprarenal gland, one minute vessel apiece from phrenic, aortic, and renal sources. Although the vessels do come from the sources just named, they are exceedingly numerous. Dividing as they course toward the suprarenal, their number sometimes attains a total of 50 or more at the periphery of the gland. In some instances their origin is chiefly phrenic; in others it is renal, the twigs being derived from the main renal artery, or, from a hilar division of the renal, with striking arborization at the margin of the gland. In some instances twigs from an accessory phrenic branch of the aorta add complexity to the pattern. Ofttimes rami of suprarenal level cross to the upper pole of the kidney, thus helping to render highly vascular the quadrilateral area above the true pedicle of the kidney.

Suprarenal and renal areas, therefore, cannot be divorced; nor can the genital visceral supply be regarded as independent of either of these, since a spermatic (or ovarian) artery may arise from a supernumerary renal. Even when the gonadal vessel arises from the aorta at the accustomed level, it may still be an element of the pedicle, coursing transversely to pass through a hiatus in the renal vein.

While it is common to find suprarenal arteries multiple to an astonishing degree, it is likewise regular to find veins disposed in simplest possible arrangement, i.e., one vein for each suprarenal gland.

The suprarenal vein of the right side is exceedingly short (page 420); it courses transversely to end quickly in the inferior vena cava. The vein of the left gland is longer; it descends to the left renal, almost always receiving the inferior phrenic vein, and, often, capsular tributaries.

Thus it is clear that suprarenal arteries are numerous, the vein single, for each gland. There is, then, no similarity in pattern between suprarenal arteries and the associated veins. Nowhere in the human body are vessels of the two categories of blood vessel as discrepant in schema as they are in the supply to this endocrine gland.

AA· PHRENICAE INFERIORES
TYPES OF ORIGIN, 700 SPECIMENS

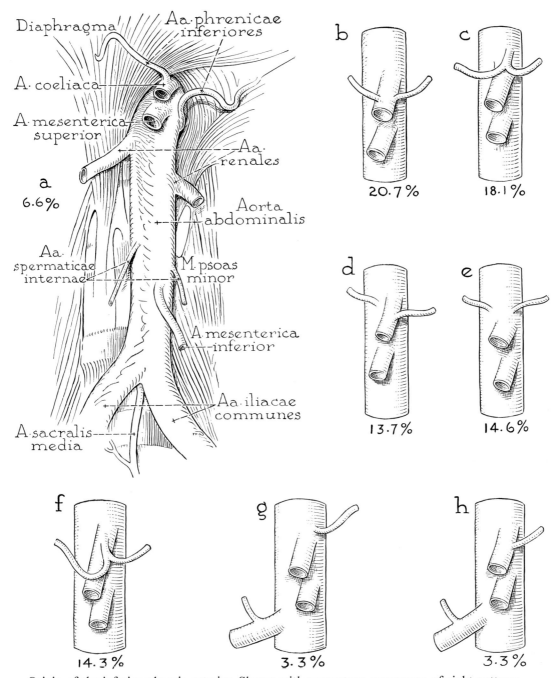

Origin of the inferior phrenic arteries. Shown with percentage occurrence of eight patterns.

a, Separately from the celiac artery (right) and the aorta (left). *b*, Separately from the celiac artery. *c*, By a common stem of aortic derivation. *d*, The reversal of the arrangement in *a*. *e*, Bilateral origin from the aorta. *f*, By a common stem from the celiac artery. *g*, From the right renal artery and the aorta (left). *h*, The reversal of the arrangement in the preceding figure. These together constitute 94.7 per cent of the total number of specimens. Among the remaining type (total of 5.3 per cent) are the vessels that arose from the following arterial sources: left gastric; hepatic; accessory hepatic; internal spermatic. No arteries derived from the splenic division of the celiac.

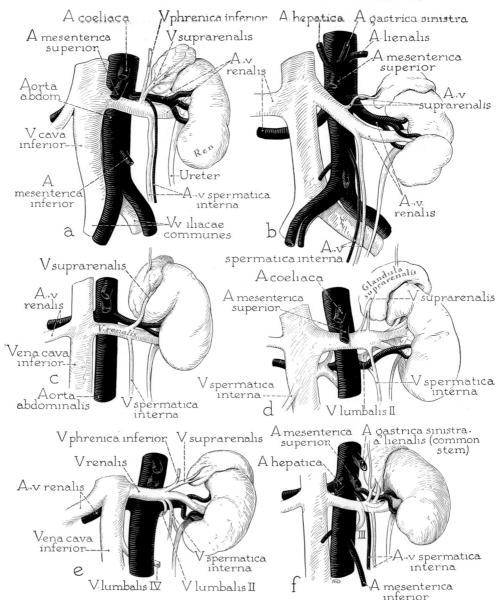

Variations in the renal form, position, and blood supply. Pages 412 to 416: Twenty examples encountered in a study of 100 consecutive specimens.

a, The most frequent arrangement of renal tributaries: the inferior phrenic and suprarenal veins enter the renal as a confluent vessel; the internal spermatic vein enters the left renal on the caudal border at a point lateral to that at which the confluent stem enters on the cranial border. The internal spermatic artery is unusual in that it accompanies the renal vessel in the medial half of the pedicle.

b, The suprarenal vein enters the renal independently, and the left internal spermatic artery arises at the usual level. The three vessels regularly derived from a celiac axis originate independently from the aorta.

c, The regular tributaries enter the renal vein opposite each other.

d, The suprarenal and internal spermatic veins are bifid; the latter sends its divergent channels into the renal vein on superficial level, and into the second lumbar vein on deep level. The renal artery courses between the arms of the Y-shaped division.

e, The second left lumbar vein ends independently in the renal, but the fourth lumbar crosses to the opposite side to become a caval tributary.

f, The third left lumbar vein ends in the renal; the suprarenal vein is double, one of the pair being confluent with the inferior phrenic. The left gastric and splenic arteries arise from a common aortic stem, whereas the hepatic (in the absence of a celiac source) leaves the aorta independently. An accessory renal artery originates as a common stem with the internal spermatic, both constituting the renal pedicle.

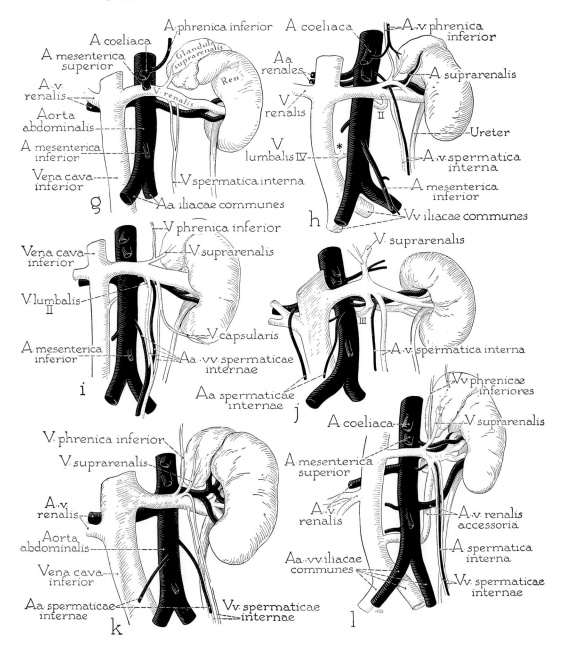

Variations in the renal blood supply, continued.

g, Bifurcation of the internal spermatic vein; the separate channels enter the renal vein lateral to the point of termination of the suprarenal.

h, The left renal vein divides; an internal spermatic artery of high origin passes through the hiatus thus formed and becomes a constitutent of the renal pedicle. The cranial element of the divided vein receives two suprarenal tributaries, one of which is confluent with the inferior phrenic vein; the caudal division receives a large second lumbar and an internal spermatic vein. One of the lower lumbar veins receives lesser tributaries from prevertebral level (at *).

i, On its caudal margin, the left renal vein receives the second lumbar vein and the divisions of a bifid internal spermatic. The lateral one of the pair is a common tributary with a capsular vessel.

j, Doubling of the left renal vein through the lateral half of its course; the visceral tributaries (suprarenal and internal spermatic) end in the superficial limb; the parietal tributary (third lumbar vein) ends in the deep limb. The left internal spermatic artery, after a short transverse course as a constituent of the renal pedicle, hooks around the Y-shaped confluens of the renal limbs; then it descends vertically with the corre-sponding vein.

(*Description is continued at bottom of page 414.*)

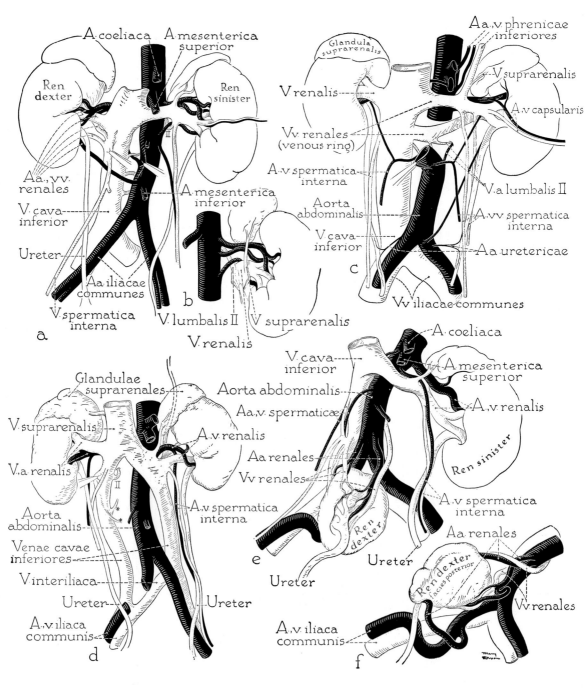

See facing page for description.

(Continuation of description of illustration on page 413.)

k, One of a pair of internal spermatic veins enters the left renal vein independently; the other forms a common channel with the suprarenal.

l, One of a pair of phrenic veins joins the suprarenal in the customary way; the other courses through the gland before establishing connection with the suprarenal drainage. Caudally the tributaries are elements of, or vessels related to, an elongate type of so-called circumaortic venous ring. The postaortic limb of the "ring" serves as an accessory renal vein (matching the course of a supernumerary artery). Then it joins the preaortic limb as the latter receives two internal spermatic veins and a single second lumbar vein. Additionally, an internal spermatic artery loops around the lumbar tributary.

Variations in renal form, position, and blood supply, continued.

a, Renal pedicles rendered complex by the presence of supernumerary arteries and veins, and by the occurrence of lumbar tributaries from retroaortic and deep paravertebral position. On the right side, the upper one of the pair of arteries reaches the renal sinus by passing dorsal to the inferior vena cava, while the other courses downward to attain a position anterior to the largest of three renal veins, but the precaval vein remains caudal to all of the other hilar elements. Small veins of generally transverse course enter the inferior vena cava from a retroaortic (prevertebral) position. On the left side, the kidney is supplied by three renal arteries that arise from the aorta in an area just caudal to the origin of the superior mesenteric artery. The lowermost of these three vessels hooks around the second left lumbar vein as the latter emerges from the substance of the psoas major muscle. The renal vein receives the lumbar vein, and the usual suprarenal and spermatic vessels. Additionally, a capsular tributary (matching an artery) reaches the renal vein through a hilar vessel as an intermediary.

b, The vascular relationships of the left renal, lumbar, and suprarenal veins in the same specimen, shown by transecting the renal vein and turning it downward.

c, A relatively simple constituency of the right renal pedicle in association with the complex arrangement of structures on the left. On the right, the single large renal vein covers the main artery in an unusually short pedicle. An accessory renal artery is derived from a somewhat larger right internal spermatic artery. This supernumerary vessel ascends to the renal hilus. From the aorta, near its bifurcation, a ureteric artery descends to the duct, terminating where the ureter crosses the right common iliac artery. On the left side, the renal vein divides near the hilus of the kidney; the parts thus produced are limbs of a so-called circumaortic venous ring. The preaortic division receives the inferior phrenic and suprarenal veins (through a common tributary), and two internal spermatic veins. The postaortic limb receives the second lumbar vein and a smaller vessel from the prevertebral or aortic connective tissue. The ventral division courses transversely from the kidney to the inferior vena cava, whereas the dorsal part passes obliquely downward to terminate in the caval vein. A vein of capsular drainage (matching an artery derived from the renal) enters the anterior portion where the latter is formed by convergence of hilar tributaries. Two left ureteric arteries arise separately from the proximal segment of the left common iliac artery. Each of them divides in midcourse and passes in a different direction. The cranial member ascends toward the renal pelvis, while the caudal one of the pair passes transversely toward the ureter. The following features warrant attention: short, common trunk for the celiac and superior mesenteric arteries; doubling of the left inferior phrenic artery; presence of a small, supernumerary renal artery on the left side which (like that of the right) arose from the internal spermatic artery.

d, Double inferior vena cava, together with different constituency of the renal pedicles. The caval channels, both of great caliber, lie to the sides of the abdominal aorta; they communicate caudally through a channel situated dorsal to the right common iliac artery. The short suprarenal vein of the right side courses horizontally to the dorsum of the inferior vena cava; the suprarenal vein of the left side descends vertically to the upper segment of the left caval channel. On the right, a small accessory renal vein is a constituent of the pedicle; on the left, a supernumerary renal vein, dorsally placed, receives a communicating stem from the azygos system of the thorax. On the right, the renal artery reaches ventral position by ascending in front of the hilar vein; on the left side, a ventral position is attained by descent of the artery in front of the larger of the two renal veins. Both caval channels receive lumbar and prevertebral tributaries (on the right, numbered and indicated by asterisk, in relation to the retracted vessel).

e and *f*, Kidneys, renal vessels, and neighboring blood vessels in a case of pelvic kidney. *f*, The anomalous kidney has been rolled lateralward in order to demonstrate its relation to the common iliac artery and vein of the right side.

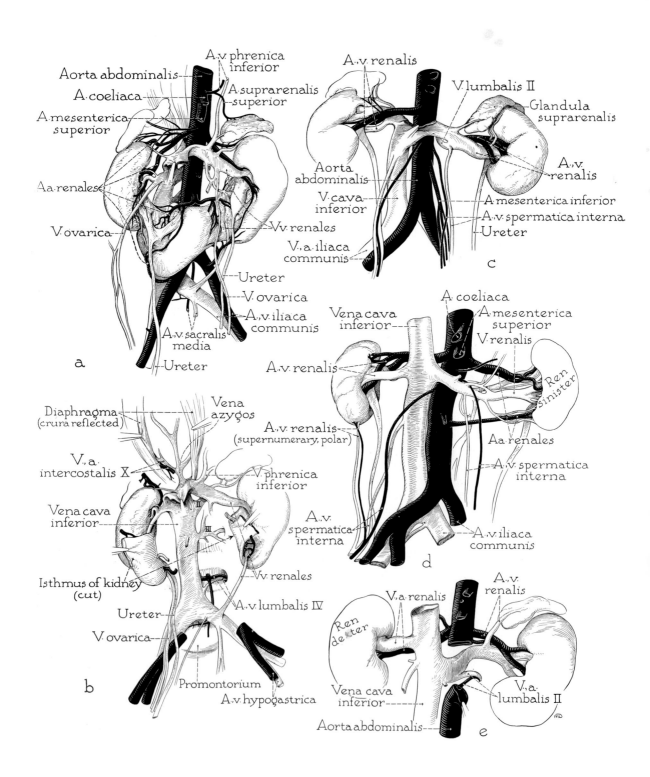

See facing page for description.

Variations in renal form, position, and blood supply, concluded.

a, The kidneys are connected by a broad isthmus of irregular form. On the right side, the ureter is formed by the junction of two main, widely separated portions that are joined below by a third. The superior one arises from the aorta below the origin of the superior mesenteric. In its descent toward the sinus of the kidney, the artery gives off one branch to the suprarenal gland and one to the superior extremity of the kidney. After the vessel skirts the superomedial border of the isthmus, it anastomoses with the second vessel of supply to the right side. The inferior member of the pair arises by a common stem with a vessel of the opposite side. In addition to the suprarenal arteries of renal origin, a small suprarenal springs from the aorta itself near the beginning of the upper renal. On the right side, the inferior extremity (lower pole) of the kidney receives two arteries from the common iliac. The renal vein of the right side receives the ovarian vein.

b, Details of deep renal anatomy in the same specimen, revealed by transecting the isthmus, and excising the aorta and its divisions and chief branches. On the right side, the ovarian vein is a tributary of the renal vein. In the midline and to the left, the azygos vein descends between the crura of the diaphragm to communicate with the inferior vena cava and the second left lumbar vein. A large left renal vein terminates in the inferior vena cava; a smaller communication descends to the left common iliac vein. The left renal vein receives the customary tributaries: inferior phrenic, suprarenal, ovarian.

c, On the right side, a single renal artery descends in front of the vein. Two small suprarenal arteries arise from the renal artery; a suprarenal vein empties into the renal vein. The internal spermatic artery arises from the aorta at renal level; the corresponding vein empties into the inferior vena cava at the lower border of the pedicle. On the left side, the renal artery descends to cover the vein by dividing into three hilar portions. The renal vein receives the following vessels as tributaries: internal spermatic vein; two suprarenals, one near the caval termination and the other near the kidney. The internal spermatic artery arises from the aorta below the lower border of the renal pedicle.

d, On the right side there is an elongated pattern at the renal sinus, the renal artery sending a descending branch to the inferior aspect of the sinus (of an unusually small kidney). At the level of the sacral promontory, the internal spermatic vein receives a vein from the inferior extremity of the kidney. On the left side, two renal arteries are present: the upper one arises from the aorta just caudal to the level of the superior mesenteric; the lower, near the level of origin of the inferior mesenteric artery. The internal spermatic artery courses transversely beneath the renal vein, passes through a hiatus in the latter, and descends vertically to the pelvis. The left renal vein receives the following tributaries from medial to lateral: suprarenal and second lumbar (above); internal spermatic and third lumbar (below); polar tributary (below). Both common iliac arteries follow a sigmoid course.

e, On the right side, the renal pedicle is of the usual type—in which the vein lies anterior to the artery. However, on the left side the hilar divisions of the renal artery descend anterior to the corresponding veins, and the second lumbar vein terminates in the renal vein.

(Illustrations on pages 412 to 414 and 416 reproduced with the permission of Surgery, Gynecology and Obstetrics.)

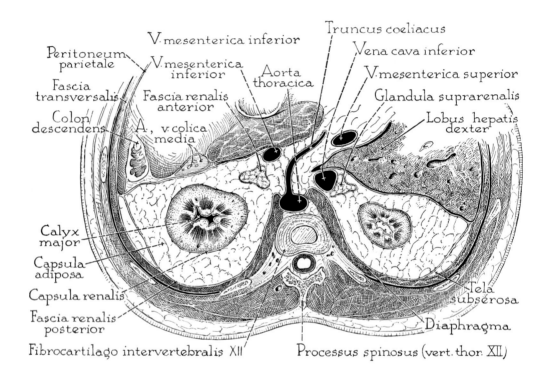

Peritoneum parietale

V. mesenterica inferior

V. mesenterica inferior

Fascia transversalis

Fascia renalis anterior

Colon descendens

A., v. colica media

Aorta thoracica

Truncus coeliacus

Vena cava inferior

V. mesenterica superior

Glandula suprarenalis

Lobus hepatis dexter

Calyx major

Capsula adiposa

Capsula renalis

Fascia renalis posterior

Fibrocartilago intervertebralis XII

Tela subserosa

Diaphragma

Processus spinosus (vert. thor. XII)

Relations of the kidneys.

Shown at the transverse level of the twelfth thoracic vertebra.

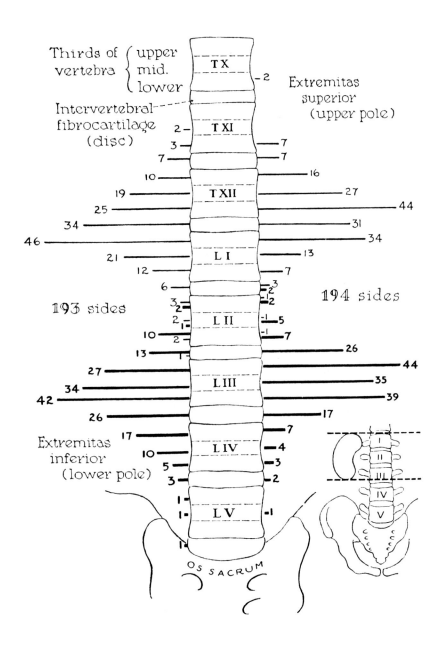

Frequency graph to record the levels of the superior and inferior extremities of kidney, upper and lower renal poles, in relation to vertebral bodies and intervertebral disc spaces.

Each of the vertebral bodies has been divided into upper, middle, and lower thirds. The levels for the superior renal extremity are indicated by means of thin lines, those for the inferior are shown by broad lines.

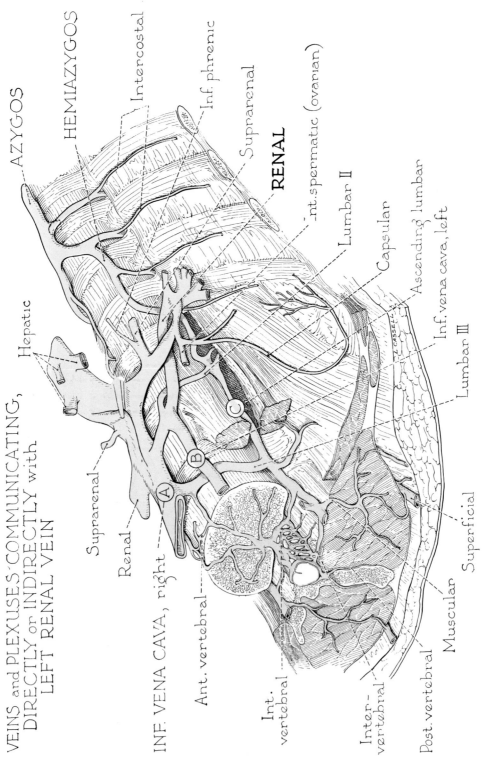

VEINS and PLEXUSES COMMUNICATING, DIRECTLY or INDIRECTLY with LEFT RENAL VEIN

AZYGOS

HEMIAZYGOS

Intercostal

Inf. phrenic

Suprarenal

RENAL

Int. spermatic (ovarian)

Lumbar II

Capsular

Ascending lumbar

Inf. vena cava, left

Lumbar III

Superficial

Muscular

Post. vertebral

Inter-vertebral

Int. vertebral

Ant. vertebral

INF. VENA CAVA, right

Renal

Suprarenal

Hepatic

Veins of the dorsum of the trunk at renal level. Recording complexity of venous pattern of left side as compared with simplicity of drainage schema on right. Semidiagrammatic composite of three specimens. See description on facing page.

On the right, the suprarenal and renal veins empty directly into the inferior vena cava (at *A*, in approximately median position upon the vertebral column). On the left, communicating directly or indirectly with the preaortic or postaortic limb of the circumaortic venous ring, are the following: left inferior vena cava (*B*, lodged in the sulcus between vertebrae and psoas muscle); ascending lumbar vein (*C*, coursing with substance of psoas); hemiazygos vein and its intercostal tributaries; inferior phrenic and suprarenal veins; capsular veins, with lesser tributaries coursing in retroperitoneal layer; lumbar veins, with tributaries from external and internal vertebral plexuses, from the dorsal axial musculature, and from the superficial fascia and integument of the back.

The following conclusions may be drawn:

1. Suprarenal arteries are very numerous although individually small; they converge upon the suprarenal gland as though it were the visceral hub of a multispoked vascular wheel (see page 410). The venous plan is simple; with exceedingly rare exceptions, there is a single vein for each gland.

2. Supernumerary renal arteries of large size are common, as are also lesser arterial branches in the suprarenal area. Accessory renal veins are infrequent. Complexity in the venous pattern is expressed, not in duplication of vessels, but in continuity of the renals with veins draining any or all of the surrounding structures.

3. The true expanse of the renal field of vascular influence becomes apparent when the usual communications of the left renal vein are grouped like a composite of several selected specimens. The left renal vein is then found at the core of an impressive set of veins and venous plexuses: inferior phrenic and suprarenal tributaries enter from above; from below and to the side come spermatic (or ovarian), capsular, lumbar, and ascending lumbar veins, and the anomalous vena cava. Additionally, communication is made with azygos and hemiazygos veins (usually through lumbars), and with the extensive set of internal and external vertebral plexuses by way of the intervertebrals and the lumbars.

4. These widespread connections bring the following structures into venous relationship with the kidney: the respiratory diaphragm; suprarenal gland, testis, ductus deferens, and ureter; the capsular and the general retroperitoneal tissue; the peritoneum; lumbodorsal, axial, and appendicular muscles (psoas major, sacrospinalis, quadratus lumborum, latissimus dorsi, and trapezius); the superficial fascia and skin; the ribs, intercostal muscles, and thoracic subserous tissue; pleura and pericardium; the vertebrae, and their discs and ligaments; the spinal cord and its meningeal coats; the visceral musculature and skeletal elements of the pelvis; the lower extremities.

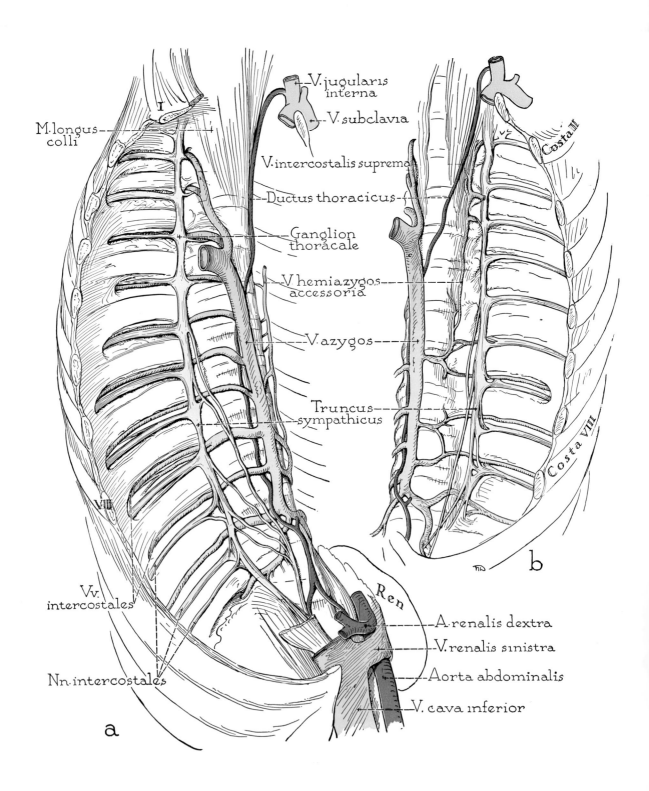

M. longus colli

V. jugularis interna

V. subclavia

V. intercostalis suprema

Ductus thoracicus

Ganglion thoracale

V. hemiazygos accessoria

V. azygos

Truncus sympathicus

Costa III

Costa VIII

b

Vv. intercostales

Nn. intercostales

Ren

A. renalis dextra

V. renalis sinistra

Aorta abdominalis

V. cava inferior

a

Azygos system of veins in relation to the ascending lumbar veins.

a, The azygos vein together with the venous channel which communicates with the ascending lumbar vein.
b, The hemiazygos vein and its lumbar communication. The lumbar portion of the parietal system is shown in the following plate of figures.

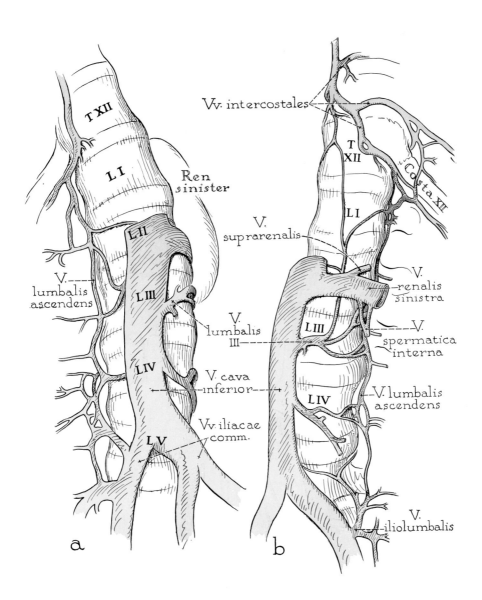

Ascending lumbar and related veins.

a, Veins of the right side; anterolateral view. The ascending lumbar vein communicates with the inferior vena cava through segmentally arranged lumbar veins and with the azygos vein.

b, Veins of the left side of the same specimen; anterolateral view. Compare preceding plate of figures (thoracic venous pattern of the same cadaver).

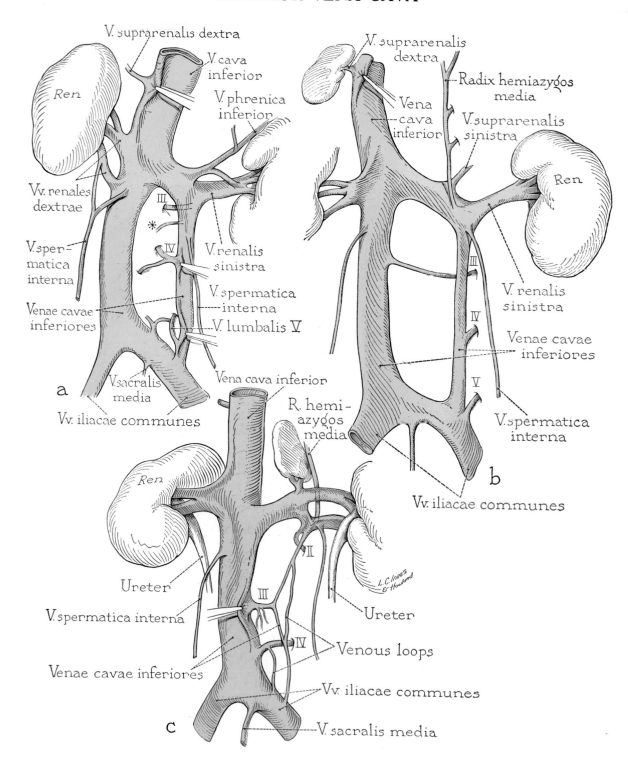

Double inferior vena cava.

a, A case in which the left caval channel approaches the caliber of the regular vein of the right side. In this and in figures *b* and *c* the lumbar communications are numbered (Roman numerals). * Indicates a vein draining the prevertebral tissue.

b, A left inferior vena cava of lesser caliber.

c, A small channel with a cross-connection at third lumbar level.

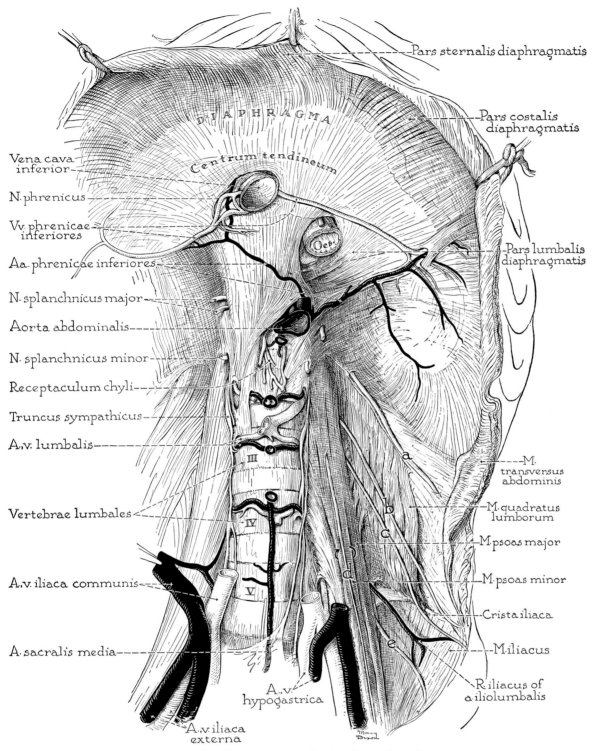

Diaphragm, lumbar muscles, and related vessels and nerves.

Portions of the diaphragm, the hiatuses and their contents; the lumbar musculature and vertebral column, together with the phrenic and lumbar blood vessels; the nerves derived from the lumbar plexus in relation to the psoas major, quadratus lumborum and iliacus muscles.

The inferior vena cava, aorta, and esophagus have been transected on the abdominal aspect of the diaphragm; the lumbar arteries have been cut where they arose from the aorta; the corresponding veins, where they entered the inferior vena cava.

In this specimen the inferior phrenic arteries arose separately; the veins enter the inferior vena cava as the latter reaches the caval hiatus in the diaphragm. The rami of the phrenic nerve are shown as they branch in the musculature.

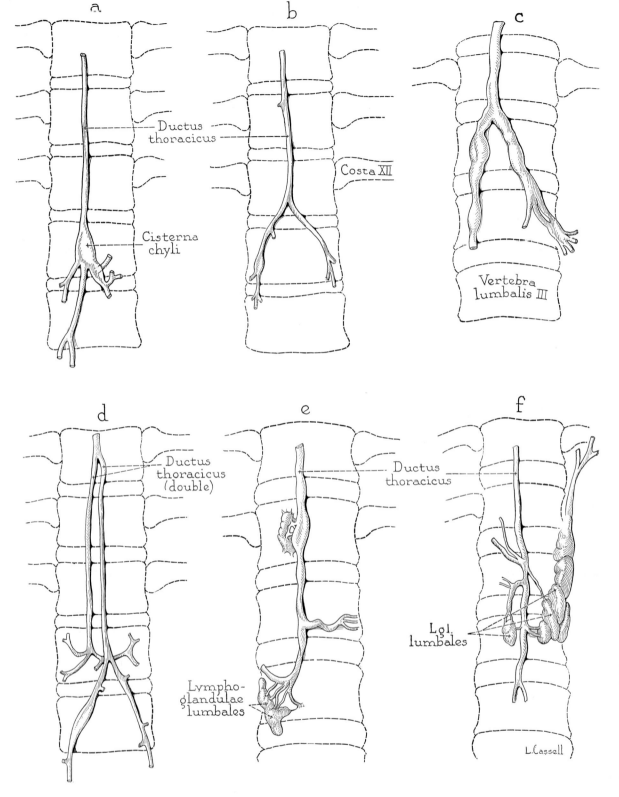

Thoracic duct. Variations in form and vertebral relations.

a and *c*, Ducts possessing sacculations of considerable size. *b* and *d*, Ducts of slender form. *e* and *f*, Ducts of elongate form.

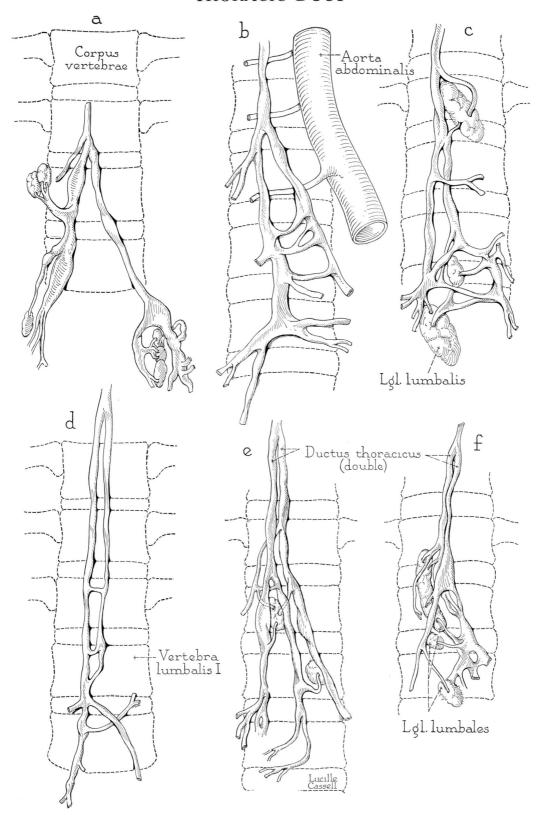

Thoracic duct. Variations, continued.

a, Duct of common, Y-shaped, form. *b* to *d*, Ducts possessing numerous anastomoses between the bilateral tributaries. *e* and *f*, Trifid ducts.

Plexus Lumbalis

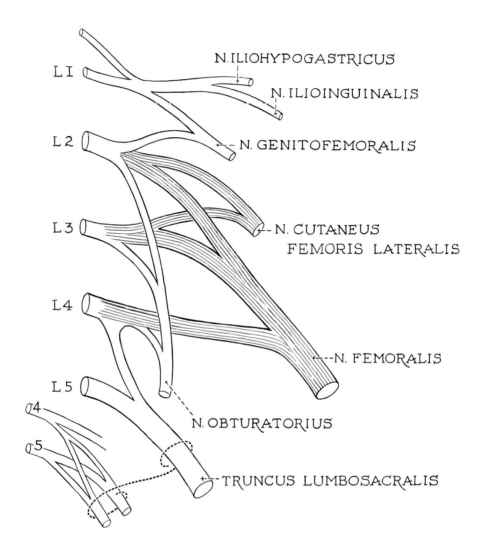

Lumbar plexus; schematic. (Adapted from Gray.)

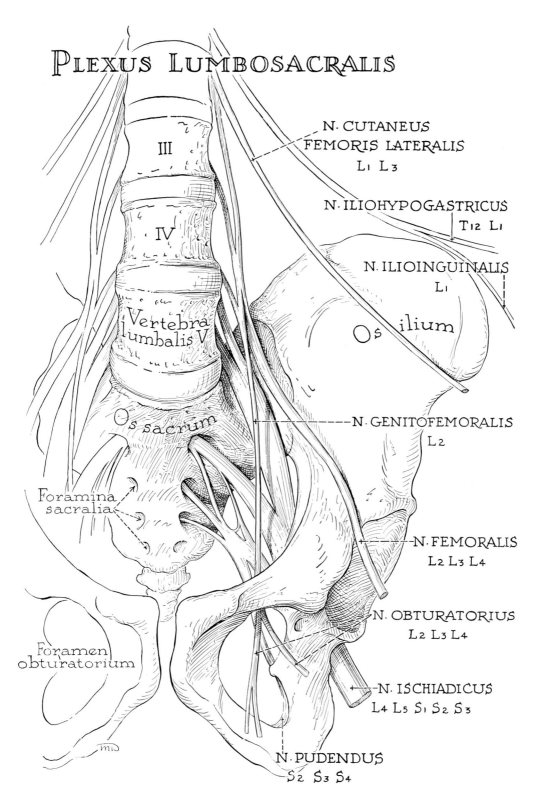

PLEXUS LUMBOSACRALIS

III

IV

Vertebra lumbalis V

Os sacrum

Foramina sacralia

Foramen obturatorium

N. CUTANEUS FEMORIS LATERALIS L₁ L₃

N. ILIOHYPOGASTRICUS T₁₂ L₁

N. ILIOINGUINALIS L₁

Os ilium

N. GENITOFEMORALIS L₂

N. FEMORALIS L₂ L₃ L₄

N. OBTURATORIUS L₂ L₃ L₄

N. ISCHIADICUS L₄ L₅ S₁ S₂ S₃

N. PUDENDUS S₂ S₃ S₄

Lumbosacral plexus.

The nerves are shown in relation to the skeletal elements of the vertebral column and pelvis. See description on page 514.

Section Seven

THE PELVIS AND PERINEUM

LIGAMENTS OF THE PELVIS.. 433

BONES OF THE PELVIS... 434

FASCIA OF THE PELVIS 435

MUSCLES OF THE PELVIS: THREE STAGES IN DISSECTION.......................... 436–438

PELVIS; AREAS OF MUSCULAR ATTACHMENT....................................... 439–442

MALE PELVIS; PERITONEUM.. 443

SIGMOID COLON; VARIATIONS: NINE SELECTED EXAMPLES......................... 444

SIGMOID COLON; VARIATIONS. SEMISCHEMATIC: TYPES, WITH PERCENTAGE OCCURRENCE. 445

SIGMOID MESOCOLON; VARIATIONS. SCHEMATIC: TYPES, WITH PERCENTAGE OCCUR-
RENCE... 446

RECTUM AND ANAL CANAL.. 447

URINARY BLADDER; EMPTY AND DISTENDED.. 448

PERINEUM AND PELVIS; SEMISCHEMATIC SECTIONS.............................. 449–451

PERINEUM, MALE AND FEMALE... 452

RECTUM; DORSAL ASPECT... 453

PROSTATE AND URINARY BLADDER... 454

PROSTATE AND SEMINAL VESICLES... 455

GENITOURINARY SYSTEM, MALE.. 456–457

GENITAL ORGANS, MALE... 458

PERINEUM, MALE: SIX STAGES IN DISSECTION.................................... 459–464

PERINEUM, FEMALE: TEN STAGES IN DISSECTION................................. 465–473

PELVIS DIAPHRAGM, FEMALE... 474

PELVIC VISCERA AND PERITONEUM, FEMALE... 475

UTERUS, VAGINA, AND OVARY.. 476

PELVIC VISCERA, FEMALE: NINE STAGES IN DISSECTION......................... 477–485

ARTERIES OF THE FEMALE PELVIS: FIVE STAGES IN DISSECTION.................. 486–490

ARTERIES AND NERVES OF THE FEMALE PERINEUM: TWO STAGES IN DISSECTION..... 491–492

ARTERIES OF THE MALE PELVIS AND PERINEUM: TEN STAGES IN DISSECTION........ 493–499

(Continued)

Obturator Artery; Variations: Eight Selected Examples.................... 500

Internal Iliac Artery; Variations: Nine Selected Examples.................. 501

Lumbopelvic Vessels and Nerves: Six Stages in Dissection................... 502–505

Nerves of the Female Pelvis: Four Stages in Dissection..................... 506–509

Nerves of the Male Pelvis: Six Stages in Dissection....................... 510–513

Lumbar and Sacral Plexuses... 514–515

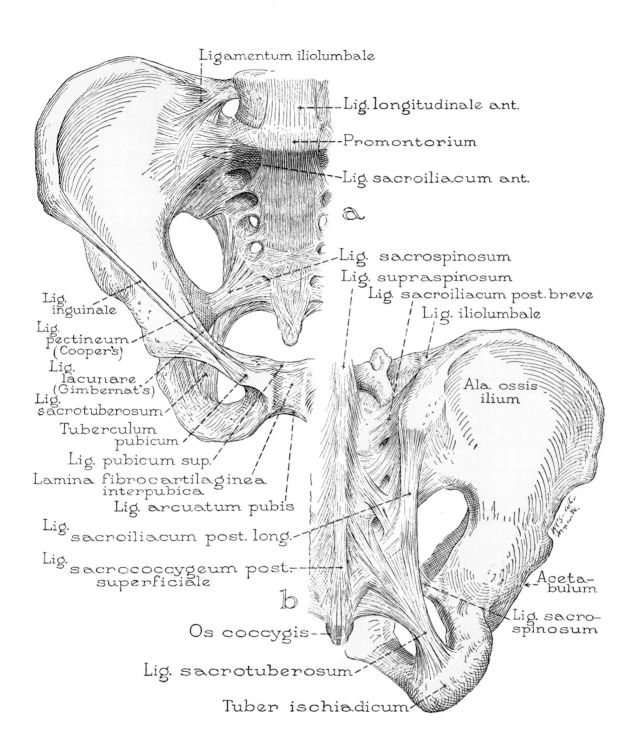

Ligamentum iliolumbale

Lig. longitudinale ant.

Promontorium

Lig. sacroiliacum ant.

a

Lig. sacrospinosum
Lig. supraspinosum
Lig. sacroiliacum post. breve
Lig. iliolumbale

Lig. inguinale

Lig. pectineum (Cooper's)

Lig. lacunare (Gimbernat's)

Lig. sacrotuberosum

Tuberculum pubicum

Lig. pubicum sup.

Lamina fibrocartilaginea interpubica

Lig. arcuatum pubis

Lig. sacroiliacum post. long.

Lig. sacrococcygeum post. superficiale

Ala ossis ilium

Aceta-bulum

Lig. sacro-spinosum

b

Os coccygis

Lig. sacrotuberosum

Tuber ischiadicum

a and *b*, Ligaments of the right half of the pelvis; anterior and posterior views.

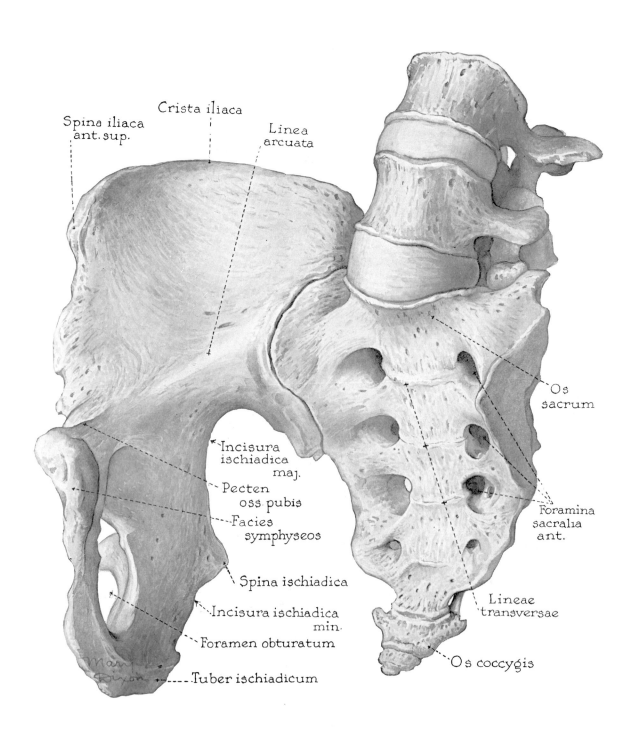

Spina iliaca
ant. sup.

Crista iliaca

Linea
arcuata

Os
sacrum

Incisura
ischiadica
maj.

Pecten
oss pubis

Facies
symphyseos

Foramina
sacralia
ant.

Spina ischiadica

Incisura ischiadica
min.

Foramen obturatum

Lineae
transversae

Tuber ischiadicum

Os coccygis

Bones of the pelvis.

The innominate bone, sacrum and coccyx (and lower lumbar vertebrae) are shown. Anterolateral view.

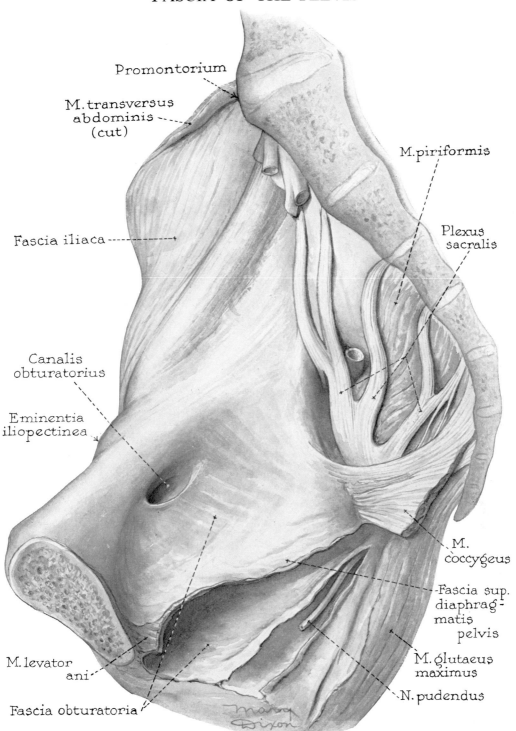

Promontorium

M.transversus
abdominis
(cut)

M.piriformis

Fascia iliaca

Plexus
sacralis

Canalis
obturatorius

Eminentia
iliopectinea

M.
coccygeus

Fascia sup.
diaphrag-
matis
pelvis

M.levator
ani

M.glutaeus
maximus

Fascia obturatoria

N.pudendus

Parietal portion of pelvic fascia.

The pelvic organs and surrounding tissues have been removed from the hemisected pelvis to expose the fasciae covering the muscles of the greater and lesser pelvis and of the lateral wall of the ischiorectal fossa. The fascia of the latter area has been incised as it forms the medial boundary of Alcock's canal. The sacral nerves are exposed, and, on still deeper level, the piriformis muscle. The sacrospinous ligament and gluteus maximus muscle bound the dissected area postero-inferiorly.

The iliopsoas fascia is shown as it lines the greater pelvis, the obturator fascia as it covers the obturator muscle in the lesser pelvis and continues medialward as the superior fascial layer of the pelvic diaphragm. The pelvic diaphragm is cut near its origin. The perineal part of the obturator fascia forms a true canal (of Alcock) as it covers the internal pudendal vessels and the pudendal nerve; here the canal is opened to show the nerve (vessels removed).

L 5

S1

M. iliacus

M. psoas maj.

N. femoralis

Canalis
obturato-
rius

C 1

M.
piriformis

M. coccygeus
(cut)

M. gluteus max.

Lig. sacrotuberosum

M. obturator int.

Tuber ischiadicum

Parietal pelvic musculature.

The muscles of the pelvic wall have been exposed by the removal of the endopelvic fascia. The following muscles have been exposed: iliacus; psoas major; obturator internus; piriformis. The gluteus maximus muscle and the sacrotuberous ligament are also shown, as are, additionally, the following bony landmarks: lumbosacral vertebral column (hemisected); tuberosity and inferior ramus of the ischium; inferior and superior rami, symphysis, and body of the pubis; anterior, inferior, and superior spines and crest of the ilium.

The iliacus and psoas major muscles are revealed as they leave the pelvis, lateral to the iliopectineal eminence, on the way to the femur; the obturator internus is seen as it makes pelvic exit through the lesser sciatic foramen; the piriformis is exposed as it leaves the pelvis through the greater sciatic foramen; the gluteus maximus muscle is in view as it descends behind the piriformis and obturator internus muscles and sacrotuberous and sacrospinous ligaments.

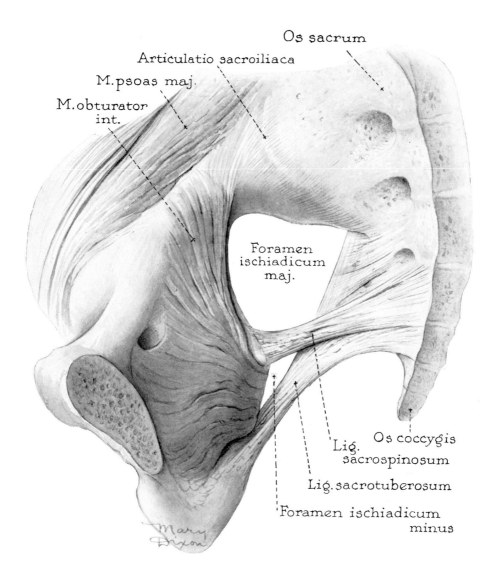

Os sacrum

Articulatio sacroiliaca

M. psoas maj.

M. obturator int.

Foramen ischiadicum maj.

Lig. sacrospinosum

Os coccygis

Lig. sacrotuberosum

Foramen ischiadicum minus

Muscles and ligaments of the pelvis.

The coccygeus and piriformis muscles have been removed to expose the sacrotuberous and sacrospinous ligaments and the other boundaries of the greater sciatic (ischiadic) foramen. The obturator internus muscle is shown as it covers the internal aspect of the bony pelvis and gains exit through the lesser sciatic foramen.

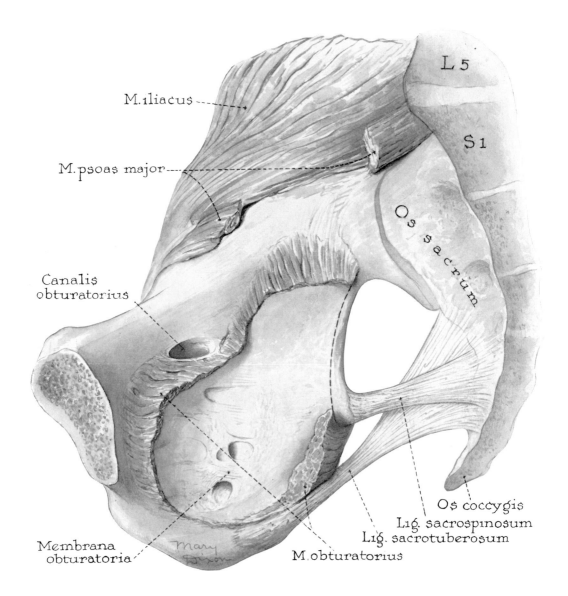

Muscles and ligaments of the pelvis.

The obturator internus muscle has now been removed, except along its line of origin and at the point of emergence from the pelvis. The psoas major has been partially removed to expose the bone at the pelvic brim.

The origin of the obturator muscle is sinuous marginally; rising on the body of the pubis, the margin lowers at the obturator canal and follows the contour of the inferior ramus of the pubis. The fibers converge upon the notch bounded by the ischial spine and tuberosity. The obturator membrane is smooth on its pelvic aspect, except where it forms the prominent obturator canal and several smaller hiatuses for the transmission of lesser blood vessels.

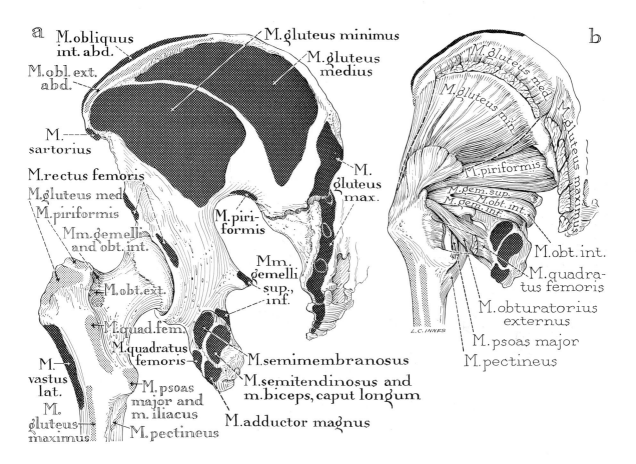

Muscles of the pelvis and thigh. Areas of attachment to bone. Viewed from behind.

a, The areas of attachment. *b*, The muscles whose origins and insertions are shown in the accompanying figure (*a*).

In these figures and in those that follow, the origin of the muscle is shown in dark pattern and labelled with heavy lettering; the insertion for each is indicated by a lighter plaque and labelled with open letters.

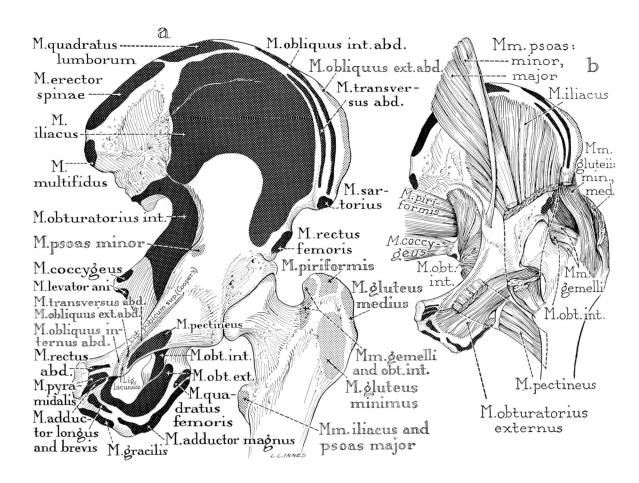

Muscles of the pelvis and thigh. Areas of attachment to bone, continued. Viewed from the front.

a, Showing the areas of attachment, origins, and insertions. *b*, The muscles. Segments of the iliopsoas and pectineus have been cut out in order to expose the deeper musculature.

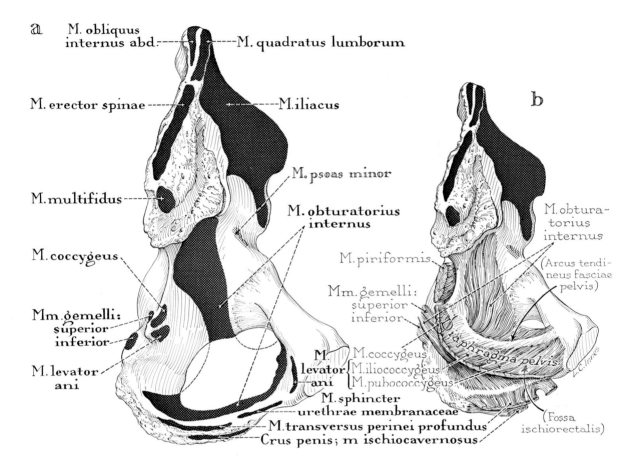

a M. obliquus internus abd.
M. quadratus lumborum
M. erector spinae
M. iliacus
b
M. psoas minor
M. multifidus
M. obturatorius internus
M. obturatorius internus
M. piriformis
(Arcus tendineus fasciae pelvis)
M. coccygeus
Mm. gemelli: superior inferior
Mm. gemelli: superior inferior
M. levator ani
M. coccygeus
M. iliococcygeus
M. pubococcygeus
M. levator ani
M. sphincter urethrae membranaceae
M. transversus perinei profundus
Crus penis; m ischiocavernosus
(Fossa ischiorectalis)

Muscles of the pelvis, continued. Areas of muscular attachment. Viewed from the medial aspect.

  a, The areas of attachment on the internal surface of the bone. b, The musculature and the space of the ischiorectal fossa between pelvic and urogenital diaphragms.

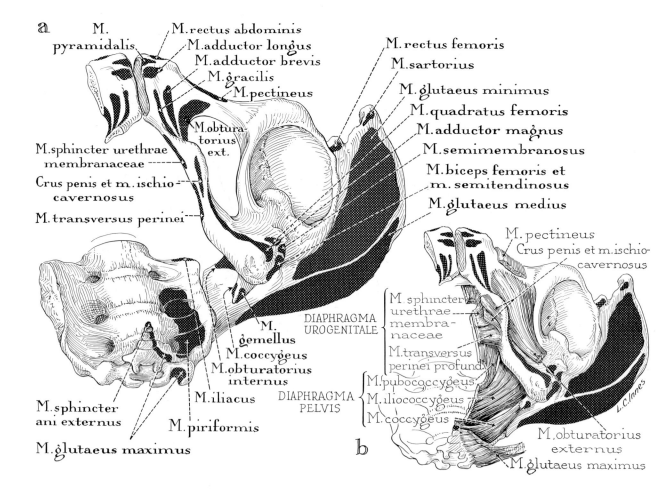

Muscles of the pelvis, concluded. Areas of muscular attachment.

a, The areas of origin. *b*, The muscles, emphasizing those that constitute the pelvic and urogenital diaphragms.

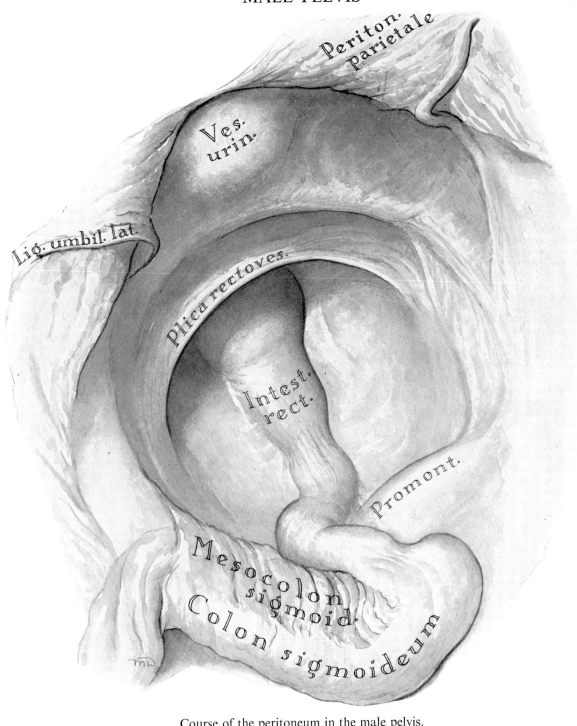

Course of the peritoneum in the male pelvis.

From the posterior surface of the anterior abdominal wall the peritoneum descends to invest the upper surface of the urinary bladder; on each side it covers, for a certain distance, the lateral surface of the lesser pelvis, before it is reflected medialward to the bladder. When the bladder is empty the peritoneum forms a fairly prominent fold, the plica vesicalis transversa, which runs transversely over the superior surface of the bladder. Less constant are smaller folds, plicae pubovesicales, which extend from the region of the vertex of the bladder toward the lateral umbilical fold. Posteriorly the peritoneum covers a small portion of the fundus of the bladder, the seminal vesicles and the seminal ducts; it then bends around to become the tunica serosa of the rectum. Between the bladder and rectum there occurs, as a consequence, the slit-like excavatio rectovesicalis. It is deepest in the middle but usually does not reach down to the prostate. This excavation is bounded above by two folds, plicae rectovesicales, which pass from the posterior part of the bladder, in arciform manner, to the lateral surface of the rectum.

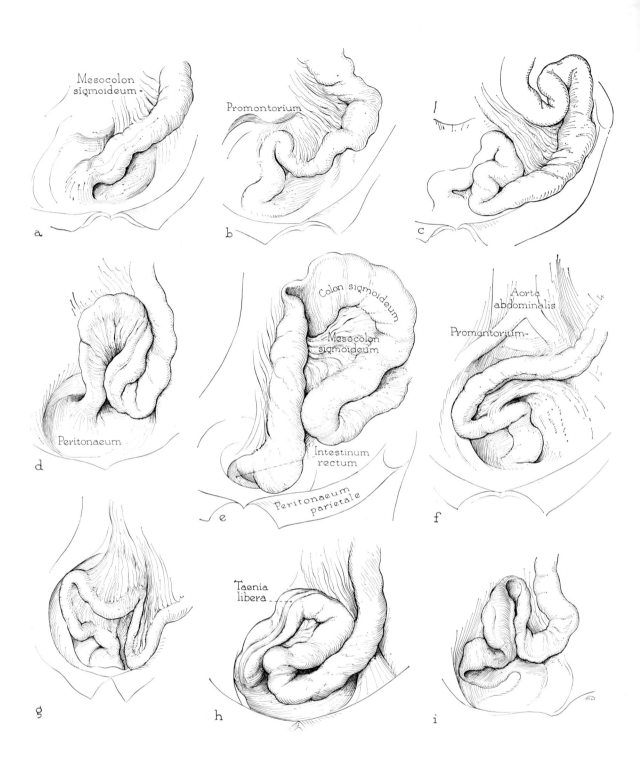

Sigmoid colon. Variations in form and position. Selected examples.

a, Colon disposed in an oblique course without contorted form. *b* and *c*, Specimens of U-shaped configuration, concavity directed toward the specimen's right. *d* and *e*, *g* to *i*, Examples of caudally-directed concavity. *f*, A loop directed toward the specimen's left, the reverse of concavity in *c*.

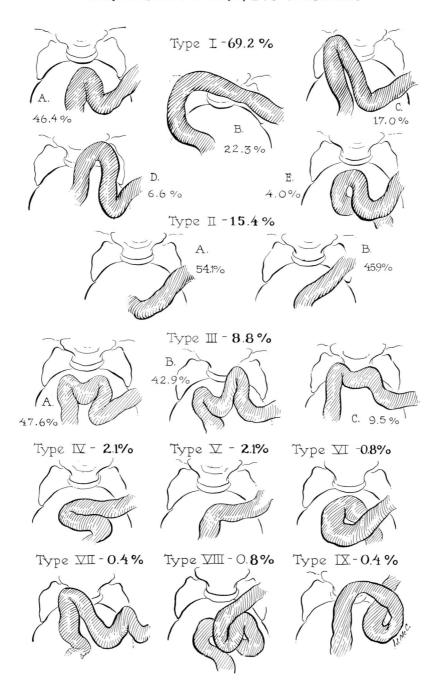

COLON SIGMOIDEUM
VARIATIONS IN FORM, 240 SPECIMENS

Type I - 69.2 %

A. 46.4 %

B. 22.3 %

C. 17.0 %

D. 6.6 %

E. 4.0 %

Type II - 15.4 %

A. 54.1%

B. 45.9%

Type III - 8.8 %

A. 47.6%

B. 42.9%

C. 9.5 %

Type IV - 2.1%

Type V - 2.1%

Type VI - 0.8%

Type VII - 0.4%

Type VIII - 0.8%

Type IX - 0.4%

Sigmoid colon. Variation in form and position. Diagrammatic.

Major types (I to IX) are illustrated, comprising varieties (A to C, etc.) within the more inclusive categories. The percentage occurrence of each type and subtype is recorded.

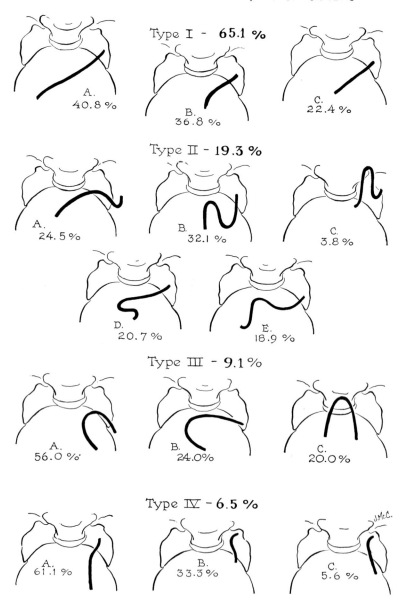

Sigmoid mesocolon. Variations in form, length, and position of the line of continuity with the parietal peritoneum. Diagrammatic.

Major types (I to IV) are illustrated, together with subsidiary variations. The percentage occurrence of each type and subtype is recorded.

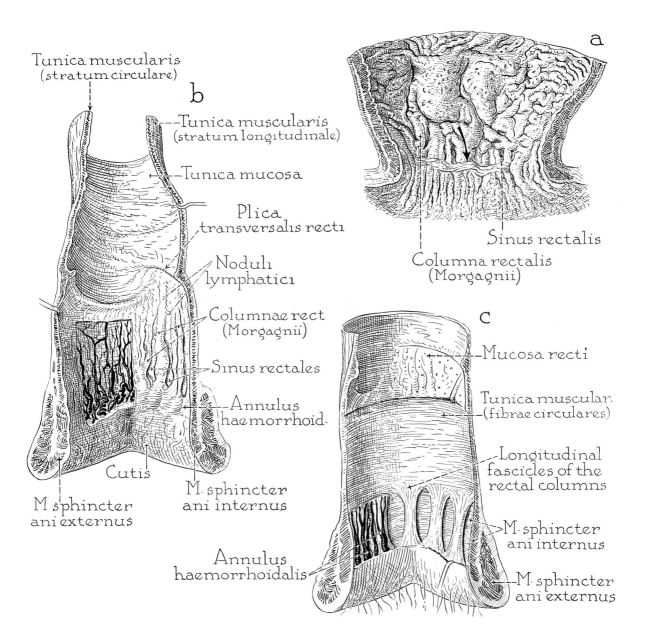

Tunica muscularis
(stratum circulare)

b

Tunica muscularis
(stratum longitudinale)

Tunica mucosa

Plica
transversalis recti

Noduli
lymphatici

Columnae rect
(Morgagnii)

Sinus rectales

Annulus
haemorrhoid.

Cutis

M. sphincter
ani externus

M. sphincter
ani internus

Annulus
haemorrhoidalis

a

Sinus rectalis

Columna rectalis
(Morgagnii)

c

Mucosa recti

Tunica muscular.
(fibrae circulares)

Longitudinal
fascicles of the
rectal columns

M. sphincter
ani internus

M. sphincter
ani externus

Rectum and anal canal; internal aspect.

In *a*, the mucous membrane (tunica mucosa) is intact (adapted from Tandler). The arrow points to the so-called mucocutaneous junction. In *b*, the mucous membrane has been partly dissected off to expose the veins of the internal hemorrhoidal plexus (after Spalteholz). In *c*, the layers have been removed to the level of the intrinsic musculature (tunica muscularis), to demonstrate the relation between the veins of the plexus and the columnar fascicles of the muscular coat (after Tandler).

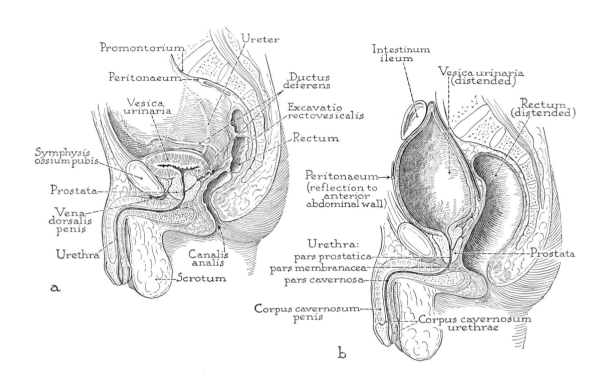

Urinary bladder and rectum.

a, Showing the organs in the empty condition. In sagittal section the bladder is three-sided. The superior surface faces upward; the posterior surface is directed both backward and downward. Inferiorly, the bladder rests upon the pelvic floor (the levator ani muscles) and the pubic symphysis.

b, The bladder and rectum distended. The distended bladder rises above the space just described, projecting into the true abdominal cavity. It assumes a bulbous form, losing the triangular configuration. (Adapted from Cunningham.)

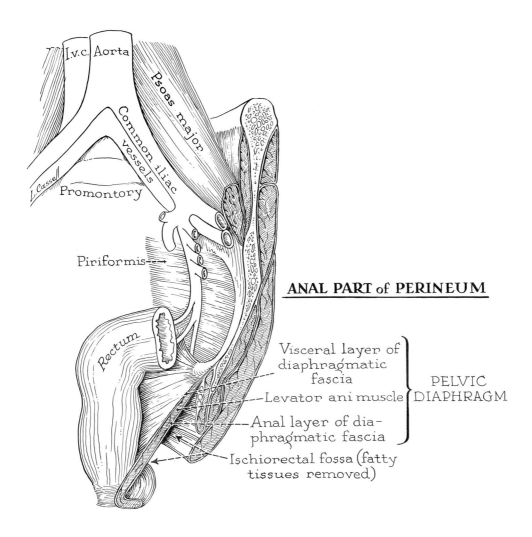

ANAL PART of PERINEUM

Visceral layer of diaphragmatic fascia
Levator ani muscle
Anal layer of diaphragmatic fascia
Ischiorectal fossa (fatty tissues removed)

PELVIC DIAPHRAGM

Frontal section through the pelvis and the anal division of the perineum; male specimen. Diagrammatic.

Superficial fatty tissue of the ischiorectal fossa and the integument have been removed in the region below the pelvic diaphragm; above the diaphragm the peritoneum and the retroperitoneal layer are omitted.

In the anal portion of the perineum, the ischiorectal fossa is bounded superiorly and medially by the inferior fascia of the pelvic diaphragm, laterally by the fascial covering of the obturator internus muscle and inferiorly by the integument. However, in the urogenital portion of the perineum (see following figure), above the superior fascia of the urogenital diaphragm on either side, the fat-filled ischiorectal fossa extends forward to the anterior limit of the perineum. The lateral boundary of the space is still formed by the parietal fascia covering the obturator internus muscle, the superior boundary by the fascia which covers the under surface of the levator ani muscle; however, the inferior boundary is the fascia, likewise diaphragmatic, on the upper surface of the urethral sphincter. This means that, whereas the fatty superficial fascia of the ischiorectal fossa in the anal region is the only layer between the skin below and the fascia of the pelvic floor above, a complex series of additional layers (related to two compartments) intervene between integument and diaphragmatic fascia in the urogenital division of the perineum.

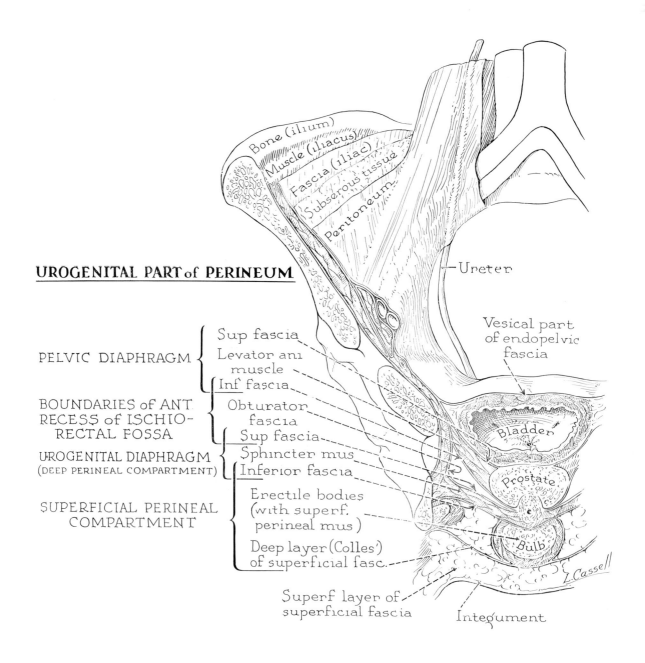

UROGENITAL PART of PERINEUM

PELVIC DIAPHRAGM { Sup fascia
Levator ani muscle
Inf fascia

BOUNDARIES of ANT RECESS of ISCHIO-RECTAL FOSSA { Obturator fascia
Sup fascia

UROGENITAL DIAPHRAGM (DEEP PERINEAL COMPARTMENT) { Sphincter mus
Inferior fascia

SUPERFICIAL PERINEAL COMPARTMENT { Erectile bodies (with superf. perineal mus)
Deep layer (Colles') of superficial fasc.

Superf layer of superficial fascia

Integument

— Ureter

Vesical part of endopelvic fascia

Bladder

Prostate

Bulb

L. Cassell

Frontal section through the pelvis and urogenital division of the perineum; male specimen. Diagrammatic. The complete series of layers and spaces are depicted from the integument inward.

In the urogenital triangle a series of important additional strata intervene between the integument and the inferior fascia of the pelvic diaphragm. These layers are: the deep membranous layer of the superficial fascia; the erectile tissue and the muscles of the superficial perineal compartment; the inferior fascia of the urogenital diaphragm; the musculature in the deep perineal compartment; the superior fascia of the urogenital diaphragm; the fatty tissue in the anterior recess of the ischiorectal fossa. Were these strata not present the succession of layers in the two subdivisions of the perineum (anal and urogenital) would be similar and, moreover, comparable to that obtaining over the body generally, namely, the integument, the fatty pannicle, and the deep fascial investment of the muscles. In the anal triangle the diaphragmatic fascial layer on the under surface of the levator ani muscle is the third reached as the dissector works inward; in the urogenital triangle, the same layer is the ninth stratum encountered.

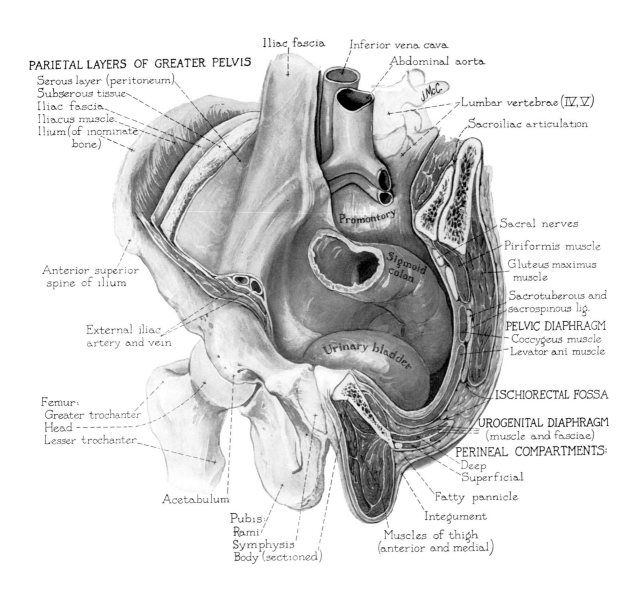

Iliac fascia   Inferior vena cava

Abdominal aorta

PARIETAL LAYERS OF GREATER PELVIS

Serous layer (peritoneum)
Subserous tissue
Iliac fascia
Iliacus muscle
Ilium (of inominate bone)

Lumbar vertebrae (IV, V)

Sacroiliac articulation

Promontory

Sacral nerves

Piriformis muscle

Sigmoid colon

Gluteus maximus muscle

Sacrotuberous and sacrospinous lig.

PELVIC DIAPHRAGM
Coccygeus muscle
Levator ani muscle

Anterior superior spine of ilium

External iliac artery and vein

Urinary bladder

ISCHIORECTAL FOSSA

UROGENITAL DIAPHRAGM
(muscle and fasciae)

PERINEAL COMPARTMENTS:
Deep
Superficial

Femur:
Greater trochanter
Head
Lesser trochanter

Fatty pannicle

Integument

Acetabulum

Pubis:
Rami
Symphysis
Body (sectioned)

Muscles of thigh
(anterior and medial)

Layers and spaces of the pelvis and perineum. Paramedian section.

In the iliac fossa, on the specimen's right, the layers of the pelvic wall are shown; in front, the external iliac vessels are transected near the point of passage through the vascular lacuna, beneath the inguinal ligament, on the way to the femoral triangle. The aorta and inferior vena cava are exposed by removal of the serous and subserous layers.

On the left side, along the cut surface of the section, the following anatomical features are demonstrated: the muscular constituents of the pelvic diaphragm; the muscular and fascial layers of the urogenital diaphragm, and the ischiorectal fossa (the anterior and posterior recesses of which are indicated by arrows); the perineal compartments, located above and below the inferior fascial layer of the urogenital diaphragm.

Compare the coronal sections, illustrated on pages 449 and 450.

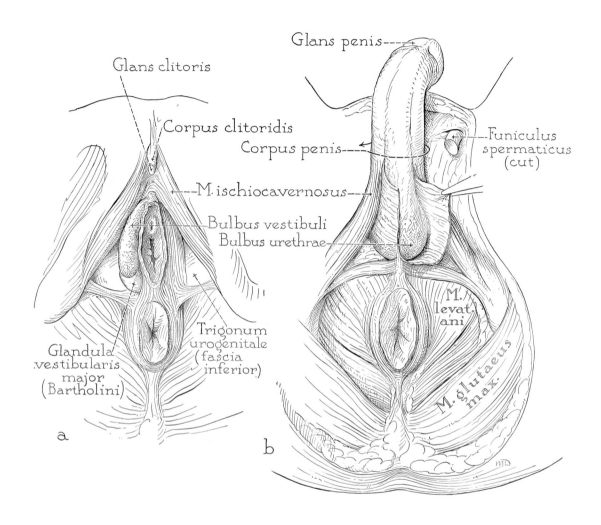

Anatomy of the male and female perineum, especially of the superficial perineal compartment.

In the male specimen (*b*), superficial perineal muscles, penile constituents, and the following boundaries of the anal portion are shown: levator ani muscle (of pelvic diaphragm) and external anal sphincter muscle. Of gluteal musculature, the gluteus maximus is included in the dissection. In the female specimen (*a*), the external anal sphincter is shown, in its relation to the superficial transverse perineal and bulbocavernosus muscles. In the male the bulbocavernosus muscle has been reflected on one side in order to expose a lateral half of the bulb of the urethra; in the female, the homologous muscle has been removed (on the reader's left) to reveal a bulb of the vestibule and the greater vestibular gland. In both specimens the crura are covered by the ischiocavernous muscles. The bulbs of the vestibule, the intermediate mass, and the glans of the clitoris are, together, homologous to the corpus cavernosus urethrae of the male.

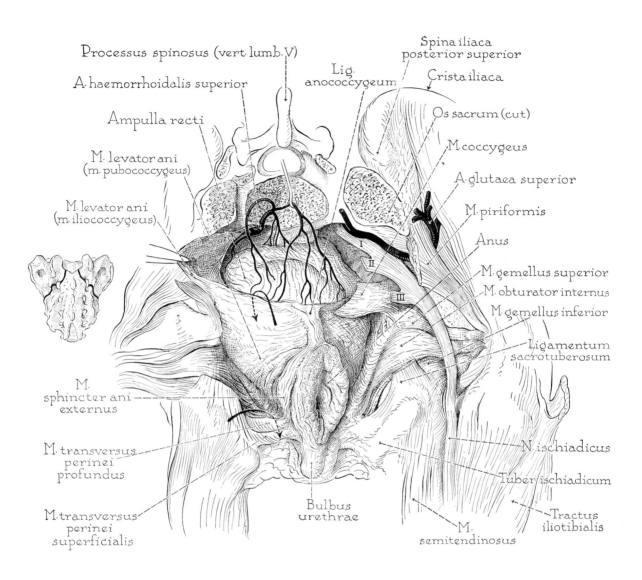

Processus spinosus (vert. lumb. V)

A. haemorrhoidalis superior

Ampulla recti

M. levator ani
(m. pubococcygeus)

M. levator ani
(m. iliococcygeus)

M.
sphincter ani
externus

M. transversus
perinei
profundus

M. transversus
perinei
superficialis

Spina iliaca
posterior superior

Lig.
anococcygeum

Crista iliaca

Os sacrum (cut)

M. coccygeus

A. glutaea superior

M. piriformis

Anus

M. gemellus superior

M. obturator internus

M. gemellus inferior

Ligamentum
sacrotuberosum

N. ischiadicus

Tuber ischiadicum

Tractus
iliotibialis

M.
semitendinosus

Bulbus
urethrae

Rectum, dorsal aspect; pelvic diaphragm and related structures.

Dorsally the sacrospinalis muscles and associated structures have been removed, together with the greater portion of the sacrum (below the level of the first sacral foramina, as indicated in the inset). The gluteus maximus muscle has likewise been removed; the piriformis and coccygeus muscles have been cut near their origins. The pelvic diaphragm has been cut away in its presacral portion, the margin retracted to reveal the rectum, the superior hemorrhoidal artery (NA, *A. rectalis superior*), and the large anterior rami (second and third, cut) which are contributory to the sacral plexus of nerves. The plexus is continued into the gluteal and posterior femoral regions chiefly as the sciatic (ischiadic) nerve. All fatty tissue has been removed from the ischiorectal fossae in the anal division of the perineum; in the urogenital portion of the perineum the dissection has been carried to the level of the superficial perineal compartment (exposing the bulb of the urethra). The upper arrow points into the retroperitoneal space situated lateral to the rectum; the lower arrow enters the anterior recess of the ischiorectal fossa.

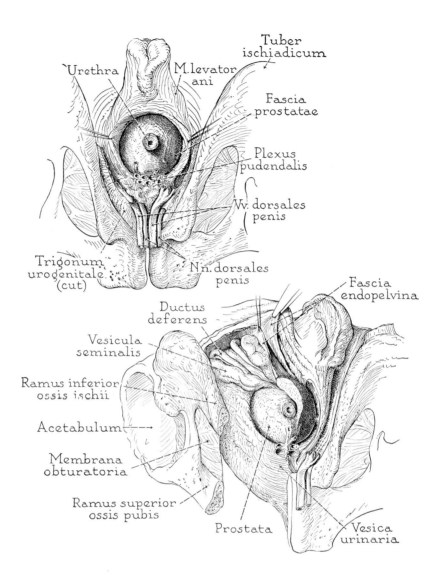

Tuber
ischiadicum

Urethra   M. levator
ani

Fascia
prostatae

Plexus
pudendalis

Vv. dorsales
penis

Trigonum
urogenitale
(cut)

Nn. dorsales
penis

Fascia
endopelvina

Ductus
deferens

Vesicula
seminalis

Ramus inferior
ossis ischii

Acetabulum

Membrana
obturatoria

Ramus superior
ossis pubis

Prostata

Vesica
urinaria

Pelvic viscera in the male, seen from the inferior, or perineal, aspect.
Same specimen as in the preceding figure.

In the upper figure the anterior portion of the pelvic diaphragm has been incised in the median plane,
and the margins retracted to expose the prostate; the organ is invested by a fascial coat derived from the
diaphragmatic portion of the pelvic fascia. Anterior to the prostate, and in retropubic position, the pudendal
plexus of veins is exposed. Marginally, in the urogenital portion of the perineum, a portion of the urogenital
diaphragm remains, as do the cut ends of the dorsal penile veins and nerves.

In the lower figure the pelvic organs are more fully exposed through removal, on the specimen's left
side, of the pelvic diaphragm and of the body of the pubis and ischium. The prostatic fascia has been dissected off the gland, and the vesical fascia removed from the urinary bladder. A portion of one lobe of the
prostate has been removed on the left side. The seminal vesicles and deferent ducts are revealed by reflection
of the endopelvic fascia.

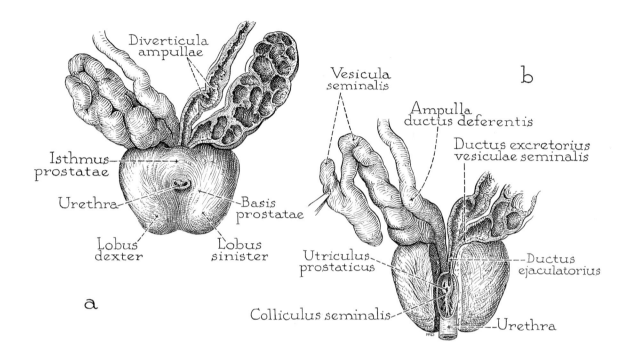

Prostate gland and seminal vesicles.

a, The prostate gland and the seminal vesicles and their ducts, viewed from the front and above. The prostate has been freed from the urinary bladder by transecting the urethra; on the specimen's left, the vesicles and their ducts have been opened.

The part here exposed is the upper surface, or base, of the gland. The area of the base between the urethral orifice and the ejaculatory ducts (shown in *b*) is the isthmus.

b, In further dissection, a wedge-shaped segment has been cut out of the gland, to include the tissue of the isthmus (see *a*) and to extend downward as far as the apex. Here the prostatic part of the urethra becomes continuous with the membranous part upon entering the urogenital diaphragm (or trigone).

The large, tortuous main duct of each seminal vesicle narrows to become the excretory duct. This duct of the seminal vesicle unites with the lower end of the ampulla of the ductus deferens to form the ejaculatory duct; the latter then enters the substance of the prostate gland, lying upon the wall of the *utriculus prostaticus.* The ejaculatory duct terminates by opening into the urethra at the *colliculus seminalis,* a small, slit-like orifice.

The prostate consists of 30 to 50 tubuloalveolar glands, embedded in a stroma of smooth muscle. Sixteen or more ducts are formed by the union of the larger number of individual glands. These open into the urethra by minute orifices located at each side of the colliculus. (Drawings adapted from Spalteholz.)

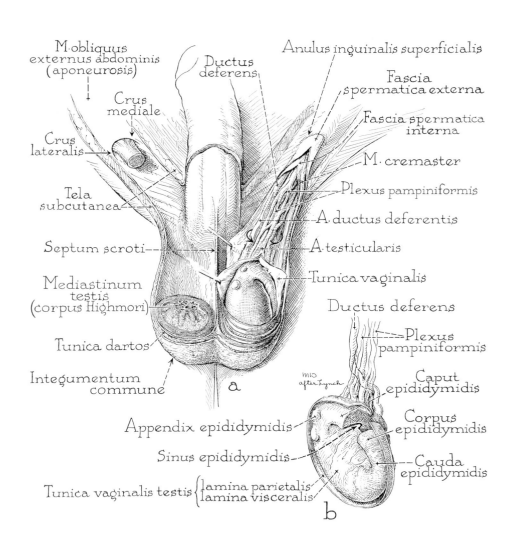

M·obliquus externus abdominis (aponeurosis)

Crus mediale

Ductus deferens

Anulus inguinalis superficialis

Fascia spermatica externa

Fascia spermatica interna

M·cremaster

Plexus pampiniformis

A·ductus deferentis

A·testicularis

Tunica vaginalis

Ductus deferens

Crus lateralis

Tela subcutanea

Septum scroti

Mediastinum testis (corpus Highmori)

Tunica dartos

Integumentum commune

a

Plexus pampiniformis

Caput epididymidis

Corpus epididymidis

Cauda epididymidis

Appendix epididymidis

Sinus epididymidis

Tunica vaginalis testis { lamina parietalis / lamina visceralis }

mb after Lynch

b

Male genital organs.

Scrotum, scrotal and funicular layers, and testis.

a, On the specimen's right side, the spermatic cord has been transected near the point of emergence from the subcutaneous inguinal ring; the margins of the ring have been defined by removal of the external spermatic fascia. The testis has been sectioned in order to demonstrate its mediastinal areas. On the opposite side the constituents of the spermatic cord (encircled) and the funicular coverings are shown (see also p. 349).

b, The parts of the testis and epididymis. The sinus is shown by cutting out a section of the body of the organ. Demonstrating also the reflection of the serous tunic from the viscus to the parietal.

(Adapted with the kind permission of Dr. Joseph E. Markee.)

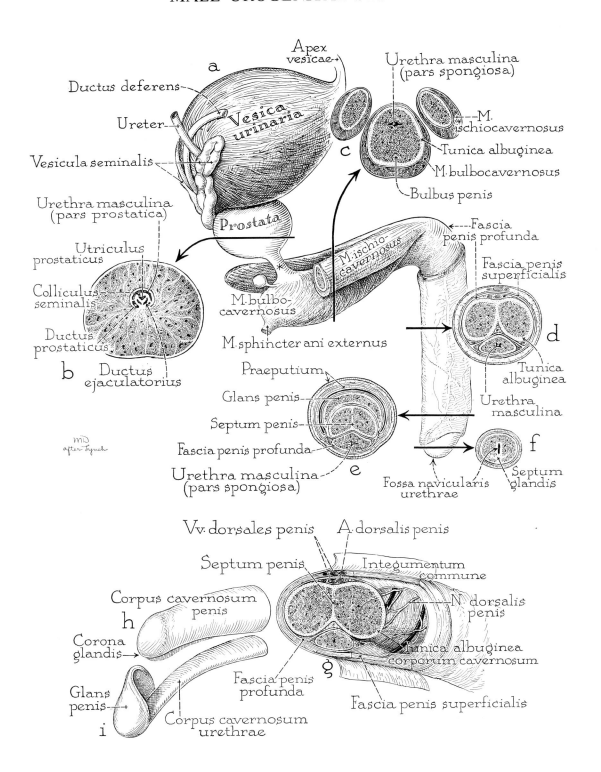

Male urogenital system.

a, The urinary bladder, prostate gland, erectile bodies, and urethra (membranous part indicated by *).
b, Transverse section through the prostate (see *b*, page 455).
c to *f*, Penile constituents at the four levels indicated in *a*.
g and *h*, Cavernous bodies intact and separated.
(Adapted with the permission of Dr. Joseph E. Markee.)

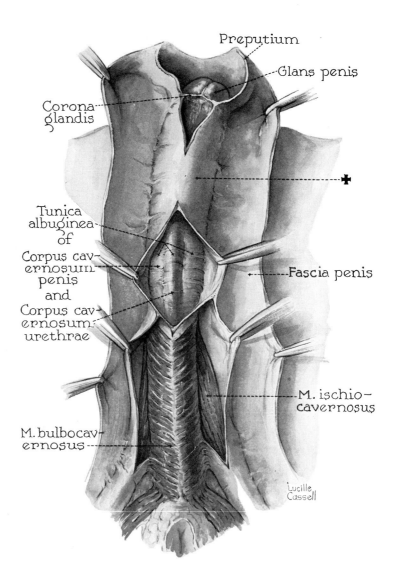

Perineal fascia.

The penis has been raised and dissection carried out along its ventral surface. The entire scrotal sac and contents have been removed to reveal the superficial perineal musculature and its fascial continuities with the penis.

A medial incision through the superficial penile fascia (dartos) permits that structure to be reflected laterally to display a thin but firm fascial layer, the deep fascia of the penis (Buck's fascia), indicated by ✚, which is closely adherent to the fibrous capsule of the corpora cavernosa penis and urethra. An incision in the median line of the deep fascia demonstrates this relationship to the corpora; another, more distal incision indicates its intimate adherence to the capsule overlying the glans. The prepuce contains between its two layers of skin a thin prolongation of the dartos.

At the base of the penis, the deep fascia is continued inferiorly over the superficial perineal muscles (bulbocavernosus, ischiocavernosus) as true muscle fascia.

The deep fascia of the penis is formed above by the outer layer of investing fascia of the external oblique muscle; below, by a prolongation of the muscle fascia of the superficial perineal muscles; laterally, by union of the upper and lower fascial layers.

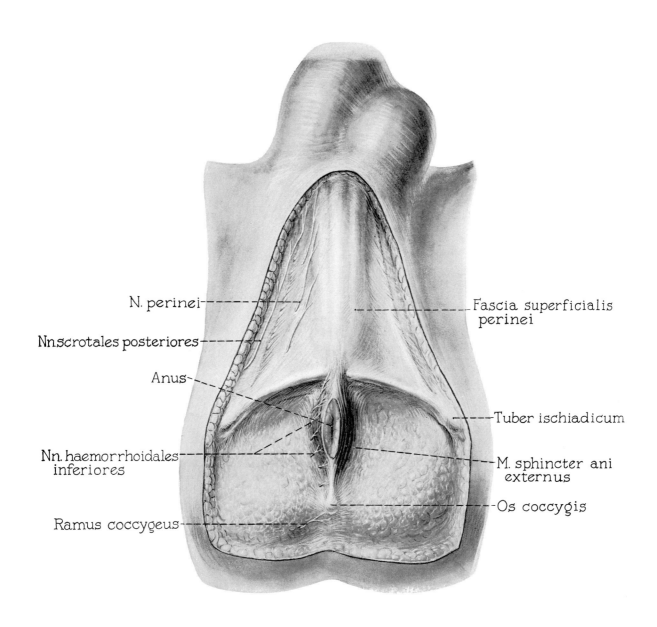

N. perinei

Nn. scrotales posteriores

Anus

Nn. haemorrhoidales inferiores

Ramus coccygeus

Fascia superficialis perinei

Tuber ischiadicum

M. sphincter ani externus

Os coccygis

Male perineum. Subcutaneous structures and perineal fascia.

Fat-laden tissue of the superficial fascia fills the ischiorectal fossae in the anal part of the perineum. In the urogenital division of the perineum, the superficial layer of the superficial fascia has been removed to expose the deep stratum. The deeper layer is virtually of aponeurotic nature. At each side, it is attached to the ischiopubic ramus and ischial tuberosity. Behind, it curves upward around the superficial transverse perineal muscle, to become continuous with the inferior fascia of the urogenital diaphragm. Thereby the layer forms the inferior boundary, or "floor," of the superficial perineal compartment (see page 465). (From Warren: Handbook of Anatomy, Harvard University Press.)

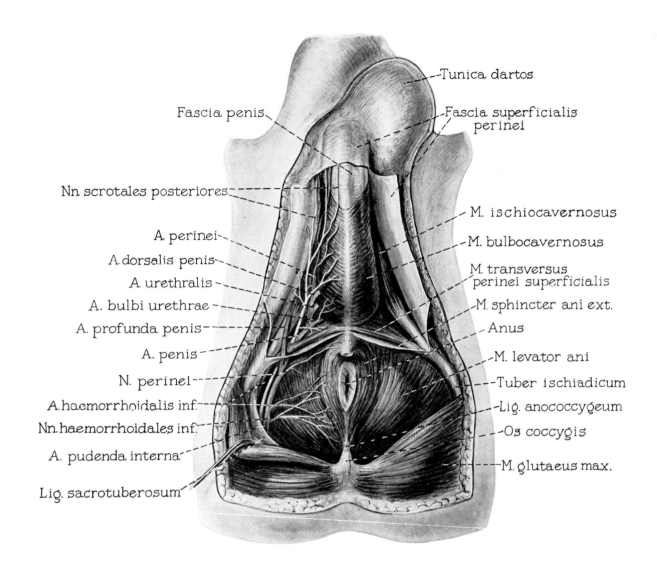

Fascia penis

Nn scrotales posteriores

A. perinei

A. dorsalis penis

A. urethralis

A. bulbi urethrae

A. profunda penis

A. penis

N. perinei

A. haemorrhoidalis inf.

Nn. haemorrhoidales inf.

A. pudenda interna

Lig. sacrotuberosum

Tunica dartos

Fascia superficialis perinei

M. ischiocavernosus

M. bulbocavernosus

M. transversus perinei superficialis

M. sphincter ani ext.

Anus

M. levator ani

Tuber ischiadicum

Lig. anococcygeum

Os coccygis

M. glutaeus max.

Male perineum. Muscles of the erectile bodies and of the pelvic diaphragm, with the related vessels and nerves.

In the anal part of the perineum, on the specimen's right side, the vessels and nerves are shown as they pass from the infrapiriform recess of the greater ischiadic (sciatic) foramen, medialward to the anal canal, and forward to the musculature of the superficial perineal compartment. In the anal triangle the pudendal vessels and nerves have been freed from the fascia of the obturator internus muscle, beneath which they occupied the so-called Canal of Alcock. The inferior hemorrhoidal artery (NA, *A. rectalis inferior*), like the accompanying nerves, supplies both the sphincteric musculature of the anal canal and the skin of the perineum.

In the urogenital part of the perineum the deep layer of superficial fascia has been cut and reflected to demonstrate the contents of the superficial perineal compartment. On the specimen's right side, the dissection has been carried to deeper level, revealing the vessels and nerves in the deep perineal compartment.

The superficial perineal muscles invest the cavernous, or erectile, bodies (exposed in the succeeding figure). The arteries of supply to the erectile tissue leave the internal pudendal by triradiate branching, to pass medialward to the bulb of the urethra, forward to the penile crus and penile glans. (From Warren: Handbook of Anatomy, Harvard University Press.)

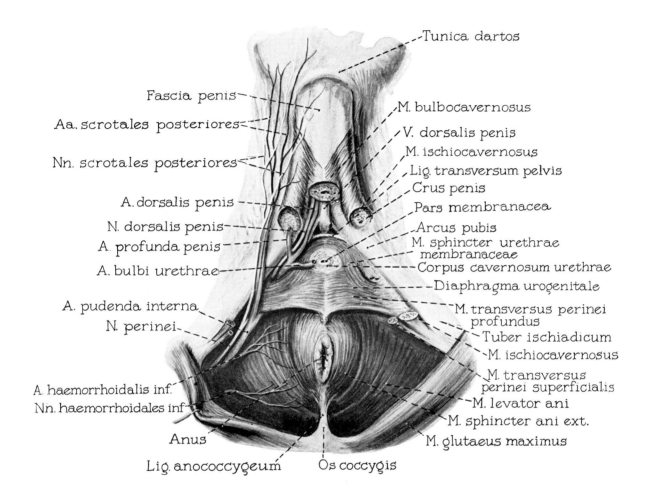

Tunica dartos

Fascia penis

Aa. scrotales posteriores

Nn. scrotales posteriores

M. bulbocavernosus

V. dorsalis penis

M. ischiocavernosus

Lig. transversum pelvis

Crus penis

Pars membranacea

A. dorsalis penis

N. dorsalis penis

A. profunda penis

A. bulbi urethrae

Arcus pubis

M. sphincter urethrae membranaceae

Corpus cavernosum urethrae

Diaphragma urogenitale

A. pudenda interna

N. perinei

M. transversus perinei profundus

Tuber ischiadicum

M. ischiocavernosus

M. transversus perinei superficialis

A. haemorrhoidalis inf.

Nn. haemorrhoidales inf.

M. levator ani

M. sphincter ani ext.

Anus

M. glutaeus maximus

Lig. anococcygeum

Os coccygis

Male perineum. Musculature of the urogenital diaphragm and blood vessels to the cavernous tissue.

In the urogenital part of the perineum the bulb of the urethra and the proximal portions of the penile crura have been removed; the inferior fascia of the urogenital diaphragm has been dissected away to expose the musculature of the diaphragm in the deep perineal compartment. The artery to the bulb of the urethra is cut; the deep artery is shown as it perforates the penile crus; the third branch of the internal pudendal, or dorsal, artery continues forward to the glans.

Small veins usually accompany the arteries, matching their course in returning to plexuses within the pelvic cavity. However, the greater venous drainage is forward. These vessels converge upon the dorsal vein of the penis, the confluent channel then entering the pelvic cavity through a small foramen bounded in front by the pubic symphysis (and pubic arcuate ligament), behind by the transverse ligament of the pelvis. This ligament is formed by fusion of the two layers of fascia of the urogenital diaphragm. (From Warren: Handbook of Anatomy, Harvard University Press.)

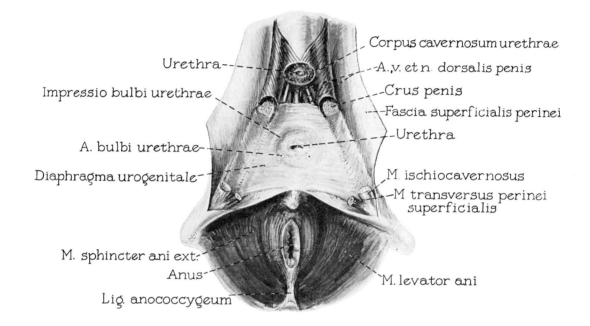

Urethra

Impressio bulbi urethrae

A. bulbi urethrae

Diaphragma urogenitale

Corpus cavernosum urethrae

A., v. et n. dorsalis penis

Crus penis

Fascia superficialis perinei

Urethra

M. ischiocavernosus

M. transversus perinei superficialis

M. sphincter ani ext.

Anus

Lig. anococcygeum

M. levator ani

Male perineum. Fascial layers of the perineal compartments.

The cavernous bodies, together with the investing muscles, are shown anteriorly where, as roots, they join to form the penile body; posteriorly, the crura remain near their attachment to the pubic arch; in the middle of the space, the bulb of the urethra is represented merely by the impression left upon the "roof" of the superficial perineal compartment. This superior boundary, or roof of the compartment (or interspace), is the inferior fascia of the urogenital diaphragm. The arteries of supply to the erectile bodies are transmitted by small openings in the fascial layer on their way from the deep to the superficial compartment. (From Warren: Handbook of Anatomy, Harvard University Press.)

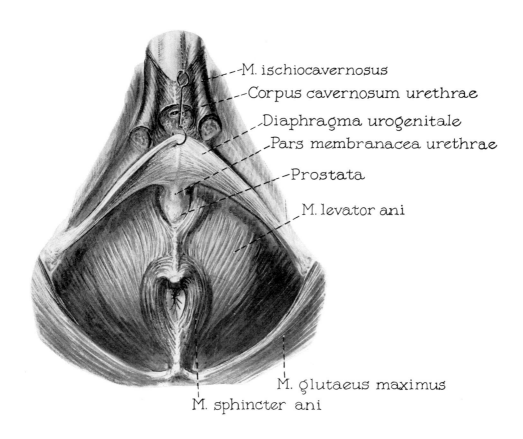

M. ischiocavernosus

Corpus cavernosum urethrae

Diaphragma urogenitale

Pars membranacea urethrae

Prostata

M. levator ani

M. glutaeus maximus

M. sphincter ani

Male perineum. Pelvic and urogenital diaphragm.

The urogenital diaphragm has been freed on its superior aspect, along the median raphe by which it was attached to the apposed surface of the pelvic diaphragm. Thus detached, it has been drawn forward as a unit, to expose the following spaces and structures: an anterior recess of the ischiorectal fossa, on each side of the middle line; a circumferential cleft at prostate level, produced by separating the prostatic fascia from the adjacent fascicles of the levator ani muscle; the basal part of the urogenital diaphragm, as it covers the deep transverse perineal muscle (compare figure on page 469). It is around the latter muscle (here concealed) that the two fascial layers of the diaphragm curve and join each other. By fusing, they close the compartment, or "pouch," posteriorly; laterally, the space is closed by attachment of the two layers to the ischiopubic rami; anteriorly, the layers unite to form a strong band, the transverse ligament to the pelvis (see figure on page 470).

The pelvic diaphragm is exposed through the greater part of its extent. Like the urogenital diaphragm, it is three-layered—fascial strata covers its inferior and superior surfaces. Here the inferior investment has been removed to expose the chief muscular constituent, the levator ani. The lesser constituent, the coccygeus, is covered by the gluteal musculature. (From Warren: Handbook of Anatomy, Harvard University Press.)

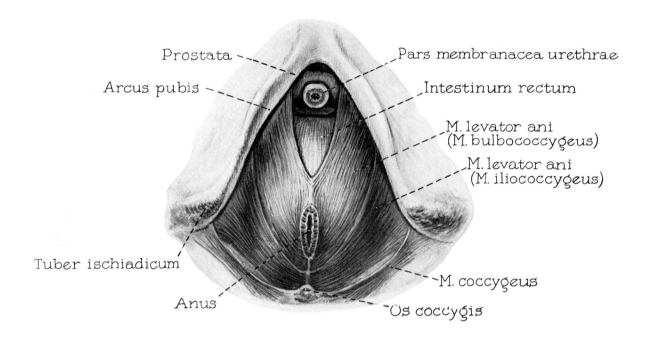

Prostata

Arcus pubis

Tuber ischiadicum

Anus

Pars membranacea urethrae

Intestinum rectum

M. levator ani
(M. bulbococcygeus)

M. levator ani
(M. iliococcygeus)

M. coccygeus

Os coccygis

Male perineum. Pelvic diaphragm.

The form and muscular component of the pelvic diaphragm are demonstrated by removal of the urogenital diaphragm (see preceding figure).

The levatores ani together form the greater part of the pelvic diaphragm; each consists of an anterior (pubococcygeal) part, and a posterior division, the iliococcygeal (also termed ischiococcygeal). The coccygei complete the diaphragm behind. The diaphragm constitutes the partition between the pelvis proper and the perineum.

Anteriorly, a median cleft transmits the urethra from the prostate gland in the pelvis to the deep perineal compartment. In the dissection the hiatus has been enlarged in order to demonstrate the prostate gland and the rectal part of the large intestine. The diaphragm supports these organs.

Posteriorly, the anal canal passes through the pubococcygeal part of the muscle (OT, bulbococcygeus).

Laterally, but out of view, the obturator internus muscle forms the boundary of the ischiorectal fossa, inferior to the line of tendinous attachment of the levator ani (see pages 435 and 441, b). Superior to the line, the same muscle constitutes the side wall of the lesser pelvis. (From Warren: Handbook of Anatomy, Harvard University Press.)

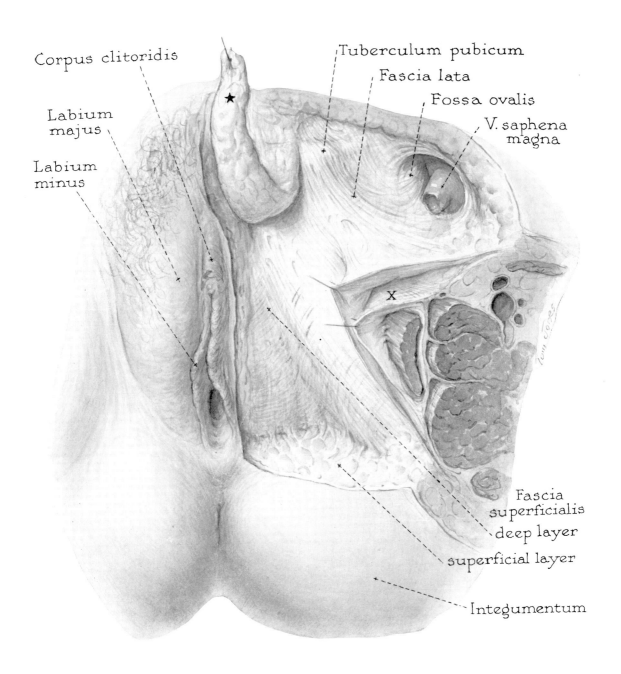

Corpus clitoridis

Labium majus

Labium minus

Tuberculum pubicum

Fascia lata

Fossa ovalis

V. saphena magna

X

Fascia superficialis

deep layer

superficial layer

Integumentum

Female perineum: subcutaneous layers.

On the reader's right the superficial layer of the superficial fascia has been removed to expose the deep (Colles') layer in the anterior, or urogenital, part of the perineum; in the posterior, or anal, part of the perineum the superficial layer, locally thickened and adipose, remains intact behind the line of cut, i.e., in the ischiorectal fossa. The sleeve of fascia lata, shown by transecting the thigh, has been freed from the muscle fascia; the latter is shown as it invests the sartorius (at X) and the adductors, freed from the muscles and retracted. The diverticular process, which contains prolongations of the inguinal layers together with the round ligament of the uterus, has been mobilized and lifted (marked with star). On the opposite half of the perineum the skin remains intact. Successively deeper dissections follow.

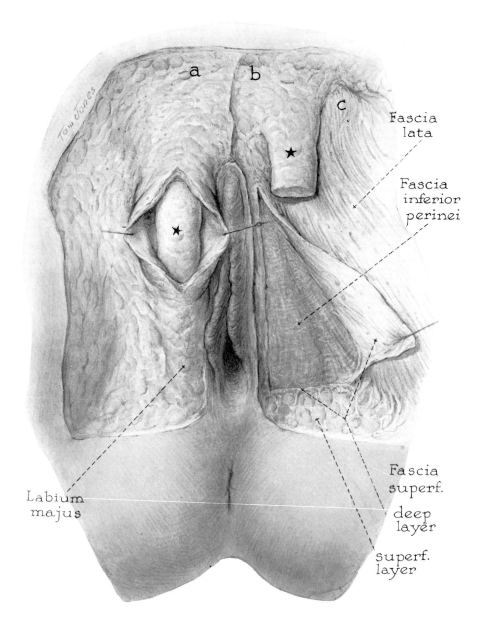

Female perineum: subcutaneous structures and fasciae of the urogenital part of the perineum.

On the left, the superficial layer of the superficial fascia has now been exposed by reflection of the skin; it has been incised longitudinally where it covers the labial portion of the diverticular process (at star). The width of the latter is demonstrated by retraction of the margins of the incision. On the right, the deep layer of the superficial fascia has been cut, the flap turned lateralward, to show the inferior perineal fascia as it covers the muscles in the superficial perineal compartment. In the anterior portion of the anal part of the perineum, on each side, much of the fat of the superficial layer has been removed from the ischiorectal fossae; over the front of the pubis the same layer has been removed in three levels to show, successively, the immediately subcutaneous tissue, a; the covering of the diverticulum, b; the diverticulum itself, at star; and the subjacent fascia lata, c.

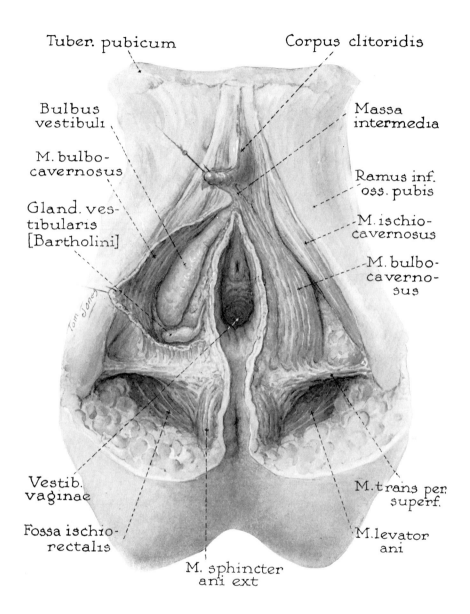

Tuber. pubicum

Corpus clitoridis

Bulbus vestibuli

M. bulbo-cavernosus

Gland. ves-tibularis [Bartholini]

Massa intermedia

Ramus inf. oss. pubis

M. ischio-cavernosus

M. bulbo-caverno-sus

Vestib. vaginae

Fossa ischio-rectalis

M. trans per. superf.

M. levator ani

M. sphincter ani ext

Female perineum: ischiorectal fossa and superficial perineal compartment.

In the anal part of the perineum the levator ani and external anal sphincter muscles of each side are shown by removal of the superficial fatty tissue. In the urogenital part of the perineum, on the right side, by cutting away the muscle fascia, the ischiocavernosus, superficial transverse perineal and bulbocavernosus muscles have been brought into view. On the left side the bulbocavernosus muscle has been reflected to expose the bulb of the vestibule and greater vestibular (Bartholin's) gland and duct. Anteriorly are seen the glans, body, and intermediate mass of the clitoris.

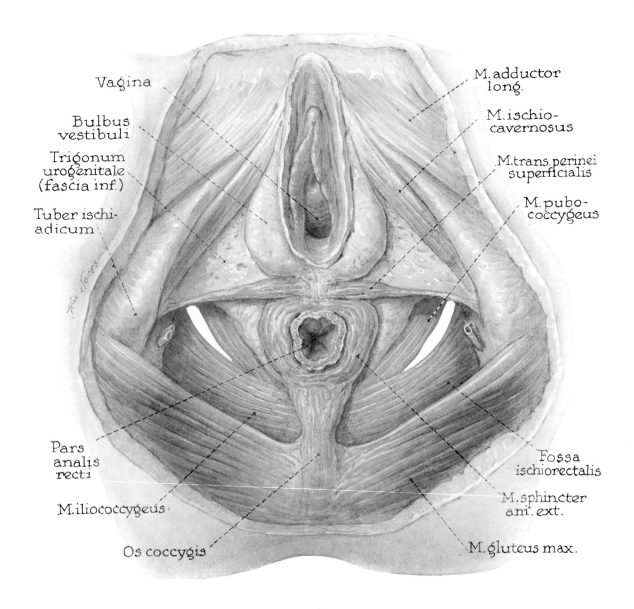

Vagina

Bulbus
vestibuli

Trigonum
urogenitale
(fascia inf.)

Tuber ischi-
adicum

M.adductor
long.

M.ischio-
cavernosus

M.trans.perinei
superficialis

M.pubo-
coccygeus

Pars
analis
recti

Fossa
ischiorectalis

M.sphincter
ani.ext.

M.iliococcygeus

Os coccygis

M.gluteus max.

Female perineum: erectile bodies (cavernous tissue) and muscles of the
superficial perineal compartment and the musculature of the pelvic diaphragm.

    In the anal triangle the fatty tissue has been entirely removed from the ischiorectal fossae, to expose
the pelvic diaphragm and the external anal sphincter. With removal, too, of the fascial investments of the
levator ani, the cleft between pubococcygeal and iliococcygeal portions is made evident. In the urogenital
triangle the layers of superficial fascia have been removed to expose the ischiocavernosus muscles; the
bulbocavernosus muscles have been dissected away, to reveal the bulbs of the vestibule. The integument of
the lesser labia and of the clitoris is intact.

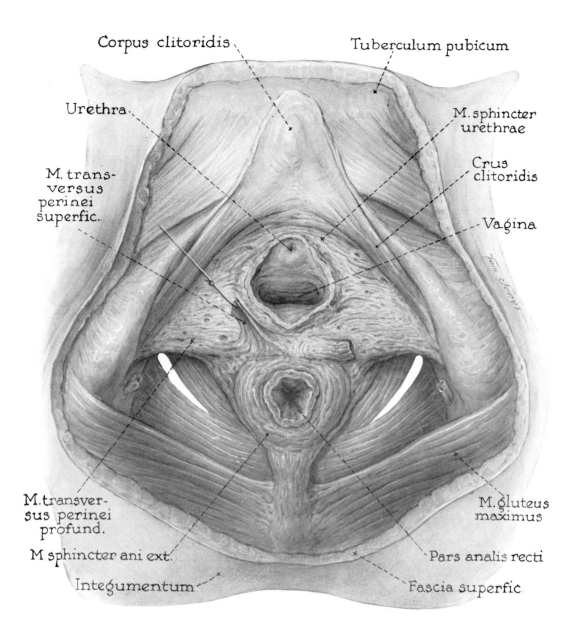

Corpus clitoridis

Tuberculum pubicum

Urethra

M. sphincter urethrae

M. transversus perinei superfic.

Crus clitoridis

Vagina

M. transversus perinei profund.

M. gluteus maximus

M sphincter ani ext.

Pars analis recti

Integumentum

Fascia superfic.

Female perineum: Muscular contents of the deep perineal compartment.

In the anal triangle the external anal sphincter has been freed somewhat in order to show the coccygeal extension of the urogenital diaphragm. In the urogenital triangle the following superficial structures of the perineum have been removed: the integument and the subcutaneous tissue; the mucous membrane of the vestibular walls; the vestibular bulbs (no intermediate mass present); the inferior fascia of the urogenital diaphragm; some of the more superficial fibers of the sphincter muscle of the membranous urethra and of the deep transverse muscles which were attached to the inferior fascia. The following structures are shown: muscles of the urogenital diaphragm; the roof of the vestibule, into which open the vagina and the urethra; a portion of the transverse ligament of the pelvis; the body of the clitoris; the inferior perineal fascia, as it invests the ischiocavernosus muscles and covers the front of the pubis; the medial portion of the superficial transverse perineal muscles (stump on left elevated to demonstrate fusion at the central tendinous point of the perineum). The transverse ligament of the pelvis (i.e., the anteriorly fused fascial layers of the urogenital diaphragm) is largely concealed by the pubic symphysis.

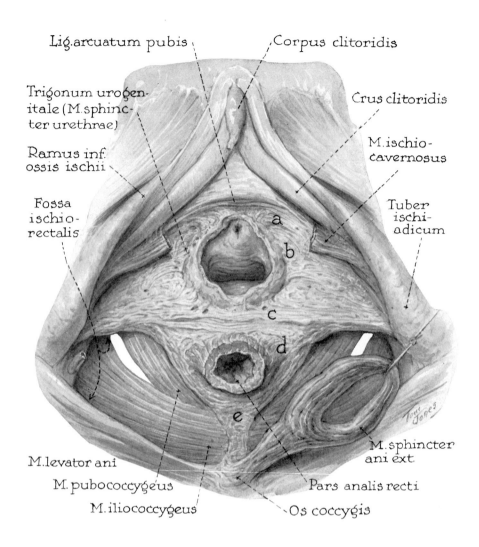

Lig. arcuatum pubis

Corpus clitoridis

Trigonum urogen-
itale (M.sphinc-
ter urethrae)

Crus clitoridis

M.ischio-
cavernosus

Ramus inf.
ossis ischii

Fossa
ischio-
rectalis

Tuber
ischi-
adicum

a

b

c

d

e

M.sphincter
ani ext.

M.levator ani

M.pubococcygeus

Pars analis recti

M.iliococcygeus

Os coccygis

Female perineum: muscles of the pelvic and urogenital diaphragms.

In the anal part of the perineum the external anal sphincter, now detached from the subjacent muscles of the urogenital and pelvic diaphragms and from the intrinsic musculature of the canal, has been drawn aside to reveal the backward-directed fibers of the urogenital triangle. In the urogenital part of the perineum the ischiocavernosus muscles have been rolled medialward away from the crura and the body of the clitoris; the superficial transverse perineal muscles have now been entirely removed to show the course of fibers at the base of the urogenital diaphragm. It is evident that the so-called sphincter of the membranous urethra is not restricted to the urogenital part of the perineum. In addition to sending muscle fibers into, and in front of, the urethra (at a), into the vaginal wall (b), across the midline between the vagina and anus (c) and into the wall of the latter (d), it is prolonged backward to a coccygeal attachment (at e). The transverse ligament of the pelvis appears as a cut edge just dorsal to the pubic arcuate ligament.

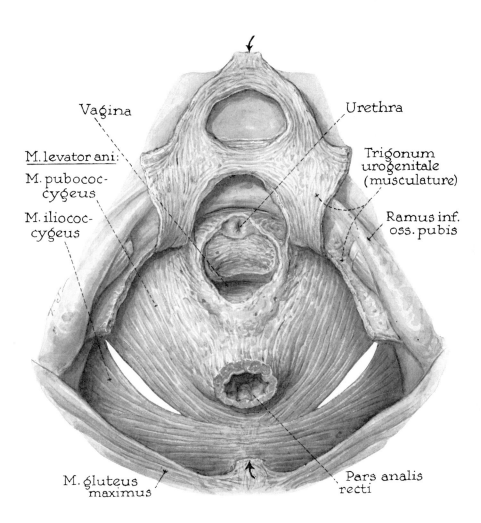

Vagina

Urethra

M. levator ani:

M. pubococ-
cygeus

M. iliococ-
cygeus

Trigonum
urogenitale
(musculature)

Ramus inf.
oss. pubis

M. gluteus
maximus

Pars analis
recti

Female perineum: musculature of the pelvic diaphragm.

The musculature of the urogenital diaphragm has been freed from the pelvic diaphragm in the midline, cut along the ischiopubic ramus on each side, and at coccygeal apex behind (see arrows); the urogenital diaphragm, thus freed from its major attachments, has been turned forward. The space exposed between the two diaphragms is the anterior recess of the ischiorectal fossa, from which all fatty tissue has been removed. The pubococcygeal and iliococcygeal parts of the levator ani are exposed by removal of their thin investing fascia (inferior fascia of the pelvic diaphragm, or anal layer of the diaphragmatic fascia). The pubococcygeus contributes supporting muscle fibers to the urethra, the vagina, and the anal canal.

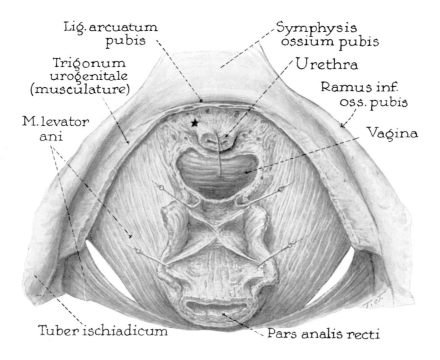

Lig. arcuatum pubis

Trigonum urogenitale (musculature)

M. levator ani

Symphysis ossium pubis

Urethra

Ramus inf. oss. pubis

Vagina

Tuber ischiadicum

Pars analis recti

Female perineum: anterior, or pubococcygeal, portion of the pelvic diaphragm.

The urogenital diaphragm has been removed except for a narrow strip of attachment along the ischiopubic rami and at the transverse ligament of the pelvis. The pelvic diaphragm has been incised in the middle line from the anal to the vaginal canal, in order to demonstrate the relation of these canals to the pelvic diaphragm and to fascial sheaths which intervene between the musculature of the pelvic diaphragm and the intrinsic musculature of the visceral canals. Like the vagina and the anal part of the rectum, the urethra receives supporting fibers from the levator ani (at star). The cleft, or space, which intervenes between the pubic arcuate and the urogenital diaphragm (or trigone) is so small that it is not evident when the perineum is viewed directly from below. The cleft transmits the dorsal clitoridal veins into the vesical venous plexus, situated with the pelvis.

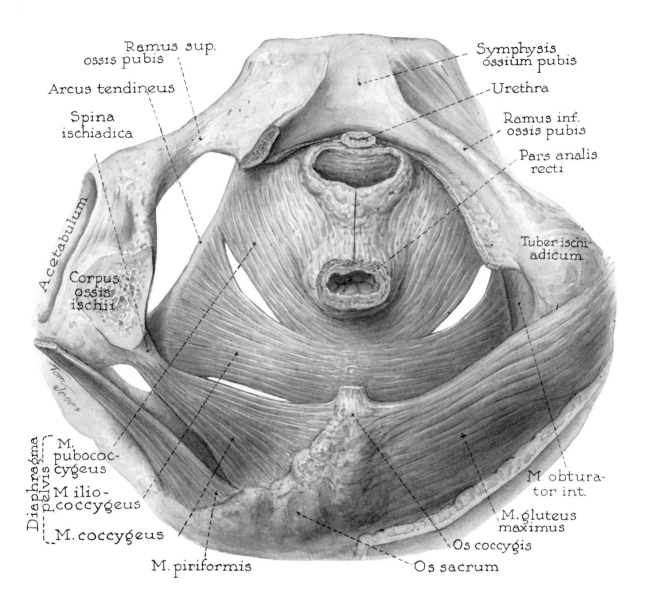

Ramus sup.
ossis pubis

Arcus tendineus

Spina
ischiadica

Acetabulum

Corpus
ossis
ischii

Tom Jones

Diaphragma
pelvis
{ M.
pubococ-
cygeus
M. ilio-
coccygeus
M. coccygeus

M. piriformis

Symphysis
ossium pubis

Urethra

Ramus inf.
ossis pubis

Pars analis
recti

Tuber ischi-
adicum

M. obtura-
tor int.

M. gluteus
maximus

Os coccygis

Os sacrum

Female perineum: pelvic diaphragm and related musculature of the urogenital diaphragm and buttock.

Portions of the right innominate bone have been removed (the inferior pubic ramus cut near the symphysis and the ischium superior to the level of the spine) to demonstrate the attachments, form and relationships of the pelvic diaphragm. The following features are especially important: the clefts between the adjacent or partially overlapping pubococcygeal and iliococcygeal elements of the pelvic diaphragm; the tendinous origin of the aforementioned divisions of the levator ani muscle; the manner in which the portion arising from the pubis passes deep to that taking origin from the spine of the ischium; the proximity of the urethra to the pubic symphysis, and the greater distance between vagina and anus; the complementary position which the coccygeus holds to the iliococcygeus (left), the manner in which it is covered by the gluteus maximus (right); the dorsal situation of the piriformis.

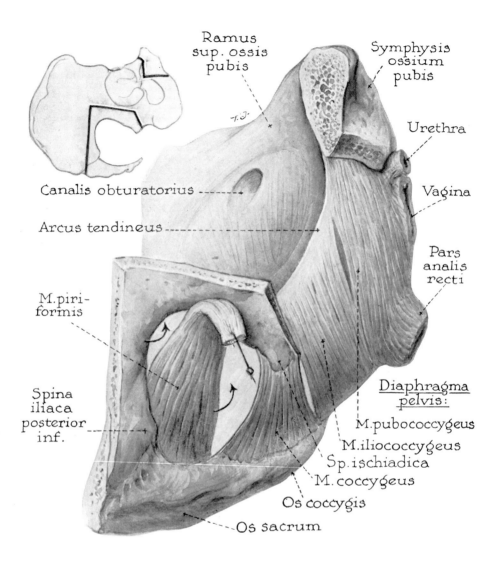

Ramus
sup. ossis
pubis

Symphysis
ossium
pubis

Urethra

Canalis obturatorius

Vagina

Arcus tendineus

Pars
analis
recti

M. piri-
formis

Spina
iliaca
posterior
inf.

Diaphragma
pelvis:

M. pubococcygeus

M. iliococcygeus

Sp. ischiadica

M. coccygeus

Os coccygis

Os sacrum

Female perineum and pelvis: the diaphragmatic and parietal musculature. Lateral view.

By cutting parasagittally through the superior pubic ramus and through the body of the ischium in front of the spine, and then by removing the bone between the pubic and ischial attachments of the levator ani (see inset), the following additional anatomical features are demonstrated: the arciform origin of the levator ani from the covering of the obturator internus (latter intact on specimen's left half); the uniformity in direction of the levator fibers; the position of the anal part of the rectum at the "spout" of the diaphragmatic "funnel"; the capaciousness of the foramina above and below the piriformis (at arrows); the relatively small size of the clefts between parts of the diaphragmatic musculature; the depth of the bony sciatic (ischiadic) notch, which is closed by the coccygeus and piriformis muscles.

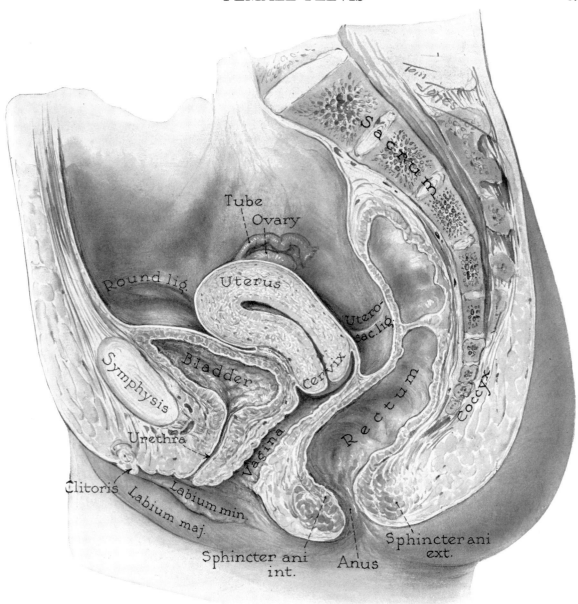

Female pelvis; sagittal section. Showing the relations of the organs and the course of the peritoneum.

Whereas in the abdominal cavity proper the parietal peritoneum is reflected upon portions of the alimentary tract in the form of a complicated series of supporting folds or mesenteries, in the pelvic division of the cavity it is for the most part merely carried over the upper surfaces of pelvic organs, adapting itself to the inequalities produced by them. By their presence it is prevented from descending to the level of the pelvic diaphragm. As the peritoneum descends from the lateral pelvic wall to the bladder, on each side of the organ a shallow depression is formed, termed the paravesical fossa. The peritoneum ascends over the bladder to cover the vesical surface of the body of the uterus, from which it is continued lateralward as the anterior layer of the broad ligament; the shallow trough-like recess thus formed is the vesicouterine excavation (uterovesical pouch). The peritoneal layer next covers the fundus of the uterus, investing all of the posterior uterus and a small upper segment of the vaginal wall; from the uterus it is again draped lateralward to form the posterior layer of the broad ligament of the uterus. From the uterus and the ligament the peritoneum passes to the front of the rectum, forming a deeper sac, the rectouterine excavation. The peritoneum reaches the rectum approximately at the junction of its lower and middle thirds; in the middle third it covers only the front of the tube, while in the upper third it clothes the sides as well; the layers of the two sides then meet above to form a mesenteric support for the sigmoid colon. In partially investing the rectum the peritoneum forms paired pouches, the pararectal fossae, bounded on each side by a crescentic fold of peritoneum, the rectouterine fold (fold of Douglas).

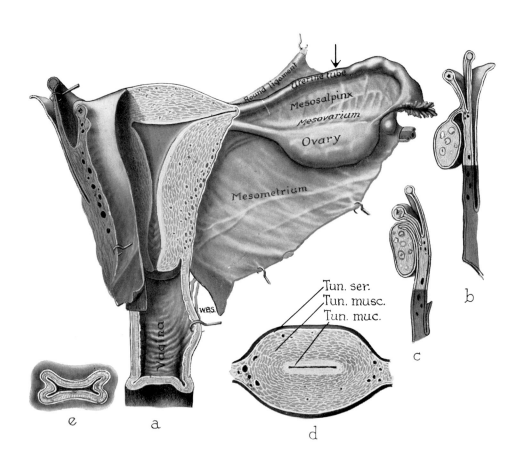

Female genital organs.

a, The female internal organs of generation, seen from behind. The broad ligament has been spread out on the right; on the left, it has been cut and turned backward. The uterus and the vagina are partially opened.

b, Schematic vertical section of the broad ligament at the level of the arrow in *a*; the mesometrium and the mesovarium have been spread apart. *c*, The same, with the portions of the ligament and the ovary in their normal relations.

d, Transverse section of the body of the uterus. *e*, Transverse section through the lower portion of the vagina; the lumen is compressed by the vaginal columns.

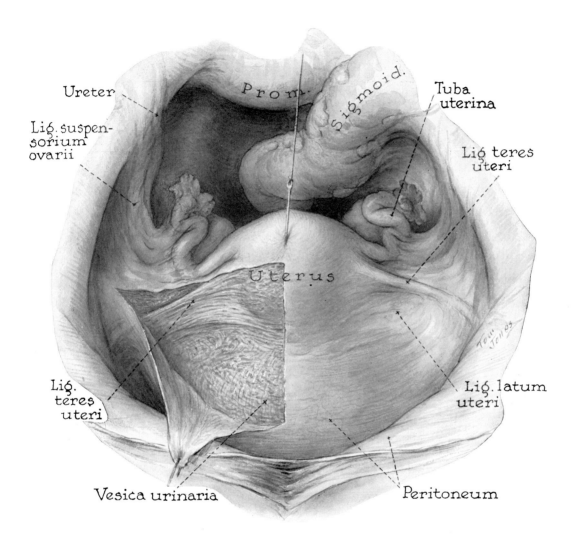

Female pelvis: subperitoneal tissue (tela subserosa)
of the broad ligament, the urinary bladder, and the uterus. Anterior view.

The uterus has been retracted from its normal anteverted position; the peritoneum has been removed, on the specimen's right, from the body of the uterus, the broad ligament, and the superior surface of the bladder.

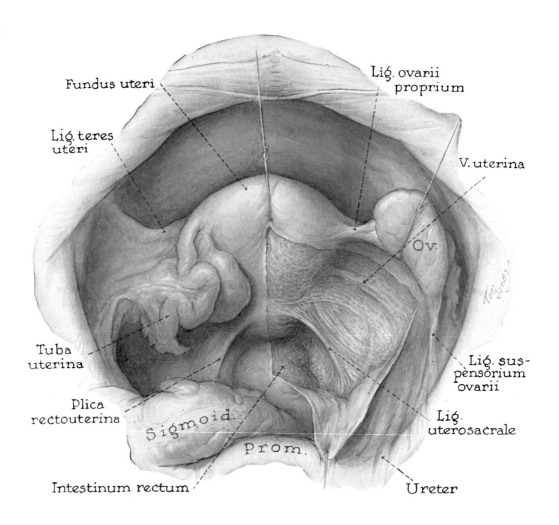

Fundus uteri

Lig. ovarii
proprium

Lig. teres
uteri

V. uterina

Ov.

Tuba
uterina

Lig. sus-
pensorium
ovarii

Plica
rectouterina

Sigmoid.

Lig.
uterosacrale

Prom.

Intestinum rectum

Ureter

Female pelvis: retroperitoneal tissue of the
uterus, the broad ligament, and the pararectal region. Posterior view.

   The uterus, the ovary, and the uterine tube have been elevated; the peritoneum has been removed from
the right half of the body of the uterus and, with it, the posterior leaf of peritoneum of the broad ligament.
In this way the subdivisions of the parametrial tissue are shown. The subserous tunic forms a thin, areolar
layer in the superior (tubal) portion of the broad ligament; it becomes thicker to contribute a sheath-like
investment for the uterine vessels; at the basal aspect of the broad ligament the tissue attains an even heavier
and stronger character, being indistinguishable from the uterosacral and cardinal ligaments.

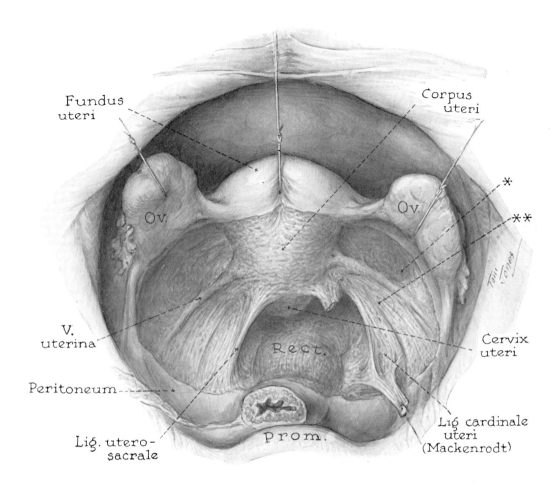

Fundus uteri

Corpus uteri

Ov.

Ov.

*

**

V. uterina

Cervix uteri

Peritoneum

Lig. utero-sacrale

Rect.

Prom.

Lig cardinale uteri (Mackenrodt)

Female pelvis: the supporting structures of the uterus. Posterior view.

The entire posterior leaf of peritoneum has been removed from the broad ligament. On the right side the uterosacral ligament has been cut to show the depth of the recess for which it forms the roof (see left side, intact). * indicates the area of thin parametrium, ** the thicker part which forms a sheath for the vessels.

The subserous connective tissue (tela subserosa, extra-, sub-, or retro-peritoneal tissue) forms a dense cobweblike packing containing a varying amount of fat, which intervenes between the fascia on the inner surface of the musculature and the peritoneum. In the abdominal cavity proper the peritoneum is rather closely applied to the internal investing fascia of the parietal muscles. Consequently, the subserous tissue forms a relatively thin layer. In the pelvis, however, the peritoneum is reflected from the wall to the organs at a level higher than the point at which the parietal fascia is continued medialward on the upper surface of the pelvic diaphragm; the considerable subperitoneal "space" thus produced is filled with connective tissue.

The subserous tissue of the pelvis is regionally modified to form a fatty areolar packing between the rectum and the sacrum; it contributes fascial sleeves for the bladder, uterus, and rectum; from the sides of the uterus, between the serous layers of the broad ligament, and backward to the hypogastric (NA, internal iliac) vessels, the tissue constitutes a plate for transmission of the uterine arteries and veins; it is thickened to merge with bands of ligamentous strength for support of the urethra and bladder and the vagina and uterus.

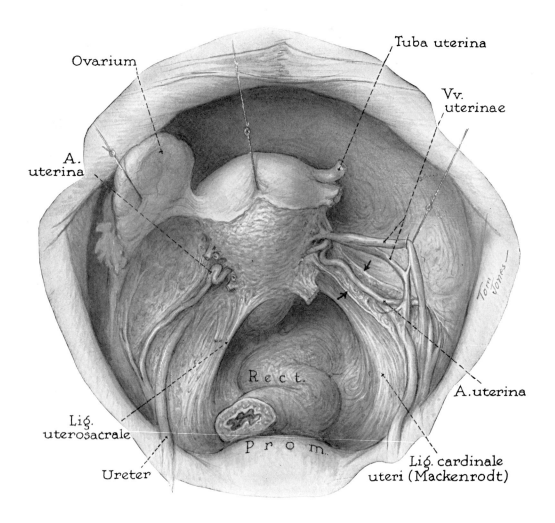

Female pelvis: structures within the broad ligament, vascular (mobilized)
and ligamentous (defined or cut).

On the right side the uterine tube and the round ligament have been cut near the uterus, in order to show the relations of the structures situated inferior to the uterine tube. The thinner part of the parametrium has been dissected away to expose the cut margins (at arrows) of the heavier tissue, which forms a sheath-like investment for the uterine vessels. In this way, also, it is demonstrated that the thickened basal part of the subserous layer becomes, essentially, the cardinal ligament. On the left side, for purposes of comparison, only part of the fibrous tissue has been removed.

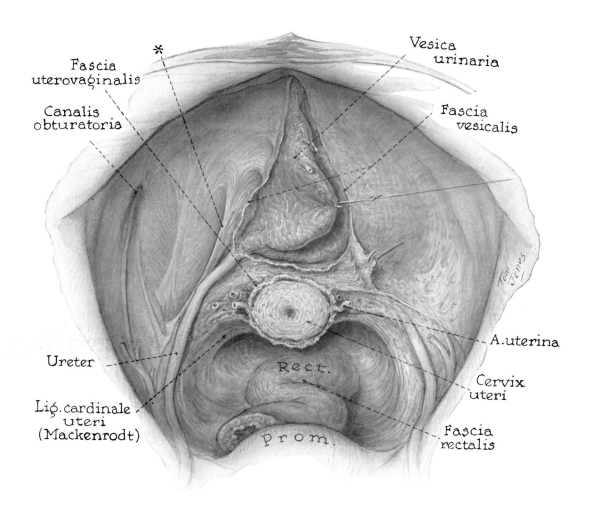

Fascia
uterovaginalis

Canalis
obturatoria

Vesica
urinaria

Fascia
vesicalis

Ureter

Rect.

A.uterina

Cervix
uteri

Lig. cardinale
uteri
(Mackenrodt)

Prom.

Fascia
rectalis

Female pelvis: basal structure of the broad ligament,
the ligamentous supports of the bladder and the uterus, and the fascial coats of pelvic organs.

On the right the uterine vessels have been excised, and the remainder of the cardinal ligament retained for comparison with the structures exposed by deeper dissection on the left. On the left side, the veins have been cut near their point of emergence from the uterine wall; here they form a pedicle, which is elongate vertically. The ureter is shown in its surgically important relation to the uterine artery, and to the fused fascial sheaths of the bladder and vagina.

In the anterior part of the pelvic cavity on the right side the fascial covering of the bladder has been partially stripped away, leaving the muscular coat exposed on the superior surface. On the left side, the vesical layer of the endopelvic fascia has been freed and has been removed to the level of continuity with the fascia of the pelvic diaphragm; a portion of the bladder has been folded upon itself toward the right. The fascia of the pelvic diaphragm is now clearly revealed, together with its upward-directed vesical and uterine sheaths. The asterisk (*) indicates the wing-like fascial support of the bladder from the superior surface of the pelvic diaphragm.

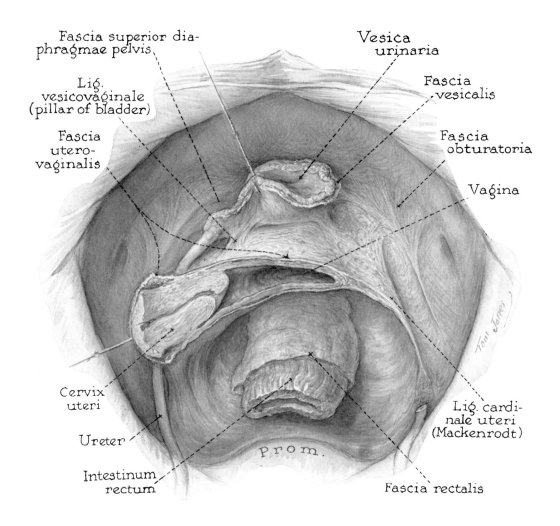

Fascia superior dia-
phragmae pelvis

Lig.
vesicovaginale
(pillar of bladder)

Fascia
utero-
vaginalis

Vesica
urinaria

Fascia
vesicalis

Fascia
obturatoria

Vagina

Cervix
uteri

Ureter

Intestinum
rectum

Prom.

Lig. cardi-
nale uteri
(Mackenrodt)

Fascia rectalis

Female pelvis: endopelvic fascia (visceral investments); ligamentous supports of the viscera.

The urinary bladder has been cut down to trigonal level, leaving, however, the ureter on the left side. The cervix of the uterus and the vagina (upper two-thirds) have been halved sagittally, the uterine collar of endopelvic fascia separated from the muscular wall. On the right side a similar continuity is demonstrated, as is also the relation of the fascial sheath to the cardinal ligament. By drawing apart the bladder and the uterus, the fusion of their adjacent sheaths is evident; this fusion is termed the vesicovaginal ligament. The looser fascial sheath of the rectum is also mobilized.

The fascia covering the pelvic surface of the obturator muscle is continuous with the iliac fascia covering the iliacus muscle in the greater pelvis. The fascia is attached to the superior ramus of the pubis, and below to the pubic arch, where it forms the fascial canal of Alcock for the pudendal vessels and nerves. Midway in its course, in the lesser pelvis, the layer gives origin to the two layers of fascia of the pelvic diaphragm. As the upper layer covers the pelvic surface of the levatores ani and coccygei muscles, it is the superior fascia of the pelvic diaphragm. The lower layer, on the perineal surface of the muscles, is the inferior fascia of the pelvic diaphragm. Usually the inferior fascia is so thin that it is scarcely distinguishable from the fatty tissue of the ischiorectal fossa.

The fascial covering of the muscles which form the pelvic diaphragm is carried upward on the viscera as the latter pierce the diaphragm. These sheaths, applied to the viscera, are definite envelopes; they may be readily freed from the intrinsic muscular coat of the organ and from the thin areolar layer which is situated just beneath the peritoneum.

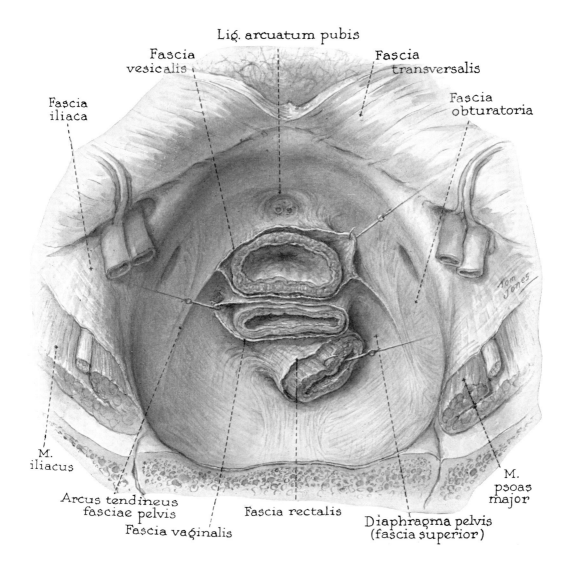

Lig. arcuatum pubis

Fascia vesicalis

Fascia transversalis

Fascia iliaca

Fascia obturatoria

M. iliacus

M. psoas major

Arcus tendineus fasciae pelvis

Fascia rectalis

Diaphragma pelvis (fascia superior)

Fascia vaginalis

Female pelvis: visceral reflections of the endopelvic fascia.

Anterolaterally, the layers of the abdominal wall have been turned forward along a medial cut; postero-laterally, on each side, the ala of the ilium has been cut horizontally, together with the iliopsoas muscle and fascia; posteriorly, the sacrum has been transected at the same horizontal level. The peritoneum and the retroperitoneal tissues have been removed to the level of the fascia lining the pelvis, to expose the latter. Within the lesser pelvis, the organs have been transected, together with their reflections of the diaphragmatic fascia; the fibrous sleeves, reflected from the diaphragmatic fascial layer, have been freed from their respective viscera and retracted. Thus, the parietal fascia (investing the pelvic surface of the obturator internus muscle) becomes the superior diaphragmatic fascia (as it descends to cover the levator ani and coccygeus muscles); then the fascia becomes visceral (as it forms separate coats for the urinary bladder, the vagina and uterus, and the rectum).

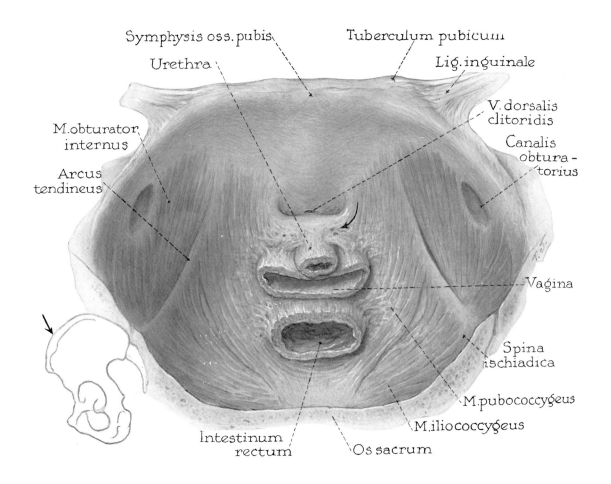

Symphysis oss. pubis

Urethra

Tuberculum pubicum

Lig. inguinale

M. obturator internus

Arcus tendineus

V. dorsalis clitoridis

Canalis obturatorius

Vagina

Spina ischiadica

M. pubococcygeus

M. iliococcygeus

Intestinum rectum

Os sacrum

Female pelvis: parietal and diaphragmatic musculature.
Viewed from above and behind; looking into the "visceral," or anterior, portion
of the pelvic bowl (arrow in inset indicates direction of view).

The musculature is exposed by complete removal of retroperitoneal and ligamentous structures, and of the fascial lining of the pelvis (including the endopelvic fascial continuations upon the viscera). The curved arrow indicates the direction of muscle fibers in the urethral portion of the pubococcygeus. The urethra, vagina, and rectum have been transected near their points of passage through the pelvic diaphragm.

The coccygeus muscle and the levator ani form, with their fellows of the opposite half of the pelvis minor, the muscular constituents of the pelvic diaphragm. Each coccygeus muscle (see following figure) is thin and quadrangular, and is situated on the anterior surface of the sacrospinous ligament. It takes origin from the spine of the ischium and, expanding, inserts into the lateral margin of the lowermost segment of the sacrum and of the upper part of the coccyx.

The levatores ani muscles and their investing fasciae together form the greater part of the pelvic diaphragm, which supports the pelvic viscera and constitutes the partition between the pelvis and the perineum. Each muscle takes origin in front from the posterior surface of the superior pubic ramus, lateral to the symphysis, and behind, from the pelvic surface of the ischial spine; between these two points it has an aponeurotic origin from the tendinous arch of the obturator fascia. The anterior fibers, which constitute the pubococcygeal part of the muscle, pass backward and medialward to be inserted as a tendinous plate into the anterior surface of the third and fourth sacral segments—where it overlies the iliococcygeal part of the levator muscle. The iliococcygeus arises from the posterior half of the tendinous arch and, to a slight degree, from the pelvic surface of the coccyx. In the precoccygeal area the fibers of the iliococcygeus are caudal to the backward extension of the pubococcygeus.

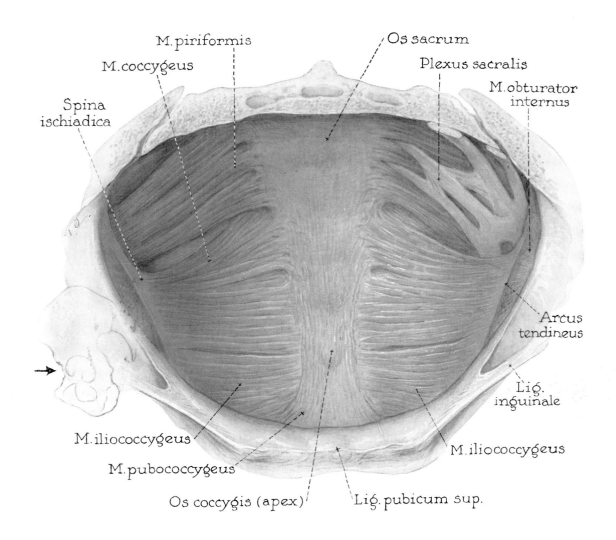

M.piriformis
M.coccygeus
Os sacrum
Plexus sacralis
M.obturator internus
Spina ischiadica
Arcus tendineus
Lig. inguinale
M.iliococcygeus
M.pubococcygeus
M.iliococcygeus
Os coccygis (apex)
Lig. pubicum sup.

Female perineum: parietal and diaphragmatic musculature.
The same specimen, viewed from the front; looking into the "parietal" or posterior part
of the pelvic bowl (see inset). Dissection as in preceding figure.

Here the pelvic floor consists of the iliococcygeal part of the levator ani muscle and the coccygeus muscle; the iliococcygeal subdivision of the levator ani is represented only by a coccygeal prolongation.

The muscles that cover the walls and constitute the floor of the pelvis minor belong to two groups: those of the lower extremity, namely, the obturator internus and the piriformis; and those that form the pelvic diaphragm, namely, the coccygeus and the levator ani (see preceding figure). The fasciae of the above muscles are continuous with one another, and likewise with the transversalis fascia of the abdomen and the aponeurotic layers of the perineal compartments; they also provide fibrous coverings for the pelvic organs.

The piriformis muscle is triangular in outline, and lies flattened against the posterior wall of the pelvis minor. It originates by three or more processes, lateral to the second, third, and fourth anterior sacral foramina; becoming narrower and more rotund, it leaves the pelvis through the upper part of the greater ischiadic foramen, for insertion into the greater trochanter of the femur. The piriformis, together with the coccygeus muscle, closes the space in the posterior bony wall of the pelvis intervening between the ischium and sacrum.

The obturator internus muscle clothes the side wall of the pelvis minor and the ischiorectal fossa; like the piriformis, it is flattened and fan-shaped. It arises from the circumference of the obturator foramen, from which its fibers converge upon the lesser ischiadic foramen; becoming tendinous, it is joined by the two gemelli, and with them is inserted into the greater trochanter of the femur.

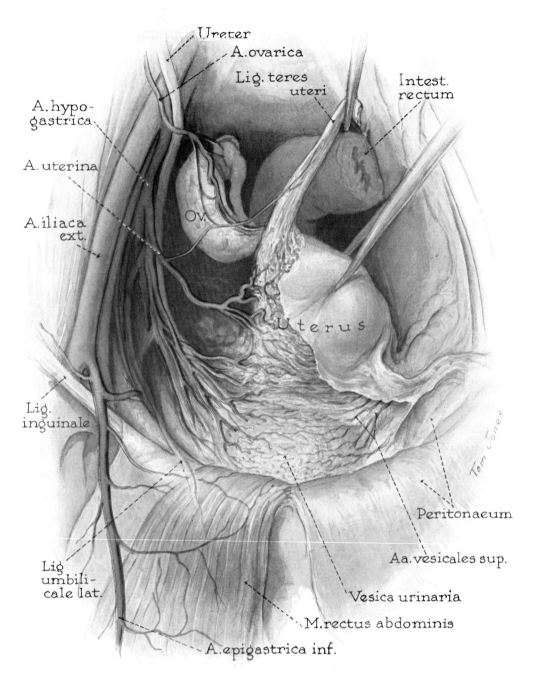

Female pelvis: vesical, uterine, and ovarian arteries.
The uterus has been retracted toward the left side. Suprapubic view.

Arteries retain their *in situ* positions; the terminal rami of the vesical arteries have been completely exposed bilaterally. The peritoneum has been almost completely removed on the right.

The vesical arteries course toward the lateral margin of the bladder. The posterior members of the group follow the ureter, resting upon it and paralleling its course; the anteriorly placed vessels descend obliquely to the bladder. Upon reaching the bladder they turn medialward to pierce, chiefly, the musculature of the superior surface, within which they anastomose with companion vessels of the opposite side.

The ovarian arteries are homologous to the internal spermatic arteries in the male. They pass between the layers of the broad ligament, below the level of the uterine tube, then inward toward the ovary through the mesovarium. The vessels divide into terminal branches which enter the hilum of the ovary, forming broad anastomoses with the ovarian rami of the uterine artery.

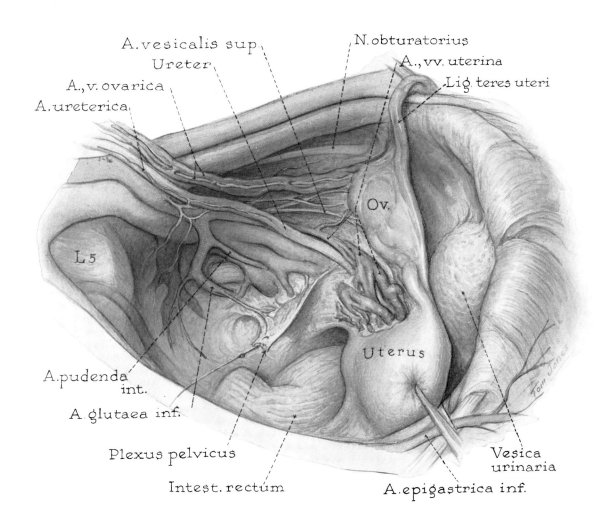

Female pelvis: arteries and veins of posterior part of left pelvis.

The uterus has been retracted to right. The peritoneum and retroperitoneal tissues have been removed from the posterior part of the left broad ligament and from the lateral wall of the lesser pelvis, thus exposing the vessels. The connective tissue containing the pelvic plexus of nerves has been partially freed and retracted by a hook toward the midline. The parametrial tissue has been removed carefully in order to retain the natural positions and relations of the pelvic viscera and blood vessels.

The uterine vessels, as an assemblage, form the greater part of the bulk of the broad ligament; the veins outnumber the branches of the uterine artery. The vessels, in crossing to the uterus from the lateral wall of the pelvis, lie above the ureter. The ureter enters the lesser pelvis by passing over the point of division of the common iliac artery into the external iliac and the hypogastric; as the duct lies just above the hypogastric artery, it receives a branch of supply; from this branch twigs are sent along the ureter as ascending and descending rami.

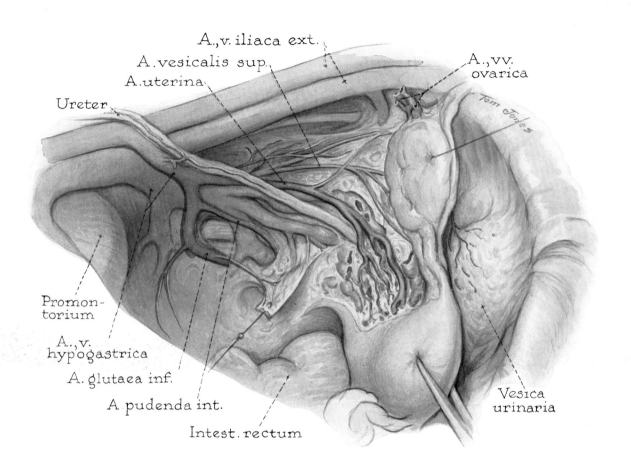

Female pelvis: uterine and related arteries.

The uterine artery has been further exposed by partial removal of the accompanying veins. All remaining structures still lie in the positions they held prior to dissection. The ovarian vessels have been transected at the point at which they leave the suspensory ligament of the ovary. The gluteal and pudendal vessels are shown as they approach the greater sciatic (ischiadic) foramen.

The uterine artery of each side lies first on the inner wall of the lesser pelvis; passing medialward and slightly forward on the fascia of the levator ani muscle, it enters the lower margin of the broad ligament. Upon reaching the cervix of the uterus it gives off a vaginal branch, which courses downward on the lateral fornix of the vagina. The main vessel follows a very tortuous course upward along the lateral margin of the uterus, giving off many spiral branches to the anterior and posterior surfaces of the organ. The uterine artery continues as a laterally directed stem, which divides into branches supplying the ovary and the uterine tube.

Beneath the peritoneum of the posterior surface of the broad ligament the most superficial of the uterine vessels are covered by a thin layer of subserous connective tissue in which are lodged the autonomic nerves of the pelvic and uterovaginal plexuses. The branches of the uterine artery, together with numerous large veins of plexiform character, are grouped in such a way that they make up a broad pedicle.

The vaginal artery (not exposed in the figure) represents the inferior vesical artery of the male. It passes medialward from its hypogastric origin to supply the vagina and bladder and forms an important anastomosis with the descending (vaginal) branch of the uterine artery.

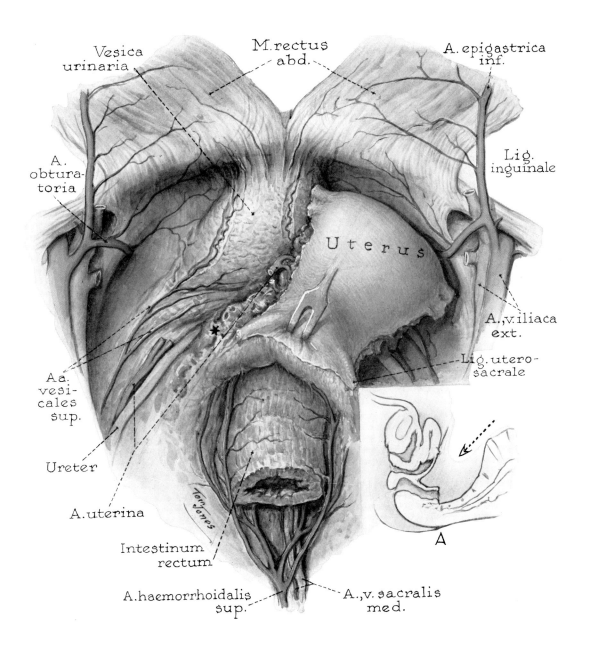

Female pelvis: arteries of the superior surface of the bladder,
the uterine "hilus," and the rectum. Seen from above.

The uterus has been drawn forward and toward the right; it remains covered with peritoneum over its posterior surface down to the level of the cervix. The vessels have been cut along the lateral aspect of the uterus and shown as constituents of a vascular pedicle. On the left the tissue of Mackenrodt's ligament has been removed posterolaterally to vaginal level (at star); this is the plane of division between vesical and uterovaginal vessels. The superior vesical arteries have been traced to the posterior surface of the abdominal wall. The rectum has been transected at the level of the fourth sacral segment; the hemorrhoidal (NA, rectal) arteries have been exposed as they course along the posterolateral aspect of the rectum. Arrow in the inset records direction of view in the main figure.

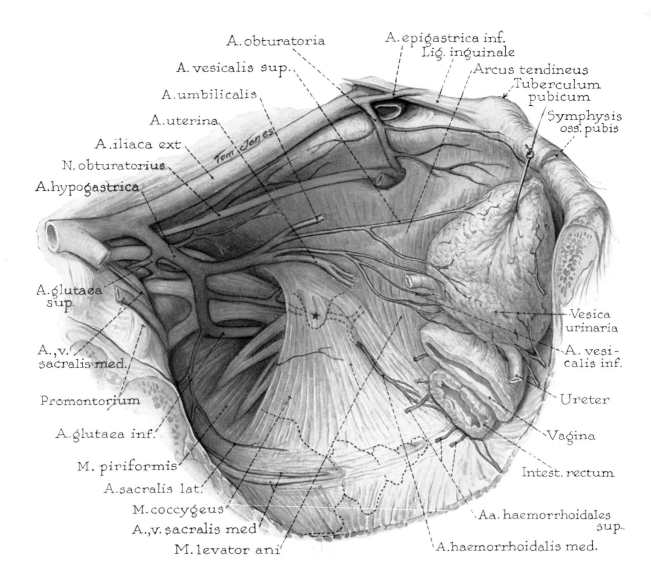

Female pelvis: arteries of the bladder, vagina, and terminal rectum. Superolateral view.

The vessels have been exposed by removal of subserous tissue, fascia of pelvic diaphragm, and endo-pelvic fascial investments. The right one-third of the pelvis has been removed by a parasagittal cut following the lateral margins of the lumbar vertebral bodies. The rectum and vagina have been transected near the pelvic floor; the urinary bladder is intact but has been pulled forward to expose its base. The external iliac vein has been removed, as have all tributaries of the hypogastric (NA, internal iliac) vein. The distal portions of the umbilical and uterine arteries have been removed. Several of the vesical branches of the anterior division of the hypogastric (NA, internal iliac) artery remain intact. The internal pudendal, the inferior gluteal, and the lateral sacral branches of the posterior division of the hypogastric are shown. The middle hemorrhoidal (NA, rectal) in this specimen arises from the internal pudendal, as frequently encountered. The positions of the sacrum, coccyx, and spine of the ischium, as well as the concealed portion of the internal pudendal artery, are indicated by dotted lines; the star marks the point where the internal pudendal artery passes external to the ischial spine, through its short gluteal course.

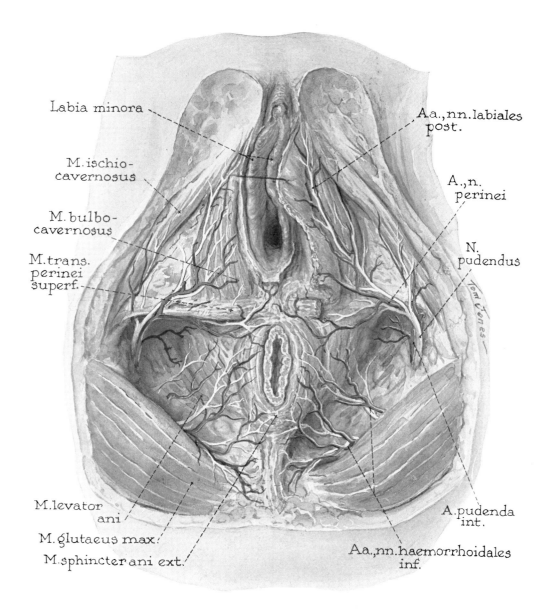

Labia minora

Aa.,nn.labiales post.

M.ischio-cavernosus

A.,n. perinei

M.bulbo-cavernosus

N. pudendus

M.trans. perinei superf.

M.levator ani

M.glutaeus max.

M.sphincter ani ext.

A.pudenda int.

Aa.,nn.haemorrhoidales inf.

Female perineum: arteries and nerves of the ischiorectal fossae and the superficial perineal compartment.

On both sides of the perineum the superficial fatty tissue has been removed to expose the inferior hemorrhoidal vessels and nerves in the anal part of the perineum; through removal of the deep layer of the superficial fascia in the urogenital part of the perineum the muscular rami of the perineal artery and the accompanying nerves are brought into view.

After piercing the obturator fascia on the lateral wall of the ischiorectal fossa, the hemorrhoidal vessels and nerves course medialward and forward toward the anal canal and the external anal sphincter. Further distalward the perineal vessels and nerves arise from the pudendals. They enter the superficial perineal compartment to supply the muscles contained therein. The posterior labial vessels and nerves arise similarly; however, they remain outside the compartment. In the superficial, fat-laden layer of the superficial fascia they pass forward, to care for the cutaneous innervation of the greater and lesser lips and adjacent areas of the perineal skin.

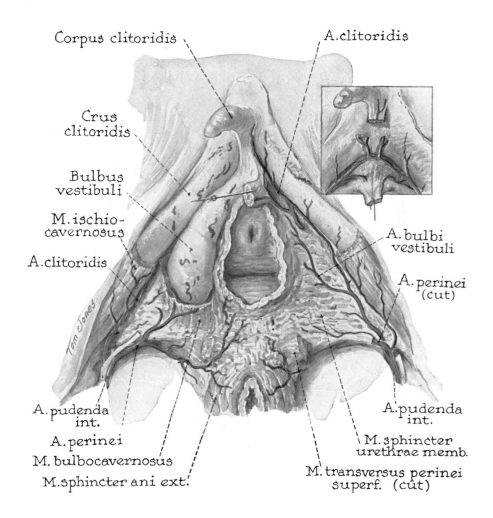

Female perineum: arteries of the superficial and deep perineal compartments in the female.

On the reader's left the branches of the perineal division of the internal pudendal artery are shown. On the opposite side the clitoridal branches are illustrated; these supply the bulb of the vestibule and the crus and body of the clitoris. On the right side, in this specimen, the clitoridal artery arises within the pelvis and pierces the pelvic and urogenital diaphragms. Inset: subpubic anastomosis of the distal portions of the clitoridal arteries.

As is recorded in this figure and in the preceding illustration, the perineal artery courses through the superficial compartment; therein it supplies the superficial transverse perineal muscle, the ischiocavernosus and bulbocavernosus muscles. The erectile bodies (the clitoridal crura and glans, and the vestibular bulbs) receive their blood supply from the more deeply placed clitoridal artery. The latter vessel traverses the deep perineal compartment, imbedded in the substance of the urethral sphincter (sphincter muscle of the membranous urethra). The branches of the clitoridal artery must pierce the inferior fascia of the urogenital diaphragm to reach the bulb of the vestibule, and the crus and the glans of the clitoris.

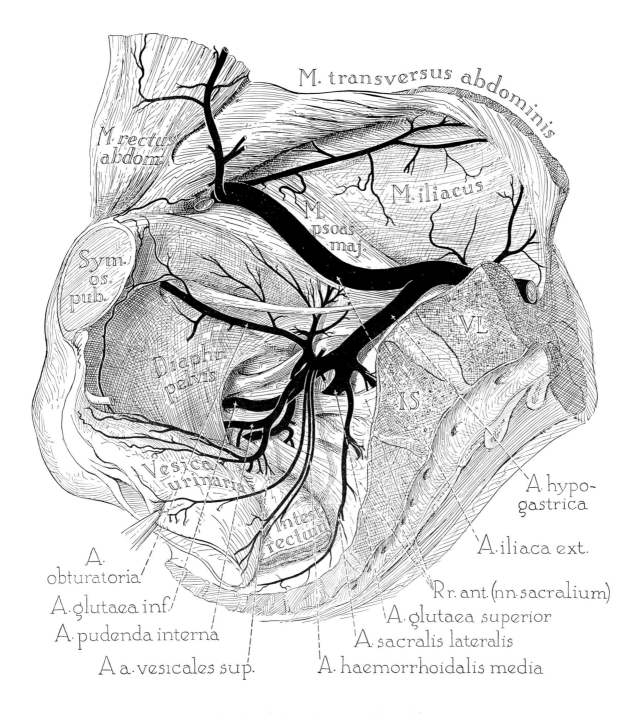

M. transversus abdominis

M. rectus abdom.

M. iliacus

M. psoas maj.

Sym. os. pub.

VL

Diaphr. pelvis

IS

Vesica urinaria

A. hypogastrica

Intest. rectum

A. iliaca ext.

A. obturatoria

Rr. ant. (nn. sacralium)

A. glutaea inf.

A. glutaea superior

A. pudenda interna

A. sacralis lateralis

A a. vesicales sup.

A. haemorrhoidalis media

Arteries of the perineum and the pelvis,
especially parietal and diaphragmatic vessels. Right side of male specimen.

Structures shown in a median sagittal section, from the symphysis to the vertebral column. All of the peritoneum, the preperitoneal connective tissue, and the parietal and visceral fasciae have been removed. Both the rectum and the bladder (the latter halved sagittally) have been drawn to the left, in order to display both the visceral and parietal branches of the hypogastric artery. The veins have been excised, to render more graphic the arterial plan. Certain of the hemorrhoidal and vesical arteries have been drawn dorsalward in order to expose the greater sciatic (ischiadic) foramen, through which gluteal and pudendal arteries leave the pelvis. In addition to pelvic structures, the anterior and anterolateral abdominal muscles are included in the dissection, principally for purposes of orientation.

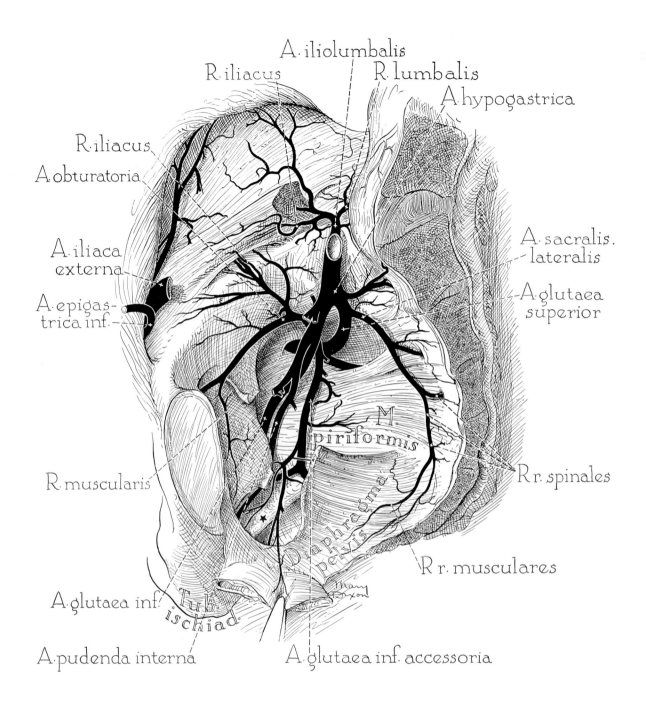

Arteries of the pelvis and the perineum; specimens as in preceding figure. Lateral view.

Only a small piece of the rectum remains, to record an unusual origin of a middle hemorrhoidal artery. Veins have been removed, as have also the following structures, or portions thereof: the right common iliac artery; the external iliac artery; the hypogastric artery (to the point of origin of the iliolumbar); the psoas major muscle, in order to expose the contained muscular branches derived from iliolumbar and obturator; the hemorrhoidal and vesical arteries; the lumbar plexus of nerves; the coccygeus and the adjacent part of the levator ani muscle, to expose the gluteal and perineal course of branches of the hypogastric artery (NA, *A. iliac interna*); the levator ani near the obturator foramen, in order to bring into view parietal rami to the obturator internus muscle; the sacrospinous ligament, to expose the sciatic notches, the internal pudendal artery in the perineum and the pelvis, and the sacrotuberous ligament (at star).

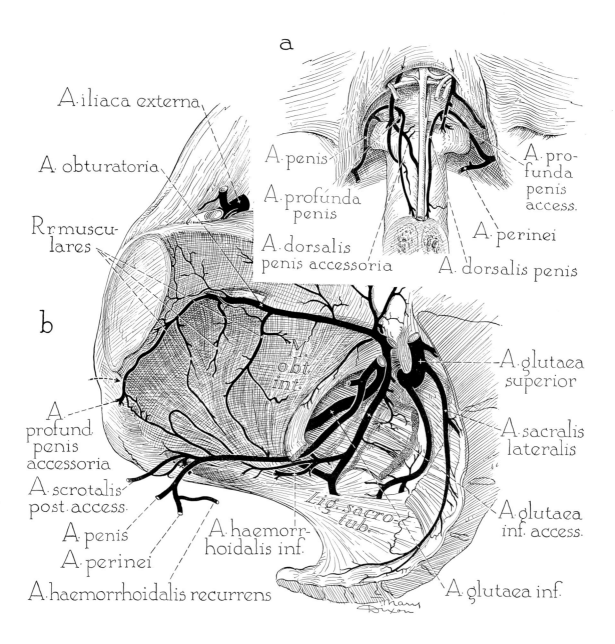

a

A. iliaca externa

A. obturatoria

R. r. musculares

A. penis

A. profunda penis

A. dorsalis penis accessoria

A. profunda penis access.

A. perinei

A. dorsalis penis

b

M. obt. int.

A. profund. penis accessoria

A. scrotalis post. access.

A. penis

A. perinei

A. haemorrhoidalis inf.

A. haemorrhoidalis recurrens

Lig. sacro-tub.

A. glutaea superior

A. sacralis lateralis

A. glutaea inf. access.

A. glutaea inf.

Arteries of the pelvis and perineum, especially the vessels of the pelvic wall and of the erectile tissue.
Specimen as in the two preceding and the six following figures.

The pelvic diaphragm has been wholly removed in *b*, in order to reveal the full course and the perineal divisions of the internal pudendal artery; in the same dissection the course of the obturator artery and its scheme of branching are demonstrated. The further course of the deep arteries of the penis (regular and accessory) is traced in *a*.

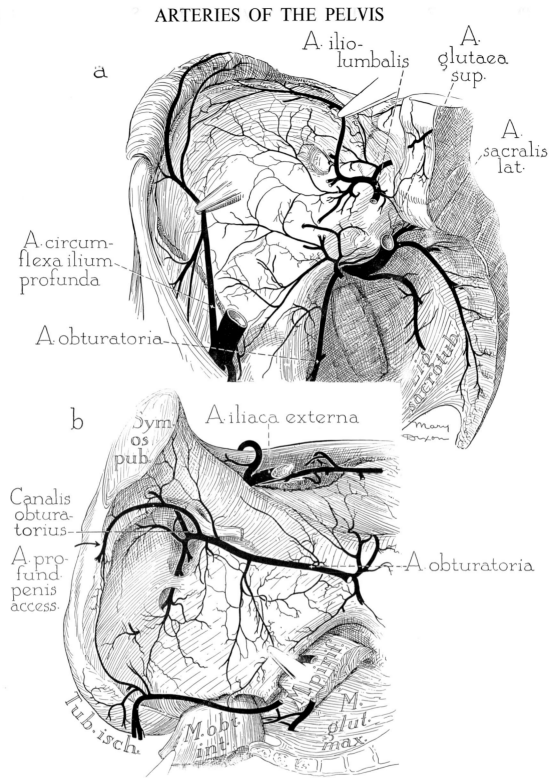

Pelvic arterial supply; deepest (osseous) level. *a*, Greater pelvis; *b*, lesser pelvis.

The iliacus muscle has been removed to the point at which it leaves the pelvis beneath the inguinal ligament. In this way the arteries of deep level are shown as they arise from the iliac circumflex, iliolumbar, and obturator. Muscular branches have also been followed into the transversus abdominis. The arteries in the region of sacral foramina, sacrum, and sacral ligaments have been excised in order to bring attention to the arteries in the iliac fossa. The piriformis muscle remains only at the margin of the great sciatic notch. The iliac circumflex artery and the iliac branch of the iliolumbar have been retracted to expose more fully their rami to the periosteum. Some of the larger muscular rami have been transected where they enter the muscles; the finer rami, which rest upon the periosteum, supply the latter, the subjacent bone, and the muscles (removed) on their deep, or attached, aspect.

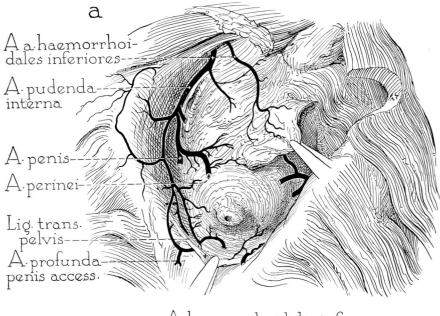

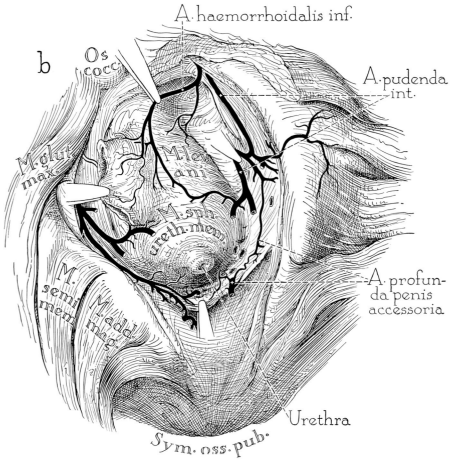

Arteries of the male perineum. Two views of the same dissection.

    On the left side (*a*), the pudendal artery has been cut near its origin, i.e., near the division of pudendal into perineal and penile. The deep artery of the penis has been removed with the distal portion of perineal artery.

    On the right side (*b*), the inferior hemorrhoidal artery (*A. rectalis inferior*) has been exposed to its origin from the internal pudendal by removing part of the gluteus maximus muscle. The perineal artery has been transected near the point of division of the pudendal into perineal and penile stems. The accessory deep artery of the penis has been cut near its point of emergence from the urogenital diaphragm (trigone).

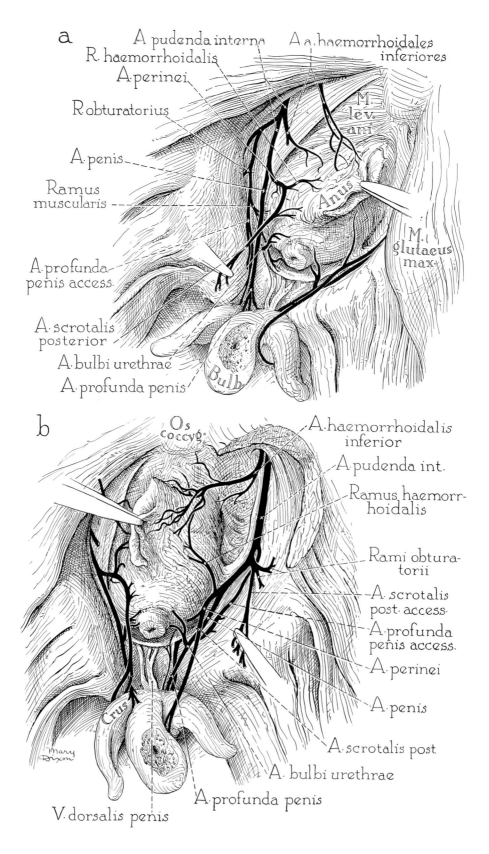

a

A pudenda interna
A.a. haemorrhoidales inferiores
R. haemorrhoidalis
A. perinei
R. obturatorius
M. lev. ani
A. penis
Ramus muscularis
Anus
A. profunda penis access.
M. glutaeus max.
A. scrotalis posterior
A. bulbi urethrae
A. profunda penis
Bulb

b

Os coccyg.
A. haemorrhoidalis inferior
A. pudenda int.
Ramus haemorrhoidalis
Rami obturatorii
A. scrotalis post. access.
A. profunda penis access.
A. perinei
A. penis
Crus
A. scrotalis post
A. bulbi urethrae
V. dorsalis penis
A. profunda penis

Mary Dixon

See opposite page for description.

Arteries of the male perineum. Two views of the same dissection;
a, Especially of the left side; *b*, especially of the right half of the perineum.

All perineal musculature (of both superficial and deep compartments) has been removed to expose the branches, within these compartments, of the internal pudendal artery. The latter vessel is shown in its course through the ischiorectal fossa. The gluteal and femoral muscles are exposed.

In general, it may be said that the internal pudendal artery descends to the lower margin of the piriformis muscle, behind the sacrospinous ligament and ischial spine, then in curving course forward along the inferior ramus of the ischium; in its course it is covered by the obturator fascia. Behind the superficial transverse perineal muscle it divides into the perineal and penile (or clitoridal) branches. Before division it gives rise to the inferior hemorrhoidal arteries (NA, *Aa. rectales inferiores*). These vessels course transversely median-ward through the fat of the ischiorectal fossa, being superficial to the muscles of the pelvic diaphragm. They anastomose with the middle hemorrhoidal (NA, *Aa. rectales mediae*) and middle sacral arteries. The perineal artery extends forward and medianward over or under the superficial transverse perineal muscle. In the male the artery supplies the scrotum by means of posterior scrotal branches; in the female corresponding branches supply the labia. It also gives off small branches to the superficial muscles of the perineum. The penile artery (in the male) runs forward in the direction of the main stem close to the inferior ramus of the pubis, within the urogenital trigone; emerging from the trigone, it is continued as the dorsal artery of the penis, below the pubic arcuate ligament. The artery to the bulb of the urethra is given off at the margin of the urogenital tri-gone; it runs medianward and forward to the urethral bulb and to the neighboring muscles. The small urethral branch courses forward and medianward to the corpus cavernosum urethrae. The deep artery of the penis arises just beneath the pubic arcuate ligament; it penetrates the crus penis on its medial surface, and runs in it partly backward, partly forward close to the penile septum; its branches anastomose with one an-other and with those of the opposite side.

In the specimen illustrated, on the left side (*a*), the inferior hemorrhoidal artery divides so as to send several twigs to the levator ani and the external anal sphincter muscles. Next, in anterior direction, a second hemorrhoidal provides two terminal twigs. An accessory penile artery, en route to the cavernous tissue, gives off branches to the obturator internus muscle; it has bulbar and deep terminal branches. The main stem continues, medial to the accessory penile artery, curving toward the central tendinous point, in which area it gives off two sets of branches, as if it were the perineal branch; continuing, it becomes a posterior scrotal, and finally attains a superficial level.

On the right side (*b*), a large internal pudendal artery gives off an inferior hemorrhoidal branch, opposite the coccyx (vessel exposed by notching the gluteus maximus muscles); from it numerous branches are sent to the levator ani. Continuing anteriorly the pudendal gives off a stem from which obturator twigs arise; other branches supply the tissue inferior to the pubic arch, and a thin branch arises as an accessory deep artery to the penis. Next, in anterior direction, a common trunk, directly medialward, sends off a backward-directed inferior hemorrhoidal and continues itself as a posterior scrotal. The internal pudendal itself con-tinues as a penile artery with bulbar and deep branches.

ARTERIA OBTURATORIA
VARIATIONS IN ORIGIN AND COURSE

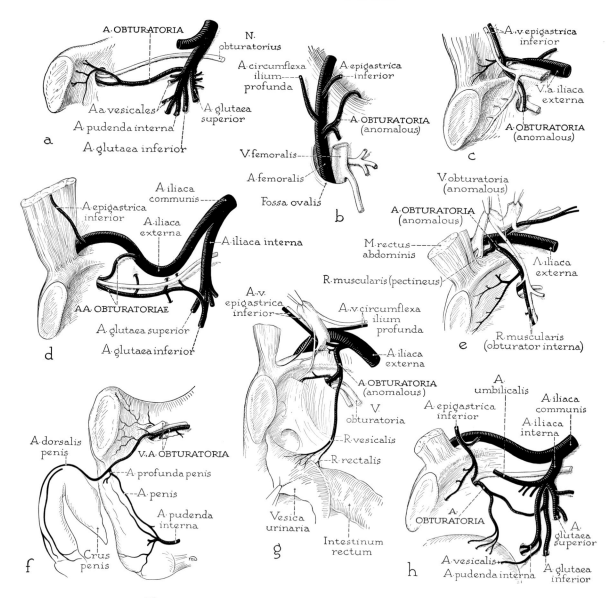

Obturator artery; selected examples from 650 body-halves.

a, Origin from the internal iliac (hypogastric) division of the common iliac artery. *b,* Derivation from the femoral continuation of the external iliac artery. *c,* Origin from the external iliac artery near the inguinal ligament. *d,* Here one of a pair of obturator arteries is a branch of the superior gluteal; the other is derived from the external iliac. *e,* Origin from a common stem (external iliac) with a muscular ramus to the pectineus. *f,* Obturator artery communicates with a penile branch of the internal pudendal. *g,* Obturator artery gives rise to the inferior epigastric, and to vesical and rectal branches. *h,* Obturator arteries originate from the inferior epigastric and the inferior gluteal branches of the internal iliac (the obturator of gluteal origin contributing to the blood supply of the urinary bladder).

In 650 body-halves, the obturator artery originated in 10 different ways, with widely varying frequency: from the main trunk of the internal iliac (BNA, hypogastric) in 23.7 per cent of cases; from the anterior division, 20.6 per cent; from the posterior division, 3.2 per cent; from the superior gluteal in 10.9, the inferior gluteal in 9.2, the internal pudendal in 2.8 per cent. The vessel was a branch of the inferior epigastric in 27.1 per cent, of the external iliac in 2.0, of the iliolumbar in 0.3. The artery was absent in 0.2 per cent of the 650 pelvic halves (right and left sides combined).

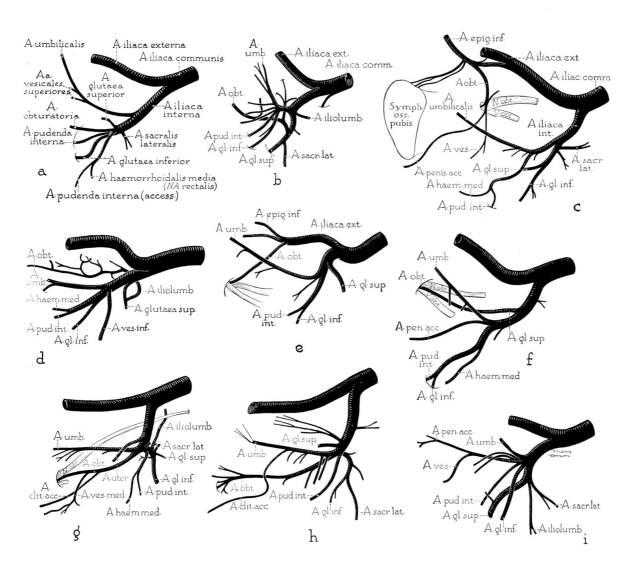

Internal iliac artery. Variations in branching.

The following are the salient features in the nine selected specimens.

a, Proximal origin of the umbilical artery, the remaining branches occurring as a spray from the terminal segment of the internal iliac (BNA, hypogastric) artery. *b*, All major branches derived from the two offsets of a large superior gluteal. *c*, An anastomotic obturator artery arising from the inferior epigastric.

d, An obturator artery derived from the iliolumbar branch of the superior gluteal, and a middle hemorrhoidal artery originating from the internal pudendal branch of the inferior gluteal. *e*, An obturator artery derived from the external iliac.

f, An obturator branch of the superior gluteal, an accessory penile arising from a common stem with the umbilical. *g*, Accessory clitoridal and middle vesical branches coming from the obturator, a back-directed common stem for the two gluteal arteries also giving rise to the iliolumbar, lateral sacral, internal pudendal, and middle hemorrhoidal (NA, middle rectal) arteries.

h, An accessory clitoridal derived from the umbilical, a common stem of origin for the inferior gluteal and the lateral sacral arteries. *i*, Separation of the internal iliac into two main divisions, each of whose largest continuing portion is a gluteal artery; the inferior gluteal is the primary or secondary source of umbilical, accessory penile, superior vesical, and internal pudendal arteries; the superior gluteal gives origin to the lateral sacral and iliolumbar arteries.

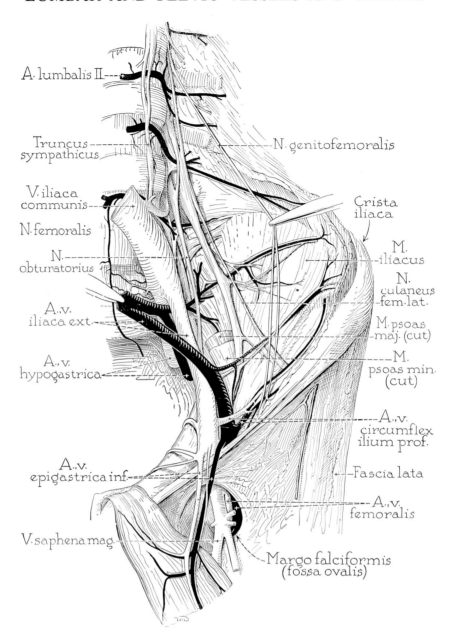

A. lumbalis II

Truncus sympathicus

V. iliaca communis

N. femoralis

N. obturatorius

A., v. iliaca ext.

A., v. hypogastrica

A., v. epigastrica inf.

V. saphena mag.

N. genitofemoralis

Crista iliaca

M. iliacus

N. cutaneus fem. lat.

M. psoas maj. (cut)

M. psoas min. (cut)

A., v. circumflex ilium prof.

Fascia lata

A., v. femoralis

Margo falciformis (fossa ovalis)

Lumbar, pelvic, and femoral vessels and nerves; anterior view.
Succeeding three figures are from the same specimen.

In the lumbar region the quadratus lumborum muscle has been removed except at the line of iliac attachment, to expose the anterior leaf of the lumbodorsal fascia and the lumbar arteries and veins as they rest upon, and pierce, this layer. In this anterior view are seen all the named nerves of the lumbar plexus as they descend upon the anterior surface, or along the medial border of, the iliacus muscle. Also shown are the iliolumbar vessels, and, particularly, the iliac arterial branch and venous tributary. The iliac vessels, like the corresponding lumbar muscular rami, are followed to the points at which they pierce the iliacus muscle. The deep circumflex iliac vessels are also traced to their muscular terminations. The inguinal ligament remains, to mark the line of division between abdomen and thigh; otherwise, the anterolateral abdominal musculature has been removed. The inferior epigastric vessels, passing from the external iliacs to the rectus muscle, are turned downward and forward with the muscle. In the thigh the skin and superficial fascia have been removed to expose the fascia lata in the area over the femoral triangle. The fossa ovalis and saphenous vein are shown for purposes of topographic relation. The only cutaneous nerve of lumbar origin encountered in this proximal area of the thigh is the lateral femoral cutaneous.

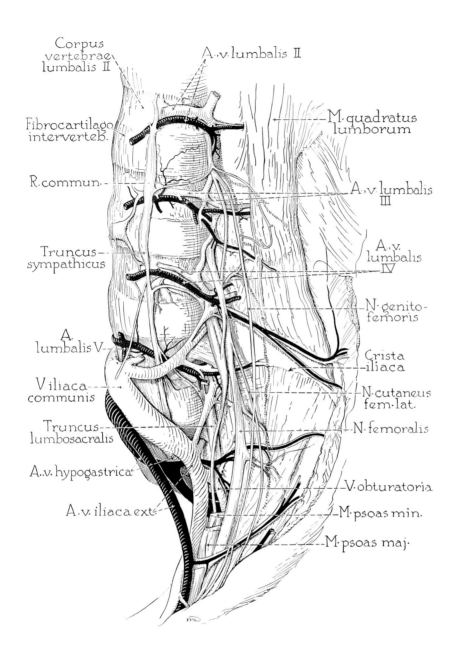

Nerves and blood vessels of the lumbar and pelvic regions; lateral view.

The psoas major muscle has been entirely removed from the lumbar region; it remains only in the anterior part of the pelvis, where it passes beneath the abdominal muscles into the thigh. The quadratus lumborum muscle is intact, as is also the iliacus. The anterolateral abdominal layers are represented only by the transversus abdominis along the line of its attachment to the iliac crest. The investing fascia has been dissected away from the lumbar and pelvic muscles. The lumbar sympathetic chain trunk remains intact; its presence serves to mark the former position of the anteromedial margin of the psoas major muscle. The following structures are exposed: the lumbar arteries and veins; the lumbar plexus and nerves derived therefrom; the ascending lumbar vein; the segmentally arranged lumbar arteries and veins; the iliac branch of the iliolumbar artery and the accompanying veins; the common iliac, hypogastric (NA, *A. iliaca interna*), and external iliac vessels; the femoral continuations of the latter.

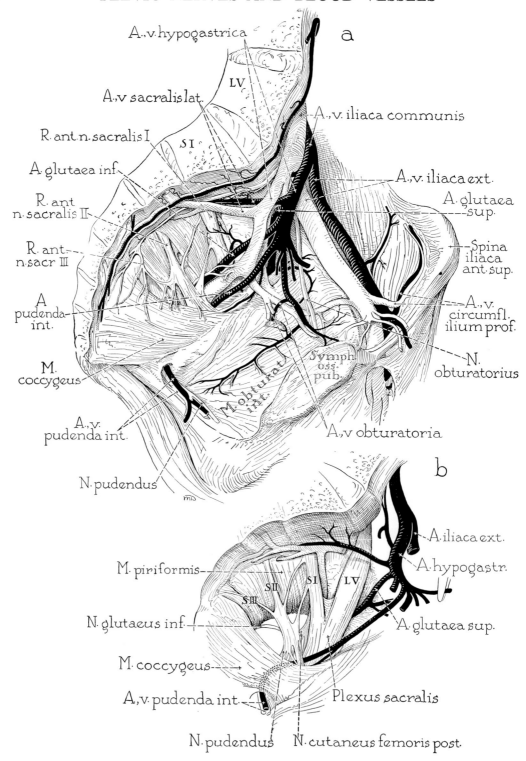

Nerves and blood vessels of the lesser pelvis; medial view.

In *a*, the veins remain in the dissection; in *b*, they have been removed, in order to demonstrate the anterior rami contributory to the sacral plexus. The levator ani muscle has been completely removed. The coccygeus muscle remains intact. The piriformis muscle is exposed in *a*, in relation to the anterior rami of the sacral nerves; the muscle is removed in *b*. The gluteal and pudendal vessels and nerves are shown; the gluteals and pudendals are shown in relation to the sacral trunks within the pelvis, while the pudendals appear again in perineal course. In the perineum the pudendal vessels and nerves rest upon the ischiopubic ramus and the antero-inferior margin of the obturator internus muscle.

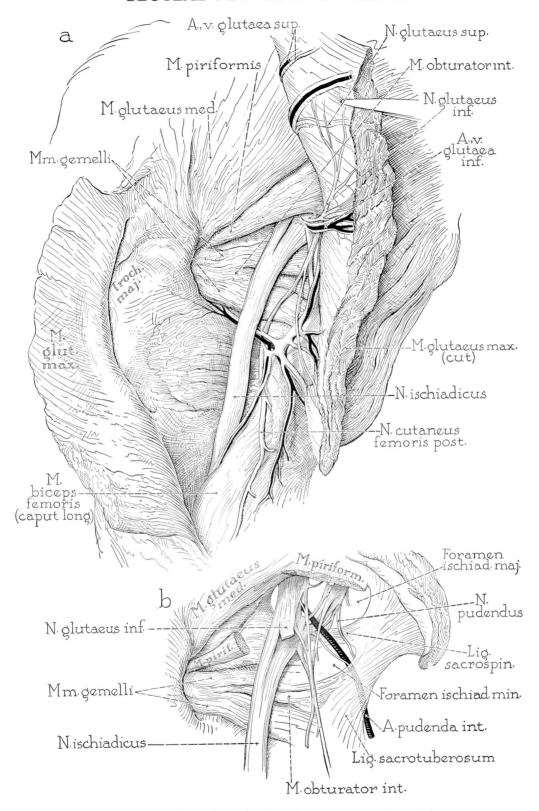

Nerves and blood vessels of the gluteal region; posterolateral views.

In *a*, the gluteus maximus muscle has been reflected; in *b*, the piriformis muscle has been removed, where it overlay the sacral plexus, and the gluteal vessels excised. The pudendal nerve and artery have been exposed in the course, through the sciatic foramina, from the pelvis into the perineum.

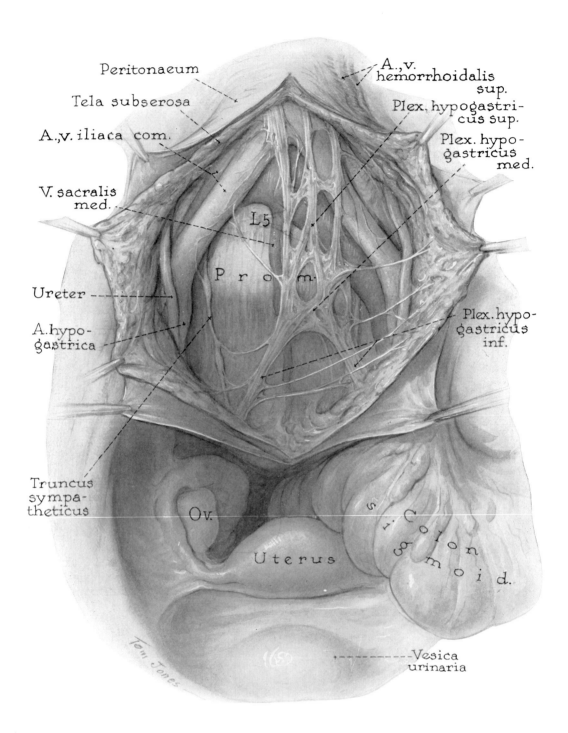

Nerves of the female pelvis. Hypogastric plexus,
in relation to the vertebral column, iliac vessels and subserous layer of tissue, and the ureters.

The peritoneal and retroperitoneal (subserous) layers have been incised vertically and reflected, in order to demonstrate the superficial and deep relations of the autonomic nerves.

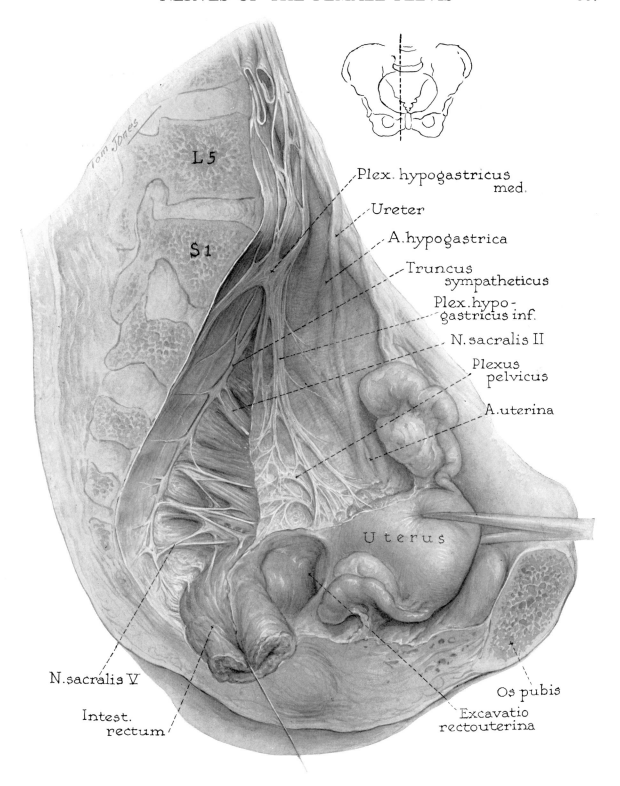

Plex. hypogastricus med.

Ureter

A. hypogastrica

Truncus sympatheticus

Plex. hypogastricus inf.

N. sacralis II

Plexus pelvicus

A. uterina

L 5

S 1

Uterus

N. sacralis V

Intest. rectum

Os pubis

Excavatio rectouterina

Nerves of the female pelvis, continued. Lateral view of the same specimen,
sectioned in parasagittal plane through pubic tubercle of the right side (see inset); deeper level.

The terminal portion of the rectum is retracted. The fibrous lamina beneath the fatty preperitoneal
layer has been freed and elevated, and a portion of it removed in order to expose the sacral plexus, the
parasympathetic nerves, the sacral sympathetic chain, and the subjacent piriformis muscle.

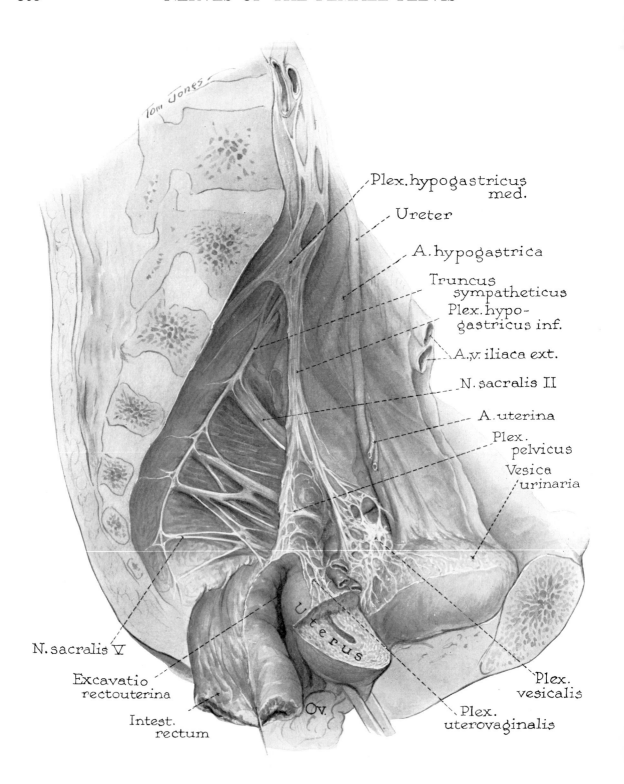

Plex. hypogastricus med.

Ureter

A. hypogastrica

Truncus sympatheticus

Plex. hypogastricus inf.

A., v. iliaca ext.

N. sacralis II

A. uterina

Plex. pelvicus

Vesica urinaria

Tom Jones

Uterus

N. sacralis V

Excavatio rectouterina

Intest. rectum

Ov.

Plex. vesicalis

Plex. uterovaginalis

Nerves of the female pelvis, dissection continued. Lateral view.

Through further removal of the heavier layer of preperitoneal tissue, the following have been more fully exposed: the anterior rami of the sacral nerves, together with rami communicating with the sympathetic trunk; offshoots of the pelvic plexus sent to the uterus, the vagina, and the urinary bladder; the distal portion of the ureter, in relation to the vesical plexus.

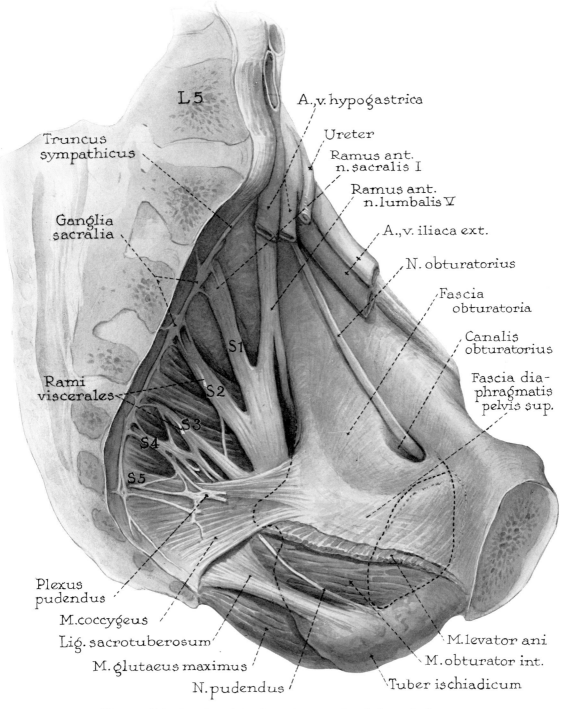

L 5

A., v. hypogastrica

Truncus sympathicus

Ureter

Ramus ant. n. sacralis I

Ramus ant. n. lumbalis V

Ganglia sacralia

A., v. iliaca ext.

N. obturatorius

Fascia obturatoria

Canalis obturatorius

S1

Rami viscerales

S2

Fascia diaphragmatis pelvis sup.

S3

S4

S5

Plexus pudendus

M. coccygeus

Lig. sacrotuberosum

M. glutaeus maximus

N. pudendus

M. levator ani

M. obturator int.

Tuber ischiadicum

Nerves of the female pelvis, dissection completed. Lateral view.
Margins of the obturator foramen and ischiadic notches are indicated by dotted lines.

The iliopsoas fascia has now been removed; the pelvic part of the obturator fascia is intact. The superior fascia of the pelvic diaphragm and the levator ani muscle remain only at their lateral attachments; the obturator internus muscle is shown, freed of fascia in its perineal part, as it courses toward the lesser sciatic (ischiadic) foramen. The sacrotuberous ligament is in view, but the sacrospinous ligament is almost completely covered by the coccygeus muscle. The obturator nerve (from the lumbar plexus) is followed to the obturator canal. The lumbosacral trunk and the five sacral nerve trunks are shown (the lower rami in the series resting upon the piriformis muscle). The sacral plexus, formed by their union, extends into the greater sciatic foramen. The pudendal nerve is followed along the perineal wall, exposed there by removal of the obturator fascia.

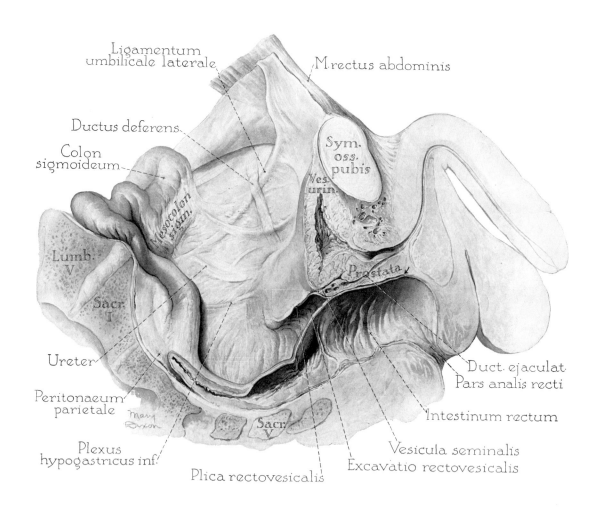

Pelvic nerves and organs in the male; peritoneal level (successively deeper levels follow).
Hemisected specimen. Showing especially the topography of the pelvic autonomic
plexus and the relations of the viscera.

　　The median sagittal section passes through the entire length of the rectum, and through the urinary
bladder, urethra, and prostate (latter hypertrophied). The section also passes through the interpubic fibrocartilage, seminal vesicles, retropubic plexus of veins, scrotum, and penile cavernous tissue.
　　Even while the peritoneum remains intact, it is evident that the distal portion of the hypogastric plexus
pursues an arciform course from upper sacral level to that of the base of the urinary bladder. It is likewise
clear that the plexus lies about midway between the ureter and the rectum, and nearer the sacrum than the
brim of the lesser pelvis. Toward the pelvic brim the lateral umbilical ligament and the ductus deferens cross
in x-fashion; toward the sacrum, the ureter follows the curve of the inferior hypogastric plexus.

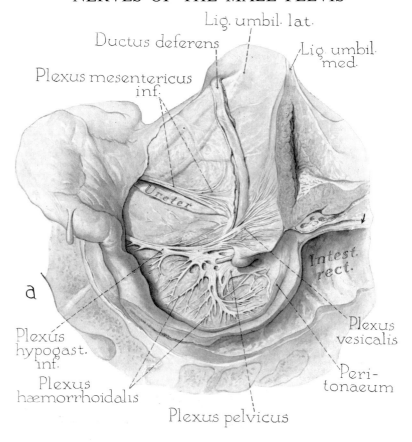

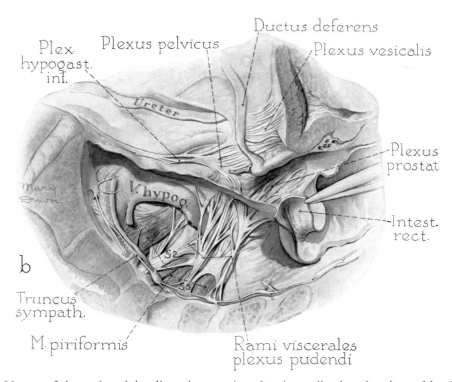

Nerves of the male pelvis; dissection continued to immediately subperitoneal level.

In *a*, the parietal peritoneum has been dissected away, together with the vesical part of the visceral peritoneum. The serous layer remains where it forms the pelvic mesocolon, and clothes the colon and rectum. The ureter, ductus deferens, and nerves have been freed from their thin stratum of subperitoneal tissue. In *b*, the heavier layer of fibrous tissue has been reflected to expose the sacral plexus.

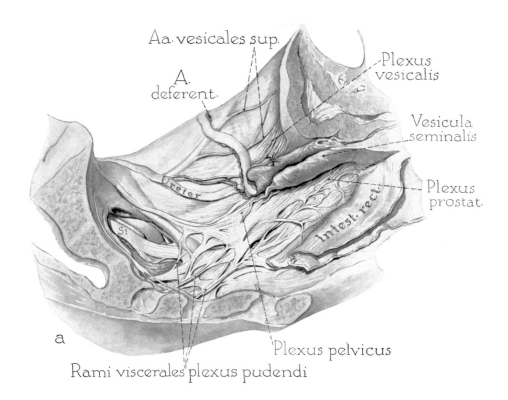

a

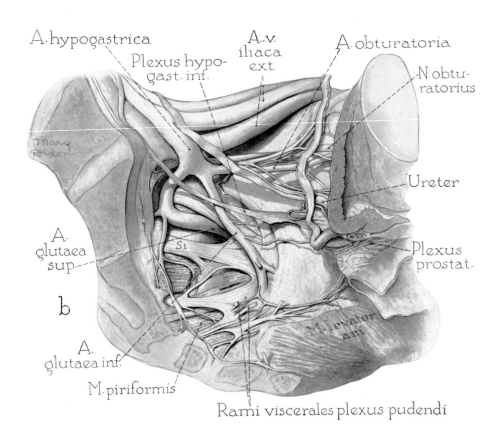

b

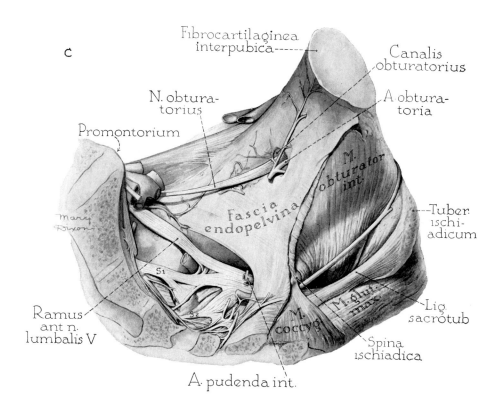

Nerves of the male pelvis; dissection carried to parietal level.

a, Form and composition of the deeper leaf of nerves. Showing the pelvic plexus, the superficial leaf of which has been entirely removed to expose the deep layer of the pelvic autonomic plexus, and the sacral rami contributing to its fabric. The nerves from the second to fourth sacral (erigens) are exposed; the anterior continuation of the pelvic autonomic plexus has been followed ventralward to the bladder, the seminal vesicles, and the prostate. The rectum, transected at coccygeal level, has been retracted. The superficial group of vessels is exposed (superior and middle vesical arteries from the obliterated hypogastric); the deep vessels (hypogastric and external iliac) remain covered by the heavy lamina of pelvic fascia.

b, Parasympathetic origin of the rami contributory to the pelvic plexus, and deep structures related to the latter. The deep relations of the pelvic plexus are demonstrated by removal of the plexus and the heavy retroperitoneal tissue which partially invests it. The transected parasympathetic nerves (visceral rami of the pudendal plexus) remain connected with the sacral plexus; the distal continuations of the autonomics have been cut as they disappear beneath the prostate and seminal vesicle. The connections between the inferior hypogastric plexus and the pelvic plexus have been severed along the inferior margin of the former. All of the retroperitoneal connective tissue has been removed, exposing the endopelvic fascia, the vessels and nerves to the pelvic viscera, the sacral and pudendal plexuses, and the larger vessels as they leave the pelvis. The superior fascia of the pelvic diaphragm has been removed, exposing the levator ani muscle.

c, Sacral plexus with derivative parasympathetic fibers (cut), and parietal and related diaphragmatic muscles and fasciae. Viscera, autonomic plexuses, and the large blood vessels have been removed. The sacral plexus has been followed to its point of exit through the greater sciatic foramen. The parietal portion of the endopelvic fascia is fully exposed; the levator ani muscle has been cut close to its origin along the tendinous arch, where the levator fibers are shown by trimming away the superior fascia of the pelvic diaphragm. The ischiorectal fossa has been freed of fat to reveal the pudendal artery (other associated vessels and nerves removed), the obturator internus muscle, the sacrotuberous ligament, and the gluteus maximus muscle.

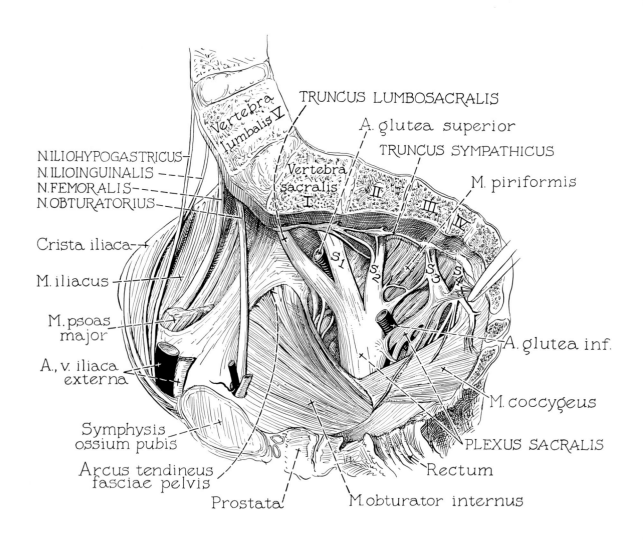

Nerves of the lumbar and sacral plexuses, shown in a hemisected male pelvis; viewed from the left side.

The anterior rami of the nerves (L4 to S5) converge toward the greater ischiadic foramen, through which they pass into the gluteal region with the piriformis muscle. Cut visceral branches are held by forceps. Also shown are motor nerves to the levator ani and coccygeus muscles (in the lesser pelvis), and several nerves from the lumbar plexus (in the greater pelvis).

Unlike the other derivatives of the anterior rami of the lumbar and sacral nerves, the iliohypogastric and ilioinguinal nerves, and the external spermatic branch of the genitofemoral pass through the antero-lateral abdominal musculature. The lumboinguinal division of the genitofemoral nerve, the femoral, and the lateral femoral cutaneous leave the pelvis beneath the inguinal ligament. The obturator nerve emerges through the upper part of the obturator foramen. The superior and inferior gluteal leave the pelvis through the greater ischiadic foramen by way of the suprapiriform and infrapiriform recesses, respectively. The ischiadic (OT, sciatic) nerve accompanies the inferior gluteal.

The lower part of the sacral plexus is named the pudendal. The largest derivative, the pudendal nerve, passes from the pelvic into the gluteal region through the infrapiriform recess; then it winds around the ischial spine, turning forward in the perineum, to course along the inferior ramus of the pubis.

(*See also page 515.*)

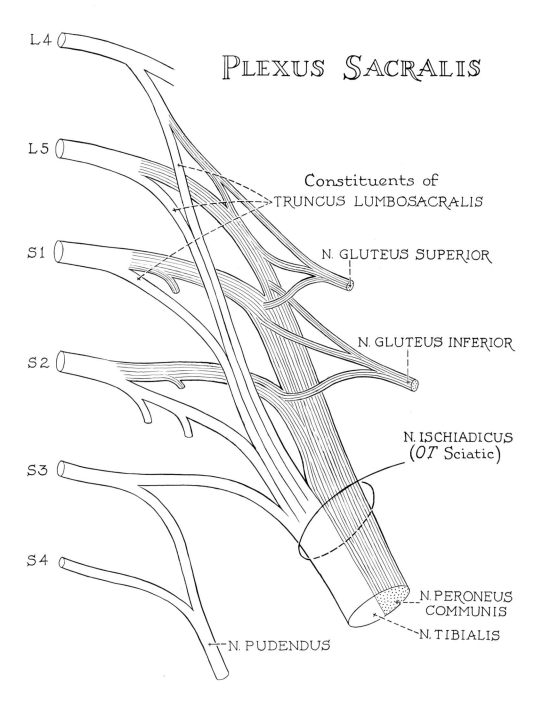

PLEXUS SACRALIS

L4

L5

S1

S2

S3

S4

Constituents of
TRUNCUS LUMBOSACRALIS

N. GLUTEUS SUPERIOR

N. GLUTEUS INFERIOR

N. ISCHIADICUS
(*OT* Sciatic)

N. PERONEUS
COMMUNIS

N. TIBIALIS

N. PUDENDUS

Sacral plexus of nerves. Diagrammatic.
Adapted from Gray.

THE LOWER MEMBER

BONES OF THE LOWER MEMBER.. 519–521

LIGAMENTS.. 522–524

BONES; AREAS OF MUSCULAR ATTACHMENT................................... 525–528
    Femur.. 525
    Tibia and Fibula... 526
    Foot.. 527–528

FEMORAL SHEATH AND BLOOD VESSELS: SEVEN STAGES IN DISSECTION.............. 529–530

FASCIA LATA: TWO STAGES IN DISSECTION..................................... 531

MUSCLES OF THE THIGH, BY GROUPS; SEMISCHEMATIC........................... 532

ANTERIOR AND LATERAL FEMORAL MUSCLES: TEN STAGES IN DISSECTION.......... 533–541

GLUTEAL MUSCULATURE: ELEVEN STAGES IN DISSECTION....................... 542–550

PIRIFORMIS MUSCLE AND SCIATIC NERVE; VARIATIONS: FOUR TYPES, WITH PERCENTAGE
    OCCURRENCE.. 551

MUSCULOFASCIAL COMPARTMENTS OF THE THIGH; SCHEMATIC................... 552

POSTERIOR FEMORAL MUSCULATURE: NINE STAGES IN DISSECTION................ 553–557

MUSCULOFASCIAL COMPARTMENTS OF THE LEG; SCHEMATIC...................... 558

POSTERIOR CRURAL MUSCULATURE: SEVEN STAGES IN DISSECTION................ 559–562

ANTEROLATERAL CRURAL MUSCULATURE: THREE STAGES IN DISSECTION........... 563–564

GASTROCNEMIUS AND SOLEUS MUSCLES; STRUCTURE........................... 565–566

MUSCLES AND TENDONS OF THE LEG, BY GROUPS.............................. 567–568

PLANTARIS TENDON; VARIATIONS: FIVE TYPES, WITH PERCENTAGE OCCURRENCE..... 569

MUSCULATURE OF THE FOOT: ELEVEN STAGES IN DISSECTION.................... 570–575

MUSCLES OF THE THIGH AND LEG; SCHEMATIC: ACTION-GROUPS.................. 576–578

SUPERFICIAL VEINS... 579–582

BLOOD VESSELS AND NERVES OF THE THIGH; ANTERIOR: FOUR STAGES IN DISSECTION.. 583–585

BLOOD VESSELS AND NERVES OF THE THIGH; POSTERIOR: EIGHT STAGES IN DISSECTION.. 586–590

BLOOD VESSELS AND NERVES OF THE LEG: SIX STAGES IN DISSECTION.............. 591–592

BLOOD VESSELS AND NERVES OF THE FOOT: THREE STAGES IN DISSECTION.......... 593

VESSELS AND NERVES OF THE THIGH AND LEG; SCHEMATIC...................... 594–598

517

(*Continued*)

SUPERFICIAL VEINS AND LYMPH GLANDS; TYPES: SIXTEEN EXAMPLES............... 599–603

FOSSA OVALIS AND CONTENTS; TYPES: SIXTEEN EXAMPLES....................... 604

TOPOGRAPHY OF FEMORAL HERNIA: SEVEN STAGES IN DISSECTION................. 605–609

INGUINOFEMORAL REGION: SIX STAGES IN DISSECTION.......................... 610–613

TOPOGRAPHY OF OBTURATOR HERNIA: FIVE STAGES IN DISSECTION................ 614–618

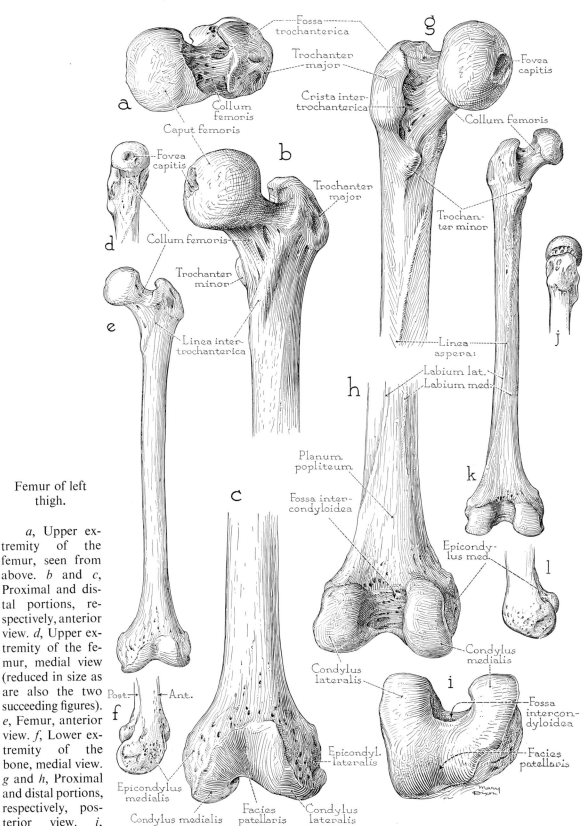

Femur of left thigh.

a, Upper extremity of the femur, seen from above. b and c, Proximal and distal portions, respectively, anterior view. d, Upper extremity of the femur, medial view (reduced in size as are also the two succeeding figures). e, Femur, anterior view. f, Lower extremity of the bone, medial view. g and h, Proximal and distal portions, respectively, posterior view. i, Lower extremity of the femur, seen from below. j, Upper extremity of the femur, lateral view (reduced, as are also the two succeeding figures). k, Femur, posterior view. l, Lower extremity of the bone, lateral view.

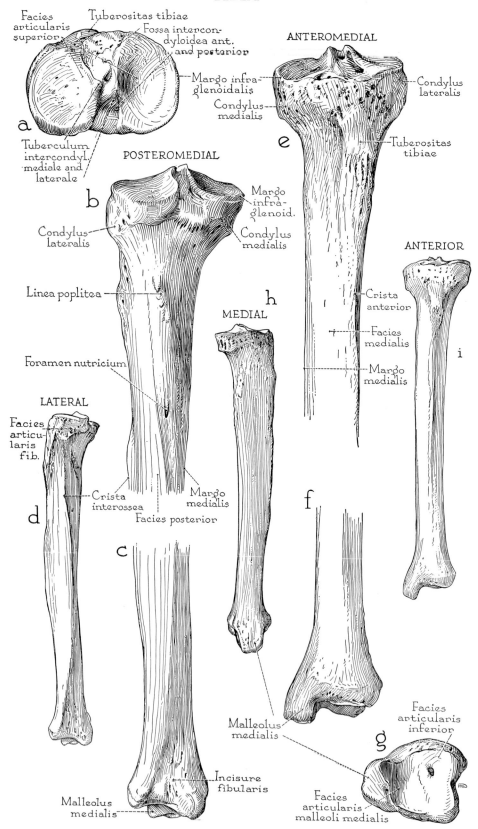

Tibia of left leg.

a, Upper extremity of the tibia, seen from above. *b* and *c,* Proximal and distal portions, respectively, posterolateral view. *d,* Tibia, lateral view (reduced, as are also *h* and *i*). *e* and *f,* Proximal and distal portions, respectively, anteromedial view. *g,* Lower extremity of the tibia, seen from below. *h* and *i,* Medial and anterior views, respectively.

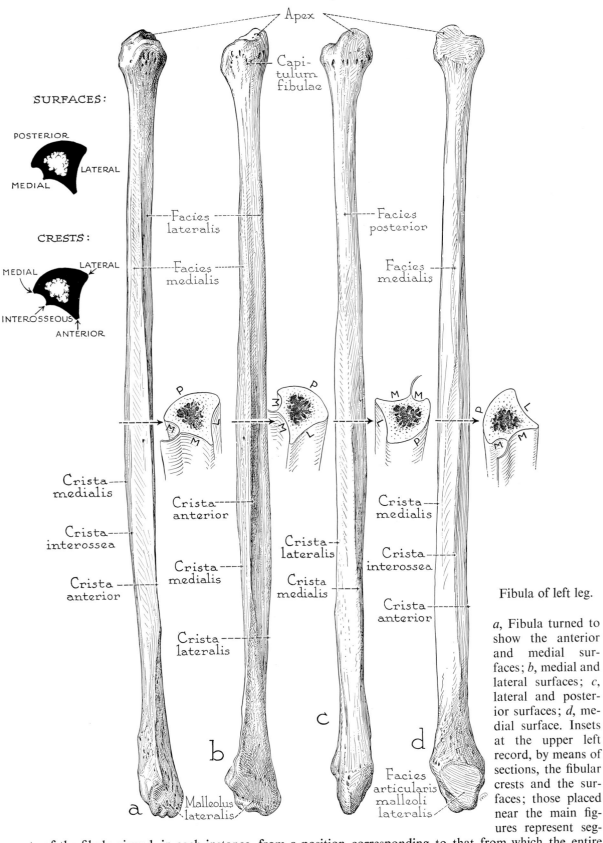

SURFACES:

POSTERIOR

LATERAL

MEDIAL

CRESTS:

MEDIAL LATERAL

INTEROSSEOUS

ANTERIOR

Apex

Capitulum fibulae

Facies lateralis

Facies medialis

Facies posterior

Facies medialis

Crista medialis

Crista interossea

Crista anterior

Crista anterior

Crista medialis

Crista lateralis

Crista lateralis

Crista medialis

Crista medialis

Crista interossea

Crista anterior

Malleolus lateralis

Facies articularis malleoli lateralis

a

b

c

d

Fibula of left leg.

a, Fibula turned to show the anterior and medial surfaces; *b*, medial and lateral surfaces; *c*, lateral and posterior surfaces; *d*, medial surface. Insets at the upper left record, by means of sections, the fibular crests and the surfaces; those placed near the main figures represent segments of the fibula viewed, in each instance, from a position corresponding to that from which the entire bone was seen. The initials M, L, and P are abbreviations for medial, lateral, and posterior, respectively.

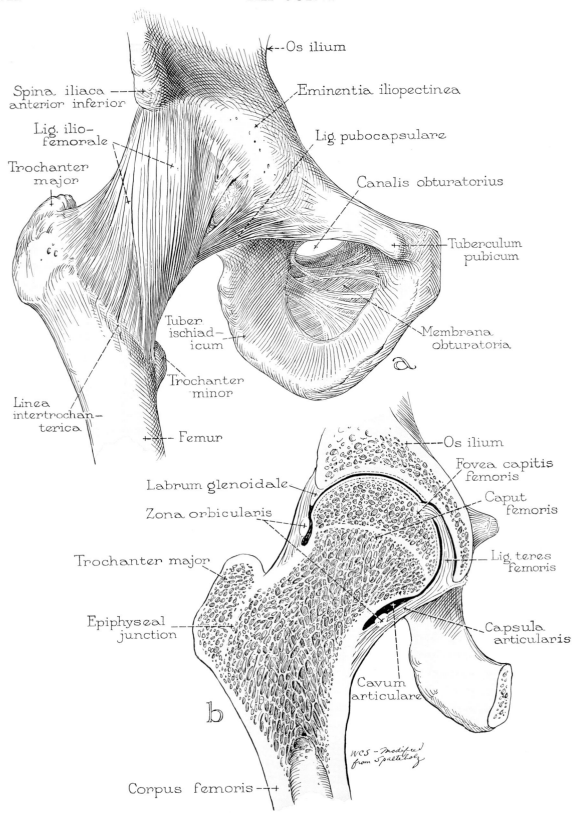

Spina iliaca anterior inferior

Lig. ilio-femorale

Trochanter major

Os ilium

Eminentia iliopectinea

Lig. pubocapsulare

Canalis obturatorius

Tuberculum pubicum

Tuber ischiadicum

Trochanter minor

Membrana obturatoria

Linea intertrochanterica

Femur

a

Labrum glenoidale

Zona orbicularis

Trochanter major

Epiphyseal junction

Os ilium

Fovea capitis femoris

Caput femoris

Lig. teres femoris

Capsula articularis

Cavum articulare

b

WCS - modified from Spalteholz

Corpus femoris

Hip joint and obturator membrane. Entire and in coronal section; anterior views.

a, Ligaments of the articulation at the hip, and the membrane which, except for the space of the obturator canal, closes the obturator foramen in the innominate bone.

b, Articular cavity, capsule and supporting ligaments, and cartilaginous lip of the hip joint.

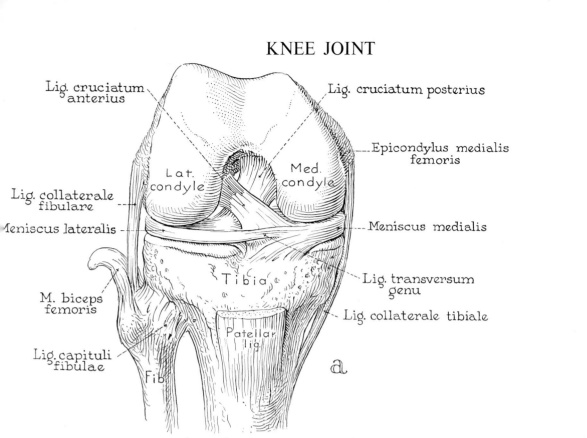

Lig. cruciatum anterius

Lig. cruciatum posterius

Lig. collaterale fibulare

Epicondylus medialis femoris

Lat. condyle

Med. condyle

Meniscus lateralis

Meniscus medialis

Tibia

Lig. transversum genu

M. biceps femoris

Lig. collaterale tibiale

Lig. capituli fibulae

Patellar lig.

Fib

a

Anterior

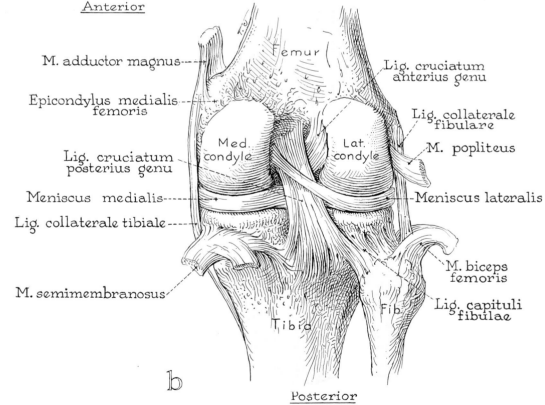

M. adductor magnus

Femur

Lig. cruciatum anterius genu

Epicondylus medialis femoris

Lig. collaterale fibulare

Med. condyle

Lat. condyle

M. popliteus

Lig. cruciatum posterius genu

Meniscus medialis

Meniscus lateralis

Lig. collaterale tibiale

M. biceps femoris

M. semimembranosus

Lig. capituli fibulae

Tibia

Fib

b

Posterior

Knee joint; anterior and posterior views.

a, Ligaments supporting the capsule as collaterals, and the ligaments and cartilaginous menisci within the capsular space. The tendons of insertion of the biceps femoris and quadratus femoris have been cut.

b, Ligaments and menisci of the knee joint. The tendon of the semimembranosus has been freed from the capsule.

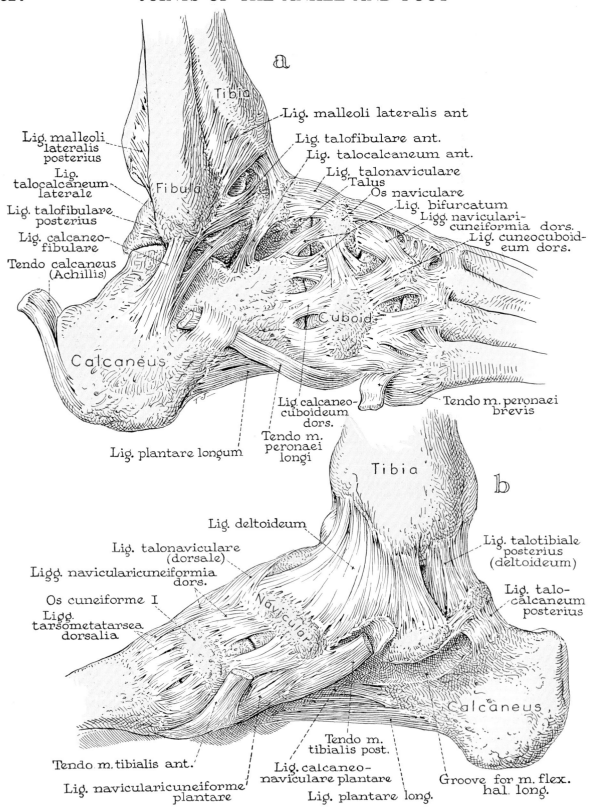

Joints of the ankle, tarsus, and metatarsus. Articular capsule removed
in order to emphasize the strengthening ligaments. Lateral and medial views.

In *a*, the calcaneal and long peroneal tendons are shown; in *b*, those of the anterior and posterior tibial
muscles.

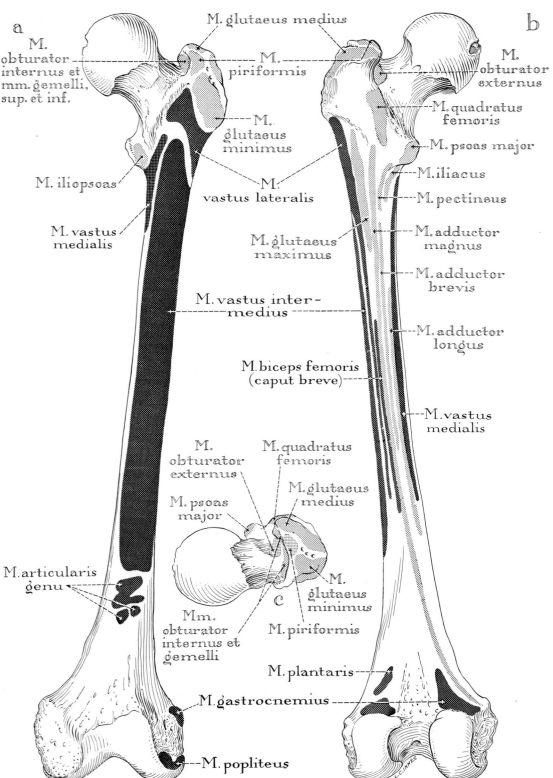

a
M. glutaeus medius
b
M. obturator internus et mm. gemelli, sup. et inf.
M. piriformis
M. obturator externus
M. quadratus femoris
M. glutaeus minimus
M. psoas major
M. iliopsoas
M. iliacus
M. vastus lateralis
M. pectineus
M. vastus medialis
M. glutaeus maximus
M. adductor magnus
M. adductor brevis
M. vastus intermedius
M. adductor longus
M. biceps femoris (caput breve)
M. vastus medialis
M. obturator externus
M. quadratus femoris
M. psoas major
M. glutaeus medius
M. articularis genu
c
M. glutaeus minimus
Mm. obturator internus et gemelli
M. piriformis
M. plantaris
M. gastrocnemius
M. popliteus

Femur. Areas of muscular attachment.

a, Anterior aspect. *b*, Posterior aspect. *c*, The superior extremity of the femur, viewed from above.

In each of these figures, and in those of the leg and foot that follow, the area of origin of a muscle is shown in darker pattern and the label in heavy lettering. The area of insertion in each instance is treated in lighter pattern and labelled with open lettering.

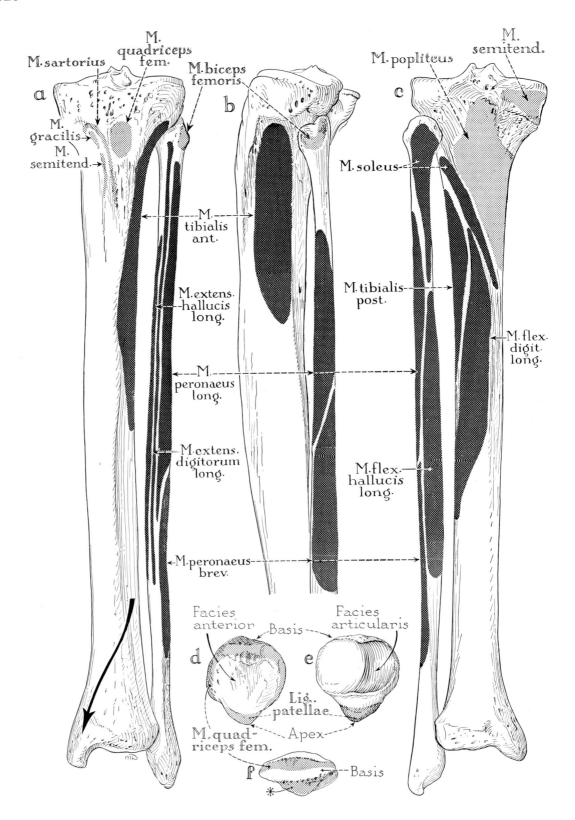

Tibia, fibula, and patella. Areas of muscular attachment.

Views of the tibia and fibula. *a,* Anterior aspect; *b,* lateral; *c,* posterior.
Views of the patella. *d,* Anterior; *e,* posterior or articular; *f,* superior (of the base).

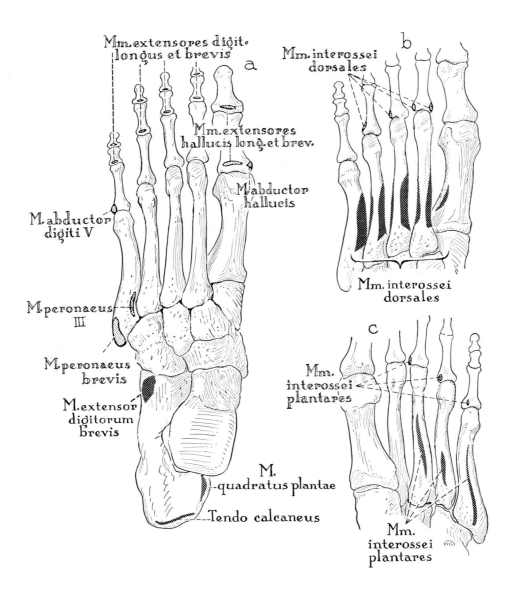

Bones of the foot. Dorsal surface. Areas of muscular attachment.

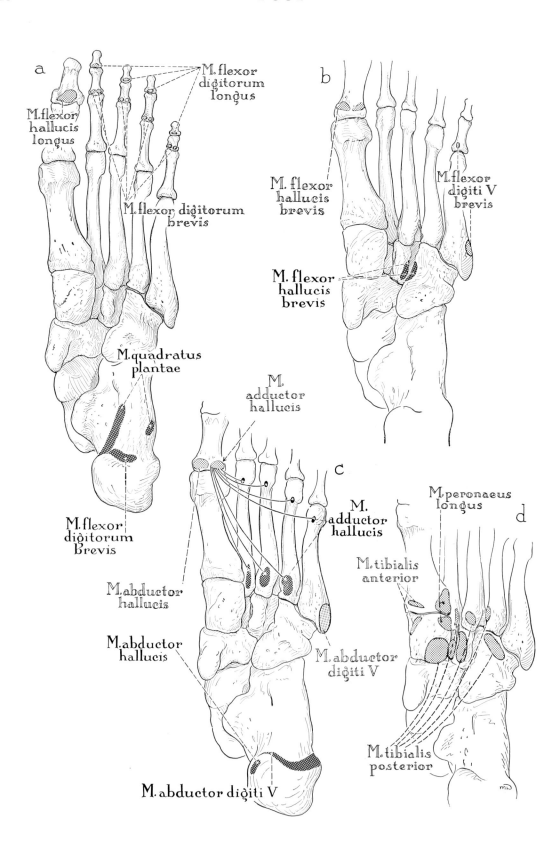

Bones of the foot. Plantar surface. Areas of muscular attachment.

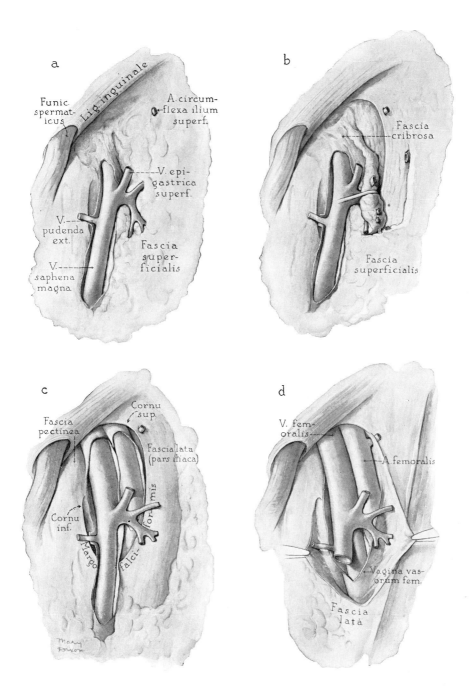

Investments of the saphenous and femoral veins; successive stages in dissection, from the superficial fascia to the fascia lata and the femoral sheath.

a, The fatty layer of superficial fascia has been partially removed at the fossa ovalis (NA, *hiatus saphenus*) to expose the subjacent membranous layer where it ensheathes the femoral and saphenous veins.

b, The fat-laden stratum has been reflected from the area lateral to the fossa and retracted medialward to show the falciform boundary of the fossa and the superior cornu. The superficial fascia is rendered cribrose by the saphenous tributaries.

c, The fatty layer has now been completely removed, thereby showing how the subjacent deep layer of fascia forms a complete sheath (opened here) for femoral vessels.

d, The sheath has been further exposed where it lies beneath the fascia lata beyond the distal edge of the falciform margin.

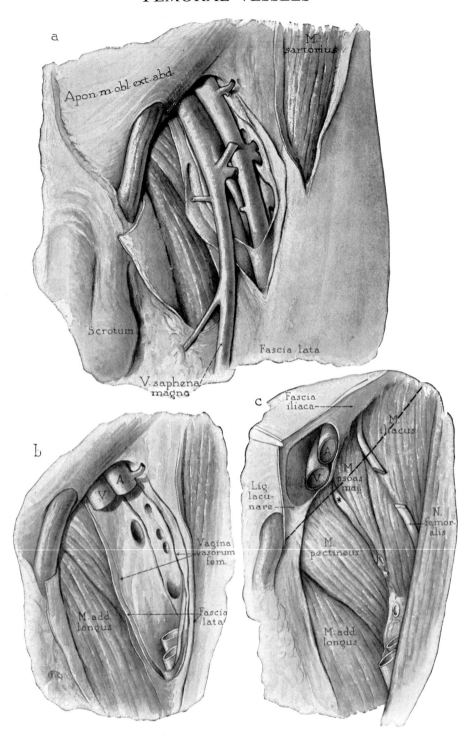

Investments of the femoral vessels; dissections continued to the muscular level.

a, The bilaminar sheath of the femoral vessels has been opened to the point where, distally, the contained vessels enter the adductor canal.

b, The floor of the sheath has been exposed by excision of the vessels. A indicates artery; V, vein.

c, In order to demonstrate the muscular relations of the femoral vessels and their sheath, the fascia lata has been entirely removed in the area of the femoral triangle. The fascia is elevated proximally (the former position of the inguinal ligament being indicated by a broken line); the position of the iliopectineal eminence is indicated by asterisk. The femoral nerve is shown as it enters the thigh through the muscular lacuna, descends in a sulcus between the psoas and iliacus, and finally crosses the latter muscle.

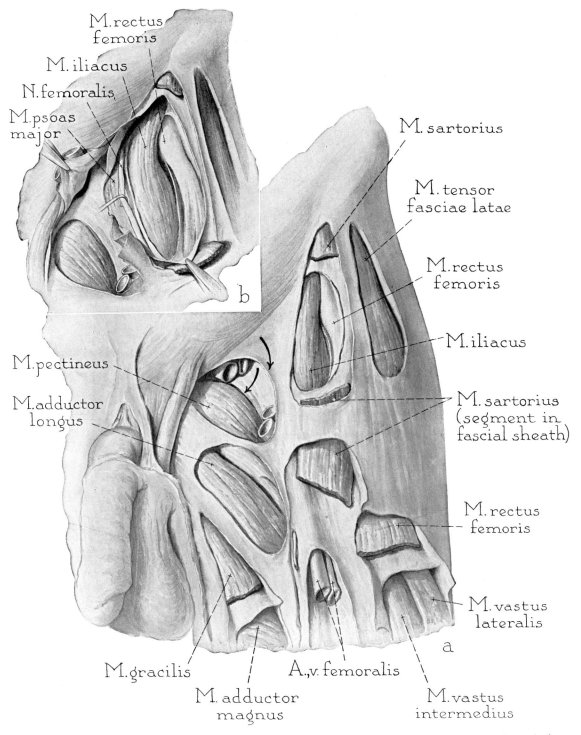

Fascia lata and intermuscular septa of the medial and anterior femoral regions; anterolateral view.

a, The fascia lata and the lesser fascial sleeves have been opened at several points to demonstrate the manner in which the muscles are invested by the femoral fascia and its septa. The pectineal fascia on the floor of the fossa ovalis (NA, *hiatus saphenus*) has been removed to expose the pectineus muscle (to the point of the arrow at the left). The femoral vessels have been transected. The fascia that forms the falciform margin of the fossa ovalis is intact (arrow at the right).

b, Deeper dissection in the proximal portion of the same region. The fascia lata, incised along the line of its continuity with the inguinal ligament, is lifted with the femoral vessels. The fascial roof of the muscular lacuna has been removed to show the psoas major and neighboring muscles.

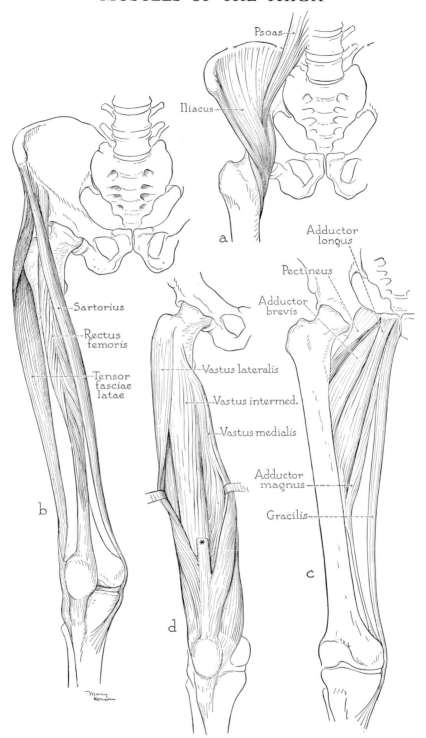

Muscles of the front and sides of the thigh, by groups.

a, The psoas and iliacus, from the lumbar portion of the vertebral column and the wall of the false pelvis, conjoined, narrow as they descend from the pelvic cavity to an insertion into the lesser trochanter on the proximal extremity of the femur. *b*, Lateral to this muscle complex the sartorius, rectus femoris, and tensor fasciae latae, arising from the anterior iliac spines, descend in divergent courses to insertions on the proximal extremities of the tibia and fibula. *c*, Medial to the iliopsoas the pectineus, the three adductors, and the gracilis arise from the pubic and ischial portions of the innominate bone. They insert into a dorsally placed linear crest (linea aspera) of the femur and into the medial condyles of the femur and the tibia. *d*, Distal to the insertion of the iliopsoas, the three vasti arise from the same line (linea aspera) and from the side and front of the femur, completely investing the shaft of the femur and joining the rectus (*). On the way to an anterior tibial insertion the tendon encloses the patella.

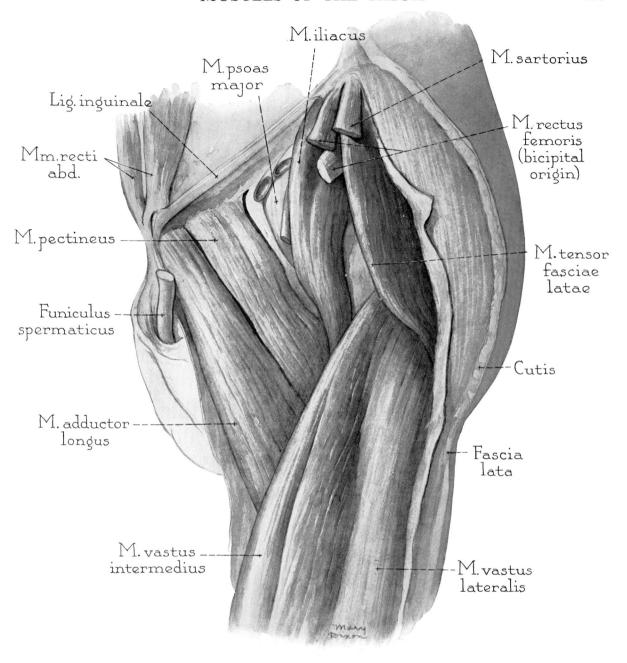

M. iliacus

M. psoas major

M. sartorius

Lig. inguinale

M. rectus femoris (bicipital origin)

Mm. recti abd.

M. pectineus

M. tensor fasciae latae

Funiculus spermaticus

Cutis

M. adductor longus

Fascia lata

M. vastus intermedius

M. vastus lateralis

Muscles on the proximal half of the thigh, within, and adjacent to, the femoral triangle.
Dissection continued.

The sartorius and rectus femoris muscles have been removed except at their origins. The tendinous acetabular head of the biceps occupies a sulcus in the iliacus. On the abdomen the recti and the inguinal ligament remain; the lateral abdominal muscles have been removed. The femoral vessels rest upon the psoas major muscle; the femoral nerve lies in the sulcus between the psoas and the iliacus muscles.

Of the muscles related to the femoral triangle, two (the adductor longus and the pectineus) arise from the superior ramus of the pubis, two (the psoas major and the iliacus) enter the thigh, beneath the inguinal ligament, from the pelvis; three (the sartorius, the rectus, and the tensor) take origin chiefly from the anterior iliac spines. The muscles of the first two sets insert into the femur, as a virtually uninterrupted plate. The iliacus and the psoas major, through a common tendon, insert into the lesser trochanter; the pectineal line, continued distalward from the trochanter, receives the insertion of the pectineus; the adductor longus, still further distalward, is implanted into the linea aspera.

The muscles of the third set diverge; the sartorius muscle inclines toward the medial surface of the thigh, the tensor remains on the lateral aspect, while the rectus descends between them to the front of the leg.

a

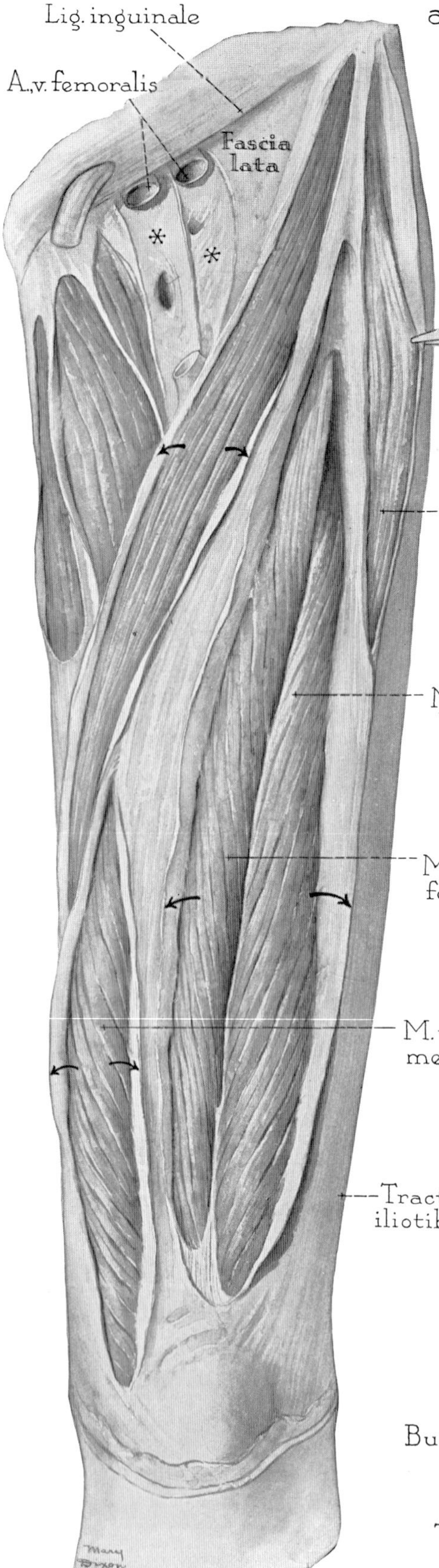

b

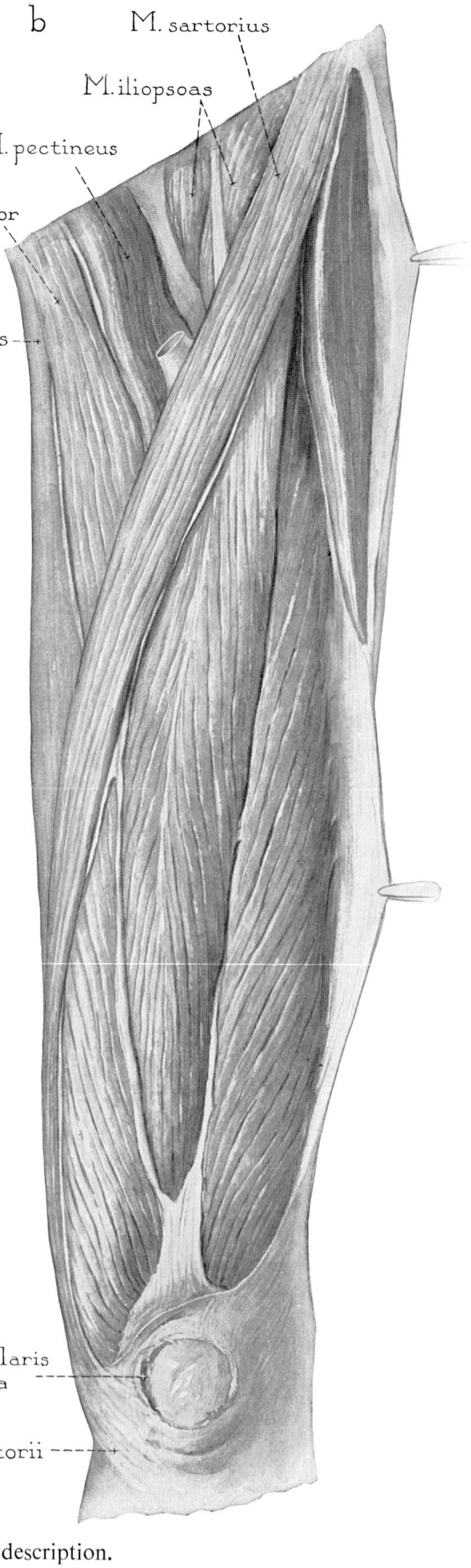

Lig. inguinale

A.v. femoralis

Fascia lata

M. sartorius

M. iliopsoas

M. pectineus

M. adductor longus

M. gracilis

M. tensor fasciae latae

M. vastus lateralis

M. rectus femoris

M. vastus medialis

Tractus iliotibialis

Bursa praepatellaris subcutanea

Tendo m. sartorii

See opposite page for description.

Anterior, lateral, and medial femoral musculature; with the investing portions of the deep fascia.

a, The integument and superficial fascia have been removed, and the fascia lata has been incised by longitudinal cuts corresponding to the long axes of the femoral muscles. At the margins of the incisions (indicated by arrows) the fascia has been retracted to expose the muscles which are contained within the fascial compartments. The compartments of the femoral sheath (at *) are opened, the vessels excised.

b, The deep investing fascia of the thigh (fascia lata) has now been largely removed, the cut edges of the intermuscular septa appearing between adjacent muscles. The fascia has been incised along the anterior margin of the tensor fasciae latae and retracted, to demonstrate the fusion of layers to form the iliotibial tract. At the knee the fascia has been removed to the line where it becomes continuous with the quadriceps tendon and the capsule of the joint; it has been removed from the patella to expose the space of the prepatellar bursa. In the proximal part of the thigh the fascia has been cut away in order to reveal the muscles that form the floor of the femoral triangle.

c, The fascia now remains only on the medial and on the lateral aspects of the thigh; in the former situation it appears as an intermuscular septum. At the knee the fascia blends with the capsule of the joint, and with the tendon of insertion of the quadriceps femoris muscle. The rectus femoris muscle has been removed except at its extremities. The sartorius has been cut in order to expose the iliopectineal fossa, for which it forms the lateral boundary. The femoral nerve enters the thigh in the sulcus between the iliacus and psoas major muscles, quickly dividing into branches for the innervation of the anterior femoral muscles.

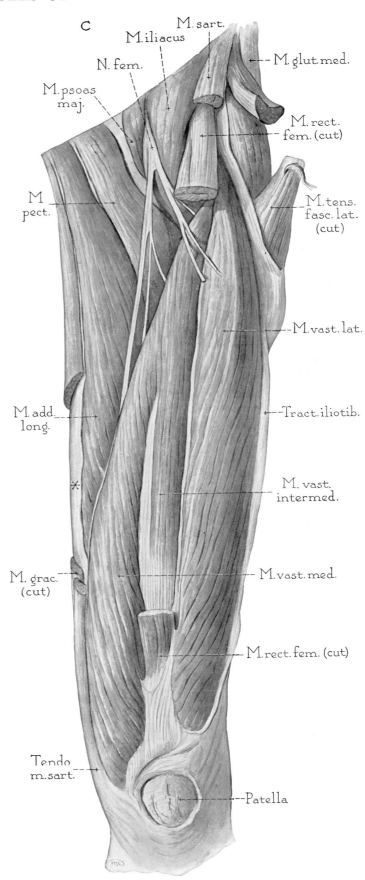

C

M. sart.
M. iliacus
N. fem.
M. glut. med.
M. psoas maj.
M. rect. fem. (cut)
M. pect.
M. tens. fasc. lat. (cut)
M. vast. lat.
M. add. long.
Tract. iliotib.
M. vast. intermed.
M. grac. (cut)
M. vast. med.
M. rect. fem. (cut)
Tendo m. sart.
Patella

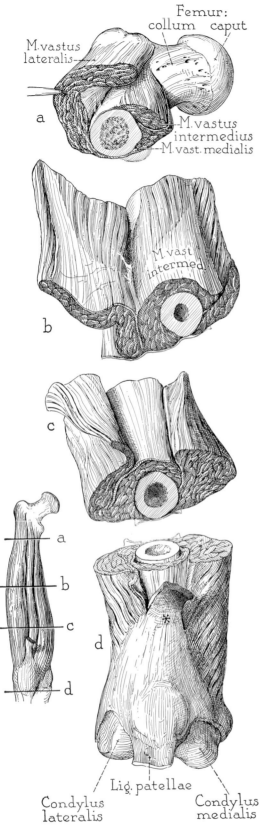

Vasti sectioned at the levels indicated in the inset, to illustrate their form and interrelationships.

a, At the level of the transection, the vastus intermedius is entirely muscular. It arises from the anterior, medial, and posterior surfaces of the femur. The vastus lateralis, although investing the lateral surface of the bone and partially covering the vastus intermedius, has no fascicular attachments to either. It is covered for part of its free (outer) surface by a heavy aponeurosis, which extends proximally to the origin from the greater trochanter.

b, The facing surfaces of the vastus intermedius and vastus lateralis are aponeurotic. The vastus medialis, on its internal surface, is in contact largely with the vastus intermedius; the medial third of the same surface forms the floor of a sulcus for the rectus femoris muscle.

c, The thin aponeurosis of the vastus intermedius fuses laterally with that on the deep surface of the vastus lateralis. The combined aponeurosis extends almost to the dorsal aspect of each of the two muscles. Between the bulging (anterior) summit of the vastus medialis and the medial margin of the vastus lateralis, the rectus femoris lies in a sulcus, the floor of which is the vastus intermedius.

d, In the region of the knee joint the fibers of the lateral and medial vasti are implanted into the sides of the tendon of the rectus femoris (at*); those of the intermediate vastus insert into the deep aspect. The tendon of the quadriceps femoris, formed by the convergence of the four muscles, encloses the patella. From the latter the patellar tendon is prolonged to the tuberosity of the tibia.

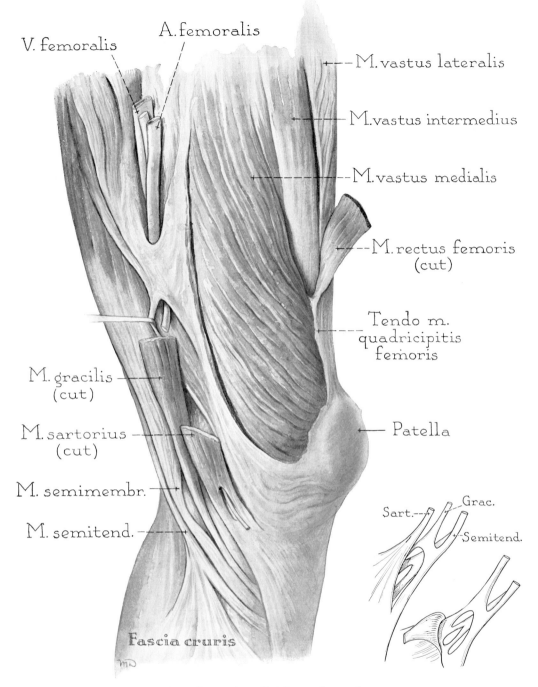

V. femoralis
A. femoralis
M. vastus lateralis
M. vastus intermedius
M. vastus medialis
M. rectus femoris (cut)
Tendo m. quadricipitis femoris
M. gracilis (cut)
M. sartorius (cut)
Patella
M. semimembr.
M. semitend.
Sart. Grac.
Semitend.
Fascia cruris

Anterior and medial femoral muscles.

The investing fascia (fascia lata) has been removed except where, posterior to the vastus medialis, it extends inward to an osseous attachment as the medial intermuscular septum. Distally the fascia blends with the capsule of the knee joint, from which it is prolonged into the leg as the crural fascia. The tendons of the sartorius, gracilis, and semitendinosus gain insertion into the crural fascia as they course toward their areas of chief attachment on the tuberosity or the medial condyle of the tibia. In this specimen the semimembranosus also inserts into the tibial tuberosity.

At their insertions the sartorius, gracilis, and semitendinosus are closely related; the tendons together form the pes anserinus (see diagrammatic figures at lower right). They converge upon the tibia from the three femoral regions; the sartorius comes from the anterior femoral region, the gracilis from the medial, and the semitendinosus from the posterior. Over the area of the medial surface of the tibial condyle, the sartorius fuses with the subjacent gracilis and semitendinosus. Through the continuity of the tendons with the fascial investment of the muscles of the leg, the several muscles greatly increase their territory of attachment.

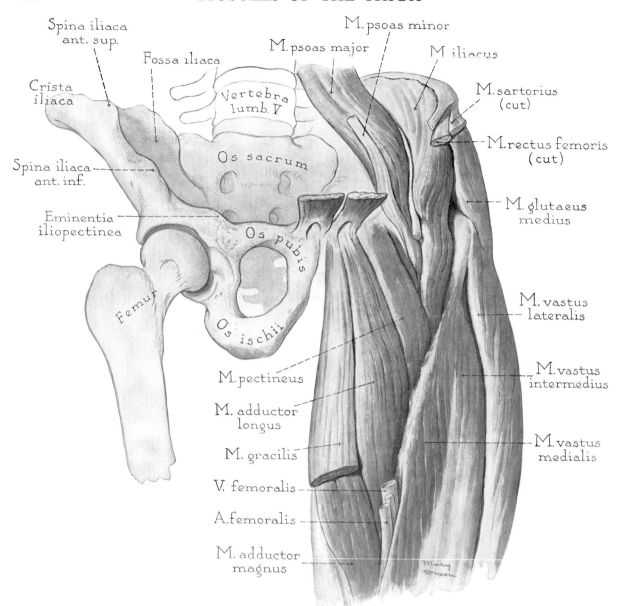

Spina iliaca
ant. sup.

Fossa iliaca

Crista
iliaca

Spina iliaca
ant. inf.

Eminentia
iliopectinea

Femur

Vertebra
lumb. V

Os sacrum

Os pubis

Os ischii

M.pectineus

M. adductor
longus

M. gracilis

V. femoralis

A. femoralis

M. adductor
magnus

M. psoas minor

M. psoas major

M. iliacus

M. sartorius
(cut)

M. rectus femoris
(cut)

M. glutaeus
medius

M. vastus
lateralis

M. vastus
intermedius

M. vastus
medialis

Femoral musculature; anteromedial view.

The tendons of origin of the sartorius, of the tensor fasciae latae, and of the rectus femoris muscles, with the adjacent inguinal ligament, have been cut in order to reveal the anterior border of the gluteus medius muscle, the iliopsoas muscle, and the associated femoral nerve. The contents of the iliac fossa (in the pelvis) and the deep boundaries of the adductor canal (in the thigh) are thereby brought into view. The overarching border of the vastus medialis forms a prominent lateral boundary for the adductor canal; the contents of the canal, namely, the femoral vessels and the accompanying saphenous nerve, rest upon the pectineus and the adductor muscles. The aponeurotic surface of the vastus intermedius muscle is shown, overlapped by the vastus lateralis. The interdigitating nature of the insertion of the gluteus medius and the origin of the vastus lateralis is demonstrated. The topographical importance of the iliopsoas is evident; it separates the muscles that arise from the anterior iliac spines from those that take origin from the rami of the pubis and ischium. On the specimen's right half are exposed the eminences and areas from which femoral muscles arise or to which they are otherwise related. The spines of the ilium give origin to the sartorius and rectus femoris, the rami of the pubis and ischium to the pectineus and the adductors, the femur to the vasti. The iliacus muscle takes origin from the internal surface of the ala of the ilium; joined by the psoas, the origin of which is vertebral, the two muscles descend in relation to the iliopectineal eminence to an insertion on the lesser trochanter of the femur.

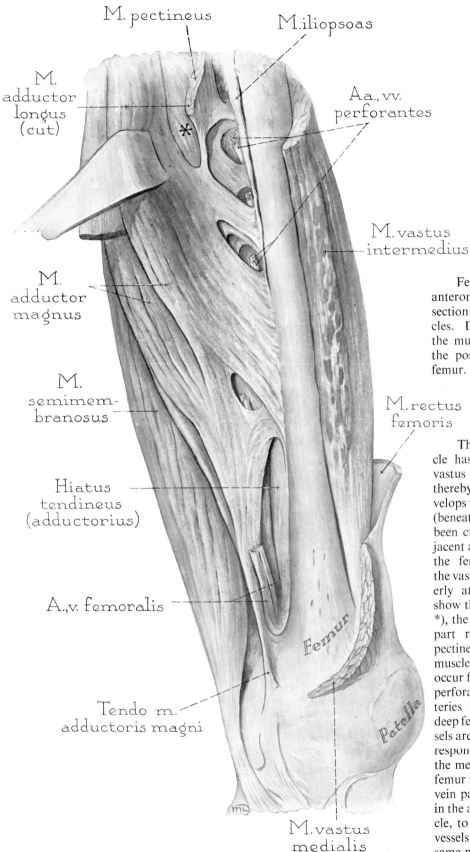

M. pectineus

M. iliopsoas

M. adductor longus (cut)

Aa., vv. perforantes

*

M. vastus intermedius

M. adductor magnus

M. semimem- branosus

Hiatus tendineus (adductorius)

M. rectus femoris

A., v. femoralis

Femur

Patella

Tendo m. adductoris magni

M. vastus medialis

Femoral musculature in anteromedial view. Deep dissection of the adductor muscles. Depicting, especially, the muscles that insert into the posterior aspect of the femur.

The vastus lateralis muscle has been removed; the vastus intermedius muscle is thereby revealed, as it envelops the femur. The gracilis (beneath the retractor) has been cut to expose the subjacent adductor. The shaft of the femur is exposed where the vastus medialis was formerly attached. In order to show the adductor brevis (at *), the pectineus has been in part removed. Within the pectineus and the adductor muscles hiatuses of large size occur for transmission of the perforating vessels; the arteries are branches of the deep femoral, the venous vessels are tributaries of the corresponding vein. Just above the medial epicondyle of the femur the femoral artery and vein pass through the hiatus in the adductor magnus muscle, to become the popliteal vessels in the fossa of the same name.

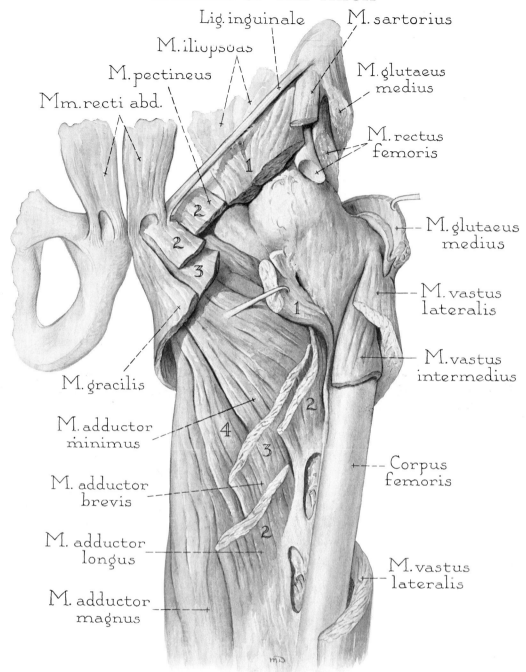

Mm. recti abd.

M. pectineus

M. iliopsoas

Lig. inguinale

M. sartorius

M. glutaeus medius

M. rectus femoris

M. glutaeus medius

M. vastus lateralis

M. vastus intermedius

Corpus femoris

M. vastus lateralis

M. gracilis

M. adductor minimus

M. adductor brevis

M. adductor longus

M. adductor magnus

Muscles of the pelvis and thigh in relation to the hip joint and to one another, in laminar succession. Deep dissection, anterior view. The cut ends of the muscles are similarly numbered, and in the succession in which they appear as they approach the femur.

The iliopsoas (psoas and iliacus), and the muscles of the adductor group situated medial thereto, are arranged as they extend from the region of the iliopectineal eminence, along the rami of the pubis, dorsalward along the inferior ramus of the ischium, to the tuberosity of the latter bone. The series begins with the iliacus and ends with the adductor magnus. The seven muscles that have femoral insertions are arranged in such a way, as they reach the femur, as to be disposed in four strata. The iliacus and psoas major, fused to produce a common tendon, make up the first layer (at 1); the conjoined tendon is prolonged downward on the iliopectineal line. The pectineus and adductor longus comprise a second layer (at 2), with insertion into the pectineal line and the linea aspera. The third layer (at 3) consists of the adductor brevis alone. The fourth layer is made up of the adductor minimus and adductor magnus (at 4). The muscles of these two layers insert chiefly into the linea aspera.

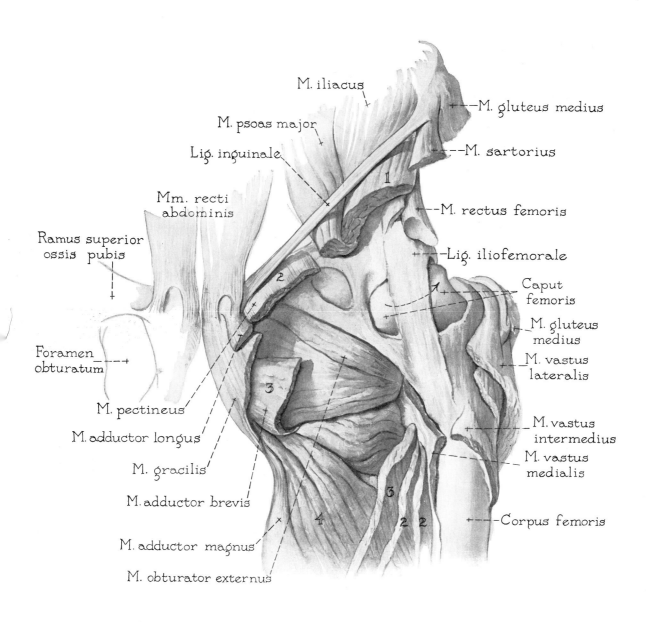

M. iliacus

M. psoas major

Lig. inguinale

Mm. recti abdominis

Ramus superior ossis pubis

Foramen obturatum

M. pectineus

M. adductor longus

M. gracilis

M. adductor brevis

M. adductor magnus

M. obturator externus

M. gluteus medius

M. sartorius

M. rectus femoris

Lig. iliofemorale

Caput femoris

M. gluteus medius

M. vastus lateralis

M. vastus intermedius

M. vastus medialis

Corpus femoris

Muscles of the pelvis and thigh in relation to the hip joint; deeper dissection.
Numbered as in the preceding figure.

The insertion of the iliopsoas has been cut away, the vasti (medius and intermedius) shown as they envelop the femur. The adductor brevis (at 3) has been slightly reflected near its insertion to show the plane of separation between the adductor minimus and the adductor magnus (the latter at 4). The bursa that lay beneath the iliopsoas muscle has been opened. The head of the femur is exposed by cutting the articular ligament to each of the medial parts of the iliofemoral ligament (beneath which an arrow is passed).

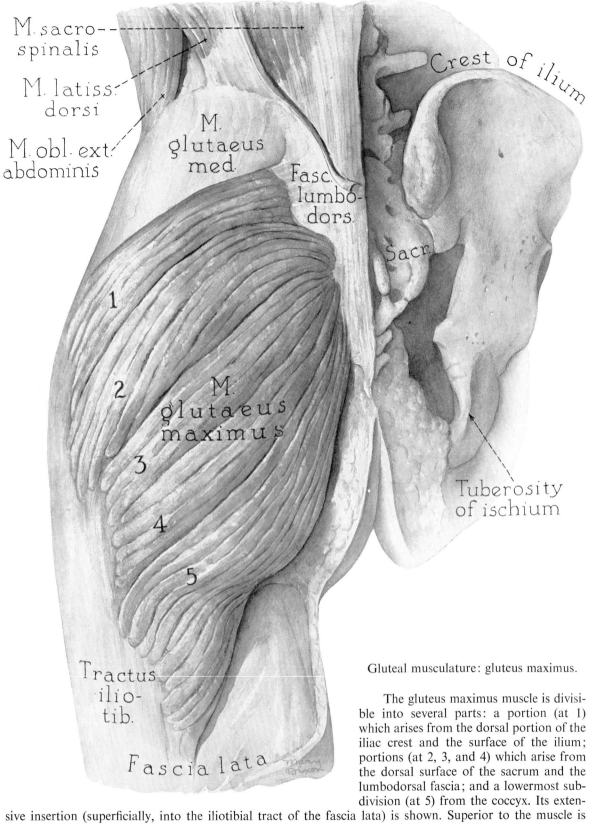

M. sacro-spinalis

M. latiss. dorsi

M. obl. ext. abdominis

M. glutaeus med.

Fasc. lumbo-dors.

Crest of ilium

Sacr.

1

2 M. glutaeus maximus

3

4

5

Tuberosity of ischium

Tractus ilio-tib.

Fascia lata

Gluteal musculature: gluteus maximus.

The gluteus maximus muscle is divisible into several parts: a portion (at 1) which arises from the dorsal portion of the iliac crest and the surface of the ilium; portions (at 2, 3, and 4) which arise from the dorsal surface of the sacrum and the lumbodorsal fascia; and a lowermost subdivision (at 5) from the coccyx. Its extensive insertion (superficially, into the iliotibial tract of the fascia lata) is shown. Superior to the muscle is the closely related gluteus medius, here still covered by fascia. In the succeeding five figures the dissection is carried to progressively deeper levels, terminating with exposure of the bone.

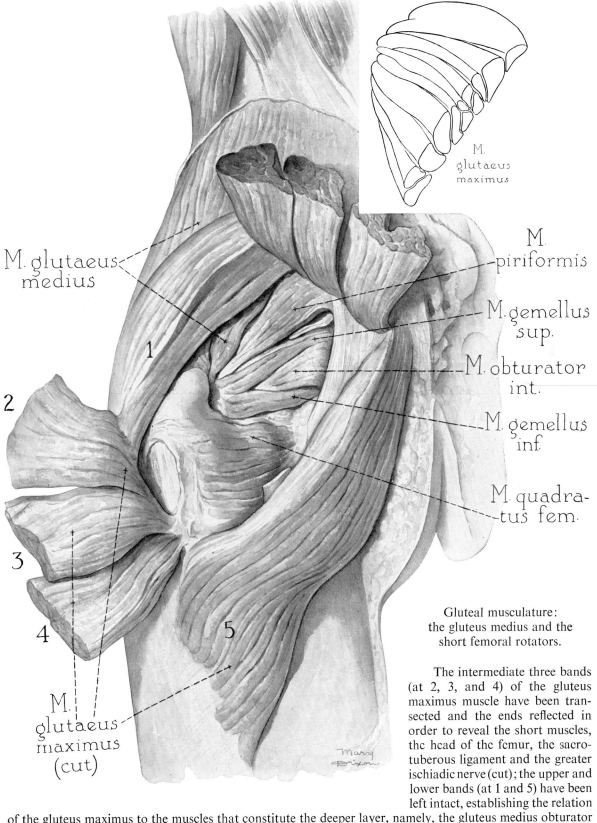

M. gluteaus maximus

M. gluteaus medius

M. piriformis

M. gemellus sup.

M. obturator int.

M. gemellus inf.

M. quadratus fem.

1

2

3

4

5

M. gluteaus maximus (cut)

Gluteal musculature:
the gluteus medius and the
short femoral rotators.

The intermediate three bands
(at 2, 3, and 4) of the gluteus
maximus muscle have been transected and the ends reflected in
order to reveal the short muscles,
the head of the femur, the sacrotuberous ligament and the greater
ischiadic nerve (cut); the upper and
lower bands (at 1 and 5) have been
left intact, establishing the relation
of the gluteus maximus to the muscles that constitute the deeper layer, namely, the gluteus medius obturator
internus, gemelli, and quadratus femoris. The bands of the gluteus maximus are made up of groups of heavy
fascicles, the groups being set off by thick septa sent inward from the investing fascia (see inset).

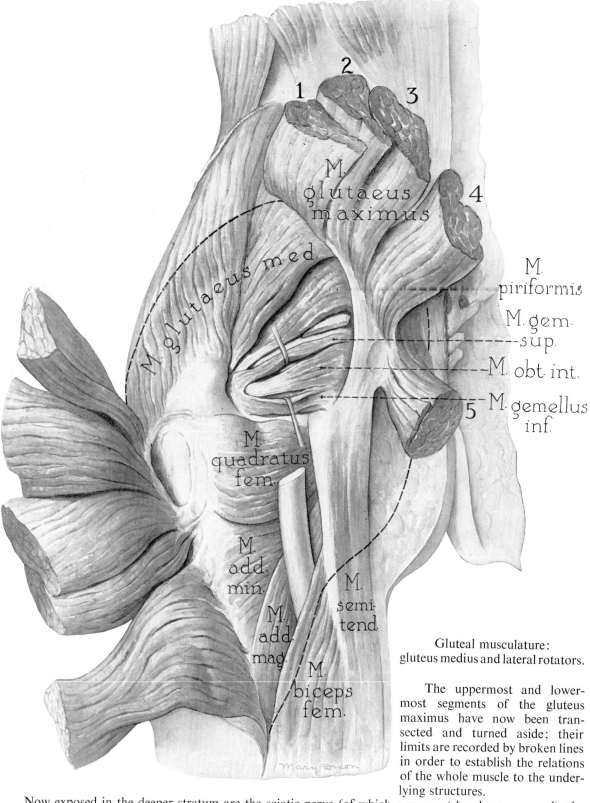

Gluteal musculature:
gluteus medius and lateral rotators.

The uppermost and lowermost segments of the gluteus maximus have now been transected and turned aside; their limits are recorded by broken lines in order to establish the relations of the whole muscle to the underlying structures.

Now exposed in the deeper stratum are the sciatic nerve (of which a segment has been removed), the gluteus medius, the piriformis muscle, the obturator internus and the gemelli (retracted to expose the obturator tendon), the quadratus femoris, the tendons of origin of the hamstring muscles (biceps femoris, semimembranosus, and semitendinosus), the adductores (minimus and magnus).

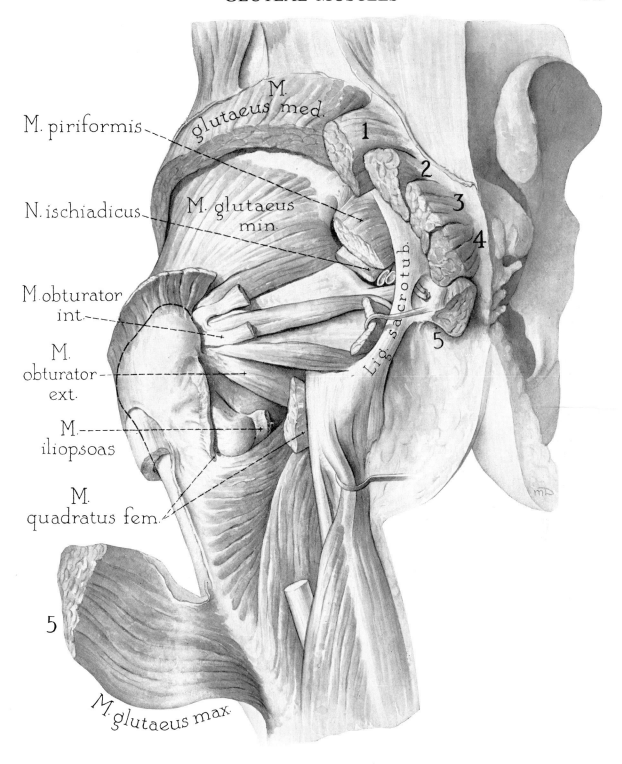

M. piriformis

M. gluteaeus med.

1

2

3

4

N. ischiadicus

M. gluteaeus min.

Lig. sacrotub.

5

M. obturator int.

M. obturator ext.

M. iliopsoas

M. quadratus fem.

5

M. gluteaeus max.

Gluteal musculature: the gluteus minimus and the short lateral rotators.

The gluteus maximus muscle has been removed except at the origin and at the insertion. The middle two fourths of the gluteus medius has been removed to show the subjacent gluteus minimus. The piriformis remains only at its extremities. The middle third of the quadratus femoris has been cut to show the obturator externus muscle, and the lesser trochanter with the tendon of insertion of the iliopsoas. The gluteal portion of the obturator internus has been similarly treated, to bring into view the underlying gemelli.

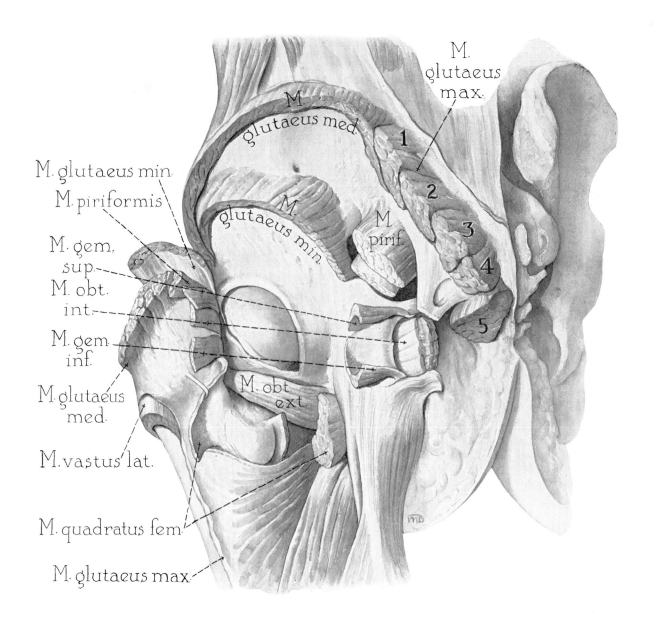

M. glutaeus max.

M. glutaeus med.

M. glutaeus min.

M. piriformis

M. gem. sup.

M. obt. int.

M. gem. inf.

M. glutaeus med.

M. vastus lat.

M. quadratus fem.

M. glutaeus max.

M. glutaeus min.

M. pirif.

M. obt. ext.

1 2 3 4 5

Gluteal region: tendons in relation to the hip joint and to skeletal landmarks.

The gluteus minimus has been removed, except near its origin at the inferior gluteal line; similarly the gluteus maximus has been cut back to its origin behind the posterior gluteal line, the gluteus medius to its origin anterior and ventral to the same line. The piriformis, the gemelli, and the quadratus femoris muscles have been removed in their middle two fourths, the obturator externus muscle and the full length of the intertrochanteric line being exposed by excising the quadratus femoris. The obturator internus muscle has been cut and turned aside, in order to display the tendinous character of its deep surface and the manner in which the fibrocartilage of the lesser sciatic notch has been sculptured by the banded tendon. The sacrotuberous ligament has been cut and the ends turned aside, revealing, below, the origin of the inferior gemellus from the ischial tuberosity and, above, that of the superior gemellus from the ischial spine and the sacrospinous ligament. The articular capsule of the hip joint has been opened to expose the margin of the acetabulum and the head of the femur. Displayed also are the origin of the vastus lateralis muscle from the postero-inferior aspect of the greater trochanter, and the insertion of the gluteus maximus muscle into the linea aspera. The latter insertion takes place through the lateral intermuscular septum as an intermediary.

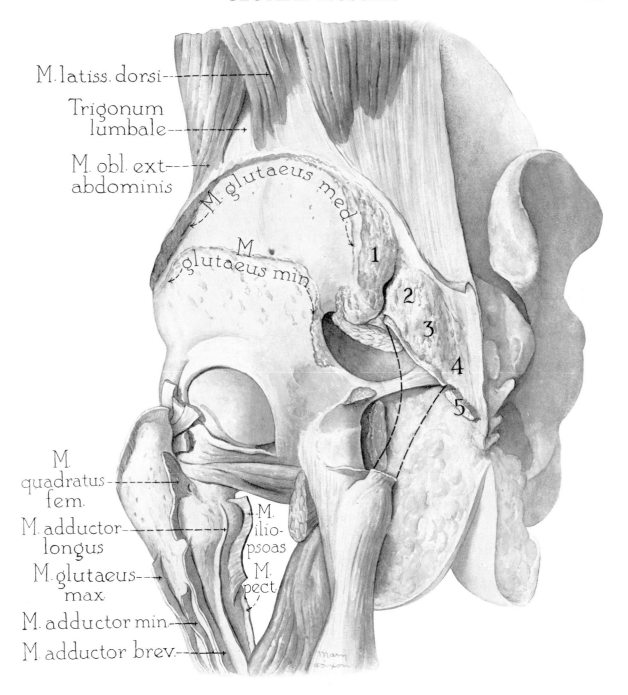

M. latiss. dorsi

Trigonum lumbale

M. obl. ext. abdominis

M. glutaeus med.

M. glutaeus min.

1
2
3
4
5

M. quadratus fem.

M. adductor longus

M. glutaeus max.

M. adductor min.

M. adductor brev.

M. ilio-psoas

M. pect.

Gluteal musculature: the areas of muscular attachment.

The three main areas of origin of the gluteus maximus are shown. The first segment arises chiefly from the roughened area of the ilium behind the posterior gluteal line. The second, third, and fourth segments constitute the intermediate area. The fifth segment is coccygeal in origin. The gluteus medius has been cut away, upward to the posterior gluteal line, the gluteus minimus to the anterior gluteal line. The piriformis has been almost totally removed, in order to exhibit its several areas of origin and to expose the boundaries of the greater sciatic foramen; from the notch both sciatic nerve and gluteal vessels have been removed. The gemelli have been excised; the obturator internus has been cut back to its pelvic portion in order to expose the full margin of the lesser ischiadic foramen. The hamstring muscles are shown as they arise from the ischial tuberosity; the sacrospinous and sacrotuberous ligaments remain only at their extremities (the margins of the latter indicated by dotted lines). On the right side the sacrospinalis (NA, *M. erector spinae*) has been excised to expose the sacrum.

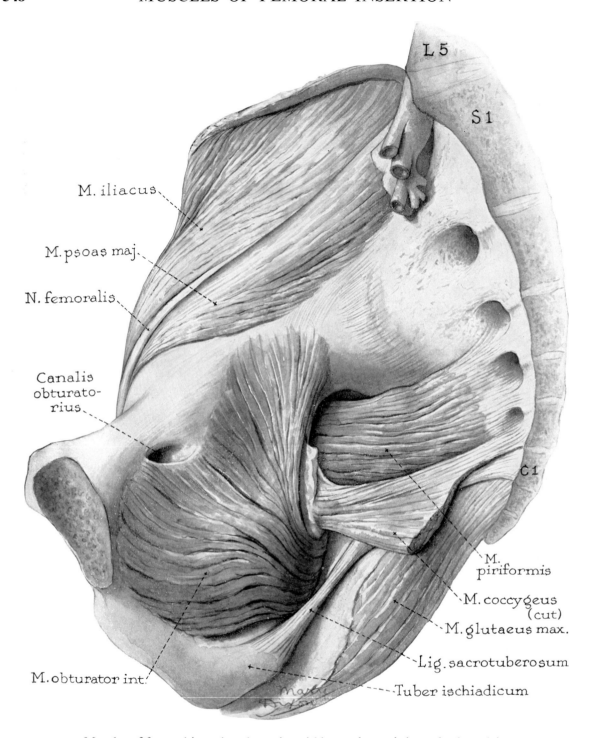

M. iliacus

M. psoas maj.

N. femoralis

Canalis obturatorius

L 5

S 1

C 1

M. piriformis

M. coccygeus (cut)

M. glutaeus max.

Lig. sacrotuberosum

Tuber ischiadicum

M. obturator int.

Muscles of femoral insertion that arise within, or descend through, the pelvis.

The muscles of vertebral and of parietal pelvic origin are shown by removal of the psoas, iliac, and obturator fasciae. The iliacus and psoas major muscles, which fuse distally to form the iliopsoas tendon, are revealed as they leave the greater pelvis just lateral to the iliopectineal eminence. In the thigh the combined tendon inserts into the lesser trochanter of the femur. Within the greater pelvis the iliacus muscle, in arising from the internal aspect of the ala of the ilium, forms the muscular floor of the iliac fossa; the psoas major muscle courses along the pelvic brim. The piriformis muscle is seen as it passes from an anterior sacral origin, through the greater ischiadic foramen, to a femoral insertion into the greater trochanter. The obturator internus muscle (see following figure) forms the muscular wall of the lesser pelvis.

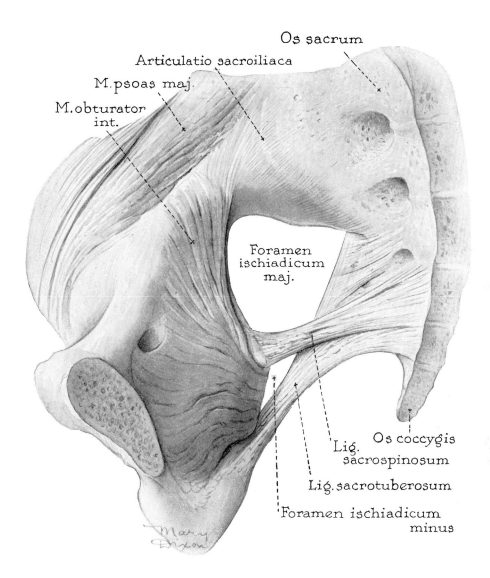

Os sacrum

Articulatio sacroiliaca

M. psoas maj.

M. obturator int.

Foramen ischiadicum maj.

Os coccygis

Lig. sacrospinosum

Lig. sacrotuberosum

Foramen ischiadicum minus

Musculature of femoral insertion and pelvic origin; dissection continued.

The coccygeus and piriformis muscles have been removed to expose the sacrospinous and sacrotuberous ligaments, as these bands convert the ischiadic (sciatic) notches into foramina. The obturator internus muscle is shown as it arises from the wall of the lesser pelvis and as it leaves the latter cavity, through the lesser ischiadic foramen, on the way to a trochanter (femoral) insertion. Since the piriformis muscle has been dissected away from the sacrum and removed, the greater ischiadic foramen is open.

Figures in the preceding series record the extrapelvic, gluteal course of the piriformis and obturator internus.

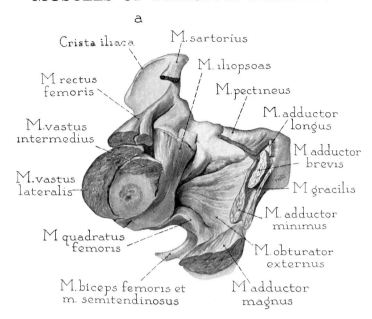

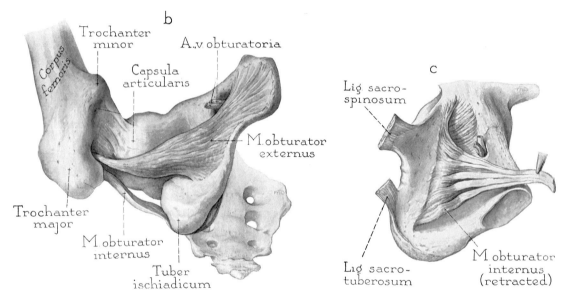

Muscles related to the hip joint.

a, Muscles chiefly of the anterior and posterior groups. The iliopsoas, obturator externus, and quadratus femoris appear in that order from before backward; the iliopsoas is partially tendinous (psoas major), partially muscular (iliacus) at the conjoined insertion into the lesser trochanter. The following muscles of the medial femoral group have been cut near their origins from symphysis of the pubis, ischiopubic ramus, and tuberosity of ischium: the adductores (longus, brevis, minimus, magnus); the gracilis. Of the posterior femoral group of muscles the long head of the biceps femoris and the semimembranosus have been cut at their common tendon of origin. Of the anterior femoral the following have been transected: rectus femoris, sartorius, pectineus.

b, Obturator externus and obturator internus muscles; viewed from below. The right half of the pelvis is shown; the thigh is flexed, to bring into view the obturator externus muscle and tendon and the adjacent tendon of the obturator internus. With removal of the other muscles of pelvic origin, the ischiopubic ramus and the tuberosity of the ischium are brought into view.

c, Obturator internus muscle; structure of the muscle and its tendon. The tendon has been cut near its insertion, retracted through the lesser sciatic (ischiadic) foramen into the pelvis, and freed from its attachment to the inner wall of the pelvis to a point near its origin; the pelvic aspect is thus turned toward the reader. The muscle fascicles converge, in groups, upon the foramen; the bands narrow as they meet to form a common tendon near the margin of the greater sciatic foramen. The surface of the foramen is correspondingly grooved.

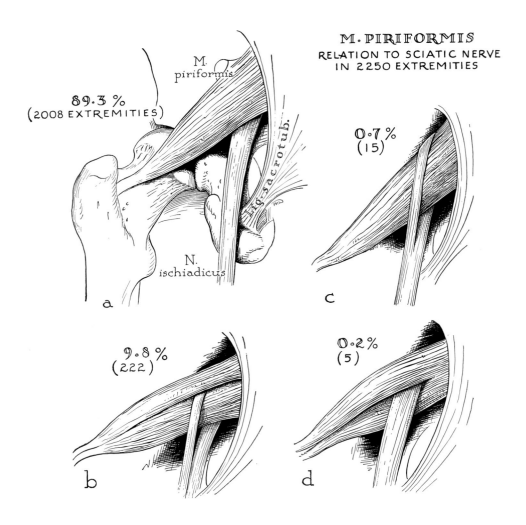

M·PIRIFORMIS
RELATION TO SCIATIC NERVE
IN 2250 EXTREMITIES

89.3%
(2008 EXTREMITIES)

0.7%
(15)

9.8%
(222)

0.2%
(5)

The relation of the sciatic (NA, ischiadic) nerve to the piriformis muscle.

a, The nerve, undivided, passes beneath the piriformis muscle in approximately 90 per cent of cases. It leaves the pelvis through the infrapiriform recess of the greater sciatic (ischiadic) foramen (see also page 505).

b, In approximately 10 per cent of cases the constituent elements, the common peroneal and the tibial, leave the pelvis separately and remain independent in their relation to the muscle. The common peroneal nerve passes through the muscle, the tibial nerve beneath it.

c and *d*, The least frequent patterns, together representing less than 1 per cent of the specimens. In *c*, the elements, separate as in *b*, enter the thigh by passing above and below the unsplit muscle; in *d*, the ischiadic nerve, undivided as in *a*, passes through the substance of the piriformis.

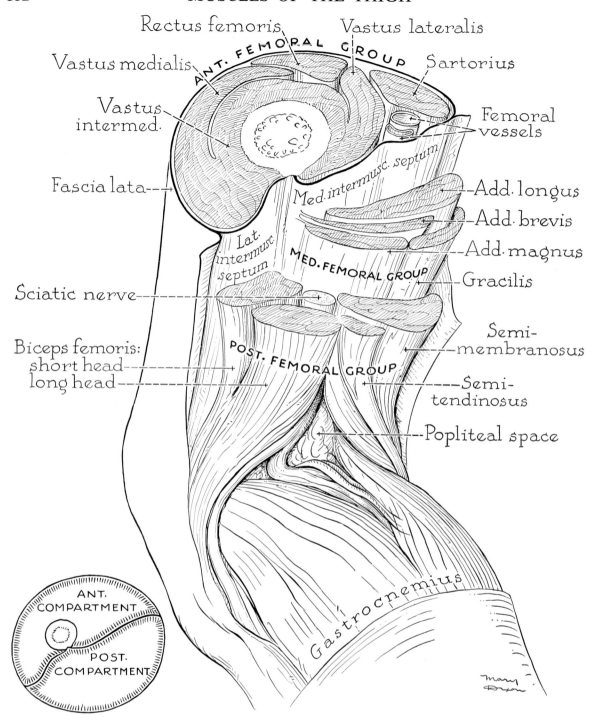

Muscles of the thigh, as contents of two osteofascial compartments
and as boundaries of the adductor canal and popliteal fossa.

The cross section, through the middle of the thigh, shows the quadriceps femoris and the sartorius of the anterior femoral group of muscles, the adductores and gracilis of the medial group, and the three hamstring muscles of the posterior group. The anterior and medial sets are enclosed in one compartment, the posterior set in another (inset). On the medial aspect of the thigh the adductor canal, housing the femoral vessels and nerve, is formed by the sartorius, vastus medialis, and adductor longus. On the dorsal aspect of the knee joint the hamstring muscles diverge. In so doing, these muscles form the boundaries of the proximal portion of the popliteal fossa. The distal boundaries of the fossa are formed by the medial and lateral heads of the gastrocnemius and by the plantaris.

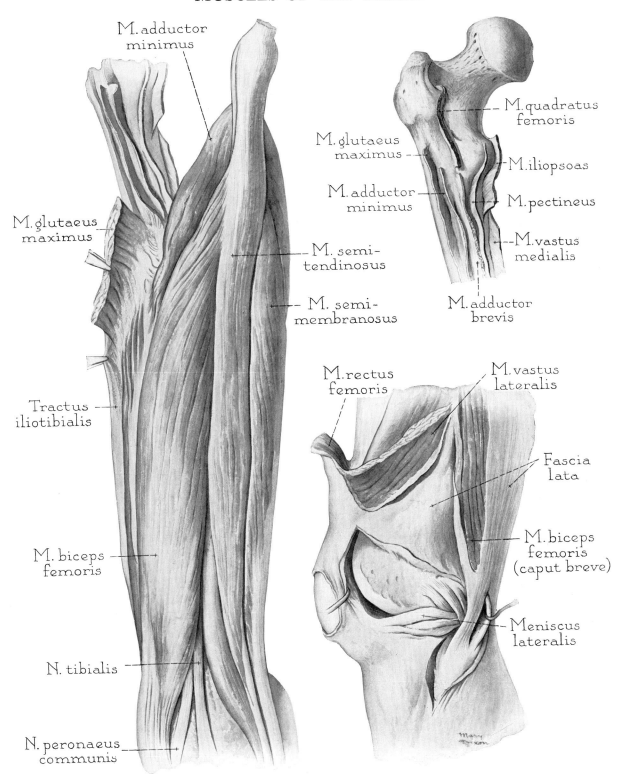

Femoral musculature; posterior and lateral views.

In the figure at the left the gluteus maximus is retracted to show its relation to the iliotibial tract. In the lower right figure the fascia lata has been removed to expose the posterior femoral muscles; the crural fascia and articular capsule have been incised to reveal the tendon of the biceps, the superficial peroneal nerve, and the structures of the joint. At the upper right are shown the muscles which insert dorsally into the proximal third of the femur.

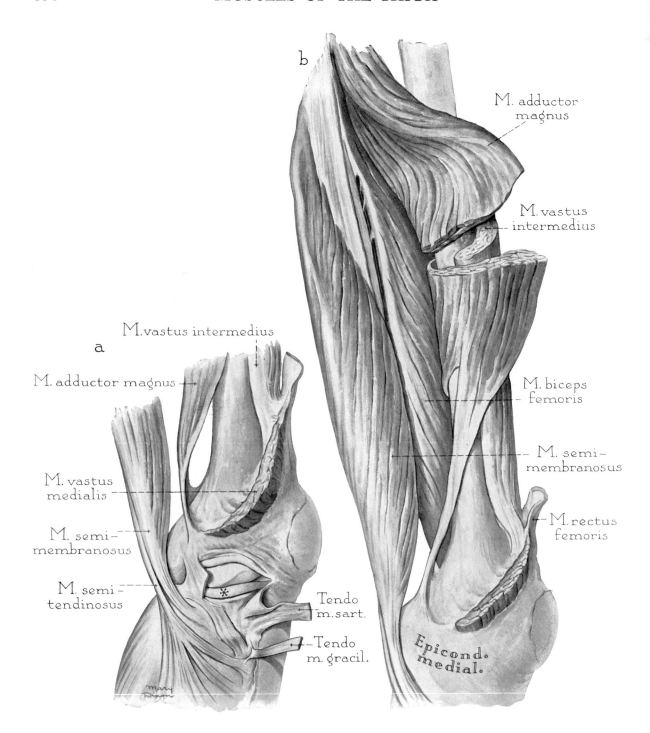

Femoral musculature; medial view. Deep dissection.

a, The vastus medialis muscle has been removed, except at its insertions; the vastus intermedius is intact, the tendon of the rectus femoris turned forward. The adductor magnus muscle is shown at its condylar insertion. The tendons of the sartorius and gracilis have been turned forward to reveal the subjacent tibial collateral ligament. The articular capsule of the knee joint has been opened to expose the medial meniscus (at *) and the medial condyle of the femur.

b, The adductor magnus has been cut transversely, and the two portions rolled medialward to expose the anterior aspect of the posterior femoral (hamstring) muscles. The vastus medialis has been cut away at its insertion.

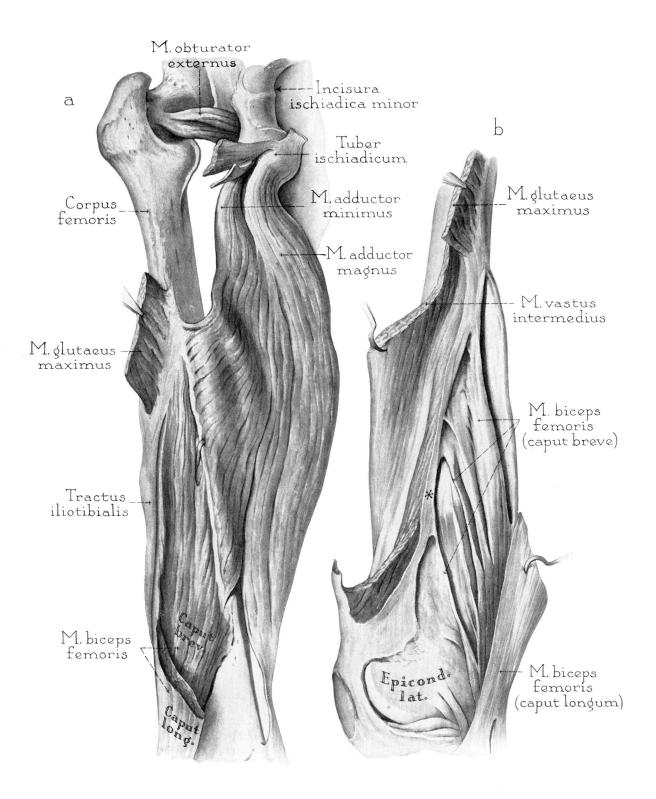

Femoral muscles; posterior and lateral views. Dissection continued. (See following page for description.)

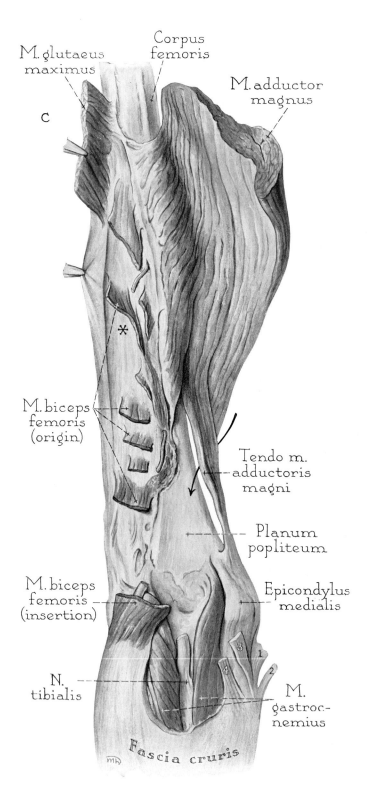

M. glutaeus maximus

Corpus femoris

M. adductor magnus

c

*

M. biceps femoris (origin)

Tendo m. adductoris magni

Planum popliteum

M. biceps femoris (insertion)

Epicondylus medialis

N. tibialis

3 1

4 2

M. gastrocnemius

Fascia cruris

mD

Femoral muscles; posterior and lateral views. Dissection concluded.

a, Medial femoral and deep posterior femoral muscles. Posterior view. The lowermost portion of the gluteus maximus has been turned lateralward to demonstrate its insertion into the lateral intermuscular septum, from which the short head of the biceps femoris takes origin. The common tendon of origin of the semitendinosus and the long head of the biceps femoris has been cut, exposing, next beneath, the tendon of origin of the semimembranosus, also transected (unlabelled at ischial tuberosity).

b, Anterior and posterior femoral muscles. The long head of the biceps femoris has been cut and retracted, the leaflike structure of the short head of the muscle being thereby demonstrated.

c, Medial and deep posterior femoral muscles; posterior view. The biceps femoris has been cut away, leaving only the slips of origin from the lateral intermuscular septum (at *). At the knee the sleeve of crural fascia has been opened to expose the heads of origin of the gastrocnemius and the tibial and common peroneal divisions of the sciatic (ischiadic) nerve. Laterally the insertion of the biceps femoris muscle is seen; medially are shown the tendinous insertions of the semitendinosus, gracilis, and semimembranosus (numbered) and the adductor hiatus (at arrow). The perforating arteries are shown as they pierce the fascial septum. The common peroneal nerve lies deep to the insertion of biceps femoris muscle.

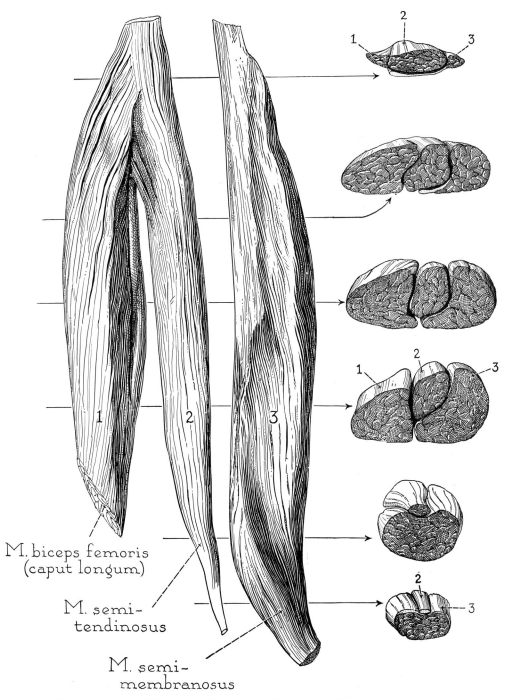

M. biceps femoris
(caput longum)

M. semi-
tendinosus

M. semi-
membranosus

Posterior femoral (hamstring) muscles of the right thigh; anterior aspect.

In the segments cut at the levels indicated, the constituent muscles are correspondingly numbered. The figure at the left shows the three muscles excised. In the main figures the semitendinosus has been separated from the semimembranosus. The figures at the right record the interrelationships of the three muscles.

At the level of the proximal segment, the semitendinosus, here broad and muscular, rests upon the flattened tendon of the semimembranosus and against the biceps femoris; the latter, in its proximal portion, is small. At the level of the next segment the rounded belly of the semitendinosus lies in a deep sulcus between the semimembranosus and the long head of the biceps femoris. At distal levels the semitendinosus attains a more superficial position in relation to the other two muscles, finally inclining medialward to rest in a sulcus on the posterior surface of the semimembranosus. Near the knee joint the semitendinosus and the semimembranosus have inclined medialward, away from the biceps femoris; the space formed between the divergent muscles is the popliteal fossa.

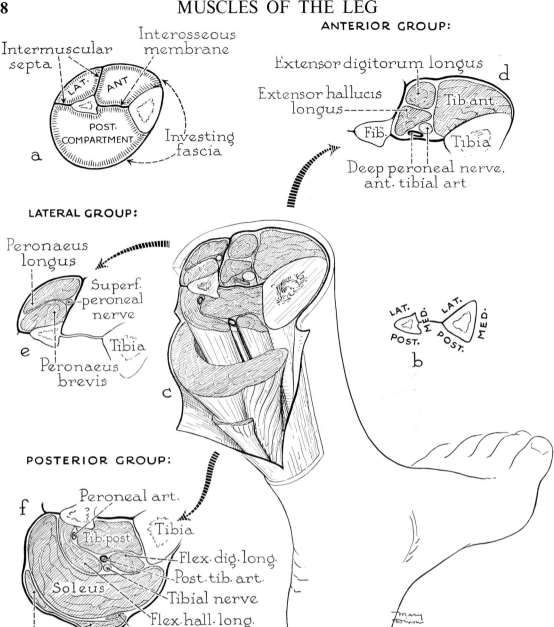

Muscles and associated structures of the leg, as contents of osteofascial compartments; diagrammatic.

a and *b*, The tibia and fibula, the interosseous membrane, the investing crural fascia, and the three intermuscular septa serve to divide the leg into three compartments.

c, The leg in cross section, showing contents of the three crural compartments.

d, The anterior compartment contains the tibialis anterior muscle, the two extensor muscles of the digits, together with the anterior tibial artery and the deep peroneal division of the common peroneal nerve. The peroneus tertius, fourth muscle in the anterior crural group, is situated distal to the level of the section.

e, The lateral crural compartment contains the peroneus longus and peroneus brevis muscles and the superficial peroneal division of the common peroneal nerve. The muscles are supplied by small rami of the anterior tibial artery and of the peroneal branch of the posterior tibial.

f, In the posterior crural compartment are lodged seven muscles arranged in three strata. The superficial layer is made up of the gastrocnemius and plantaris; the intermediate layer is formed by the soleus; the deep layer is composed of the tibialis posterior and the two digital flexors. The popliteus is situated at a level proximal to that of the section. In this compartment are the tibial nerve, the posterior tibial artery, and the latter's peroneal branch.

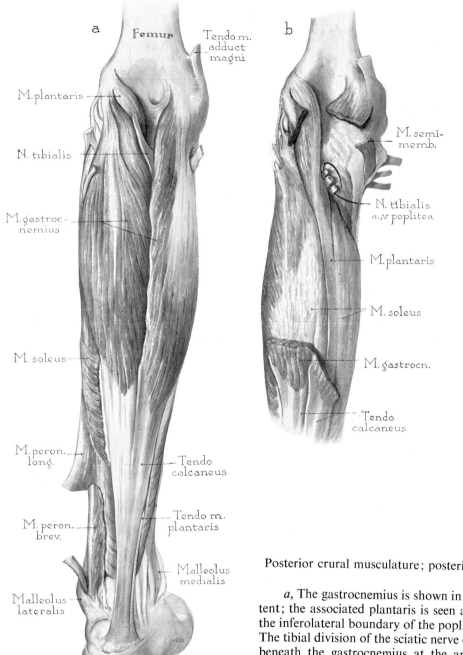

a Femur
Tendo m. adduct. magni
M. plantaris
N. tibialis
M. gastroc-nemius
M. soleus
M. peron. long.
Tendo calcaneus
M. peron. brev.
Tendo m. plantaris
Malleolus medialis
Malleolus lateralis

b
M. semi-memb.
N. tibialis a., v. poplitea
M. plantaris
M. soleus
M. gastrocn.
Tendo calcaneus

Posterior crural musculature; posterior views.

a, The gastrocnemius is shown in its full extent; the associated plantaris is seen as it forms the inferolateral boundary of the popliteal fossa. The tibial division of the sciatic nerve disappears beneath the gastrocnemius at the apex of the fossa. To either side of the distal half of the gastrocnemius muscle projects a portion of the subjacent soleus. The slender tendon of the plantaris courses along the medial border of the strong calcaneal tendon. The muscles of the thigh have been removed.

b, The main portion of the gastrocnemius has been removed to expose the soleus and the plantaris. The broad aponeurosis of origin of the soleus, which is carried downward upon the muscle, covers almost its entire posterior surface; becoming denser and narrower, it is inserted into the deep surface of the calcaneal tendon. The ribbon-like tendon of the plantaris crosses the soleus. The popliteus muscle is covered by a heavy investing fascia. The posterior tibial vessels and the tibial nerve disappear beneath the plantaris.

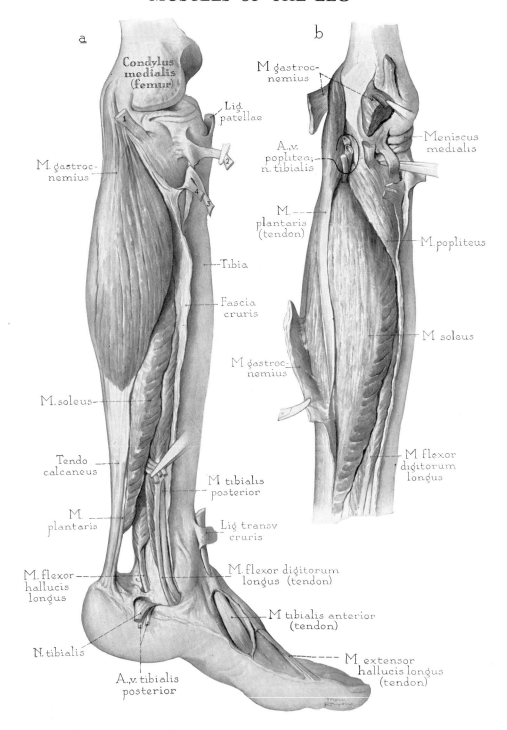

Posterior crural musculature: first and second layers, in medial view.

   a, Gastrocnemius is intact. The extent of the subcutaneous surface of the tibia is shown; from its posterior limit arises the layer of the crural fascia which invests the muscles of the calf. Tendons of insertions of the semimembranosus, sartorius, gracilis, and semitendinosus have been reflected (numbered, in order, 1 to 4).

   b, Exposed by the removal of the gastrocnemius are the following: soleus, plantaris, and popliteus muscles; tendon of insertion of the semimembranosus; the posterior tibial vessels and tibial nerve. The tendon of insertion of the adductus magnus is left attached to the condylar tubercle. In front of the soleus and the flexor digitorum longus the tibial attachment of the crural fascia is shown. The capsule of the knee joint is opened to show the meniscus and tibial collateral ligament (lifted by forceps).

Posterior crural muscles:
deep stratum in posterior view.

a, The plantaris has been cut at its extremities, the distal portion turned downward with the calcaneal tendon. The soleus (at 2) has likewise been cut; portions of the tibial and fibular origins and the tendon of calcaneal insertion remain. By removal of the superficial and the intermediate groups of muscles, the third stratum is exposed. It consists of the flexor hallucis longus (at 5), the flexor digitorum longus (at 3) and the tibialis posterior (at 4). The tibialis posterior is largely covered by the flexor of the hallux and medially by the flexor of the digits. The latter muscle arises through an elongate fascial band which is attached laterally to the posterior tibial muscle. The flexor digitorum longus arises largely from the fibrous septum between the muscle and the tibialis posterior, and, in this way, indirectly from the tibia. The peroneus longus muscle is cut distally and drawn backward, in order to demonstrate its origin from the lateral surface of the fibula. The peroneus brevis is exposed in its distal portion. The popliteal fascia is removed to reveal the popliteus muscle (at 1). The arrow passes through the hiatus between heads of the soleus muscle.

b, The heads of the gastrocnemius and the plantaris have been drawn aside to expose the condyles of the femur, which are now revealed by opening the articular capsule. The menisci and the posterior cruciate ligament are also shown. The popliteus muscle (at 1) has been reflected toward its insertion, the tibial origin of the soleus cut away (at 2). The flexor hallucis longus has been removed, leaving the posterior surface of the fibula largely exposed. The flexor digitorum longus (at 3) has been freed from the subjacent tibialis posterior (at 4), along the farther margin of the former's aponeurotic stripe of origin. The tibialis posterior is fully exposed and the tibial and fibular origins seen. The ankle joint has been opened posteriorly.

c, With removal of the posterior crural muscles, their areas of origin are demonstrated. The present stage has progressed beyond that pictured in *b* in respect to the following features: removal of the popliteus and the peroneus longus (to expose the more distally placed peroneus brevis); removal of the flexors and of the posterior tibial (to expose the posterior surface of the two bones); exposure of the interosseous membrane and the hiatus within the latter, through which pass the posterior tibial vessels.

(*b* and *c* on following page.)

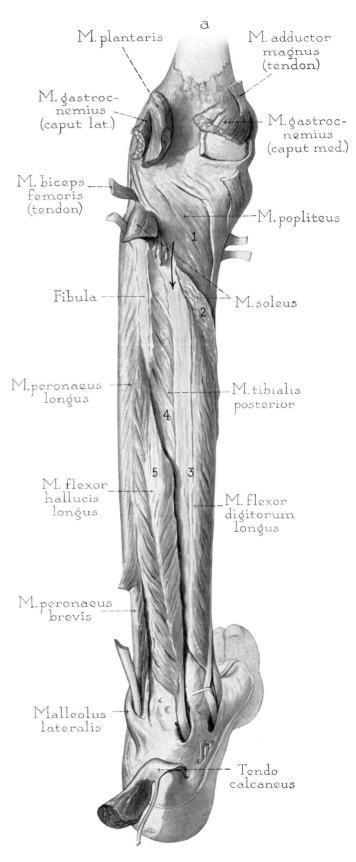

a

M. plantaris

M. adductor magnus (tendon)

M. gastrocnemius (caput lat.)

M. gastrocnemius (caput med.)

M. biceps femoris (tendon)

M. popliteus

Fibula

M. soleus

M. peronaeus longus

M. tibialis posterior

M. flexor hallucis longus

M. flexor digitorum longus

M. peronaeus brevis

Malleolus lateralis

Tendo calcaneus

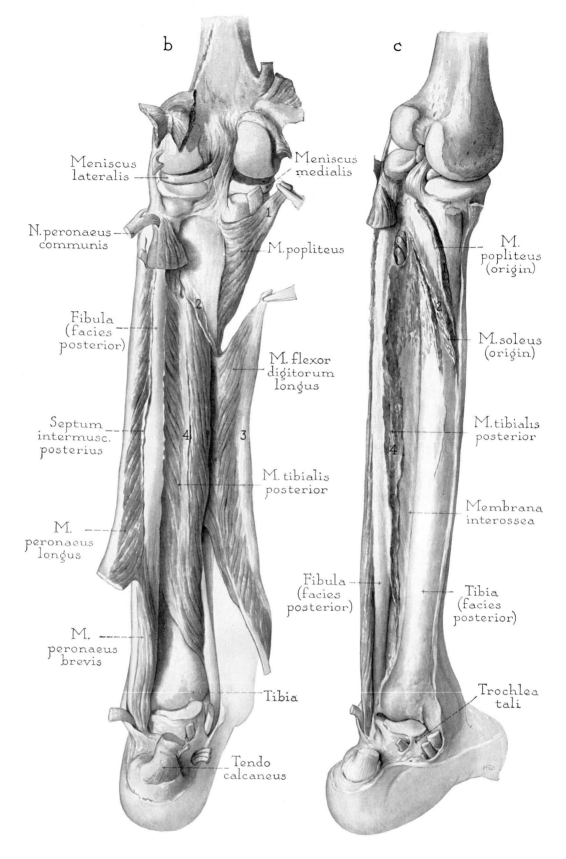

b

c

Meniscus lateralis

Meniscus medialis

1

N. peronaeus communis

M. popliteus

M. popliteus (origin)

Fibula (facies posterior)

M. soleus (origin)

M. flexor digitorum longus

Septum intermusc. posterius

M. tibialis posterior

M. tibialis posterior

Membrana interossea

M. peronaeus longus

Fibula (facies posterior)

Tibia (facies posterior)

M. peronaeus brevis

Trochlea tali

Tibia

Tendo calcaneus

Posterior crural muscles: deep stratum in posterior view (continued). (See preceding page for description.)

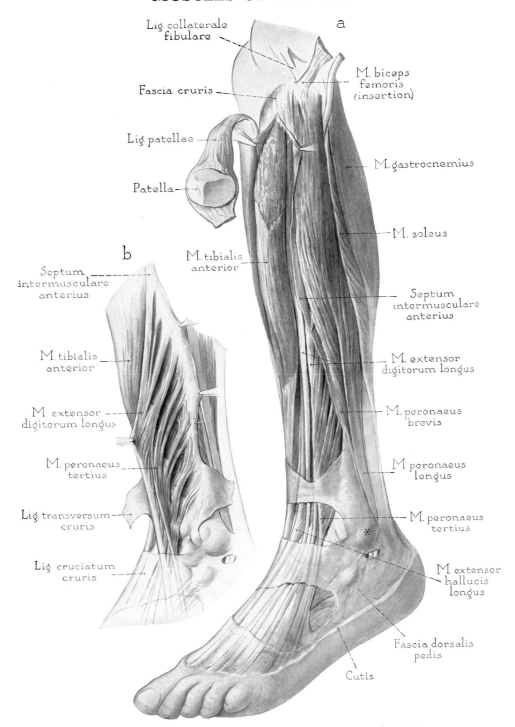

Lig. collaterale fibulare

Fascia cruris

Lig. patellae

Patella

M. tibialis anterior

Septum intermusculare anterius

M. tibialis anterior

M. extensor digitorum longus

M. peronaeus tertius

Lig. transversum cruris

Lig. cruciatum cruris

a

M. biceps femoris (insertion)

M. gastrocnemius

M. soleus

Septum intermusculare anterius

M. extensor digitorum longus

M. peronaeus brevis

M. peronaeus longus

M. peronaeus tertius

M. extensor hallucis longus

Fascia dorsalis pedis

Cutis

b

Anterior and lateral crural musculature; left leg, in lateral view.

a, The crural fascia has been removed except in the following areas: over the proximal extremity of the tibialis anterior muscle, where the latter arises in part from the deep or internal surface of the fascia; along the crest of the tibia where the fascia forms the medial boundary of the anterior osseofascial compartment; in the groove between the tibialis anterior and the peronei, where the fascia forms the lateral boundary of the anterior compartment; in the region of the ankle where the fascia is thickened to form the transverse crural and cruciate ligaments. The ligaments converge upon the lateral malleolus (at *). The tendon of the quadriceps femoris has been cut and turned downward. On the dorsum of the foot the fascial layers have been removed to expose the long extensor tendons.

b, Structure of extensor digitorum longus, demonstrated by drawing the muscle sharply forward.

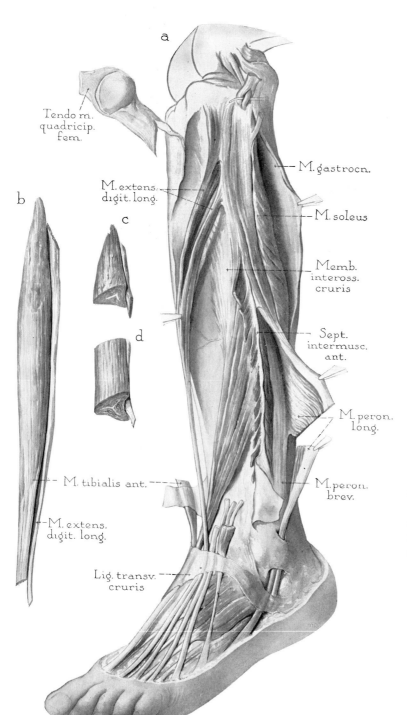

Tendo m.
quadricip.
fem.

M. extens.
digit. long.

b

c

d

M. tibialis ant.

M. extens.
digit. long.

Lig. transv.
cruris

a

M. gastrocn.

M. soleus

Memb.
inteross.
cruris

Sept.
intermusc.
ant.

M. peron.
long.

M. peron.
brev.

Anterior and lateral crural muscles, second stratum; tibialis anterior and extensor digitorum longus removed.

a, Lateral to the tibia is situated the interosseous membrane, from the proximal portion of which the tibialis anterior arises. The superficial part of the extensor digitorum longus muscle has been drawn forward, the middle two fourths of the deep portion of the extensor removed. The peroneus longus muscle has been removed in its distal fifth to expose the peroneus brevis.

b, Tibialis anterior and associated proximal portion of extensor digitorum longus; both excised.

c and *d*, Sections of the tibialis anterior and the extensor digitorum longus muscles, at the first and second thirds.

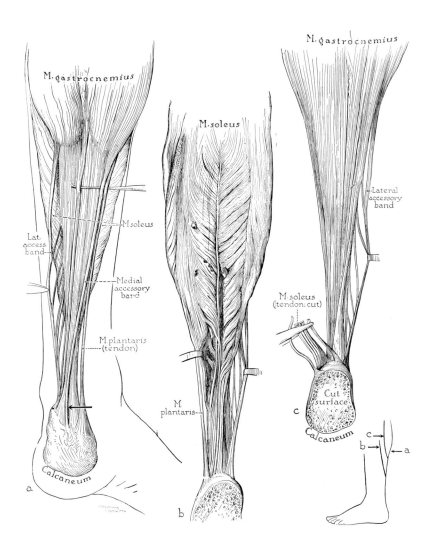

Gastrocnemius and soleus. Structure of the muscles and their tendons.

a, The banded structure of the calcaneal tendon, seen from the superficial, or posterior, surface. Demonstrating the manner in which the bands incline toward the lateral margin of the tendon. The inclination is such that a medial band reached the middle of the calcaneus (at arrow).

b, The bipenniform character of the soleus muscle, as seen from the deep, or anterior, surface.

c, The banded character of the calcaneal tendon, seen from the deep, or anterior, surface (compare *a*). The lateral bands incline medialward.

The inset records the directions of the views.

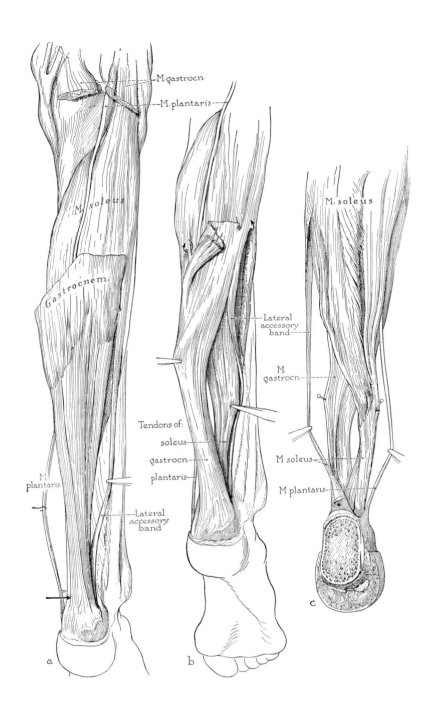

Structure of the tendons of the gastrocnemius, soleus, and plantaris.
Posterior (*a* and *b*) and anterior (*c*) views.

The components of the calcaneal tendon, derived from the gastrocnemius and soleus muscles, are shown, as well as the plantaris tendon and the accessory bands of the calcaneal tendon.

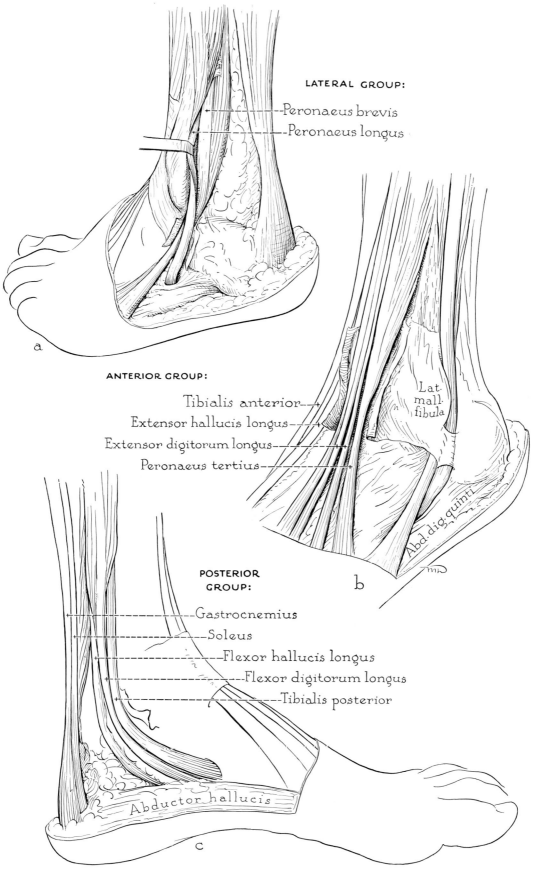

LATERAL GROUP:
Peronaeus brevis
Peronaeus longus

a

ANTERIOR GROUP:
Tibialis anterior
Extensor hallucis longus
Extensor digitorum longus
Peronaeus tertius

Lat. mall. fibula

Abd. dig. quinti

b

POSTERIOR GROUP:
Gastrocnemius
Soleus
Flexor hallucis longus
Flexor digitorum longus
Tibialis posterior

Abductor hallucis

c

Tendons and muscles of the leg. (See following page for description.)

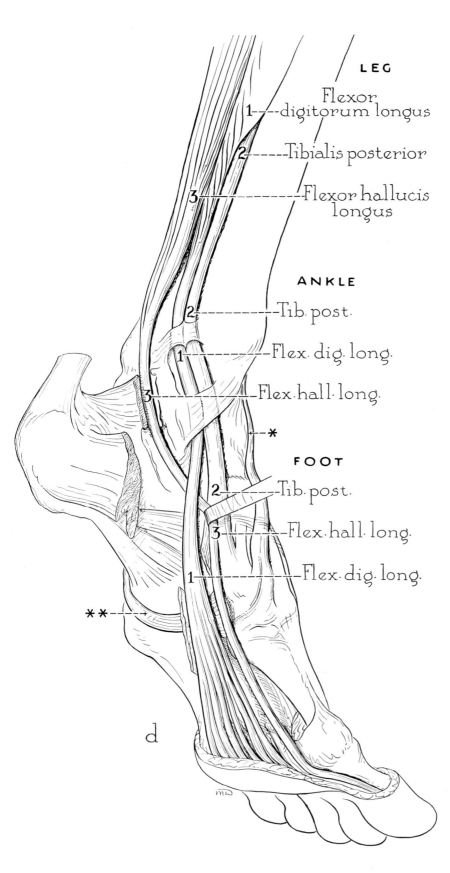

LEG

1 --- Flexor digitorum longus

2 ----- Tibialis posterior

3 ----- Flexor hallucis longus

ANKLE

2 ------- Tib. post.

1 ------- Flex. dig. long.

3 ------- Flex. hall. long.

- - *

FOOT

2 ------- Tib. post.

3 ------- Flex. hall. long.

1 ------- Flex. dig. long.

** - - - +

d

Tendons and muscles of the leg.

a, The tendons of the two lateral crural muscles reach the side and plantar surface of the foot by descending beneath the peroneal retinacula and behind the lateral malleolus of the fibula. The tendon of the shorter muscle (peroneus brevis) terminates on the fifth metatarsal bone; the tendon of the longer one (peroneus longus) crosses the sole to the first metatarsal bone.

b, The tendons of the four anterior crural muscles reach the dorsal surface of the foot by passing beneath the transverse and cruciate crural ligaments. The tibialis anterior and peroneus tertius descend to metatarsal attachments on opposite sides of the foot; the digital extensors, between the marginally situated tendons, insert into the phalanges.

c, The tendons of the deep posterior crural muscles incline medialward; they reach the plantar surface of the foot by passing beneath the laciniate ligaments, behind the medial malleolus; their insertions are chiefly tarsal and phalangeal.

The tendons of muscles of the superficial layer (gastrocnemius and plantaris) and the tendon of the single muscle of the intermediate stratum (soleus) terminate on the superior surface of the calcaneus; they do not reach the sole.

d, The tendons of the three muscles of the deep posterior crural group change position in relation to each other as they pass from the leg to the sole of the foot. In the leg, the succession from medial to lateral side is as follows: flexor digitorum longus, tibialis posterior, flexor hallucis longus. At the ankle, the second (intermediate) member of the triad attains median position, the order then being 2, 1, 3. In the foot the originally third (lateral) member passes beneath the first (medial) member, the order finally being 2, 3, 1.

Other associated tendons and ligaments are shown (tibialis anterior tendon at *, peroneus longus tendon at **, and long plantar ligament).

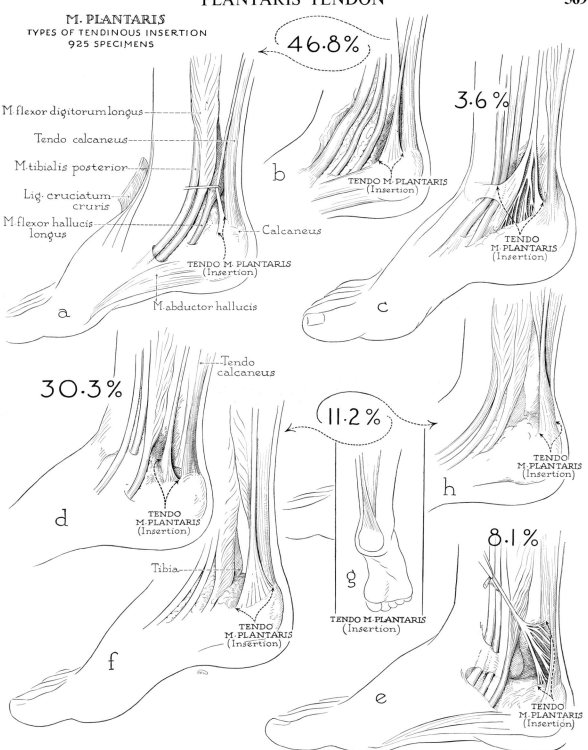

M. PLANTARIS
TYPES OF TENDINOUS INSERTION
925 SPECIMENS

46·8%

3·6%

M.flexor digitorum longus

Tendo calcaneus

M.tibialis posterior

Lig. cruciatum cruris

M.flexor hallucis longus

Calcaneus

TENDO M. PLANTARIS (Insertion)

M.abductor hallucis

TENDO M. PLANTARIS (Insertion)

TENDO M.PLANTARIS (Insertion)

a

b

c

Tendo calcaneus

30·3%

11·2%

TENDO M.PLANTARIS (Insertion)

Tibia

TENDO M.PLANTARIS (Insertion)

TENDO M.PLANTARIS (Insertion)

h

d

f

g

TENDO M.PLANTARIS (Insertion)

8·1%

e

TENDO M.PLANTARIS (Insertion)

Tendon of the plantaris muscle; major types of insertion,
with percentage occurrence of each in 925 extremities.

a, Attachment to the calcaneus as a part of the calcaneal tendon (the degree of separation varied). *b*, A broader, fan-shaped insertion prolonged forward on the calcaneus toward, or to, the origin of the abductor hallucis. *c*, An even more extensive implantation, employing the laciniate ligament. *d*, Insertion separately into the calcaneal bone, crosswise between the *tendo calcaneus* and the tibia. *e*, Elongate attachment to the anterior surface and medial border of the calcaneal tendon, usually by numerous bands, with occasional prolongation forward on the superior surface of the body of the calcaneus. *f* to *h*, Insertion not only into the calcaneus anterior to the combined tendon of the gastrocnemius and soleus, but also posteriorly to cover part (*f*) or all (*g*, *h*) of the *tendo calcaneus* on the superficial aspect of its distal extremity.

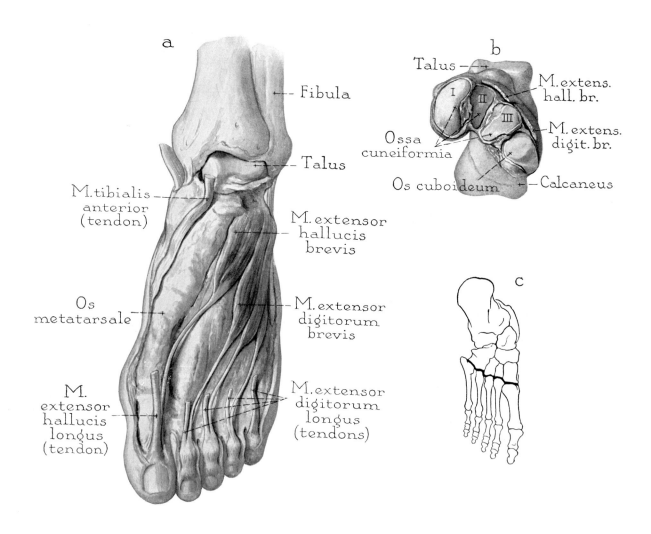

Muscles of the dorsum of the foot.

a, The tendons of the long digital extensor have been cut near their points of junction with the corresponding short tendons. The short extensors are fully exposed; the broad character of the whole muscle is apparent, as is also the lateral position of the muscle bellies at their calcaneal origin. The muscle arises chiefly from the lateral and superior surfaces of the body of the calcaneus. The medial element of the muscle is the extensor hallucis brevis. The articular capsule of the ankle joint has been opened. The interossei are covered by their investing fascia. Over the short extensors the thin muscle fascia has been removed.

b, Transverse arch of the foot; at the distal end of the tarsus, seen from the front. The tarsus has been disarticulated from the metatarsus. The assemblage is placed in the position assumed when the individual is standing, in order to demonstrate the depth of the concavity on the plantar surface. On the dorsum of the foot the transected extensor digitorum brevis is seen.

c, Left foot in plantar view. The heavy line at the tarsometatarsal junction indicates the site of the disarticulation in *b.*

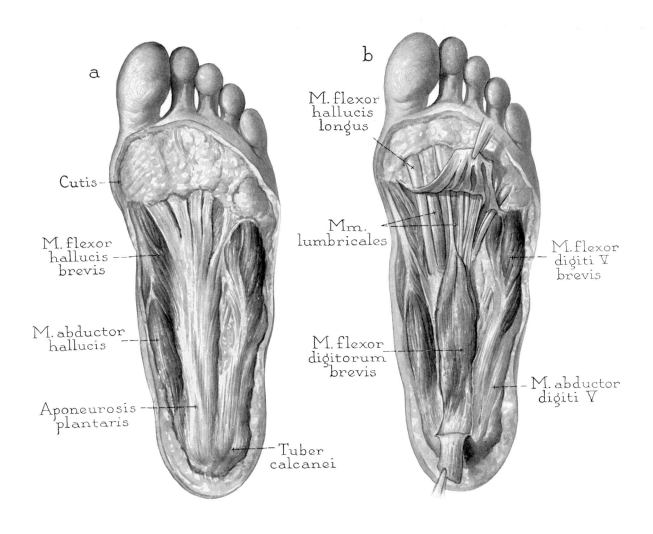

a

b

M. flexor
hallucis
longus

Cutis—

M. flexor
hallucis
brevis

Mm.
lumbricales

M. flexor
digiti V
brevis

M. abductor
hallucis

M. flexor
digitorum
brevis

Aponeurosis
plantaris

M. abductor
digiti V

Tuber
calcanei

Layers of the sole of the foot.

a, Plantar aponeurosis. The fascial layer lies deep to a thick superficial stratum of fatty tissue. The entire layer is divided into three portions, namely, marginal thinned divisions, and a thick intermediate part. The intermediate part covers the long digital flexors and associated muscles; the thinned lateral and medial parts cover, respectively, the intrinsic muscles of the small toe and the hallux. The intermediate part divides below the metatarsal bones into digital processes. In the following figures successively deeper layers are shown.

b, Muscles of the sole. Superficial layer: flexor digitorum brevis, abductor hallucis, and abductor digiti quinti. The central portion of the plantar fascia has been cut, the ends turned away in order to expose the short flexor; the calcaneometatarsal thickening of the lateral part has been left intact, as have also the two abductor muscles. For an appreciable distance distalward from the attachment of the plantar aponeurosis to the calcaneus, the flexor digitorum brevis arises from the deep surface of the aponeurosis; fragmented fascicles represent points of former attachment.

The flexor digitorum brevis is not a simple, flattened muscle belly, but actually is disposed in three strata. The superficial layer gives origin to a single tendon, for the second digit; the intermediate layer sends its tendon to the third digit; the deep portion gives off two attenuate tendons.

The abductor hallucis and the abductor digiti quinti are seen on the margins of the foot. The cut margins of the intermuscular septa are seen on each side of the flexor digitorum brevis.

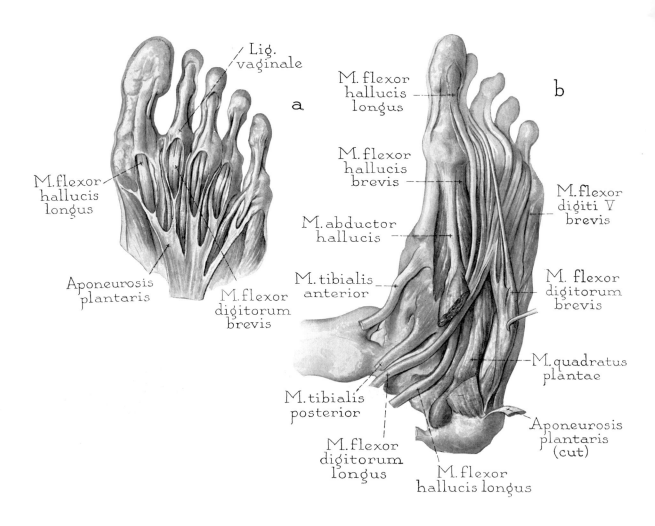

Ligament vaginale

M. flexor hallucis longus

a

M. flexor hallucis longus

Aponeurosis plantaris

M. flexor digitorum brevis

M. flexor hallucis longus

M. flexor hallucis brevis

M. abductor hallucis

M. tibialis anterior

M. tibialis posterior

M. flexor digitorum longus

M. flexor hallucis longus

b

M. flexor digiti V brevis

M. flexor digitorum brevis

M. quadratus plantae

Aponeurosis plantaris (cut)

Layers of the sole of the foot, continued.

a, The flexor tendons and their sheaths in relation to the plantar aponeurosis. The central portion of the plantar aponeurosis has been transected near the point at which it divides into the five digital processes. The processes have been followed to their insertions, the distal clefts cleared to show the structures they transmit. Through the cleft in each process pass the long and short flexor tendons. To the medial side of each of the lateral four processes lies a lumbrical muscle.

b, Musculature of the sole, especially of medial side; inferomedial aspect. The following muscles of crural origin are here followed to the sole of the foot, their tendons having been transected near the ankle joint: the tibialis anterior, tibialis posterior, flexor digitorum longus, and flexor hallucis longus. The following intrinsic muscles of the foot are shown in detail: the abductor hallucis brevis; flexor hallucis brevis, quadratus plantae, and flexor digitorum brevis. The tendon of the flexor hallucis longus passes into the sole on the fibular side of the digital flexor; crossing the deep surface of this tendon, it receives a small slip therefrom. This area of crossing is exposed by removal of the middle third of the main muscle belly of the abductor hallucis. The flexor digitorum longus enters the sole by passing along the medial margin of the sustentaculum tali. Crossing the tendon of the flexor hallucis longus, it divides into four parts, which pass to the second to the fifth toes. The abductor hallucis is superficial in position and of relatively large size; the origin from the medial process of the calcaneus is shown, as it covers the origin of the subjacent medial head of the quadratus plantae. The medial head of the quadratus plantae has been exposed, by excision of the proximal portion of the abductor hallucis, proximalward to its origin from the medial process of the tuber calcanei; the lateral is still covered by the flexor digitorum brevis. The origin of the flexor digitorum brevis from the medial process of the calcaneus is revealed.

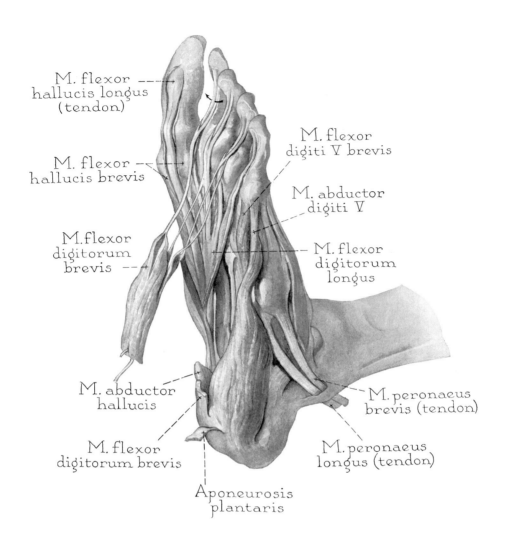

M. flexor hallucis longus (tendon)

M. flexor hallucis brevis

M. flexor digitorum brevis

M. abductor hallucis

M. flexor digitorum brevis

M. flexor digiti V brevis

M. abductor digiti V

M. flexor digitorum longus

M. peronaeus brevis (tendon)

M. peronaeus longus (tendon)

Aponeurosis plantaris

Muscles of the sole of the foot, continued.

Showing especially the muscles of the lateral aspect. The tendons of the following muscles of crural origin have been followed into the sole of the foot: peroneus brevis, peroneus longus, flexor hallucis longus, and flexor digitorum longus. The following intrinsic muscles of the plantar surface are shown: abductor digiti quinti, flexor digitorum brevis, flexor digiti quinti brevis, and quadratus plantae. The central part of the plantar aponeurosis and the origin of the abductor hallucis are shown as cut ends. The flexor digitorum brevis has been freed and retracted; on the second digit an arrow passes over its divisions and under the corresponding tendon of the flexor digitorum longus. The tendon of the peroneus brevis passes behind the lateral malleolus, to an insertion into the tuberosity of the fifth metatarsal. The tendon of the peroneus longus passes behind the lateral malleolus of the fibula, in a retromalleolar groove; it crosses the lateral surface of the calcaneus in the groove above the trochlear process, then through the peroneal groove on the inferior surface of the cuboid. The origin of the abductor digiti quinti, from the tuber and body of the calcaneus, is seen. The heavy muscle belly tapers toward the point where it becomes tendinous; the tendon lies in a sulcus in the short flexor muscle, on the way to an insertion into the lateral surface of the first phalanx of the little toe. The flexor digiti quinti brevis is grooved to form a sulcus for the tendon of the abductor. The flexor digitorum brevis has been cut and drawn backward.

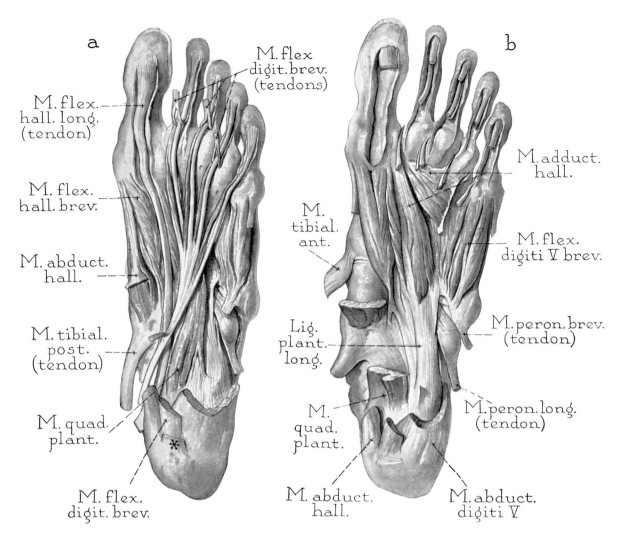

a

M.flex.
hall. long.
(tendon)

M. flex.
hall. brev.

M. abduct.
hall.

M. tibial.
post.
(tendon)

M. quad.
plant.

M. flex
digit. brev.
(tendons)

M. flex.
digit. brev.

M.
tibial.
ant.

Lig.
plant.
long.

M.
quad.
plant.

M. abduct.
hall.

b

M. adduct.
hall.

M. flex.
digiti V brev.

M. peron. brev.
(tendon)

M. peron. long.
(tendon)

M. abduct.
digiti V

Musculature of the sole.

a, The long digital flexor and the short flexors of the great and of the small toe. On the medial side of the foot, the long (crural) tendons of the tibialis posterior, flexor digitorum longus, and flexor hallucis longus have been drawn away from the ankle joint; on the lateral side (peroneal retinacula removed) the tendon of the peroneus longus has been cut and retracted. The following intrinsic muscles of the first layer have been cut: abductor hallucis, flexor digitorum brevis, and abductor digiti quinti. Of the muscles of the second layer, the flexor digitorum longus, the quadratus plantae, and the lumbricales are intact. The flexor hallucis brevis and the flexor digiti quinti brevis are in view. The tendon of the peroneus longus, exposed by removal of the abductor digiti quinti, crosses to an insertion on the opposite side of the foot, into the first metatarsal and first cuneiform bones. The broad calcaneal end of the abductor digiti quinti has been cut near its origin to expose the flexor digiti quinti brevis next below.

b, The adductor and flexor of the great toe and the flexor of the small toe. Shown cut and retracted are the long tendons (crural) from the lateral crural compartment (peroneus longus, peroneus brevis), and those from the anterior and posterior compartments (tibialis posterior and tibialis anterior). All of the muscles originating from the calcaneus have been cut. The lumbricales remain only in their distal reaches, the long digital flexor in the phalangeal portions. The muscles of the third stratum, and the associated ligaments, are now exposed. The peroneus longus occupies a cleft from the margins of which arise muscles of this third stratum, namely, the adductor hallucis (oblique head) and the flexor digiti quinti brevis. The tendon of the peroneus brevis has been drawn aside in order to display its insertion into the fifth metatarsal bone. Of the adductor hallucis, the transverse head arises from the articular capsules of the second, third, and fourth metatarsophalangeal joints; the oblique head takes origin from the long plantar and calcaneocuboid ligaments, and from the arch over the peroneus longus tendon.

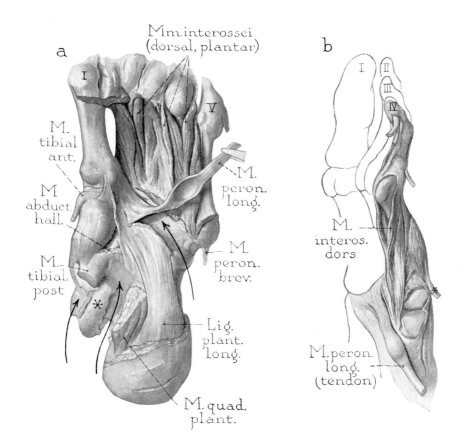

Plantar musculature; dissection concluded.

a, Showing the interosseous muscles and the associated ligaments. The muscles of the fourth stratum have been exposed by removal of the adductor hallucis, flexor hallucis brevis, and flexor digiti quinti brevis. The tibialis posterior has been cut close to attachment, the groove (arrow at the left) in which it lay being shown. The groove is situated above the sustentaculum tali of the calcaneus. The relation of the tibialis anterior to the approximated ends of the cuneiform and fifth metatarsal is shown by opening the joint between these two bones. The groove (at the middle arrow) for the tendons of the flexor digitorum longus and flexor hallucis longus on the under surface of the sustentaculum tali (at *) is shown. The long plantar ligament has been cut, in order to reveal the tunnel for the peroneus longus tendon; the latter has been turned aside (for the area of the arrow at the right) in such a way as to show the contained fibrocartilaginous nodule and the tuberosity of the cuboid over which it is moulded. The medial head of the quadratus plantae, transected, is exposed by removal of the overlying abductor hallucis. The origin of the oblique head of the adductor hallucis from the obliquely placed arch over the peroneus longus tendon is shown, fragments of the muscle being present on the long plantar ligament in that position.

b, Interosseous muscles. Lateral view of the plantar interosseous between fifth and fourth metatarsals. The metatarsal and the phalanges of the fifth digit have been removed.

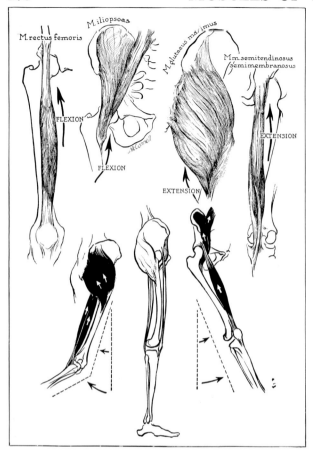

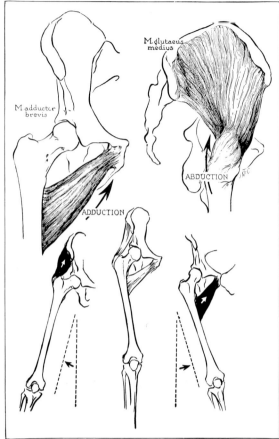

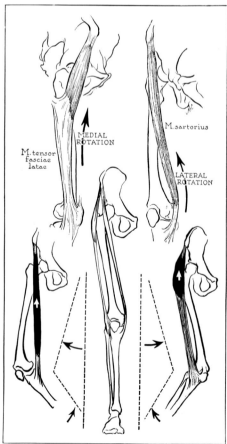

Muscles of the thigh; schematic.
Arranged in action-groups.

Upper left, The actions of flexion and extension at the hip and knee, and the muscles of the pelvic, gluteal, and femoral regions that produce the actions.
Upper right, The actions of adduction and abduction.
Lower left, Rotation, medial and lateral.

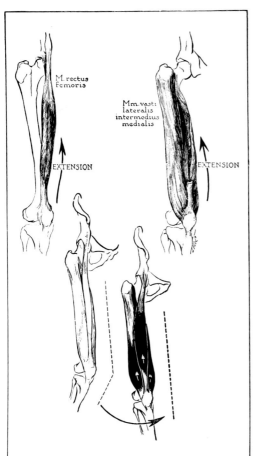
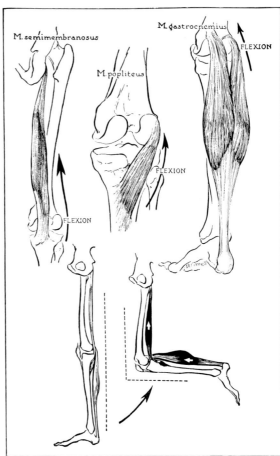

Muscles of the thigh and leg; schematic. Arranged in action-groups. Series continued.

Left, The action of extension at the knee joint, and the muscles of pelvic and femoral origin that produce this action.

Right, The action of flexion at the knee joint, and the muscles of the posterior femoral and posterior crural position that produce this action.

In these sets of illustrations, and in those on the preceding and following pages, the figures at the top in each group portray the muscles; the figures at the bottom serve to demonstrate the movements.

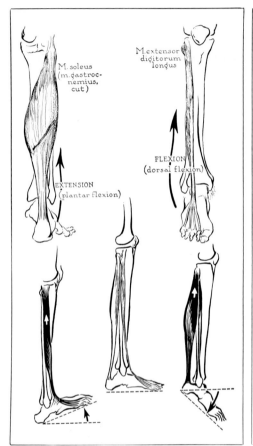
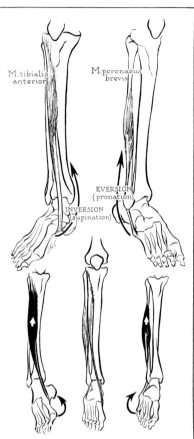

Muscles of the leg; schematic. Arrangement in action-groups. Series concluded.

Left, The actions of extension (plantar flexion) and flexion (dorsal flexion) at the ankle joint, and the three muscles of the posterior and lateral crural groups that take part in these actions.

Right, The actions of inversion (supination) and eversion (pronation), and two muscles of the anterior and lateral crural groups that produce these opposing actions.

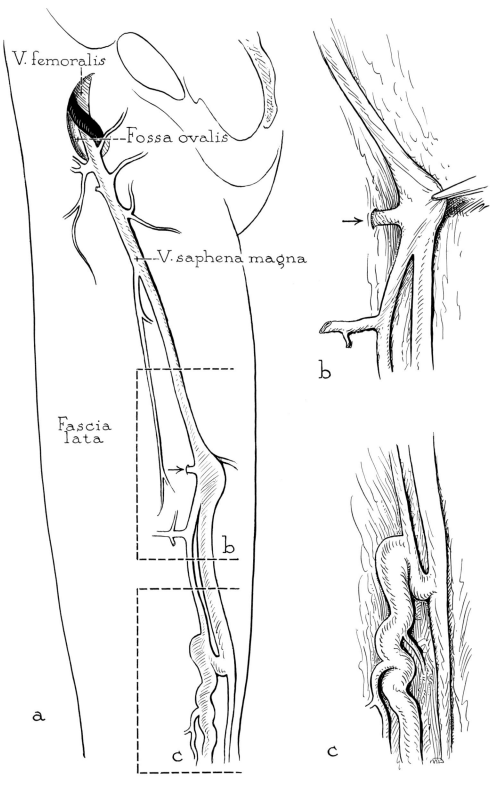

Veins of the thigh.

a, Chief veins of the anterior and medial aspects of the right thigh.

b, Tributaries, superficial and deep, of the saphenous vein, shown by retracting the latter medialward. The area, here shown in detail, is that marked in the midportion of figure *a*.

c, Area of varicosity in the saphenous vein. The area is that marked in the lower portion of figure *a*.

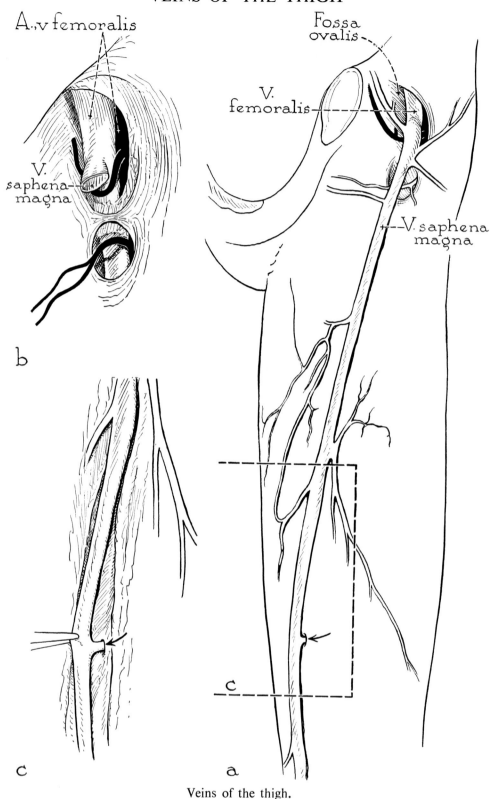

Veins of the thigh.

a, Chief veins of the superficial position on the anterior and medial aspects of the left thigh.

b, The femoral vein and its saphenous tributary (cut) in relation to the femoral artery in the fossa ovalis (NA, *hiatus saphenus*). In this specimen there occurs an accessory fossa, through which a branch of the femoral artery attains superficial level.

c, Deep tributary, from the femoral musculature; like all similar vessels, this muscular tributary reaches the saphenous vein (retracted from its channel in the fatty pannicle) by passing through a small hiatus, or fault, in the fascia lata.

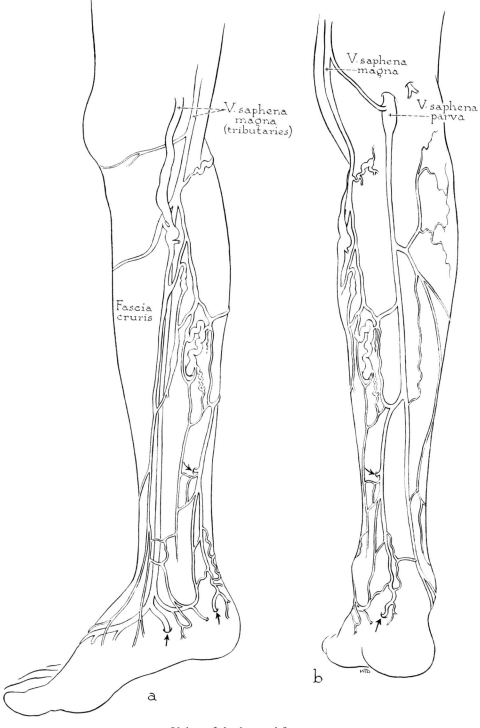

Veins of the leg and foot.

For this, and for the preceding and following figures of the four plates of illustrations of venous anatomy, the same specimen was employed for dissection. In all, the deep fascial sleeve remains intact.

a, Veins of the medial aspect of the right leg and foot. In this specimen varicosities occurred in the veins of both the thigh and leg. Upper arrows point to the areas of varicosity; lower arrows indicate points at which deep veins emerge through the fascia of the foot to reach venous channels of superficial location.

b, Veins of the posterior and medial aspects of the right leg. Arrow points to the opening in the fascia lata through which the small saphenous vein reaches the popliteal vein in the fossa of the same name.

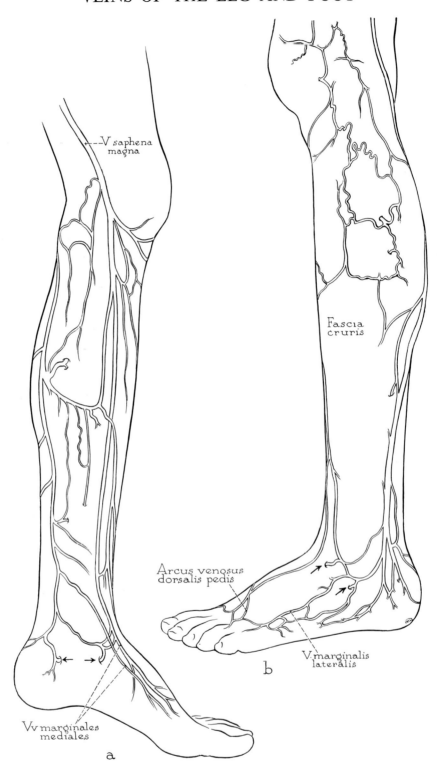

Veins of the leg and foot.

    a, Veins of the medial aspect of the left leg and foot. Arrows indicate points of communication through the crural and pedal fascia, between superficial and deep veins.

    b, Veins of the lateral aspect of the left leg. Veins in the region of the knee, while not yet varicosed, are markedly tortuous. Here, as in figure *a*, points of communication between veins external and internal to the crural and pedal fascia, are indicated by arrows.

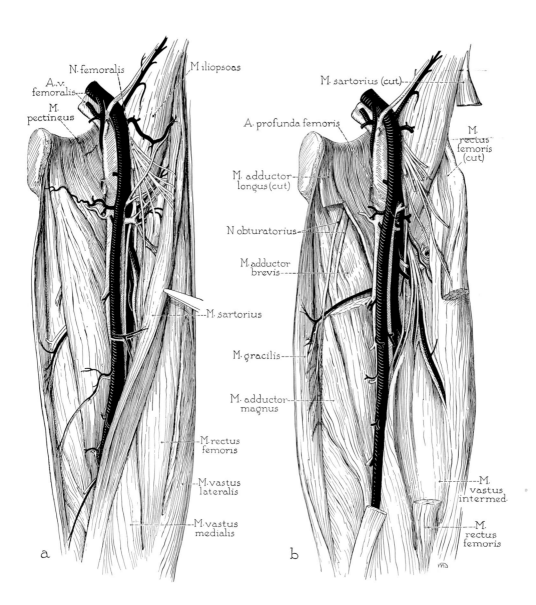

Vessels and nerves of the thigh; anterior aspect.

a, The femoral artery, vein, and nerve are shown as they course from the pelvis through the femoral tri-angle and into the adductor canal. The space of the canal is opened by retraction of the sartorius muscle.

In the following five figures the dissection of the vessels and nerves of the anterior and medial aspects of the thigh is carried to successively deeper levels.

b, The further course of the femoral vessels and nerves, and of the deep femoral artery, shown by the excision of the middle two fourths of the sartorius muscle; the obturator nerve is exposed by removal of a segment of the adductor longus muscle.

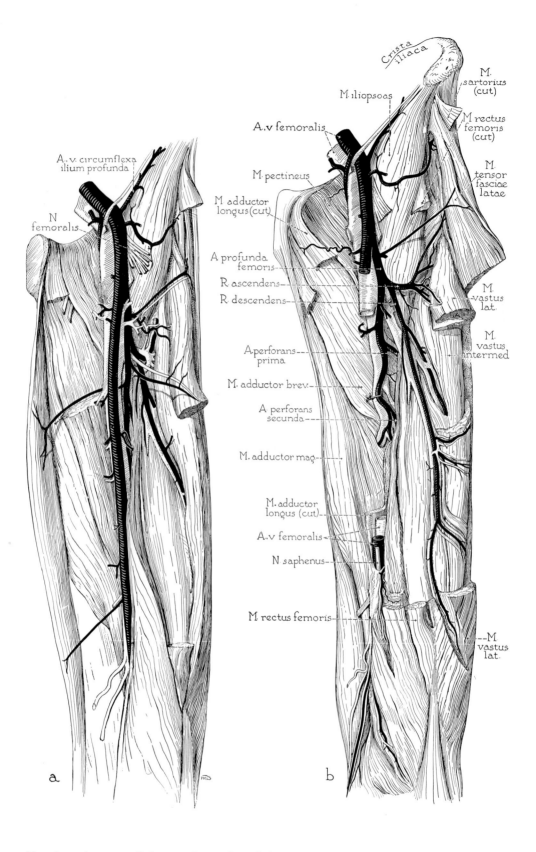

Vessels and nerves of the anterior and medial aspects of the thigh. Dissection continued.

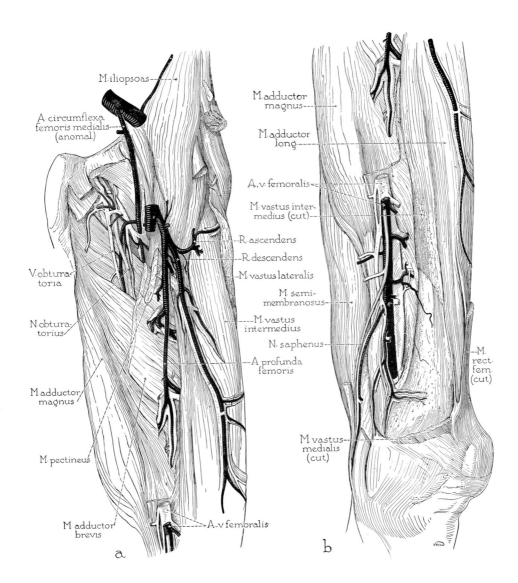

Vessels and nerves of the anterior and medial femoral regions. Dissection concluded.

a, The perforating branches of the deep femoral artery are shown, as well as the corresponding tributaries of the profunda femoris vein (the latter excised). Similarly, the obturator vessels and nerves are exposed by excision of a segment of the adductor brevis.

b, The course of the distal portion of the femoral vessels is fully demonstrated by removal of the vastus medialis muscle.

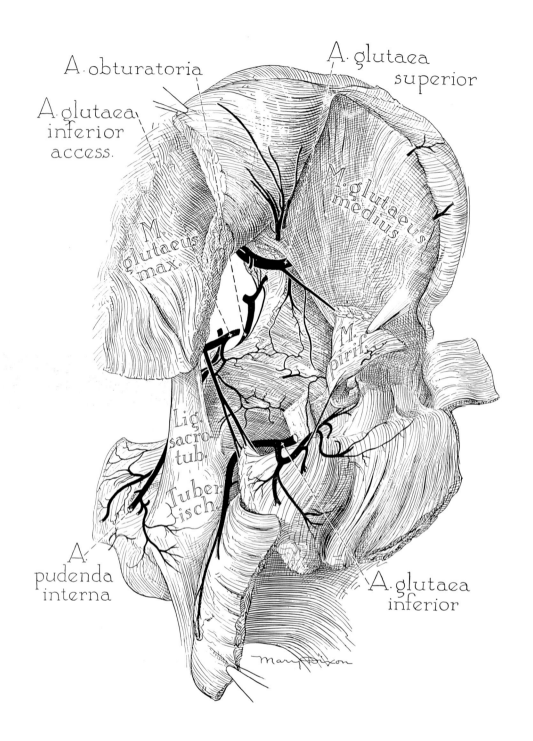

Gluteal arteries. Posterolateral view of the innominate bone.

    The superior and inferior gluteal arteries and the internal pudendal artery are shown by reflection of the following muscles: the gluteus maximus, quadratus femoris, piriformis, and associated gemelli. The deep division of the superior gluteal artery is seen as it passes beneath the gluteus medius muscle; the internal pudendal artery is traced through the lesser sciatic notch (deep to the sacrotuberous ligament), and into the perineum.

    The following two figures carry the dissection to deeper levels.

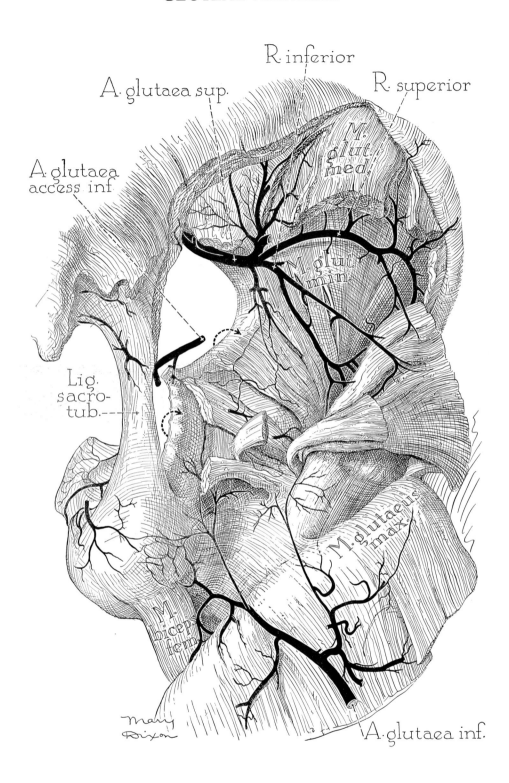

R inferior

A. glutaea sup.

R. superior

A. glutaea access inf.

M. glut. med.

M. glut. min.

Lig. sacro-tub.

M. glutaeus max.

M. biceps fem.

A. glutaea inf.

Gluteal arteries. Dissection continued.

The deep division of the superior gluteal artery is followed into the plane between the gluteus medius and gluteus minimus, both of which muscles are supplied by rami derived from the superior and inferior divisions. The inferior gluteal artery (here transected) supplies the gluteus maximus muscle.

Arrows pass through the sciatic (ischiadic) foramina.

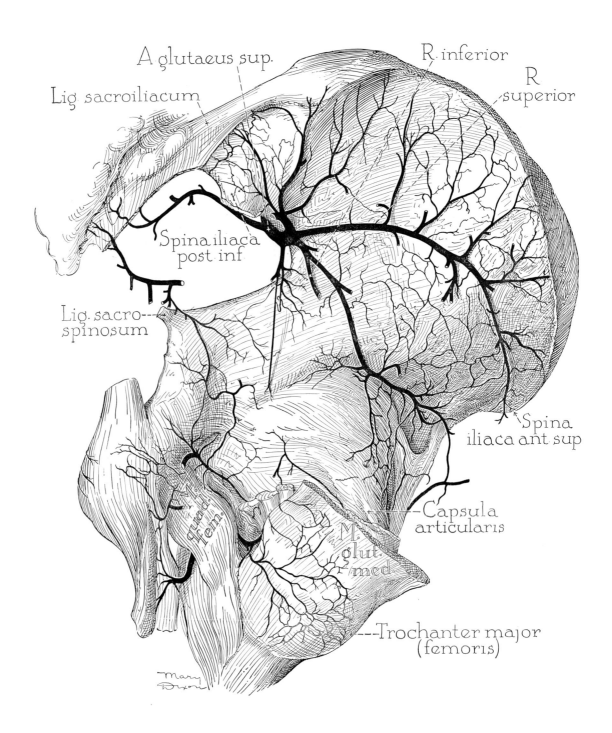

Gluteal arteries. Dissection concluded.

The finer branches of the gluteal arteries have been traced to periosteal level; muscular rami have been cut. The deep rami supply the periosteum, the underlying bone, and, from osseous level, send lesser branches into the overlying muscles.

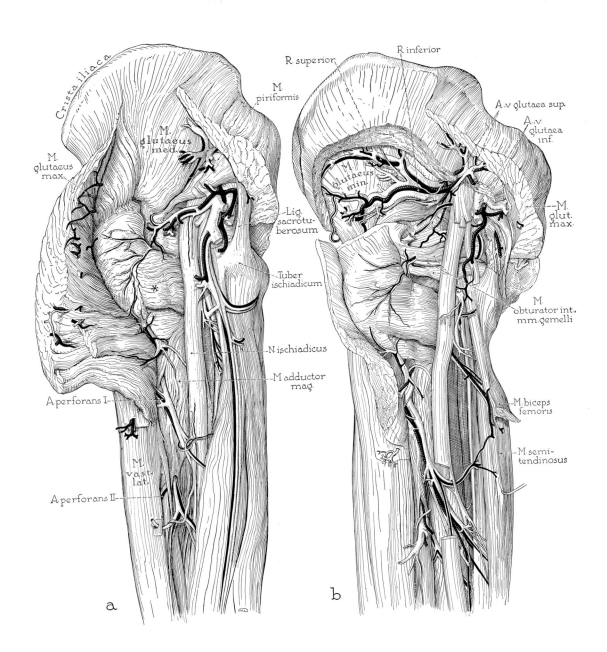

Vessels and nerves of the buttock and of the posterior aspect of the thigh.

a, The superficial division of the superior gluteal artery and tributary to the corresponding vein. Shown, transected, by reflection of the gluteus maximus muscle. On the same plane appear the inferior gluteal vessels. The sciatic (ischiadic) nerve and the perforating rami of the deep femoral vessels are shown by retraction of the hamstring (posterior femoral) muscles.

b, The deep divisions of the superior gluteal vessels and nerves are exposed by excision of the middle third of the gluteus medius muscle.

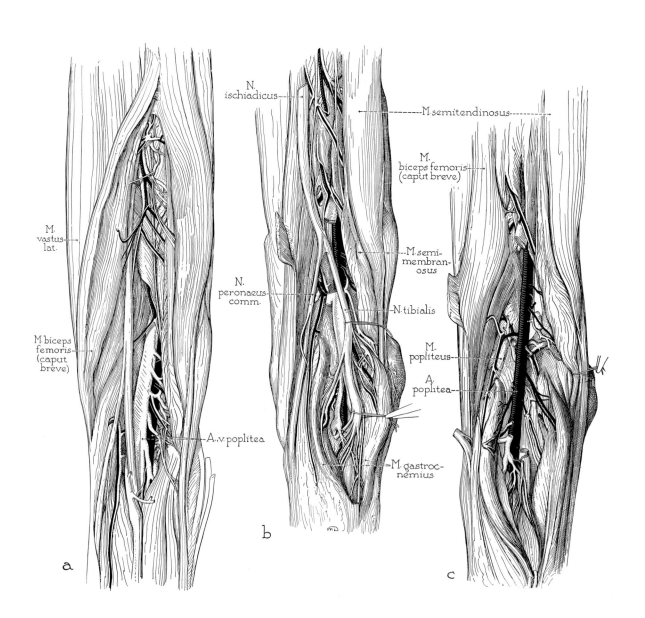

Vessels and nerves of the posterior femoral and crural regions,
especially of the popliteal fossa. Dissection continued.

a, The popliteal and perforating arteries, and the sciatic nerve and its divisions (common peroneal and tibial); shown by retraction of the biceps femoris muscle.

b, Further exposure of the same vessels and nerves, through removal of the long head of the biceps femoris.

c, Complete exposure of the popliteal artery, through excision of the veins and nerves.

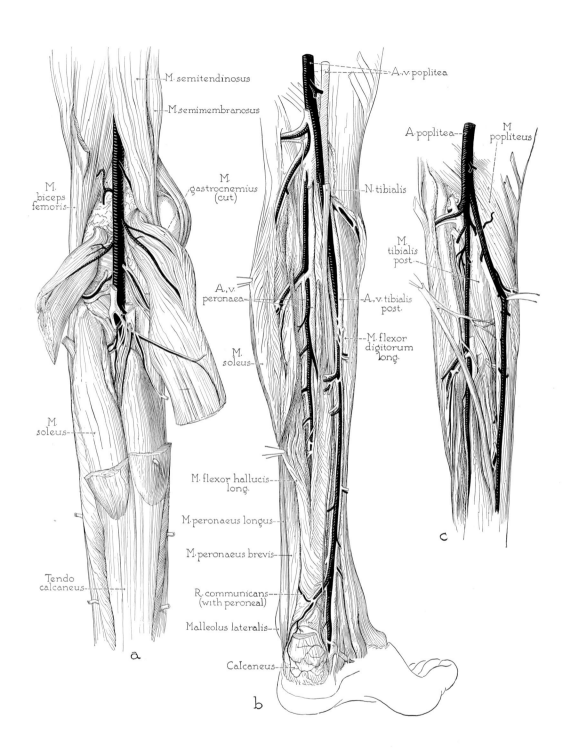

Vessels and nerves of the posterior crural region. Successively deep levels.

a, The popliteal artery in the popliteal fossa and in the space distal thereto; the latter continuation of the fossa is opened by reflection of the gastrocnemius muscle.

b, The posterior tibial vessels and the tibial nerves, revealed by reflection of the soleus muscle.

c, The arterial pattern clarified by excision of the veins.

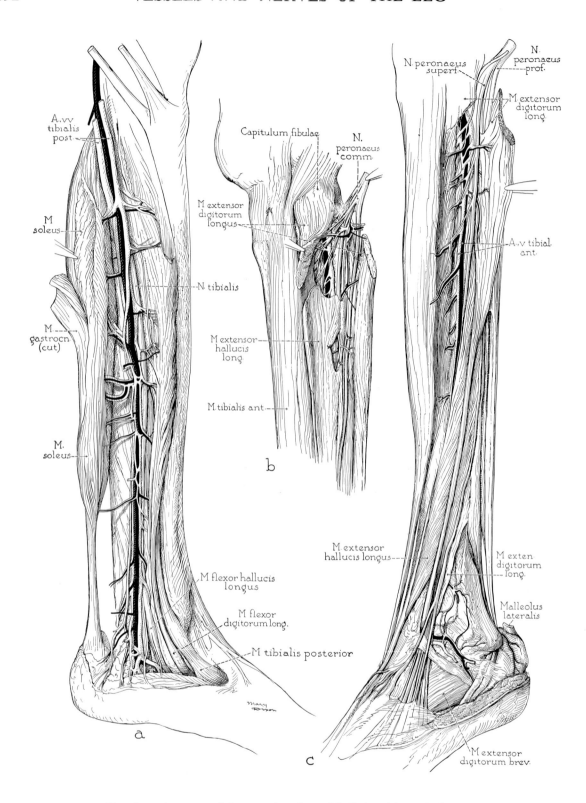

Vessels and nerves of the crural regions. Medial and lateral views.

a, The vessels and nerves of the posterior crural region, shown by retraction of the soleus muscle.
b, The vessels and nerves of the lateral crural region, deep to the peroneus longus.
c, Those of the anterior crural region, deep to the extensor digitorum longus.

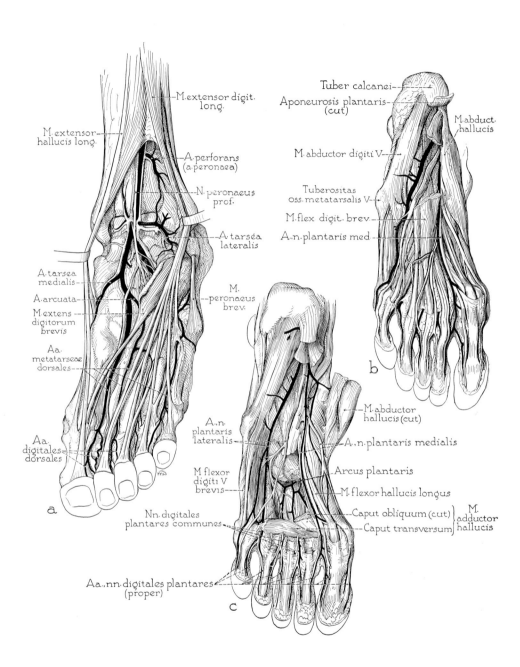

M.extensor digit. long.

M.extensor hallucis long.

A.perforans (a.peronaea)

N.peronaeus prof.

A.tarsea lateralis

A.tarsea medialis

A.arcuata

M.extens digitorum brevis

Aa. metatarseae dorsales

M. peronaeus brev.

Aa. digitales dorsales

A.,n. plantaris lateralis

M flexor digiti V brevis

Nn. digitales plantares communes

Aa.,nn.digitales plantares (proper)

a

Tuber calcanei

Aponeurosis plantaris (cut)

M.abduct. hallucis

M.abductor digiti V

Tuberositas oss.metatarsalis V

M.flex digit. brev.

A.n.plantaris med

b

M.abductor hallucis (cut)

A.,n.plantaris medialis

Arcus plantaris

M.flexor hallucis longus

Caput obliquum (cut)

Caput transversum

M. adductor hallucis

c

Vessels and nerves of the foot. Dorsal and plantar surfaces.

a, Vessels and nerves of the dorsum of the foot, shown by retraction of the long extensor tendons, and by excision of part of the short extensor.

b and c, Vessels and nerves of the plantar surface of the foot, at intermediate and deep levels.

VESSELS AND NERVES OF THE THIGH
COURSE OF ARTERIES AND NERVES IN RELATION TO
ANTERIOR AND MEDIAL FEMORAL MUSCLES

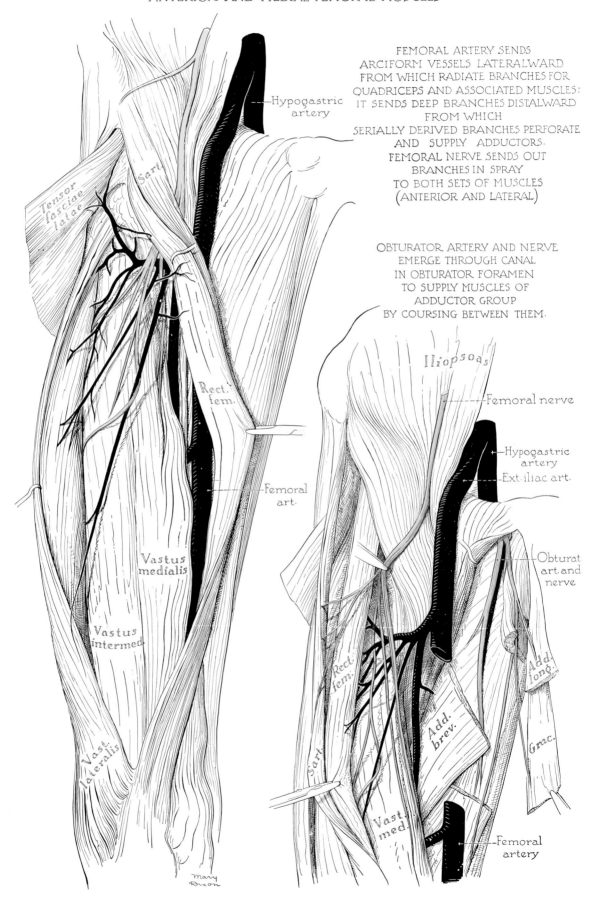

FEMORAL ARTERY SENDS
ARCIFORM VESSELS LATERALWARD
FROM WHICH RADIATE BRANCHES FOR
QUADRICEPS AND ASSOCIATED MUSCLES:
IT SENDS DEEP BRANCHES DISTALWARD
FROM WHICH
SERIALLY DERIVED BRANCHES PERFORATE
AND SUPPLY ADDUCTORS.
FEMORAL NERVE SENDS OUT
BRANCHES IN SPRAY
TO BOTH SETS OF MUSCLES
(ANTERIOR AND LATERAL)

OBTURATOR ARTERY AND NERVE
EMERGE THROUGH CANAL
IN OBTURATOR FORAMEN
TO SUPPLY MUSCLES OF
ADDUCTOR GROUP
BY COURSING BETWEEN THEM.

Hypogastric artery

Tensor fasciae latae

Sart.

Rect. fem.

Femoral art.

Vastus medialis

Vastus intermed.

Vast. lateralis

Iliopsoas

Femoral nerve

Hypogastric artery

Ext. iliac art.

Obturat. art. and nerve

Rect. fem.

Add. long.

Sart.

Add. brev.

Grac.

Vast. med.

Femoral artery

Mary Dixon

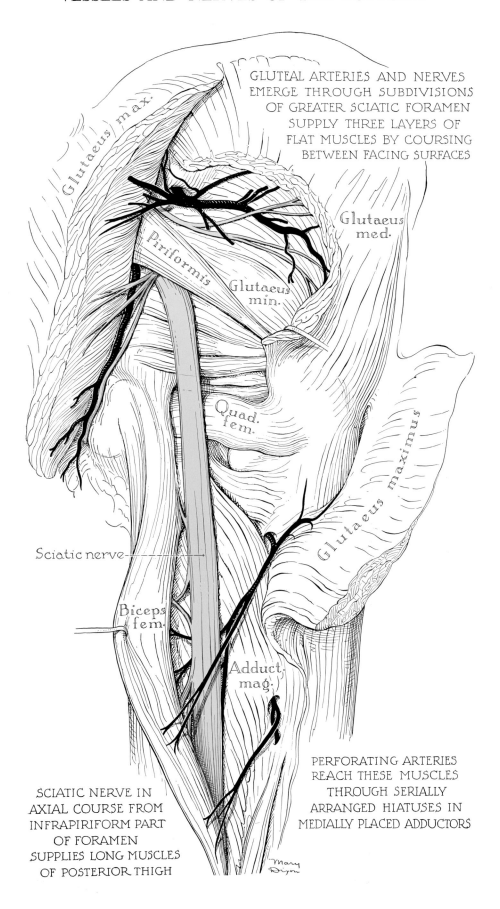

GLUTEAL ARTERIES AND NERVES
EMERGE THROUGH SUBDIVISIONS
OF GREATER SCIATIC FORAMEN
SUPPLY THREE LAYERS OF
FLAT MUSCLES BY COURSING
BETWEEN FACING SURFACES

Gluteus max.

Piriformis

Glutaeus med.

Glutaeus min.

Quad. fem.

Glutaeus maximus

Sciatic nerve

Biceps fem.

Adduct. mag.

SCIATIC NERVE IN
AXIAL COURSE FROM
INFRAPIRIFORM PART
OF FORAMEN
SUPPLIES LONG MUSCLES
OF POSTERIOR THIGH

PERFORATING ARTERIES
REACH THESE MUSCLES
THROUGH SERIALLY
ARRANGED HIATUSES IN
MEDIALLY PLACED ADDUCTORS

Mary Dion

OBTURATOR NERVE:
PASSES FROM PELVIS TO THIGH
THROUGH OBTURATOR FORAMEN, DIVIDING THEREIN
ANTERIOR DIVISION:
DESCENDS BEHIND PECTINEUS, BETWEEN
ADDUCTORS LONGUS AND BREVIS TO GRACILIS
INNERVATING THEM.
POSTERIOR DIVISION:
PASSES DISTALWARD BETWEEN
ADDUCTORS BREVIS AND MAGNUS, SUPPLYING
THESE MUSCLES

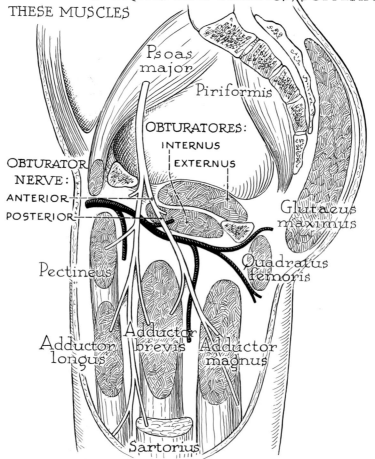

ANTERIOR TIBIAL ARTERY REACHES ANTERIOR COMPARTMENT BY PASSING
THROUGH HIATUS IN INTEROSSEOUS MEMBRANE; SENDS RAMI THROUGH
INTERMUSCULAR SEPTUM INTO LATERAL COMPARTMENT

DEEP PERONEAL NERVE ACCOMPANIES ARTERY, AFTER PASSING AROUND
FIBULA AND THROUGH SEPTUM SEPARATING COMPARTMENTS.
SUPERFICIAL PERONEAL NERVE REMAINS IN LATERAL COMPARTMENT.

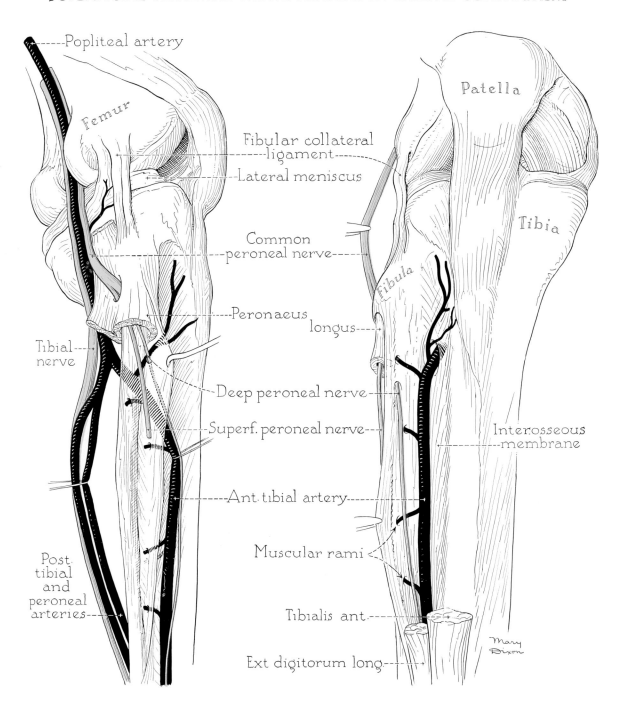

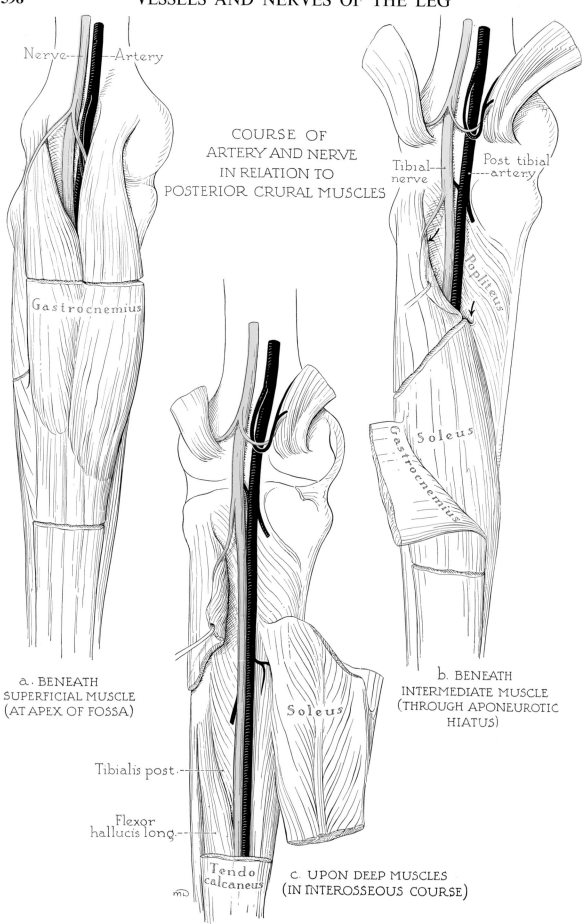

Nerve - - - - Artery

Gastrocnemius

COURSE OF
ARTERY AND NERVE
IN RELATION TO
POSTERIOR CRURAL MUSCLES

Tibial- nerve

Post tibial ---- artery

Popliteus

Soleus

Gastrocnemius

a. BENEATH
SUPERFICIAL MUSCLE
(AT APEX OF FOSSA)

b. BENEATH
INTERMEDIATE MUSCLE
(THROUGH APONEUROTIC
HIATUS)

Soleus

Tibialis post. - - -

Flexor
hallucis long. - - -

Tendo
calcaneus

mD

c. UPON DEEP MUSCLES
(IN INTEROSSEOUS COURSE)

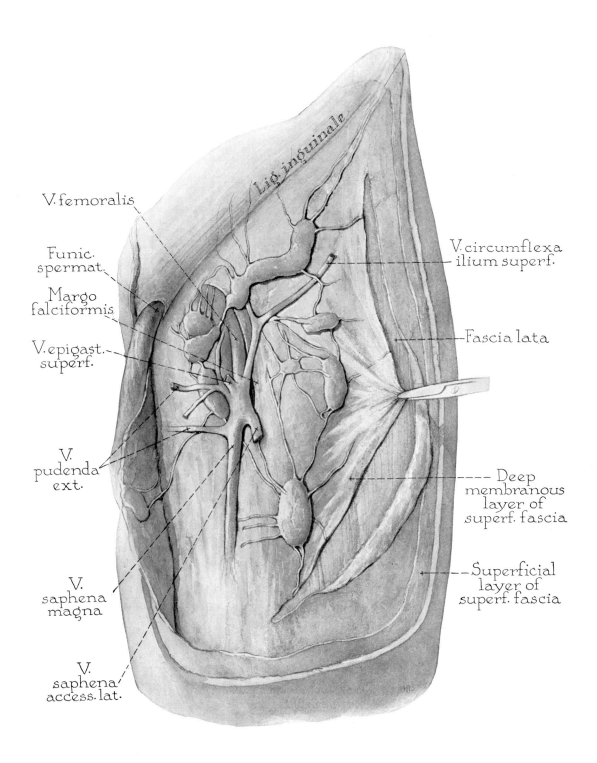

V. femoralis

Funic. spermat.

Margo falciformis

V. epigast. superf.

V. pudenda ext.

V. saphena magna

V. saphena access. lat.

Lig. inguinale

V. circumflexa ilium superf.

Fascia lata

Deep membranous layer of superf. fascia

Superficial layer of superf. fascia

Saphenous vein and its tributaries, and the inguinal lymph glands.

The superficial layer of the superficial fascia has been removed to reveal the deep layer with its contained inguinal lymph glands and the veins of the saphenous system to which the glands are intimately related. The deep layer of the superficial fascia has been incised and partially freed from the subjacent fascia lata.

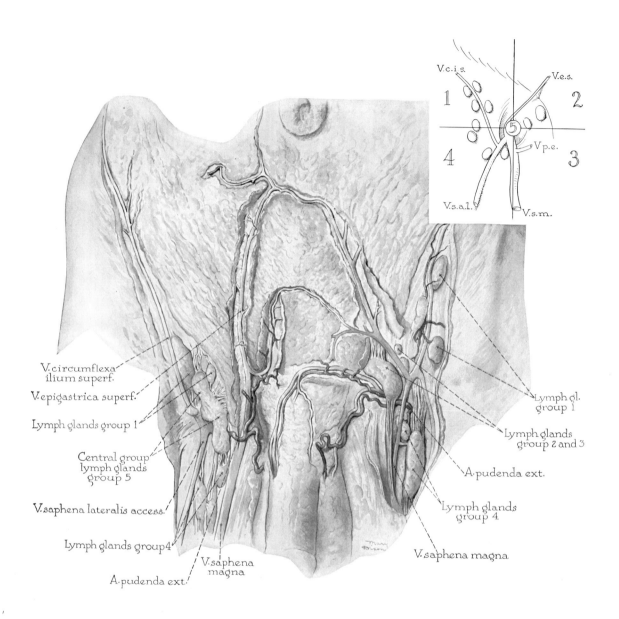

Superficial veins and lymph glands of the anterior femoral and adjacent inguinal and pudendal regions;
right and left sides.

    The superficial fatty stratum is here left intact except where it contains lymphatic glands and blood vessels. The vessels have not been transected, but are exposed *in situ* by removing the immediately surrounding adipose tissue. In this way the extent of the lower abdominal, proximal femoral, and pudendal areas of vascular and lymphatic drainage is depicted, and the fascial level of the glands and vessels recorded.

    In the inset are shown, diagrammatically, the saphenous vein and tributaries in relation to the inguinal glands of most frequent occurrence. The glands are separable into five groups; four of the groups are bounded by lines that meet at the saphenofemoral junction; the fifth group would lie upon the vessels at the latter junction. Abbreviations: V.c.i.s., vena circumflexa ilium superficialis; V.e.s., vena epigastrica superficialis; V.p.e., vena pudenda externa; V.s.a.l., vena saphena accessoria lateralis; V.s.m., vena saphena magna.

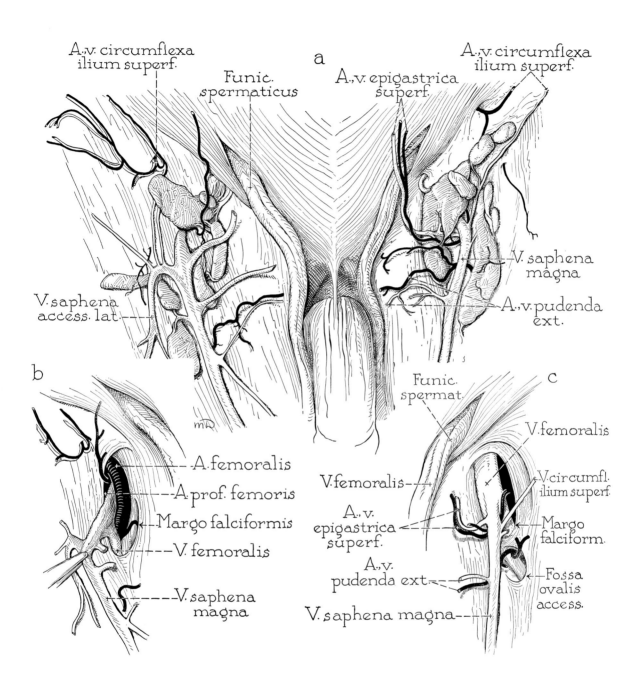

a

A.v. circumflexa
ilium superf.

Funic.
spermaticus

A.v. epigastrica
superf.

A.v. circumflexa
ilium superf.

V. saphena
magna

V. saphena
access. lat.

A.v. pudenda
ext.

b

A. femoralis

A. prof. femoris

Margo falciformis

V. femoralis

V. saphena
magna

c

Funic.
spermat.

V. femoralis

V. femoralis

V. circumfl.
ilium superf.

A.v.
epigastrica
superf.

Margo
falciform.

A.v.
pudenda ext.

Fossa
ovalis
access.

V. saphena magna

Anterior femoral and adjacent regions: *a*, of the right and left sides; *b* and *c*, of the right and left sides of
the specimen illustrated in *a*.

The superficial fascia has been removed to expose the inguinal lymph glands as they lie in relation to the
blood vessels (*a*). The lymphatic glands have been removed in order to expose the femoral vessels in the fossa
ovalis (NA, *hiatus saphenus*) and the branches of the artery and the tributaries of the vein to which the glands
were related (*b* and *c*).

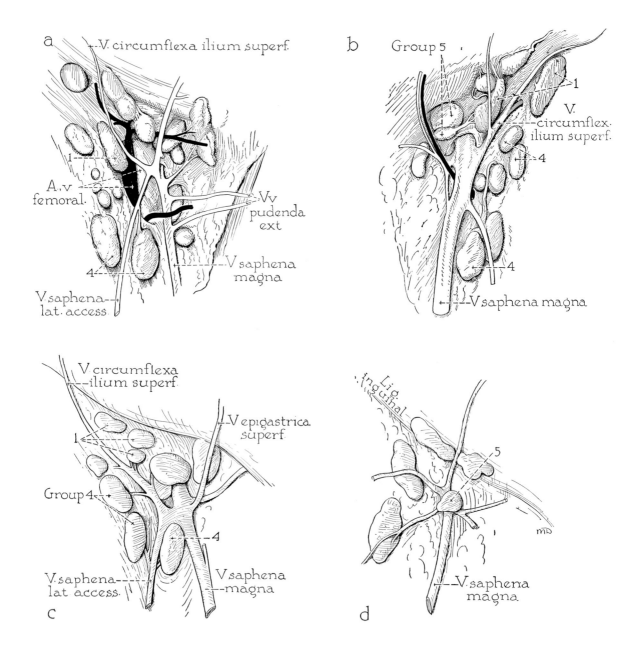

Types of arrangement of the inguinal lymph glands: *b*, Of the left groin; others of the right side. The numerals refer to the groups in the inset on page 600.

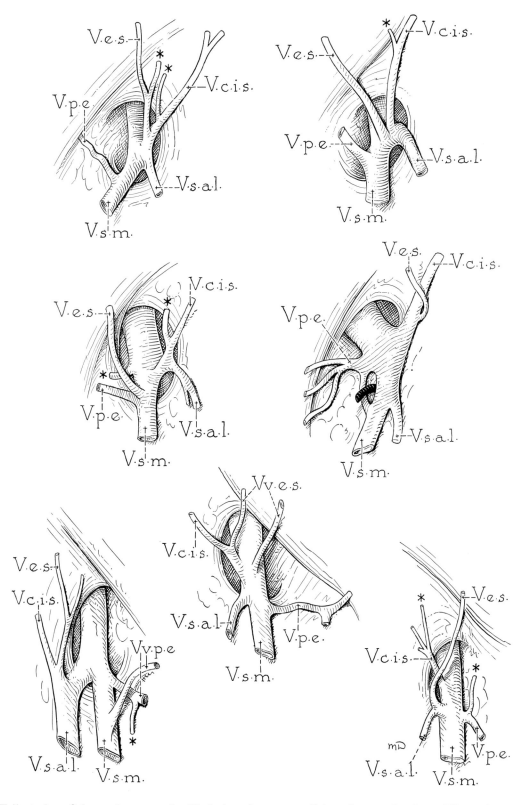

Tributaries of the saphenous vein. Variations in pattern. Selected examples from 500 specimens. For key to abbreviations, see following page. * indicates small vein draining lymph glands.

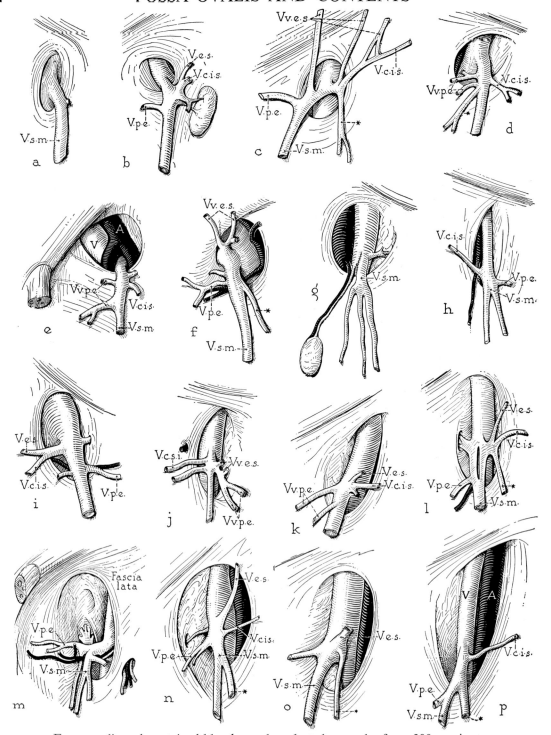

Fossa ovalis and contained blood vessels; selected examples from 200 specimens.

In outline, the fossa (NA, *hiatus saphenus*) is occasionally almost circular (*b* and *g*). However, it is usually oval (*a, d, h* to *m*); when thus compressed, the narrowness may be striking (*h* and *j*). Occasionally the fossa is dart-shaped, with the pointed end directed downward (*n* and *p*). Frequently accessory hiatuses occur within the space of the fossa proper, transmitting muscular tributaries to the larger veins.

The smallest fossa in the 200 specimens was 1.6 cm. in length, 1.7 cm. in width (*b*); the narrowest measured 1.0 cm. (*a*); the shortest, 1.6 cm. (*b*). The largest fossa was 8.5 cm. in length, 3.5 cm. in width.

Abbreviations: *V.c.i.s., Vena circumflexa ilium superficialis* (superficial iliac circumflex vein); *V.e.s., Vv.e.s., Vena epigastrica superficialis* (superficial epigastric vein or veins); *V.p.e., Vv.p.e., Vena pudenda externa* (external pudendal vein or veins); *V.s.m., Vena saphena magna* (great saphenous vein). * indicates an accessory saphenous vein (*Vena saphena accessoria*).

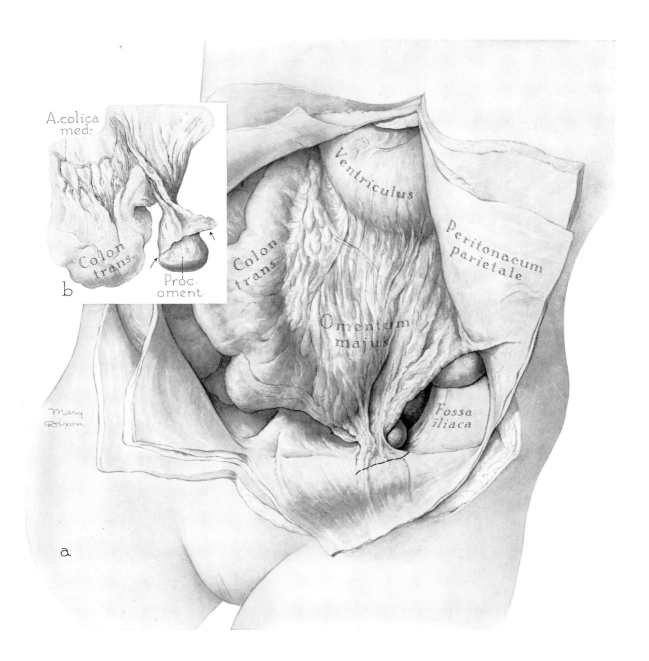

Abdominal contents in a case of femoral hernia in a female cadaver.

a, The omentum, with the transverse colon at its distal margin, formed an apron which almost completely obscured the coils of intestine. On the left side the omentum was locally fastened by a narrow band (along broken line) to the abdominal wall over the roof of the femoral canal. A nodule of the omentum occupied the femoral canal (orifice of latter, 1 cm. in diameter).

b, The hernia mass, removed from the femoral canal, has been turned upward to demonstrate form and size. Prior to removal the omentum was cut (at arrows) from the area of anterior fixation to the parietal peritoneum.

As shown in succeeding steps in the dissection, the hernia occupied the femoral canal and became sub-cutaneous upon reaching the fossa ovalis.

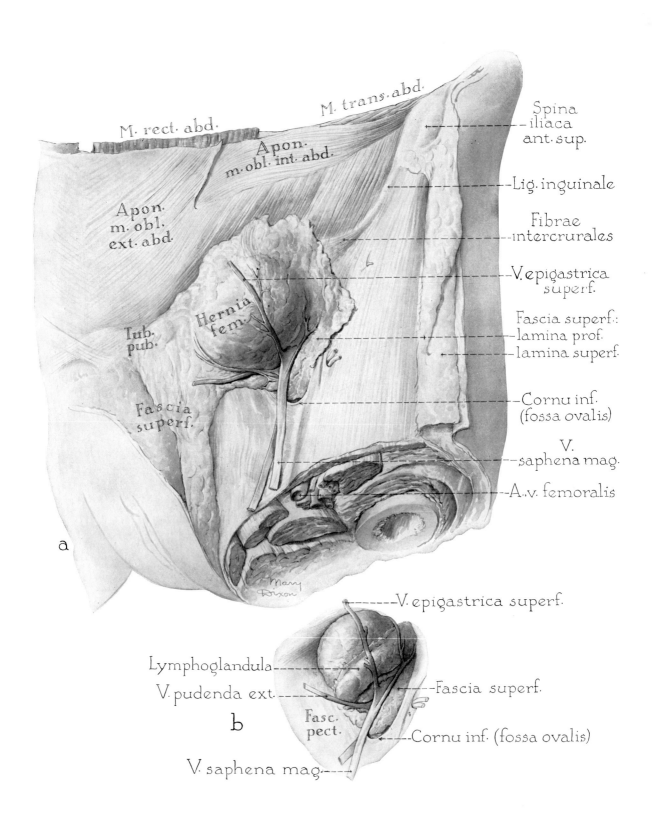

See opposite page for description.

The femoral hernia, in relation to the external fascial and aponeurotic layers
of the inguinal and proximal femoral regions (same specimen).

a, The superficial fascia has been removed except in the territory of the hernia and in the pudendal area medial thereto. The aponeurosis of the external oblique muscle and the fascia lata are exposed, as is also the fossa ovalis in the latter layer (at inferior horn of the falciform margin). The hernia produces a circular bulging in the overlying superficial fascia. The superficial veins form a basket-like support for the hernia.

b, The hernial mass with related structures.

As the succeeding figures (page 608) will demonstrate, a femoral hernia comes to occupy the medial one of the three compartments within the femoral sheath. The space within the saccular protrusion is continuous with that of the peritoneal cavity; the parietal peritoneum, thus displaced, is covered by subserous and fascial coats. These layers press outward along the vascular lacuna, beneath the inguinal ligament, and into the "empty" compartment of the femoral sheath.

The descent of a femoral hernia is, therefore, at first almost directly downward into the femoral fossa. Resistance to descent is offered, behind, by aponeurotic and ligamentous structures at the pubic pecten, and, in front, by the lacunar ligament. However, within the vascular lacuna the femoral vein and the investing sheath constitute a resilient lateral wall. Further progress caudalward brings the process into the lower portion of the femoral canal, where it impinges upon the overlying superior cornu of the fossa ovalis. After passing this point, the herniating mass is suddenly relieved of ventral constriction; as a consequence, it presses against the integument in angulated course. While the neck of the process must remain small in size, the distal mass of the tumor may increase in bulk (page 606). Having attained the fossa ovalis, and carrying the bilaminar femoral sheath forward as an envelope, the hernia impinges upon the deep layer of the fatty pannicle of the thigh.

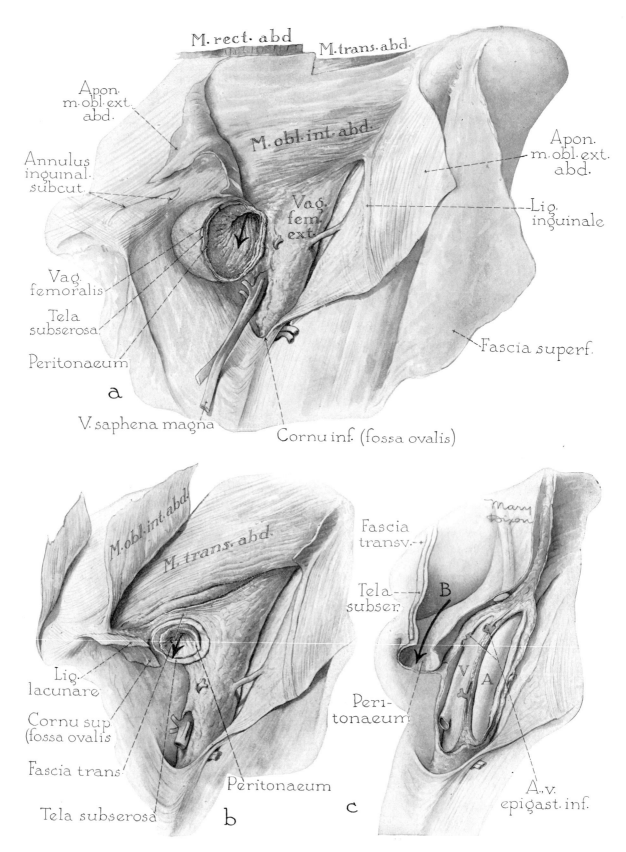

The hernial sac; its composition and inguinofemoral continuities (same specimen).

a, The aponeurosis of the external oblique muscle has been reflected; with it the fascia lata has been turned aside after cutting vertically through the superior cornu of the falciform margin of the fossa ovalis (NA, *hiatus saphenus*). The lateral wall of the sac has been cut away. In this way the following features are demonstrated: the laminar nature of the hernial sac derived in part from the femoral sheath; the relation of the orifice (at arrow) to the part of the sheath that invests the femoral vessels; the form and position of the sheath. The sac is composed of three layers, namely, the fascia of transversus abdominis muscle, the subserous connective tissue, and the peritoneum. The femoral sheath is made up of the outer and intermediate of these three layers.

b, The orifice of the hernial sac in relation to deep inguinal and femoral structures. The sac has been transected at its neck; the internal oblique has been turned aside to expose the subjacent transversus abdominis. As the sac passes through the femoral canal it is bounded medially by the lacunar ligament (here cut and turned downward), laterally by the portion of the femoral sheath that transmits the femoral vein, superiorly by the muscular lower margin of the transversus abdominis and ligamentous termination of the external oblique (inguinal ligament here cut and turned aside), and inferiorly by the superior ramus of the pubis (covered by the pectineus muscle and the pectineal fascia). The outer lamella of the femoral sheath is made up of the fascial coverings of the transversus and iliopsoas muscles prolonged into the thigh. Its surface (here exposed) is irregular, owing to the presence of fat in the contiguous layer of connective tissue. The latter, carried into the thigh as an extension of retroperitoneal tissue in the pelvis, forms the internal layer of the femoral sheath and immediately surrounds the vessels (exposed in *c*).

c, The compartments of the femoral sheath, their investments, contents, and interrelationship. The hernial sac, in the medial one of the three compartments, has been opened in front, its constituent layers demonstrated by carrying the incisions vertically upward through the deep layers of the inguinal wall. Its space (transversed by arrow B) is continuous with that of the peritoneal cavity. The bilaminar division of the sheath, which houses the femoral vessels, has been opened to demonstrate the continuity of its strata with those of the abdomen. The hernial sac is thus a diverticulum of the parietal peritoneum which, covered by subserous and fascial coats, pressed outward through the vascular lacuna beneath the inguinal ligament to occupy the "empty" compartment of the femoral sheath.

The pathway taken by a femoral hernia, then, must be at first almost directly downward into the femoral fossa, declination of the superior surface of the pubic bone carrying the process forward through the femoral ring. The herniating structures meet a restraining arch of aponeurotic fibers formed by that part of the femoral sheath which is securely attached to the pubic pecten. Further resistance is offered by the lacunar ligament. But within the vascular lacuna the femoral vein and the investing sheath form a resilient lateral wall. Further progress inferiorly brings the process into the lower reaches of the femoral canal, where it impinges upon the overlying superior cornu of the fossa ovalis. After passing this point, the process is suddenly relieved of anterior constriction, and can press toward the integument in angulated course. While the neck of the process must remain small in size, the distal mass of the tumor may thus increase in bulk. In this situation, carrying the bilaminar femoral sheath forward as an envelope, the hernia impinges upon the deep layer of the superficial fascia, as the latter locally covers the fossa ovalis.

Considering anterior hernial orifices together, the femoral canal (with the ring) represents an anatomical arrangement standing between inguinal and obturator canals in point of structural weakness. Tendency toward hernial protrusion through the inguinal wall is greatly increased by the presence of a congenital serous sac, and by exposure to the trauma and intra-abdominal tension of walls that are distensible. The femoral orifice is a narrow one, encircled in front by an aponeurotic arch, bounded by the lacunar ligament medially, and supported behind by a bony ridge. It is weakened only by the existence of potential space in the femoral ring and canal, and by resilience of the large blood vessels on its medial aspect. The obturator orifice, narrower still, is effectively bounded by an osseoligamentous rim; the obturator canal not only possesses peritoneal, preperitoneal, and ligamentous tissues to support it internally, but also is well barricaded externally by the layered musculature of the thigh (see pages 614 to 618).

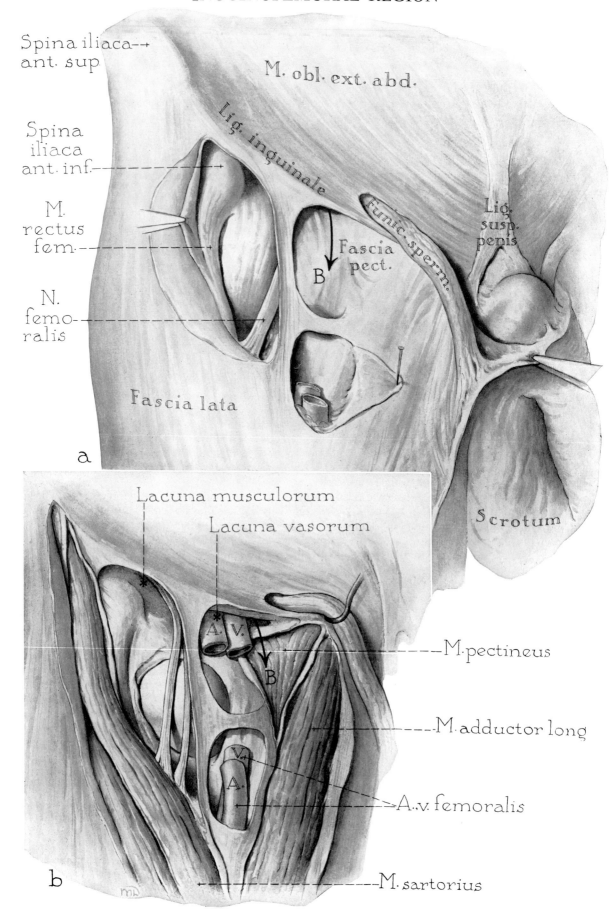

Spina iliaca→ ant. sup

M. obl. ext. abd.

Spina iliaca ant. inf.

Lig. inguinale

Funic. sperm.

Lig. susp. penis

M. rectus fem.

Fascia pect.

B

N. femoralis

Fascia lata

Scrotum

a

Lacuna musculorum

Lacuna vasorum

A.V.

B

M. pectineus

M. adductor long

V.
A.

A. v. femoralis

M. sartorius

b

Two stages in the dissection of spaces and contained structures in the inguinofemoral region.

a, The superficial fascia has been removed, exposing in the inguinal and proximal femoral regions, respectively, the aponeurosis of the external oblique muscle and the fascial investment (fascia lata) of the muscles of the thigh. The external spermatic fascia has been removed in order to expose the spermatic cord and to reveal the crural boundaries of the subcutaneous inguinal ring. The femoral vessels have been removed from the fossa ovalis (saphenous hiatus). The course of a femoral hernia is indicated by the arrow B, which here emerges from the femoral ring. Distal to the fossa ovalis an artificial window has been cut in the fascia lata to demonstrate the further course of the femoral artery and vein. A similar opening has been made in the fascia, lateral to the fossa ovalis, into the space of the muscular lacuna, from which the iliopsoas muscle has been removed, but in which the femoral nerve remains intact.

b, The investing sleeves of fascia have been cut away in such manner as to reveal the muscles and associated structures that bound the femoral triangle. Marginally the triangular space is bounded by the sartorius and adductor longus muscles; the floor is formed in part by the pectineus muscle. The iliopsoas, removed from the muscular lacuna together with the subjacent portion of the articular capsule, would form the floor of the space laterally. The stumps of the transected femoral vessels remain in the vascular lacuna. The small orifice situated on the medial aspect of the femoral vein is the femoral ring through which a hernia would pass from the abdomen into the thigh, in the direction of the arrow B, to occupy the fossa ovalis (NA, *hiatus saphenus*). The hernia would be surrounded by the lamellae of the femoral sheath and would lie beneath the superficial fascia.

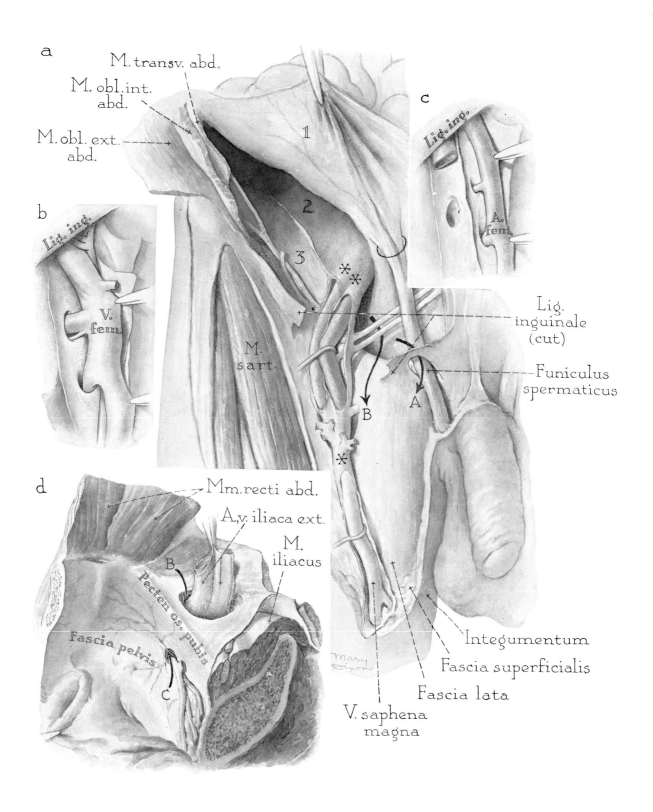

a

M. transv. abd.

M. obl. int. abd.

M. obl. ext. abd.

c

Lig. ing.

A. fem.

b

Lig. ing.

V. fem.

1

2

3

**

M. sart.

Lig. inguinale (cut)

Funiculus spermaticus

B

A

d

Mm. recti abd.

A, v. iliaca ext.

M. iliacus

B

Pecten os. pubis

Fascia pelvis

C

*

V. saphena magna

Integumentum

Fascia superficialis

Fascia lata

Structures related to the regions of inguinal, femoral and obturator herniae.

a, The abdominal layers have been incised along the inguinal ligament; the peritoneum (at 1), with the coils of small intestine, has been lifted to show the retroperitoneal connective tissue (at 2) and the subjacent pelvic fascia (at 3). The sites of inguinal and femoral herniation are indicated (by arrows A and B, respectively). The site of the orifice of the abdominal inguinal ring is marked by a circle. The fascia lata has been reflected to expose the sartorius as the muscle forms the lateral boundary of the femoral triangle. The subserous (retroperitoneal) layer, indicated by **, is carried downward from the iliac vessels upon their femoral continuations (at *); from these larger vessels arise the deep circumflex iliac (laterally) and the inferior epigastric (medially).

b, The femoral sheath of the opposite thigh has been opened to show the femoral vein; the vessel has been retracted in order to demonstrate the manner in which its tributaries are invested by tubular continuations of the sheath.

c, Artery, with branches; vein excised. *d*, Anterolateral portion of a pelvis, viewed from within; sagittal section to the left of the midline. The viscera and subserous tissue have been removed; the external iliac vessels have been cut and lifted in order to emphasize the tubular character of the vascular lacuna. Medial to the vein is the femoral ring (at arrow B). Vessels converge upon the internal orifice of the obturator canal (arrow C). The iliacus and psoas muscles and the femoral nerve occupy the muscular lacuna.

An indirect inguinal hernia would transverse the inguinal canal in indirect course, from the abdominal orifice (encircled by the ring, *a*), through the subcutaneous fault in the fibers of the external oblique aponeurosis (at arrow A in *a*, between the crura of the ring) to some point beyond the aponeurotic hiatus. Its immediate investment would be the peritoneum, which, as a vaginal process, would be more progressively dilated as herniation progressed. A femoral hernia would, in a more direct course, pass beneath the inguinal ligament upon the pecten of the pubis and between the lacunar ligament medially and the femoral vein laterally (at arrows B, *a* and *d*). An obturator hernia would enter the internal orifice of the obturator canal (*d*, at arrow C).

On the internal aspect, the abdominal wall presents an oval fovea corresponding in position to the femoral ring. Here, as elsewhere, the peritoneum of the fovea rests upon a stratum of connective, known as retroperitoneal (subperitoneal or subserous) tissue. Externally, both on the abdomen and in the proximal thigh, the superficial fascia is bilaminar in character. The deeper portion is locally thickened through inclusion of fat, subcutaneous vessels, and lymph glands. As the subserous tissue is prolonged upon the femoral continuations of the external iliac vessels, it is in turn covered by fascia derived from the parietal musculature. These are, respectively, inner and outer laminae of the femoral sheath. They are carried downward through the vascular lacuna (beneath the inguinal ligament), to lie deep to the superficial fascia of the thigh where the fault in the investing fascia (fascia lata) brings them into contact. The same relations are acquired by any herniating mass which, coming to occupy the most medially situated space in the femoral sheath—namely, the femoral canal—passes in succession through the femoral ring, femoral canal, and fossa ovalis, to subcutaneous position.

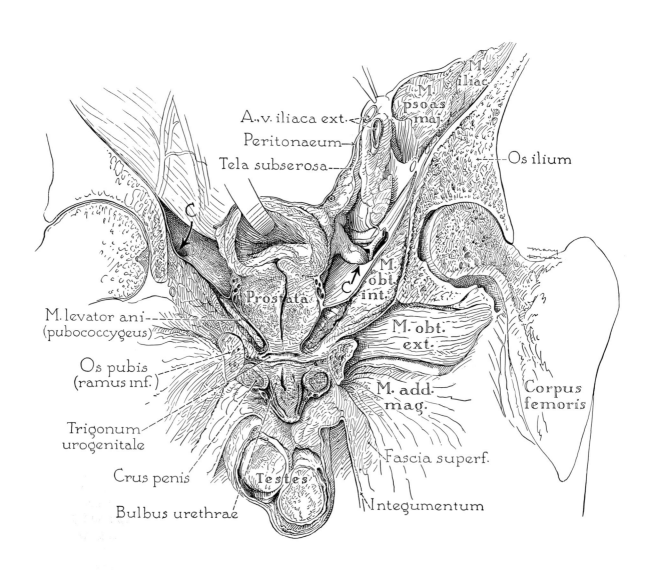

A.,v. iliaca ext.

Peritonaeum

Tela subserosa

M. iliac

M. psoas maj.

Os ilium

C

Prostata

M. obt. int.

M. levator ani (pubococcygeus)

M. obt. ext.

Os pubis (ramus inf.)

M. add. mag.

Corpus femoris

Trigonum urogenitale

Crus penis

Testes

Fascia superf.

Bulbus urethrae

Integumentum

Coronal section of the pelvis of an adult male, viewed from behind.

The section passes posterior to the obturator canals. It cuts the pubococcygeal portion of the levator ani, the sphincteric musculature and fasciae of the deep perineal compartment, the cavernous bodies and muscles in the superficial perineal compartment, the scrotum and testes, and the adductor and obturator muscles of the proximal part of the thigh. Peritoneum and preperitoneal tissue have been elevated on the right side to demonstrate a hernialike lobule of the preperitoneal layer (at arrow C) and the related obturator, artery, vein, and nerve. These layers have been removed on the left (empty obturator canal indicated by arrow). The heavy preperitoneal layer is chiefly fatty; it is relatively thin in the greater pelvis, but thick in the lesser pelvis where it passes between the external iliac vessels and the urinary bladder.

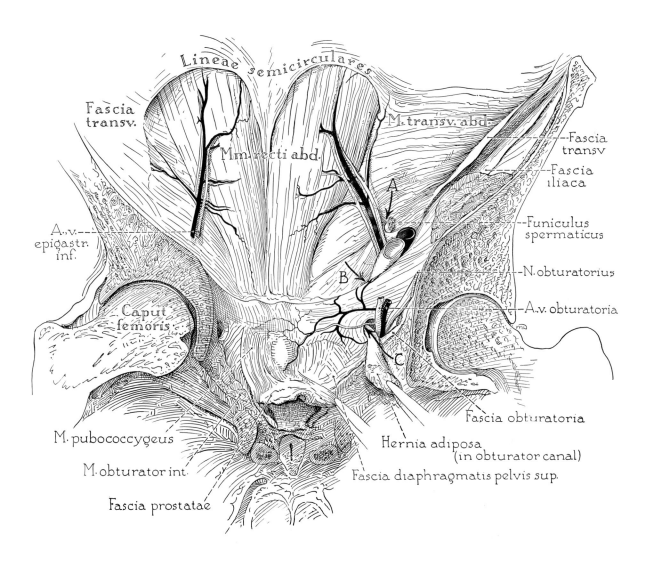

Same specimen, deeper dissection.

The peritoneum and the retroperitoneal tissue have been removed. The hernia adiposa is a finger-like process of the subserous tissue; it has been transected and pulled downward. On the left side the investing fascia has been removed from the levator ani, and from the muscles of the anterior abdominal wall. Additionally, the obturator vessels have been mobilized, the structures of the spermatic cord cut at the abdominal inguinal ring (arrow A) and the iliac vessels transected near the point where they pass beneath the inguinal ligament. On the anterior abdominal wall the serous and subserous strata have likewise been removed. On the left half the internal investing (transversalis) fascia of the transversus abdominis muscle is intact; on the right it has been cut and reflected downward, to reveal the muscle itself. The three hernial areas are thus exposed, and their general relations shown: the inguinal (arrow A) within musculofascial tubes prolonged from the lower abdominal wall; the femoral (arrow B) bounded by ligaments, bone, and blood vessels; the obturator (arrow C), a hiatus in a ligament which is strongly buttressed by the obturator muscles on both the inner (pelvic and outer femoral) aspects.

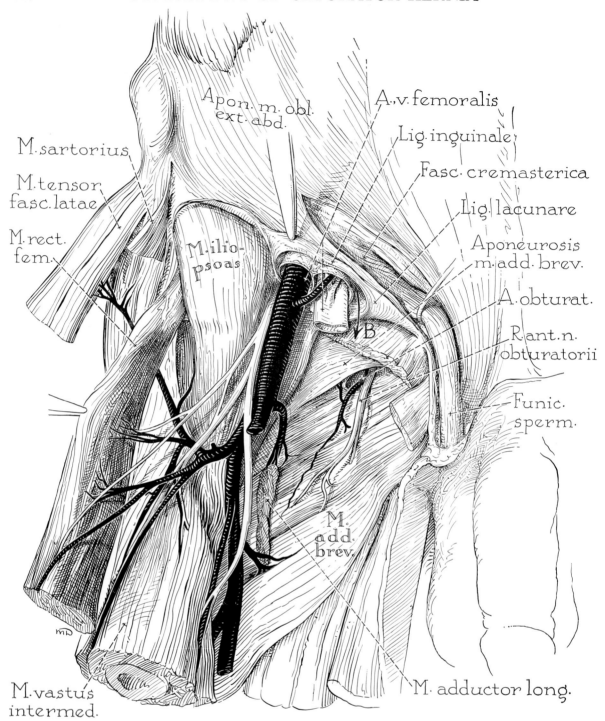

Same specimen, viewed from the front.

In the inguinal region the external oblique aponeurosis has been reflected along the line of the subcutaneous inguinal ring, to expose the internal oblique layer and its cremasteric prolongation upon the spermatic cord. The iliopsoas muscle is shown laterally in the muscular lacuna; also exposed are the femoral vessels, the femoral canal (arrow B) of the vascular lacuna, and the lacunar ligament, which bounds the femoral canal medially. Laterally, the tensor fasciae latae, the sartorius, and the rectus femoris muscles have been cut and turned aside. The femoral vessels, and the pectineus and adductor longus muscles have been cut. By removal of these structures of the obturator area, the aponeurotic origin of the adductor brevis is shown; the aponeourosis overhangs the superior margin of the obturator canal. Beneath this edge the obturator artery and the anterior branch of the obturator nerve emerge, to descend upon the adductor brevis muscle (the latter intact behind the adductor longus).

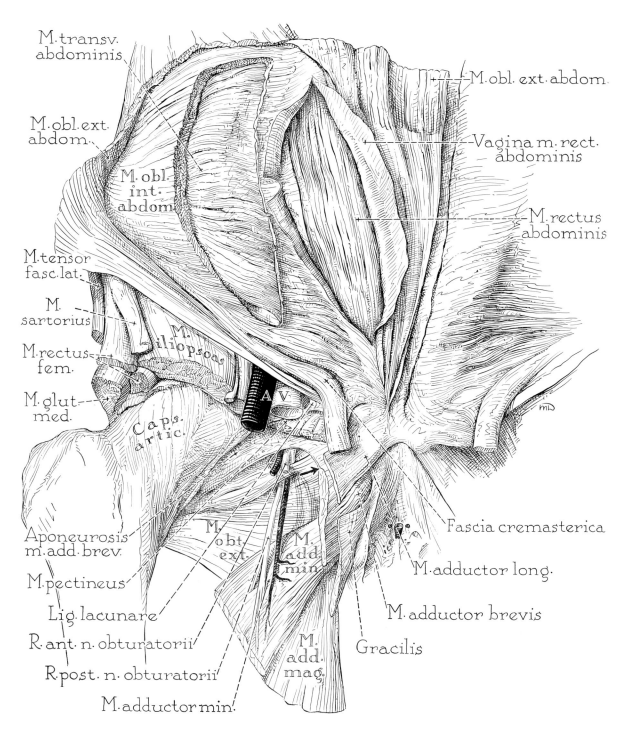

M. transv. abdominis

M. obl. ext. abdom.

M. obl. int. abdom.

M. tensor fasc. lat.

M. sartorius

M. iliopsoas

M. rectus fem.

M. glut. med.

Caps. artic.

A. V.

Aponeurosis m. add. brev.

M. pectineus

Lig. lacunare

R. ant. n. obturatorii

R. post. n. obturatorii

M. adductor min.

M. obt. ext.

M. add. min.

M. add. mag.

M. obl. ext. abdom.

Vagina m. rect. abdominis

M. rectus abdominis

Fascia cremasterica

M. adductor long.

M. adductor brevis

Gracilis

Same specimen, dissection continued.

The external oblique has been turned aside, and a window cut in the internal oblique to reveal the subjacent transverse abdominal muscle. The rectus sheath has been opened by a longitudinal incision. In the thigh the following muscles have been cut: tensor fasciae latae; sartorius; rectus femoris (both heads); iliopsoas; pectineus; adductor longus; adductor brevis; adductor magnus; obturator externus. The adductor brevis has been cut in such a way as to demonstrate that the adductor brevis muscle arises not only from the inferior pubic ramus, but also from the superior ramus (lateral to the arrow) and from the capsular tissue of the hip joint. The anterior division of the obturator nerve has been cut near the point of emergence from the foramen; the posterior division remains intact.

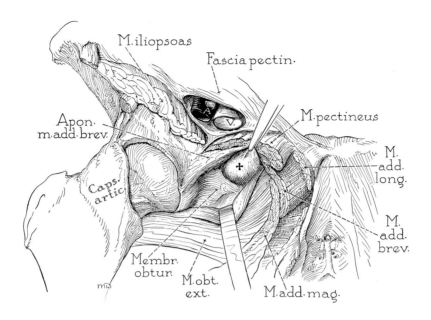

Same specimen. Dissection concluded; carried to the level of the obturator membrane and obturator canal.

The capsule of the hip joint has been partly removed to show the relation between the obturator structures and the head of the femur. The pectineus and the adductor longus have been cut close to their origins. The adductor brevis muscle and its aponeurosis have been retracted cranialward with the underlying hernial protrusion (at +). The obturator externus has been freed from the obturator membrane, and retracted caudalward. It is hereby demonstrated that the origin of the adductor brevis extends lateralward to fuse with the capsule of the hip joint, and that, in being thus prolonged, it normally covers the external aperture of the obturator canal (latter here occupied by a hernial mass).

As these dissections demonstrate, muscles, membranes, and ligaments guard the obturator canal. The orifices are small; the canal transmits lesser nerves and vessels.

In the femoral region, on the other hand, the "space" within the sheath is filled in approximately the lateral two-thirds by vessels, but is empty (save for areolar tissue and lymphatic elements) in its medial one-third (see pages 608 and 609). The peritoneum rests almost directly against the internal orifice (femoral ring) of the canal; only a thin stratum of retroperitoneal tissue intervenes. The latter relationship makes for weakness against herniation. However, some strength is lent by other factors, namely, a strong ligament (lacunar) medially, a taut ligament (inguinal) superiorly, a bone (pubis) inferiorly, and vessels (femoral) laterally.

The inguinal is even less resistant than the femoral. In descent of an indirect hernia a funicular "space" is merely made more capacious, displacement of investing coats being possible on three of the four aspects. In succession, the abdominal orifice is dilated, the inguinal opening distended, and the space bounded by the crura at the subcutaneous "ring" is widened. Once the peritoneal diverticulum is occupied, further extension is not hindered by presence of strongly resisting structures. When the hernia has reached a point midway between the "rings," the overlying external oblique is represented by fascia bridging the gaps between the aponeurotic crura; the crura are displaceable and the fascia is extensible. The cremasteric derivative of the internal oblique is regularly fascial and the funicular derivative of the transverse abdominal muscle is usually of like structure. As the hernial mass advances, it dilates in succession, a serous layer (the processus vaginalis), a thin subserous stratum and three layers which are chiefly fascial. Of the three areas, the inguinal is least well guarded by musculature and skeletal structure; the obturator is most effectually barricaded. Upon the basis of anatomical structure it would be expected that herniation would occur in the following order of frequency: inguinal, femoral, and obturator—an order actually obtaining, as evidenced by laboratory and clinical records.

INDEX

The indexing is designed to meet the special needs of the student in the laboratory. Throughout, the arrangement is selective; it guides the student to the illustration, or to sets of figures, which most serviceably portray the topographical features of an area or the gross anatomy of the particular structures encountered therein.

ABDOMEN, 311–429
  components, description, 3, 4
  musculature, anterolateral, 313
    layers, 314–318
Acetabulum, 433
Acromion, 139
Adminiculum lineae albae, 342
Adrenal gland, 416
Ala(ae)
  magnae oss. sphenoidalis, 23
  ossis ilium, 433
  parvae oss. sphenoidalis, 23
  vomeris, 28
Ampulla(ae)
  ductus deferentis, 409
  recti, 453
Angulus(i)
  mandibulae, 31
  mastoideus oss. parietalis, 26
  oculi, 97
  parietalis oss. sphenoidalis, 26
  scapulae, 139
  superior pyramidis, 24
Ankle joint, 524
Annulus(i)
  femoralis, 330
  fibrocartilagineus membranae tympani, 69
  haemorrhoidalis (zona), 447
  inguinalis, deep, 330
    female, 332
    male, 334
    subcutaneous, 332
Ansa hypoglossi, 84
Anthelix, 68
Antitragus, 68
Antrum
  mastoideum, 72
  tympanicum, 72
Anus, 447
Anvil (incus), 69, 72
Aorta
  abdominal, branches of, 365
  arch, 260
  ascending branches, anterior view, 252
    variations, 261–264

Aorta (Continued)
  thoracic, 281, 282
Apertura
  aquaeductus vestibuli, 20
  canaliculus cochleae, 24
  sinus sphenoidalis, 23
Apex (Apices)
  capituli fibulae, 521
  pulmonis, 201, 269
  pyramidis, 13
Aponeurosis(es)
  inguinalis, continuities, 328–331
  of abdominal muscles, 322
  palmaris, 208
  plantaris, 371, 572
Appendix
  fibrosa hepatis, 379
  vermiformis, blood supply, 369
    variations, 387–389
Aquaeductus
  cerebri (Sylvii), 87, 88
  vestibuli, 75
Arachnoidea
  encephali, 92
  spinalis, 294
Arcus (arch)
  anterior atlantis, 224, 227
  aortae, in situ, 260
    variations of branching, 262–264
  palmaris. See Arcus volaris.
  pharyngopalatinus, 50
  posterior atlantis, 224, 227
  superciliaris, 25
  tendineus
    fasciae pelvis, 483
    m. levatoris ani, 473
  venosus
    digitalis, 187
    dorsalis pedis, cutaneus, 582
    juguli, 129
    vertebrae, 223
  volaris, deep, arterial, 210–213
    variations, 218
    superficial, variations, 217
Arteria(ae). See also Vessels.
  alveolaris inferior, 48

Arteria(ae) (Continued)
  anonyma, 115
  appendicularis, 406
  arcuata, 593
  auricularis posterior, 48
  axillaris, 188, 190
  basilaris, 94
  brachialis, 190, 196
    variations, 201
  brachiocephalic, 115
  bronchialis, origins, variations, 270
    posterior aspect, 292, 293
    types, 270
  buccinatoria, 48
  bulbi
    urethrae, 498
    vestibuli (vaginae), 492
  caecalis, 406
  carotid, external, branches, 111
    internal, branches, 94
  carotis
    communis, 115
    externa, 117
    interna, 117
  cerebelli
    inferiores, 94
    superior, 85, 94
  cerebri
    anterior, 87, 94
    media, 93
    posterior, 94
  cervicalis
    ascendens, 124
    profunda, 135
    superficialis, 124
  ciliares posteriores, 80
  circumflexa
    humeri anterior, 188, 194
    humeri posterior, 188, 194
    ilium profunda, 496
    ilium superficialis, 601
    scapulae, 194, 195
  clitoridis, 492
  coeliaca, branches, 367, 392
  colic, 403
    variations in origin, 404, 405

Arteria(ae) (Continued)
  collaterales ulnaris, 201
  communicans
    anterior, 94
    posterior, 94
  coronaria (cordis)
    dextra, 280
    sinistra, 280
  cystic, variations, 393, 394
  deferentialis, 512
  digitales
    pedis, 593
    volares communes, 200, 212
    volares propriae, 212, 213
  dorsalis
    nasi, 47
    pedis, 593
    penis, 495
  epigastrica
    inferior, in abdominal wall, 327, 608
      internal view, 341, 615
    superficial, 601
    superior, 246
  esophageal, 281, 282
  ethmoidales, 64, 86
  femoralis
    course and tributaries, 583–585
    in femoral triangle, 616
    profunda, 584
    sheath of, 330
  frontalis, 47–49
  gastricae, 397, 398
    diagrammatic, 365
  gastroduodenalis, 397–399
  gastroepiploicae, 397
    omental branches, 362
  glutaeae, external course, 505
    intrapelvic course, 493–495
    posterolateral views, 586–588
  haemorrhoidalis
    inferior, 491
    media, 490
    superior, distribution, 498
      origin, 407
  hepatica, 378
  hepatica propria, 378
  hypogastrica, 486–490
    variations in branching, 501
  iliocolica, 402
    variations in origin, 404, 405
  iliaca
    communis, 504
    externa, 490
  iliolumbalis, 494
  infraorbitalis, 47
  intercostalis
    anterior, 257
    posterior, 256
    suprema, 287
  interossea
    dorsalis, 197
    recurrens, 197
    volaris, 200
  intestinales, 400, 401
  labial branch, of facial, 47, 48
    of perineal, 491
  laryngea superior, 115
  lienalis, 397, 398
    diagrammatic, 365
    in situ, 364
  lingualis, 111
  lumbales, 425

Arteria(ae) (Continued)
  mammaria
    interna, 257
    origins, 255
    superficialis, 254
  maxillaris
    externa, 47, 48
    interna, 48, 49
  mediana, 199, 205
  meningea media
    origin, 49
    in dura mater, 93
  mentalis, 48
  mesenterica
    inferior, 369
      variations, 407
    superior, branch of, 368
      variations, 404, 405
  metacarpeae
    dorsales, 214
    volares, 212, 213, 215
  metatarseae, 593
  musculophrenica, 257
  nasales, 64
  obturatoria, in thigh, 594
    pelvic branches, 495, 496
    variations, 500
  occipitalis, origin, 48
    course, 135
  oesophageae, 281, 282
  of buttock, 595
  of cecum and vermiform appendix, 402
  of duodenum and pancreas, 399
  of forearm, posterior, 197
    relations to nerves, 205
    and hand, anterior, 199, 200
      palmar relations, 216
  of hand, dorsal, osseous relations, 214
    lateral and palmar views, 212, 213
    palmar (diagrammatic), 215
  of head, deep, 49
  of iliac fossa, 496
  of penis, 495
  of perineal compartments, female, 492
  of perineum, male, 497–499
  of shoulder, 188
    and arm, dorsal views, 195, 196
  of small intestine, 400, 401
  of stomach, pancreas and spleen, 392
  of upper abdominal organs, 397, 398
  of vermiform appendix, variations, 406
  omentales, 397
  ophthalmica, 86
  ovarica, 486–488
  palatina
    ascendens, 50
    descendens, 50
    major, 50
    minor, 64
  palpebrales mediales, 47
  pancreaticae, 398
  pancreaticoduodenales, 397, 398
  pelvic, medial aspect, 493, 494
    perineal, 493–499
  penis, 495
  perforantes, 589
  perinei, female, 491, 492
    male, 497, 498
  peronaea, 597
  pharyngea ascendens, 50

Arteria(ae) (Continued)
  phrenica inferior, 410, 411
  plantares, 593
  poplitea, 590, 591
    terminal branches, 597
  princeps pollicis, 210
  profunda
    brachii, 195
    femoris, 584, 585
    penis, 497, 498
  pudenda
    externa, 600, 601
    interna, origin, 488
      course and branches, 494, 495
  pulmonalis, origin, 280
    branches, 273
  radialis, 198, 199, 205
    variations, 201
  recurrens
    radialis, 200, 201
    ulnaris, 200
  renalis, 412–414
  sacralis
    lateralis, 493–495
    media, 489, 490
  scrotales posteriores, 498
  sigmoideae, 403, 404
  spermatica
    externa, 330
    interna, course, 351, 352
      origin, 412–414
  sphenopalatina, 64
  spinales, 94
  sternocleidomastoidea, 49
  subclavian, origin and branches, 119
    retrotracheal, 264
    topography of, 261
  sublingualis, 49
  submentalis, 48
  subscapularis, 188
  supraorbitalis, 47, 48
  suprarenal, 410
  tarseae, 593
  temporales
    media, 48, 49
    profundae, 49
    superficialis, 47
  thoracalis lateralis, 189, 190
  thoracoacromialis, 190
  thoracodorsalis, 189
  thymicae, 259
  thyreoidea
    inferior, 115, 121
    superior, 115, 121
  tibialis
    anterior, 597
    posterior, 598
  to anterior muscles of thigh, 594
  to posterior muscles of thigh, 595
  tonsillaris, 50
  tracheales, 281
  transversa
    colli, 115
    faciei, 47
    scapulae, distribution, 188
      origin, 115
  tympanica anterior, 49
  ulnaris, 199, 200, 205
    variations, 201
  umbilicalis, 490
  ureterica, 487
  uterina, 486–488

Arteria(ae) (Continued)
  vertebralis, course, 120
    terminus, 94
  vesicales, 490
Articulatio. See also *Joints.*
  carpometacarpeae, 145, 146
  cubiti, 144
  intermetacarpeae, 145, 146
  metacarpophalangeae, 145, **146**
  radiocarpea, 145, 146
  radioulnaris, 144–146
  sacroiliaca, 437
  scapulohumeral, 143
  tarsometatarsea, 524
  tibiofibularis, 523, 524
Articulations of the phalanges (hand),
  145, 146
Arytenoid cartilage, 131
Atlas, 224
Atrium cordis
  dextrum, 275–278
    wall, variations, 279
  sinistrum, 275–278
Attachments, muscular. See *Muscles, attachments.*
Auditory canals, 73–75
Auricula of ear, 66–68
Axilla, boundaries and contents, 202
  cavity, 156
  muscles, deep dissection, 160
  nerves and muscles, deep, 126
  vessels and nerves, 189, 190
Axis
  of spine, 224
  optica, 83

Back (and thorax), 221–309
  components, 4
  musculature, 232–239
  skeletal parts, 223–227
Basis
  mandibulae, 31
  stapedis, 75
Bicuspid teeth (premolars), 32
Bifurcatio tracheae, 267
Bladder. See *Vesica.*
Bone(s). (For individual bones see *Os.*)
  carpal, relations to extensor tendons,
    183
    relations to flexor tendons, 182
  cranial, from within, 91
  of ear, *in situ*, 69
  of foot, 527, 528
  of pelvis, anterolateral view, 434
Brachial plexus. See *Plexus.*
Brain, arteries and veins, at base, 94
  inferior aspect, 90
  lateral aspect, 89
  midsagittal section, 89
  posterior aspect, 90
  veins of, superficial, 93
Bronchi, 292, 293
  subdivisions of, 267
Bulbus
  oculi, 81–84
  olfactorius, 85
  urethrae, 450, 452
  vestibuli, 467, 468
Bursa, omental, 354

Caecum. See *Cecum.*
Calcaneus, 524
Camera oculi, 83
Canal for tensor tympani muscle, **72**
Canalis(es)
  analis, 447, 448
  caroticus, foramina of, 24
  condyloideus, 22
  facialis, 72
  femoralis, 608
  hypoglossi, 22
  incisivus, 29
  inguinalis, 348, **349**
  mandibulae, 54
  obturatorius, 435
  pharyngeas, 23
  pterygoideus, 23
  semicirculares, 74, **75**
Capitulum
  fibulae, 521
  humeri, 141
  mallei, 72
  mandibulae, 31
  radii, 142
  stapedis, 72
  ulnae, 142
Caput
  femoris, 519
    section of, 522
  humeri, 141
  in situ, 195, 197
Cardia, of stomach, **383**
Cartilago
  alaris major, 64
  alaris minor, 64
  arytaenoidea, 131, 134
  corniculata, 131
  cricoidea, 133, 134
  epiglottica, 133, 134
  nasi lateralis, 64
  septi nasi, 64
  thyreoida, 131, 133, 134
    muscular attachments, external, 130
Caruncula lacrimalis, 77
Cauda
  equina, 296, 297
  helicis, 68
Cavitas glenoidalis scapulae, 139
Cavity(ies), cranial, dissections (internal),
  85, 86
    fossae and orbits, 85
  peritoneal, 370
Cavum
  conchae, 68
  epidurale, 294
  peritonaei, 357
  subarachnoideale, 294
  subdurale, 294
  tympani, 69, 70
Cecum, 387, 388
  attachment of (variations), 390
  internal view, 391
  relations of (variations), 387–389
Cellulae
  ethmoidales, 37
  mastoideae, 37
  tympanicae, 70
Centrum tendineum (diaphragmatis), 245
Cerebellum, 93–95
  section, 87
  hemispheres, 90
Cerebrum, 87–93

Cerebrum (Continued)
  convolutions, 92
  cortex, 92
  gyri, 92
  lobes, 89
  peduncles, 86
  sulci, 92
Cervical plexus, 123
Cervix uteri, 475, 479, 481
Chest, muscles of, 156–160
Chiasma opticum, 90
Chorda
  obliqua, 144
  tympani, 49
Chorioidea, 83
Ciliary body, 83, 84
Ciliary processes, 83, 84
Circulation, cerebrospinal, 53
  collateral arterial, head, neck, thorax,
    52
Circulus arteriosus (Willisi), 94
Circumferentia articularis radii, ulnae,
  142
Cisterna
  chyli, 426, 427
  of brain, 53
Clavicle, ligaments, 143
  muscular attachments, **149**
Clavicula, 140
Clitoris, 467
Coccyx, 224
  attachments of, 434–436
Cochlea, 73–75
  window, 74
Colliculus seminalis, 409
Collum
  anatomicum humeri, 141
  chirurgicum humeri, 141
  femoris, 519
  mandibulae, 31
  radii, 142
  scapulae, 139
  vesicae felleae, 384
Colon
  ascendens, arteries, 403–405
    attachment (developmental), 355
      variations, 390
    in situ, 359
  descendens, arteries, 404
    attachment, 354, 355
    in situ, 361
  sigmoideum, arteries of, 403
    attachment, 357
    in situ, 370
    relations, 351
    variations, 444, 445
  transversum, arteries, 403–405
    attachment, 360, 361, 363
    in situ, 359
    relations, 363, 364
Columna(ae)
  rectales (Morgagnii), 447
  renales (Bertini), 408
  vertebralis, 226
Commissura (cerebri)
  anterior, 87, 88
  posterior, 87
Compartment(s), interosseous (of hand),
  palmar view, 211
  midpalmar, 208, 209
    cross section, 210
  of perineum, 450, 451

Concha(ae)
  auriculae, 68
  nasales (bones), **27**
    dissection of, 64
Condylus(i)
  occipitalis, 22
  femoris, 519, 523
  tibiae, 520
Conjunctiva, 79
Conus
  arteriosus, 276
  elasticus laryngis, 131
  medullaris, 296
Cor. See *Heart*.
Cord, spermatic, investments of, 349
    layers of, 334
  spinal, level of termination, 295, 296
    segments of, 297
    transverse sections, 294
Cornea, 83
Corniculate cartilage, 131
Cornu (cornua)
  anterius ventriculi lateralis, 88
  cartilaginis thyreoideae, 131
  coccygea, 224
  inferius marginis falciformis, 529
  inferius ventriculi lateralis, 88
  superius marginis falciformis, 529
  superius ventriculi lateralis, 88
Corpus
  callosum, 87, 88
  cavernosum urethrae, 457
  ciliare, 83
  clitoridis, 467
  fornicis, 87, 88
  incidus, 72
  linguae, longitudinal section, **87**
    cross section, 132
  mammillare, 87
  mandibulae, 31
  ossis hyoidei, 131
  penis, 452
  pineale, 87, 88
  sphenoidalis, 23
  sterni, 140
    internal relations, **246**
  uteri, 479
  ventriculi, 383
  vertebrae, 223
  vesicae felleae, 384
  vitreum, 83
Cranium. See also *Skull*.
  fossae, 35
  internal topography, 94
Crest. See *Crista*.
Cricoid cartilage, 131–134
Crista(ae)
  ampullaris, 75
  anterior tibiae, 520
  buccinatoria, 31
  conchalis, 27, 29, 30
  frontalis, 19, 25
  galli, 19, 27
  iliaca, 434, 542
  infratemporalis, 23, **33**
  interossea
    fibulae, 521
    radii, 142
    tibiae, 520
    ulnae, 142
  intertrochanterica, 519
  m. supinatoris, 142

Crista(ae) (Continued)
  nasalis, 28–30
  occipitalis externa, 22
  sacrales, 224
  sphenoidalis, 23
  tuberculi majoris, 141
  tuberculi minoris, 141
  urethralis, 409
Crus (crura)
  anthelicus, 68
  clitoridis, 470, 492
  helicis, 68
  incudis, 69, 72
  of inguinal ring, 349
  penis, 498, 614
  stapedis, 72
Cuneus, 87
Cupula pleurae, 106
Curvaturae ventriculi, 383
Cusps of heart valves, 276–278
Cymba conchae, 68

DENS EPISTROPHEI, 227
Diaphragma
  pelvis, 450–452
    female, 484, 485
      inferior aspect, 471–473
      lateral aspect, 474
      muscles of, 464
    respiratoria, inferior aspect, 425
      superior aspect, 245, 253
    sellae, 86
    urogenitale (male), external aspect, 461, 462
      sections of, 450, 451
Digestive tube, 359–364
Diploe, 92
Divisions of body, primary, 3, 4
Dorsum
  linguae, 132, 134
  sellae, 23
Ductus
  arteriosus, Botalli, 274
    diagram, 272
  Botalli, 274
  choledochus, 378, 379
  cochlearis, 73
  cysticus, 384
  deferens, diagrammatic, 409
    in situ, 348, 349
  ejaculatorii, 510
  endolymphaticus, 74
  hepaticus, 378, 379
  lacrimalis, 77
  lingualis, 87
  nasolacrimalis, 77
  pancreaticus, 384
    accessorius, 384
  parotideus, 59, 60
  perilymphaticus, 74
  prostaticus, 409
  saccularis, 74, 75
  Santorini, 384
  semicircularis, 74, 75
  Stenonis, 59, 60
  submaxillaris, 49
  thoracicus, lumbar portion (variations), 426, 427
    position and connections, 286, 287

Ductus (Continued)
  utricularis, 74, 75
  Whartoni, 49
  Wirsungi, 384
Duodenum, arteries, 398, 399
  form (variations), 385
  in situ, 384
Dura mater
  encephali, 92–94
  spinalis, 294–296

EAR, 65–75
  air cells, 70
  auricula, 66–68
  cochlear structures, 73
  external, development of, 66
  internal acoustic meatus, fundus, 76
  labyrinth, bony
    in situ, 71
    sections, 75
  parts of, diagrammatic, 74
  tympanic cavity and environs, 72
Eminentia
  iliopectinea, 435
  pyramidalis, 72
Emissaria (veins), 92
Encephalon, 87–95
Epicondyli
  femoris, 519, 523
  humeri, 141, 144
Epicranius, 40
Epididymis, 409
Epiglottis, 131–134
Epistropheus (axis), 224, 227
Erectile bodies, 450
Esophagus, arteries of, 281, 282
  at diaphragm, 245
  posterior views, 292, 293
  relations in neck, 107
  sagittal view, 87
Ethmoidal cells, 37, 38
Eustachian (auditory) tube, 70, 74
Excavatio
  rectouterina (cavum Douglasi), 507, 508
  rectovesicalis, 510
Extremitas
  acromialis claviculae, 140
  sternalis claviculae, 140
Extremity, lower, 519–604
  upper, 139–220
Eye, 78–84
  bulb and socket, anterior view, 79
    ciliary region, 84
    horizontal section, 83
    layers of its wall, 81
  bulbus oculi (description), 78
  muscles of, 79–82

FACE, frontal section, 132
  muscles of, 41–43
Facies
  articularis
    acromialis claviculae, 140
    epistrophei, 224
    incudi, 72
    malleoli lateralis, 520, 521

Facies (Continued)
  articularis
    malleoli medialis, 520, **521**
    sacri, 224
    sternalis, 140
    tibiae inferior, 520
    tibiae superior, 520
    vertebrae, 223, 224
  cerebralis
    oss. frontalis, 25
    sphenoidalis, 23
    temporalis, 24
  costalis scapulae, 139
  dorsalis scapulae, 139
  fibulae, 521
  frontalis, oss. frontalis, 25
  humeri, 141
  inferior pyramidis, 24
  infratemporalis sphenoidalis, 23
  malaris, oss. zygomatici, 30
  maxillaris, oss. palatini, 30
  medialis palatini, 30
  orbitalis
    oss. frontalis, 25
    sphenoidalis, 23
    zygomatici, 30
  patellaris femoris, 519
  posterior pyramidis, 24
  radii, 142
  symphyseos, 434
  temporalis
    oss. frontalis, 25
    oss. temporalis, 24
  tibiae, 521
  ulnae, 142
Falx
  cerebri, 94
  inguinalis (aponeurotica), 337
Fascia(ae)
  colli, 101, 102
  cremasterica, abdominal level, 332
    in scrotum, 349, 350
  cruris, 558
  diaphragmatis pelvis, 483
    diagrammatic, 450
  dorsalis pedis, 563
  endopelvina, female, 482, 483
    male, 513
  hypothenaris, 208
  iliaca, 435
    diagrammatic, 450
  iliopsoas, 331
  inguinalis, continuities of, 328–331
  inguinofemoral, 610, 611
  innominata, 346
  lata, 599, 610
  lumbodorsalis (thoracolumbalis), 234
    cross section, 325
    sacral limits, 542
  manus, 208–211
  obturatoria, 435
    diagrammatic, 450
  parotideomasseterica, 42
  pectinea, 610
    in section, 331
  pelvis, diagrammatic, 449, 450
    female, 483
    medial view, 435
  perinei, female, 466
    penile portion (male), 458
  prostatae, 454
  psoas, 331
  rectalis, 481–483

Fascia(ae) (Continued)
  renalis, 418
  spermatica externa, interna, 349, 350
  temporalis, 48
  thenaris, 208
  transversalis, external layer, 317
    internal layer, 318
  uterovaginalis, 481, 482
  vesicalis, 481, 482
Femur, articulations, 522, 523
  external topography, 519
  relations of shaft, 536
Fenestra cochleae, vestibuli, 72, **75**
Fetus, ductus arteriosus in, 274
  skull in, 17
Fibrae intercrurales, 346
Fibrocartilago
  interpubica, 513
  intervertebralis, 227
Fibula, external topography, 521
  ligaments of, 523, 524
Fila radicularia n. spinalis, 299
Filum terminale, 296
Fissura
  antitragicohelicina, 68
  longitudinalis cerebri, 92, **93**
  orbitalis
    inferior, 29
    superior, 19, 23
  petrotympanica, 24
  pterygoidea, 23
  tympanomastoidea, **24**
Flexura
  duodeni inferior, 385
  duodeni superior, 385
  duodenojejunalis, 385
Fluid, cerebrospinal, 53
Fontanelles, 17
Foot, ligaments of, 524
  muscles of, 570–575
  muscular attachments, 527, **528**
  vessels and nerves, 593
Foramen (foramina)
  caecum, oss. frontalis, 25
  carotica, 24
  ethmoidalia, 35
  infraorbitale, 29
  interventriculare, 88
  intervertebrale, 227
  ischiadicum, internal aspect, **549**
    nerves in, 505
  majus, 437
  minus, 437
  jugulare, 19, 20
  lacerum, 35
  magnum, 22
  mandibulare, 31
  mastoideum, 24
  mentale, 31
  Monroi, 88
  nasale, 29
  nutricium, 141, 142
  obturatum, 434
  occipitale magnum, **22**
  of skull, 19, 20
  of sphenoid bone, **23**
  opticum, 35
  ovale (cordis), 279
  palatina, 30
  parietale, 26
  rotundum, 35
  sacralia, 224

Foramen (foramina) (Continued)
  spinosum, 16
  supraorbitale, 25
  stylomastoideum, 16
  zygomasticofaciale, 30
  zygomasticoorbitale, 30
Forearm
  arteries and nerves, anterior, 199, 200
    deep, 199, 200
  nerves and vessels, anterior, 198
    superficial, 198
Fornix cerebri, 87, 88
Fossa
  coronoidea, 141
  cranial, 35, 36
  cubital, deep dissection, 206
    structures in, 198
  digastrica, 31
  ductus venosi, 380
  iliaca, 605
  iliopectinea, 330
  infraspinata, 139
  intercondyloidea femoris, 519
    tibiae, 520
  ischiorectalis, female, 468
    in section, 449
  jugularis, 16
  mandibularis, 24
  mastoidea, 24
  occipitalis, 22
  of gallbladder, 380
  olecrani, 141
  ovalis fasciae latae (hiatus saphenus), 502
    variations in, 603, 604
  pterygoidea, 23
  radialis humeri, 141
  retroureterica, 409
  subarcuata, 19, 20
  subscapularis, 139
  supraspinata, 139
  trochanterica, 519
  venae cavae, 380, 381
    umbilicalis, 380
  vesicae felleae, 380
Fossulae fenestrae cochleae, 72, 74
Fovea(ae)
  capitis femoris, 519
  capituli radii, 142
  centralis (retinae), 83
  inguinales, 352
  pterygoidea processus condyloidei, 31
  sublingualis, 31
  submaxillaris, 31
  supravesicalis, 348, 352
Foveolae
  gastricae, 383
  granulares (Pacchioni), 92
Frenula valvulae coli, 391
Fundus
  uteri, 479, 480
  ventriculi, 383
  vesicae felleae, 384
Funiculus spermaticus, 352

GALEA APONEUROTICA, 42
Gallbladder, anomalies, 396
  cystic artery, duct, 382
  internal view, 384

Ganglion(a)
cervicalia, 124, 125
ciliare, 55
sacralia, 509
semilunare, 86
sphenopalatinum, 55
submaxillare, 49
thoracalia, 286
trunci sympathici, 286
Gaster. See *Stomach.*
Glabella, 25
Glandulae(a)
Bartholini, 467
Brunneri, 384
duodenales, 384
gastricae (propriae), 383
inguinal lymph, 602
lacrimales, 54
mammary, arteries of, 254, 255
parotis, 59–61
pituitaria, 87, 88
prostatae, 455, 457
sublingualis, 49
submaxillaris, 124
suprarenales, 414
thyreoidea, 122
vestibularis major, 467
Glans
clitoridis, 452
penis, 452
Granulationes arachnoideales (Pacchioni), 92
Greater tuberosity (of humerus), 141
Gyri cerebri, 87

Hallux, 570–574
Hamulus
lacrimalis, 29
pterygoideus, 23
Hand, arteries and nerves of, 212–220
layers of, 185, 186
muscles of, 153, 154
muscular attachments, 152
Haustra coli, 391
Head, 13–96
parts of, 3
section of, sagittal, 87
Heart, apex of, 276
atrium, left, 280
right, 277, 278, 280
auricle, left, 276
base of, superior view, 276(d)
great vessels, 271–275
in situ, anterior, 252
ventricle, left, 277, 278, 280
right, 277, 278, 280
serous sac, 275
Helix, 68
Hepar. See *Liver.*
Hernia, fatty, 333, 615
femoral, 605–609
inguinal, 346–352
obturator, 614–618
Hiatus
adductor, 556
canalis facialis, 35
maxillaris, 29
sacralis, 224
saphenus, 502

Hiatus (Continued)
semilunaris, 38
tendineus (adductorius), 539
Hilus
lienis, 386
pulmonis, 268, 269
renalis, 408
Hip bone, 434
Hip joint, 522
Humerus, 141
Hyoid bone, 131
Hypophysis (glandula pituitaria), 87, 88

Ileum, 360, 361
Ilium, 433, 434
Impressiones hepatis, 379
Incisura(ae)
anterior auris, 68
cerebelli, 93
clavicularis sterni, 140
costales sterni, 140
ethmoidalis, 25
fibularis, 520
frontalis, 25
intertragica, 68
ischiadicae, 434
jugularis
oss. occipitalis, 22
temporalis, 24
mandibulae, 31
mastoidea, 24
parietalis, 24
scapulae, 139
semilunaris ulnae, 142
sphenopalatina, 30
terminalis, cartilaginis auris, 68
ulnaris radii, 142
Incus, 69, 72
Infundibulum hypophysis, 86
Inscriptiones tendineae, 318
Integumentum abdominis (section), 325
Intestinum
blood supply, 368
caecum, 357
crassum (colon), 360
ileum, 361
jejunum, 361
mesenteries of, 361
rectum, 447, 449
tenue (parts of), 360, 361
Iris, 82, 83
Ischium, 433, 434
Isthmus
cartilaginis auriculae, 68
faucium, 132
glandulae thyreoideae, 87

Jaw, lower, 31
upper, 29
Jejunum, 360, 361
Joints. See also *Articulatio.*
ankle and foot, 524
elbow and radioulnar, 144
forearm (distal) and hand, 145, 146
hip, 522
muscular relations, posterior, 545

Joints, hip, (Continued)
tendinous relations, posterior, 546
knee, 523
shoulder, 143

Kidney(s), calyx, 408
pelvis, 408
position of (retroperitoneal), 358
variations, 419
relations (cross section), 418
substantia of, 408
variations, 414–417
Knee, cap, 535, 537
joint, 523

Labium(a)
laterale, mediale femoris, 519
majora, minora pudendi, 465
valvulae coli, 391
Labrum glenoidale articulationis coxae, 522
Labyrinthus ethmoidalis, 27
Lacrimal apparatus, 77
Lacrimal bone, 29
Lacrimonasal duct, 77
Lacuna
musculorum, 610
vasorum, 610
Lamina(ae)
cribrosa, 27
fibrocartilaginea interpubica, 433
lateralis, 23
oss. ethmoidalis, 27
papyracea, 27
perpendicularis, 27
processus pterygoidei, 23
quadrigemina, 86, 88
spiralis ossea, 73
tragi, 68
Larynx, 131
relation to pharynx (posterior), 134
Lateral ventricle, 88
Leg, cross section, 558
Lens crystallina, 83
Lesser tuberosity (of humerus), 141
Lien, 386
Ligamentum(a)
accessoria volaria, 145
acromioclaviculare, 143
annulare radii, 144
anococcygeum, 453
apicis dentis, 227
Arantii, 381
arcuatum pubis, 433
arteriosum, 273
basium (ossium metacarpalium)
dorsalia, 145, 146
volaria, 145, 146
bifurcatum, 524
broad (of uterus), 477
dissected, 488, 489
calcaneofibulare, 524
calcaneonaviculare plantare, 524
capituli
costae radiatum, 227
fibulae, 523
capitulorum (ossium metacarpalium)
transversum, 145

Ligamentum(a) (Continued)
cardinale uteri, 479
carpi
dorsale, 183, 186
radiatum, 145
transversum, 208, 209
carpometacarpea, 145, 146
collaterale
fibulare, 523
radiale, 144
tibiale, 523
ulnare, 144
collateralia
carpi, 145, 146
digitorum, 145, 146
coracoacromiale, 143
coracoclaviculare, 143
coronarium hepatis, 379
costotransversaria, 227
cruciatum cruris, 563
cuboideonaviculare dorsale, 524
deltoideum, 524
denticulatum, 294
falciforme hepatis, 379
flavum, 227
fundiforme penis, 313
gastrolienale, 357
Gimbernati, 433
hamatometacarpeum, 145
Hesselbachi, 342
iliofemorale, 522
iliolumbale, 433
inguinale (Pouparti), 332
interfoveolare, 342
interspinalia, 227
laciniatum, 569
lacunare, 433
latum uteri, 477
longitudinalia, 227
malleoli lateralis, 524
navicularicuneiformia, 524
nuchae, 239
of ankle and foot, 524
of hip joint, 522
of knee joint, 523
of pelvis (topography), 433
ovarii proprium, 478
patellae, 563
pectineum, 433
phrenicolienale, 386
pisohamatum, 145
pisometacarpeum, 145
plantare longum, 524
pubicum superius, 433
pubocapsulare, 522
radiocarpea, 145, 146
sacrococcygea, 433
sacroiliaca, 433
sacrospinosum, 437
sacrotuberosum, 437
sphenomandibulare, 48
stylohyoideum, 133
supraspinale, 227
suspensorium ovarii, 477
talocalcanea, 524
talofibularia, 524
talonaviculare (dorsale), 524
talotibialia, 524
tarsometatarsea dorsalia, 524
teres
femoris, 522
hepatis, 379

Ligamentum(a) (Continued)
teres
uteri, external view, 332
internal view, 477
transversum
atlantis, 227
cruris, 563
genu, 523
triangularis hepatis, 379
umbilicale
laterale, 511
mediale, 511
uterosacrale, 478, 479
vaginalia, 204
venosum, 381
ventriculare, 131
vertebrale, 227
vesicovaginale, 482
vocale, 131
Limbus
alveolaris, 31
fossae ovalis, 279
Vieussenii, 279
Linea(ae)
alba, 313
arcuata, 434
aspera femoris, 519
Douglasi, 318, 341
intertrochanterica, 522
mylohyoidea, 31
nuchae inferior, superior, 22
obliqua mandibularis, 31
poplitea, 520
semicircularis
external view, 318
internal view, 341
semilunaris, 318
Spigeli, 318
temporales, 26
transversae oss. sacri, 434
visus, 83
Lingua
cross section, 132
in situ, 49
longitudinal section, 87
Liver, form of (variations), 377
lobes and attachments, 379
porta hepatis and posterior view, 380
venous circulation of, 381
vessels of, 378
Lobulus
auriculae, 68
paracentralis, 87
Lobus
azygos, 266
cerebri, 90
frontalis, 90
hepatis, 381
pulmonis, 265
pyramidalis, 109
Lungs, in situ, anterior view, 251
lobes of, 265
root of, 268, 269
tracheobronchial subdivisions, 267
Lymph glands, inguinal, 599–602

MALLEOLUS
lateralis (of fibula), 521
medialis (of tibia), 520

Malleus, 69
Mandibula, 31
Manubrium
mallei, 69
sterni, 140
Margo(gines)
falciformes, 601
frontalis
oss. parietalis, 26
oss. sphenoidalis, 23
humeri, 141
infraglenoidalis, 520
lambdoideus, 22
mastoideus, 22
occipitalis
oss. parietalis, 26
oss. temporalis, 24
parietalis oss. temporalis, 24
radii, 142
scapulae, 139
sphenoidalis oss. temporalis, 24
squamosus oss. parietalis, 26
supraorbitalis oss. frontalis, 25
temporalis oss. sphenoidalis, 23
ulnae, 142
zygomaticus, 23
Massa intermedia
cerebri, 87
clitoridis, 467
Mastication, muscles of, 44–46
Mastoid process, 24
Maxilla, 29
Meatus (porus) acusticus
externus, bony, 24
section of, 69
internus, aperture, 24
section of, 75
Mediastinum, 272, 273
anterior views, 259, 260
dissection, posterior, 292, 293
superior, vessels of, 129
Medulla
oblongata, 94
spinalis, 294–299
Membra (limbs), components, 4
lower, 519–618
upper, 137–220
Membrana(ae)
atlantooccipitales, 227
hyothyreoidea, 122
interossea
antibrachii, 200
cruris, 562
obturatoria pelvis, external view, 522
internal view, 438
quadrangularis, 131
Reissneri, 73
tectoria, of ear, 73
of skull, 227
tympani, 69
vestibularis, 73
Meninges, diagrammatic, 53
encephali, 92, 93
falx cerebri, in situ, 94
spinales, 299
Menisci articulares, 523
Mesentery, cross sections, 355, 356
development, 353–356
of small intestine, 360, 361
Mesocolon, 363
sigmoid (variations), 446
Midpalmar compartment, 208, 209

Modiolus, 73
Molar teeth, 32
Mouth cavity, 50
Muscles. See *Musculus(i)* for individual muscles.
  abdominal, 313–319
    at inguinal region, 336–339
    costal relations, 320
    internal dissection of, 342, 343
  abductor pollicis longus, variations, 180
  adductors, of thigh, 539, 540
  adjacent to hip joint, anterior view, 540, 541
    posterior, 544–546
  appendicular, thoracic attachments, 243
    vertebral attachments, 232–235
  at hip joint, anteroinferior view, 550
  attachments for mastication, 33
    mandibular, anterior, 130
    on femur, 525
    on foot, 527, 258
      tibia and fibula, 526
    on gluteal region, 547
    on hyoid bone, 130
    on occipital bone, 34
    on thyroid cartilage, external, 130
  axial, 230, 231
  back and shoulder, superficial, *in situ*, 232
  biceps brachii, variations, 171
  cervical, topography of, 249
  crural, lateral views, 563, 564
    posterior, deep, 561, 562
      medial aspect, 560
      superficial, 559
  extensors of hand, variations, 207
  facial, 41–43
  forearm, deep dissection at origins, 206
  gastrocnemius-soleus complex, 565, 566
  gluteal, 542–547
    origins and relations, 439–442
  hamstring, cross sections, 557
  innervation of, table, 304, 305
  neck, posterior, 237, 238
    posterolateral, 236
  neck and shoulder, progressive dissection, 232–239
  obliques of abdomen (variations), 340
  of arm, anterior view, 167
    anterolateral and anteromedial views, 170
    posterior view, 168
  of arm and forearm, 155
  of axillary region, deep, 243
  of back, 1st layer, 161
    2nd layer, 162, 163
  of chest, 240–244
    deep, 159, 160
      description, 244
    superficial, 157, 158
  of ear, 67, 68
  of femoral insertion, intrapelvic, 548, 549
  of foot, 570–575
    dorsal, 570
    plantar, superficial layer, 571
  of forearm, action at wrist, 181
    extensors, lateral view, 177

Muscles, of forearm, (Continued)
  extensors, superficial, 176
  flexors, 172–174
  medial and posterior dissections, 178
  pronators, 175
  of hand, 153, 154
    cross section, 185
  of head, neck and trunk, posterior, 228–230
  of leg, 558–566
    osteofascial compartments, sections, 558
  of mastication, attachments, 33
    topography, 44–46
  of shoulder, anterior view, 165
    posterior, deep dissection, 166
      superficial, 164
  of suboccipital region, 239
  of thigh, 532–541
    by groups, 552
    medial view, deep, 554
    posterior and lateral views, superficial, 553
    posterolateral, deep, 555, 556
  of thigh and leg, actions, schematic, 576–578
  of thoracic wall, anterior internal, 246
  palmar, in relation to flexor tendons, 204
  pectoral topography of, 248, 249
  pelvic, lateral internal, 436
  pelvis-thigh interrelations, anteromedial, 538
  plantar, deep layers, 574, 575
  scapular, anterior view, 243
    attachments, posterior, 233, 235
    deep posterior view, 235
  terminology of, 147, 148
  thigh, anterior and medial, 533–539
    by groups, 532
    in fascial investments, 531
  trunk, by layers, 228–231
Musculus(i)
  abductor digiti quinti
    of foot, 571, 573
    of hand, 204
    hallucis, 571, 572
    pollicis brevis, 204
    pollicis longus, 176, 177
  adductor femoris, 532
    hallucis, 574
    pollicis, 204
  anconaeus, 197
  antitragicus, 68
  aryepiglotticus, 131
  arytaenoideus, 131
  auricularis
    anterior, 42
    posterior, 42
    superior, 42
  biceps
    brachii, 167
      variations, 171
    femoris, 553–557
  brachialis, 169, 172
  brachioradialis, 172–174
  buccinator, 43
  bulbocavernosus, female, 467
    male, 457, 458

Musculus(i) (Continued)
  caninus, 42
  ciliaris, 83
  coccygeus, 435, 436
  constrictores pharyngis, 133, 134
  coracobrachialis, 167, 169
  corrugator, 43
  cremaster, 339
  cricoarytaenoideus, 131
  cricothyreoideus, 131
  deltoideus, anterior view, 157
    posterior view, 164
  depressor septi, 43
  digastricus, 99
  epicranius, 40, 42
  extensor carpi radialis
    brevis, 177, 178
    longus, 177, 178
    tendons of, 181
  extensor carpi ulnaris, 178
  extensor
    digiti quinti proprius, 176
    digitorum
      brevis, 570
      communis, 176
      longus, 563
    hallucis
      brevis, 570
      longus, 563, 564
    indicis proprius, 178
    pollicis
      brevis, 177, 178
      longus, 177, 178
  flexor
    carpi radialis, 179
    carpi ulnaris, 178, 179
    digiti quinti brevis, of foot, 571
      of hand, 173
    digitorum
      brevis, 571, 572
      longus, 561
      profundus, 173
      sublimis, 172
    hallucis
      brevis, 572, 573
      longus, 561
    pollicis
      brevis, 173
      longus, 173
  frontalis, 40
  gastrocnemius, 559, 560
  gemelli, 543, 544
  genioglossus, 87
  geniohyoideus, 109
  glossopalatinus, 50
  glutaeus
    maximus, 542
    medius, 544, 545
    minimus, 545, 546
  gracilis, 532
  helicis
    major, 68
    minor, 68
  hyoglossus, 108
  iliacus, 436, 538
  iliococcygeus, 473, 474
  iliocostales, 230
  iliopsoas, 538
  incisivus labii inferioris, 43
  infraspinatus, 164

Musculus(i) (Continued)
  intercostales
    externi, 242
    interni, 242
  interossei
    of hand, 210
  ischiocavernosus, 452
  latissimus dorsi, insertion, 166
    origin, 234
    relations, 228
  levator
    ani, 164
      section of, 449
    palpebrae superioris, 80, 82
    scapulae, 235–237
    veli palatini, 134
  longissimus, 230
  longus
    capitis, 116
    colli, 286
  lumbricales
    of foot, 573, 574
    of hand, 209
  masseter, 44
  mentalis, 41
  mylohyoideus, 106
  nasalis, 41
  obliquus
    capitis inferior, 239
    capitis superior, 239
    externus abdominis, 314
    inferior oculi, 79
    internus abdominis, 315
    superior oculi, 80
  obturator
    externus, 550
    internus, 548, 549
  occipitalis, 42
  oculi, 79–82
  omohyoideus, 105
  opponens
    digiti quinti, 182
    pollicis, 180, 182
  orbicularis
    oculi, 41
    oris, 41
  ossiculorum auditus, 69
  palmaris
    brevis, 208
    longus, 179
  papillares, 277, 278
  pectineus, 532, 533
  pectoralis
    major, dissections of, 241, 242
      in situ, 240
    minor, *in situ*, 242
      variations, 250
  peronaeus
    brevis, cross section, 558
      in situ, 563
      tendons, 567
    longus, cross section, 558
      in situ, 563
      tendons, 567
    tertius, 563
  pharyngopalatinus, 132, 134
  piriformis
    external view, 543
    internal view, 548
  plantaris, 559, 560
  popliteus, 561, 562
  procerus, 41

Musculus(i) (Continued)
  pronator
    quadratus, 173
    teres, 169
  psoas
    major, 436
      cross section, 325
    minor, 538
  pterygoideus
    externus, 46
    internus, 46
  pubococcygeus, 473
  pyramidalis, 332
    variations, 335
  quadratus
    femoris, 544
    labii
      inferioris, 41–43
      superioris, 41–43
    lumborum, 503
      cross section, 325
    plantae, 572, 574
  quadriceps femoris, 534, 535
    cross sections, 536
  recti oculi, 79–82
  rectus
    abdominis, 318
      variations, 324, 325
    capitis posterior
      major, 239
      minor, 239
    femoris, 534–536
  rhomboideus
    major, 233
    minor, 233
  risorius, 41–43
  sacrospinalis, 230, 235
    cross section, 325
  sartorius, 532, 534
  scalenus
    anterior, 106, 107
    medius, 106, 107
    posterior, 106, 107
  semimembranosus, 553, 554
  semispinalis, 238, 239
  semitendinosus, 553, 554
  serratus
    anterior, anterior view, 160
      posterior view, 235
    posterior
      inferior, 229
      superior, 229
  soleus, 559, 560
    cross section, 558
  sphincter ani
    externus, 447
    internus, 447
  sphincter urethrae membranaceae, 497
  spinales, 230
  splenius, 235, 236
  stapedius (tendon), 72
  sternocleidomastoideus, 99
  sternohyoideus, 104–106
  sternothyreoideus, 104
  styloglossus, 108
  stylohyoideus, 104, 105
  stylopharyngeus, 108
  subclavius, 160
  subscapularis, 165, 166
  supinator, 172
  supraspinatus, 140
  temporalis, 44, 45

Musculus(i) (Continued)
  tensor
    fasciae latae, 533
      origin, 584
    plicae Douglasi, 341
    tympani, 72
  teres
    major, 164, 166
    minor, 168
  thyreoarytaenoideus, 131
  thyreoepiglotticus, 131
  tibialis
    anterior, 563
    tendon, 560
    posterior, 561, 562
  tragicus, 68
  transversus
    abdominis, 338
      variations, 340
    perinei profundus superficialis, 469
    thoracis, 246
  trapezius, 161
  triangularis, 41, 42
  triceps brachii, 167, 168
  vasti, 534, 535
  zygomaticus, 41–43

Nares, 64
Navel (umbilicus), 313
Neck, 99–135
  anterior and lateral regions
    progressive dissection of, 110–114
    arteries of, 115
      connections with aorta, 117, 118
    deep anatomy (description), 127
      structures, anterolateral, inferior
        part, 116
    fascia (cross section), 101
      description, 101, 102
    musculature, anterior view, 106
      anterolateral views, 104, 105
      lateral (deep), 107
      platysma, 103
      suprahyoid, 108, 109
    nerves, superficial, plexus of, 123
      muscles and deep, 126
    parts of, 3
    posterior (nuchal region), 135
    section of, sagittal, 87
    triangles of, 99, 100
    veins of, anterior, 129
    vessels and nerves, superior aspect,
      191, 192
    of thyroid gland, 121
Nervus(i)
  abducens, 81
  accessorius, 100
  acusticus, 90
  alveolares, 54, 55
  auricularis magnus, 123, 124
  auriculotemporalis, 47–49
  autonomic, cervical sympathetic, 124
    neck and thorax, 306
  axillaris, 193
  buccinatorius, 48
  cardiaci, 306
  cervicales, 123
  common peroneal, relation, branches,
    597

Nervus(i) (Continued)
cranial, at base of brain, 95
list of attributes, 96
craniosacral, diagrammatic, 308
cutaneous areas, 300–303
cutaneus antebrachii
lateralis, 187
medialis, 187
cutaneus femoris
lateralis, 502
posterior, 505
digitales
dorsales manus, 220
volares communes, proprii, **219**
dorsalis penis, 454
ethmoidalis anterior, 64
facialis, 57–62
course, relations, 57
types of branching, 62
variations, 62
femoralis, pelvic course, 503
in thigh, 535
from cervical plexus, 123
from lumbar plexus, 502, 503
frontalis, external view, 47
internal view, 82
genitofemoralis, 502
glossopharyngeus, 95
glutaei, 595
haemorrhoidales, 491
hypoglossus, 49
origin, 95
iliohypogastricus, 326
ilioinguinalis, 326
infraorbitalis, 49
infratrochlearis, 54
intercostales, 256
autonomic connections of, 288
intercostobrachiales, 189
interosseus
dorsalis, 197
volaris, 200
ischiadicus, in thigh, 505
origin, 429
variations, 551
labiales posteriores, **491**
lacrimalis, 80
laryngeus
inferior, 124
superior, 124
lingualis, 49
lumbales, 428
mandibularis, 55
massetericus, 54
maxillaris, 55
medianus, 199
origin, 203
relation to pronator teres muscle
(variations), 206
mentalis, 54, 56
musculocutaneus, 202, 203
mylohyoideus, 49
nasales, 64
nasociliaris, 80
nasopalatinus, 64
obturatorius, 509
course, diagrammatic, 596
in thigh, 594
origin, 428
occipitalis, 123
major, 123
minor, 123

Nervus(i) (Continued)
oculomotorius, 80, 81
of abdominal wall, 326, 327
of face, deep, 48, 49
of forearm, deep relations to arteries,
205
posterior, 197
of forearm and hand, anterior, 199,
200
relations (palmar), 216
of hand, cutaneous, dorsal, 220
palmar, 219
lateral and palmar views, 212
of head, superficial, 47
of leg, 591, 592
of pelvis, female, 506–508
male, 511–513
of shoulder and arm, 193–196
of thigh, anterior, 583–585
olfactorius, 95
ophthalmicus, 55
opticus, 80–82
palatini, 55
perinei, 491
peronaeus
communis, 597
profundus, 597
superficialis, 597
phrenicus
in neck, 125
origin, 123
in thorax, 272
pudendus, 509
radialis
in axilla and arm, 195, 196
in forearm (superior branch), 197
in hand, 220
recurrentes, 283
sacrales, 509
saphenus, 584, 585
sciatic, course and relations, 589, 590
variations, 551
spinal, in situ, 294
origins of, 299
rami, diagrammatic, 298
splanchnic, origins, 288
suboccipitalis, 227
subscapulares, 194
supraclaviculares, 123
supraorbitalis, 47
suprascapularis, 193
supratrochlearis, 54
sympathetic, abdominal and pelvic,
373, 374
cervical, upper thoracic, 125
trunk, thoracic, 286–288
temporales profundi, 49
thoracalis longus, 189, 190
thoracodorsalis, 189
thoracolumbar, diagrammatic, 309
tibialis, 597, 598
to anterior muscles of thigh, 594
trigeminus, 55
roots of, 95
trochlearis, 81
ulnaris, in axilla, 203
in forearm, 199
in hand, superficial branch, 220
palmar part, 213
vagus, in neck and thorax, 306, 307
origin, 95
zygomaticus, 47

Newborn, skull in, 17
Nodes, inguinal lymph, 599–602
Nose, 63, 64
accessory cavities of, 37–39
Nucha, structures of, 135

OBTURATOR FORAMEN, 434
Odontoid process, 224, 227
Oesophagus. See *Esophagus.*
Olecranon, 142
Omental bursa, 364
diagrammatic, 354
Omentum(a), lesser, structures in, 363
lesser and greater, 362
of stomach, development, 353
Ora serrata, 83
Orbit, contents, lateral view, 82
superior views, 80, 81
vertical section, 82
dissections from above, 85, 86
muscular origins in, 80
relations to cranium, 85
Organon, auditus, 65–76
olfactus, 64
spirale (Cortii), 73
visus, 78–84
Organs, genital, female, interrelations of
parts, 476
peritoneal surface, 477
posterior relations, 478–480
pelvic, female, midsagittal section, 475
urogenital, 409
pelvic, male, 510
Orientation, by planes, 5
Orificium
ureteris, 409
urethrae
externum, 469
internum, 409
Os(Ossa)
calcis (calcaneus), 524
capitatum, 145, 146
carpi, 145, 146
coccygis, 433, 434
coxae, 433, 434
cuboideum, 524, 570
cuneiformia, 524, 570
ethmoidale, 27, 28
frontale, 25
hamatum, 145, 146
hyoideum, 131
ilium, 433, 434
ischii, 433, 434
lacrimale, 29
lunatum, 145
manus, 145, 146
multangulum
majus, 146
minus, 146
nasale, 29
naviculare
manus, 146
pedis, 524
occipitale, 22
palatinum, 30
parietale, 26
pisiforme, 145, 146
pubis, 434
sacrum, 434

Os(Ossa) (Continued)
  sphenoidale, 23
  temporale, 24
  triquetrum, 146
  zygomaticum, 30
Ossicula
  auditus, 72
  pharyngeum tubae auditivae, 68, 69
Ovary, 478–480

PACCHIONIAN DEPRESSIONS, 92
Palatum
  durum, 50
  molle, 50
  musculature, 50
  topography, 50
Palatine tonsil, 50
Palm, muscles of, 204
Palmar arch. See *Arcus volaris.*
Palmer digital arteries, 215
Palmer fascia, 208–211
Pancreas, ducts and duodenal relations, 384
  in situ with related structures, 364
Panniculus adiposus, 324, 325
Papilla(ae)
  duodeni, 384
  lacrimalis, 79
  nervi optici, 83
  renalis, 408
  Santorini, 384
Parametrium, 478, 479
Paries membranaceus tracheae, 131
Parotid gland, 120
Pars
  analis recti, 447
    in situ, 468
  basilaris oss. occipitalis, 22
  centralis ventriculi lateralis, 88
  ciliaris retinae, 83
  horizontalis oss. palatini, 30
  mastoidea oss. temporalis, 24
  membranacea urethrae, 409
  nasalis
    oss. frontalis, 91
    pharyngis, 87
  oralis pharyngis, 87
  orbitalis oss. frontalis, 91
  petrosa oss. temporalis, 16, 19
  tensa membranae tympani, 72
  tympanica oss. temporalis, 16
Patella, 535, 537
Pecten oss. pubis, 434
Pedicle, hepatic, description, 395
Pedunculus cerebri, 86
Pelvis, 433–515
  components, 4
  female, arteries, 486–490
    endopelvic fascia removed, 490
    midsagittal section, 475
    progressive dissection, 477–484
  ligaments of, topography, 433
  male, peritoneal surface, 443
    sagittal section, 448
  muscles, topography, 439–442
  paramedian section, 451
  renalis, 408
Penis, 452

Penis (Continued)
  parts and investments, 457
Pericardium, at roots of great vessels, 272
  attachments to great vessels, 275
Pericranium, 40
Perineum, female, 491, 492
  deep structures, 469–473
  musculature, 467, 468
  superficial aspect, 465, 466
  layers, coronal (frontal) section, 449, 450
  male, arteries and nerves, 460, 461
    at prostatic level, 463
    superficial features, 459
  muscles of, external relations, 452
Periorbita, 85
Peritoneum, description, 372
  lines of visceral reflection, 371
  surfaces of, anterior view, 357
    posterior view, 358
Pes anserinus, 537
Phalanges digitorum manus, 145, 146
Pharynx, musculature, internal view, 134
  external view, 133
  oral and laryngeal, anterior view, 132
  posterior view, opened, 128
Pia mater
  encephali, 92, 93
  spinalis, 294
Pineal body, 87
Pituitary body (hypophysis), 87, 88
Planes, standard orientation, 5
Planum
  nuchae, 22
  popliteum, 519
Platysma, 103
Pleura, cupula of, 116
Pleurae, 256
Plexus
  brachialis, *in situ,* 202
    parts of, 203
  cervicalis, anterior, 123
  dentalis
    inferior, 54
    superior, 54
  haemorrhoidalis, 511
  hypogastricus, 506, 507
  lumbar, 428
  lumbosacral, 429
    vertebral relations, 297
  pampiniformis, veins, 346
  pelvicus, 507
  prostaticus, 511
  pudendus, 509
  sacralis, diagram, 515
    pelvic relations, 514
    roots of, 509
  sympathici
    abdominal and pelvic, 374
    celiac and renal, 373
  uterovaginalis, 508
  vesicalis, 508
Plica(ae)
  caecalis, 388
  circulares, 384
  epigastrica, 348
  ileocaecalis, 387
  Kerkringi, 384
  rectouterina, 478
  rectovesicales, 443
  transversales recti, 447

Plica(ae) (Continued)
  umbilicales, 348
  vocalis, 87
Plowshare bone (vomer), 28
Pons (Varoli), 94
Popliteal space, 590
Porta hepatis, 380
Porus (meatus) acusticus
  externus, 68
  internus, 24
Position, anatomic, 5
Praecuneus, 87
Processus(i)
  alaris, 28
  alveolaris, 29
  anterior mallei, 72
  articulares, of vertebrae, 223, 224
  ciliares, 83
  clinoidei, 23
  condyloideus, of mandible, 31
  coracoideus, 139
  coronoideus
    mandibulae, 31
    ulnae, 142
  ethmoidalis, 27
  frontalis, 29
  frontosphenoidalis, 30
  intrajugularis, 20
  jugularis, 22
  lacrimalis, 27
  lenticularis, incudis, 72
  mastoideus, 24
  orbitalis, 30
  palatinus, 29
  pterygoidei, 23
  pyramidalis, 30
  sphenoidalis oss. palatini, 30
  spinosus, 223, 224
  styloideus
    oss. temporalis, 24
    variations, 18
    radii, 142
    ulnae, 142
  stylomastoideus, 16
  temporalis oss. zygomatici, 30
  transversi, 223, 224
  uncinatus oss. ethmoidalis, 27
  vaginalis
    oss. sphenoidalis, 23
    peritonaei, 330
      in spermatic cord, 349
  vermiformis, 387–389
  xiphoideus, 140
  zygomaticus
    frontalis, 25
    temporalis, 24
Promontorium
  of middle ear cavity, 72
  of pelvis, 433, 435
Prostate gland, 409
  inferior view, 454, 463
  section, 341, 457
Protuberantia
  mentalis, 31
  occipitalis
    externa, 22
    interna, 22
Pubes, symphysis of, 433, 434
Punctum lacrimale, 79
Pupil, 81
Pylorus, 383
Pyramides renales (Malpighii), 408

RADIUS, 142
Radix mesenterii, 384
Ramus(i)
  alveolares superiores n. maxillaris, 54, 55
  anteriores nn. cervicales, 120, 123
  buccales n. facialis, 57, 60
  cervicalis (colli) n. facialis, 57, 60
  delteoideus a. thoracoacromialis, 189, 190
  dentales
    inferiores, 54
    superiores, 54
  digastricus n. facialis, 49
  frontalis n. frontalis, 54
  gingivales superiores nn. alveolares, 54
  mammarii a. axillaris, 254
  marginalis mandibulae n. facialis, 57, 60
  oesophagei n. vagi, 307
  ossis
    ischii, 341
    pubis, 454
  pectorales a. thoracoacromialis, 255
  perforantes a. metacarpae dorsalis, 214
  temporales
    n. facialis, 57, 60
    superficiales n. auriculotemporalis, 47
  viscerales plexus pudendi, 509
  zygomatici n. facialis, 57, 60
  zygomaticofacialis, 54
Raphe palpebralis lateralis, 77
Recessus
  epitympanicus, 68
  ileocaecales, 387
  laterales ventriculi quarti, 62
  opticus, 88
  suprapinealis, 88
Rectum, 447–449
  dorsal aspect, 453
Region(s), gluteal, deep structures, 505
  inguinal, 328–352
    female, 322, 333
    internal surface, 348
  inguinofemoral, topography, 612, 613
  of body, superficial, 6–9
  umbilical, internal aspect, 344
Ren. See *Kidneys.*
Retina, 83
Ribs, 259
Rima palpebrarum, 77
Rings. See *Annulus.*
Roots of spinal nerves, 298
Rostrum sphenoidale, 23

SAC, of inguinal hernia (contents), 351
Saccule, 74, 75
Saccus
  endolymphaticus, 74, 75
  lacrimalis, 77
Sacrosciatic foramina, 437
Sacrum, 434
Scala
  media, 74
  tympani, 74
  vestibuli, 74
Scalp, 40

Scapha, 68
Scaphoid (navicular) bone, 146
Scapula, 139
Sclera, 83
Scrotum, 530
  layers (in hernia), 350
Sella turcica, 23
Semicanalis m. tensoris tympani, 72
Semicircular canals, 74, 75
Seminal vesicles, 409
Septum
  atriorum, 279
  intermuscular, medial of thigh, 537
  linguae, 87
  nasi, 87
  nasi osseum, 132
  orbitale, 77
  pellucidum, 88
Sheaths, extensor, of hand, 183
  of palmar tendons, 182
  rectus abdominis muscle, 317, 318
    variations, 324, 325
  synovial, of palm, 184
Shoulder, blade (scapula), 139
  joint, 143
  muscles of, 164–168
  vessels and nerves, dorsal aspect, 193
    ventral aspect, 194
Sinus(es)
  coronarius cordis, 275, 276
  frontalis, 64, 85
    opened (unlabeled), 77
  maxillaris, 132
  paranasal, 37–39
  parasigmoidalis, 92
  pericardial, 275
  petrosus
    inferior, 94
    superior, 94
  sphenoidalis, 38, 87
  transversus, 94
  venosus sclerae (canalis Schlemmi, Lauthi), 83
Skeleton as a whole, 226
Skin, nerve supply of, 300–303
Skull, adolescent, inferior view, 16
  lateral view, 14
  adult, anterior view, 15
    external views, 13
  exterior, description, 21
  fontanelles of, 17
  interior, basal features, 19, 20
    description, 21
  superior views, 17
  tables, 25
Space, suboccipital, 135
Spermatic cord, 346, 349
Sphenoid bone, 23
Spina(ae)
  angularis, 23
  frontalis, 25
  helicis, 68
  iliacae, 588
  ischiadica, 434
  mentalis, 31
  nasalis
    oss. maxillaris, 29
    oss. palatina, 30
  scapulae, 139
  suprameatum, 24
Spinal column, 223–226
Spiral ligament, 73

Spleen, 386
Splenic artery, 398
Squama
  frontalis, 19
  occipitalis, 22
  temporalis, 24
Stapes, 72
Sternum, 140
Stirrup (stapes), 72
Stomach, 383
  form of (variations), 376
  omental attachments, 362
Stria vascularis, 73
Styloid process, 24
Subarachnoid space, 92
Subdural space, 92
Substantia medullaris (of kidney), 408
Sulcus(i)
  arteriae occipitalis, 16
  arteriosi, 26
  auriculae, 68
  caroticus, 23
  chiasmatis, 23
  infraorbitalis, 29
  intertubercularis. 141
  lacrimalis, 29
  longitudinales cordis, 280
  mylohyoideus, 31
  nervi radialis, 141
  petrosus
    inferior, 19
    superior, 19
  pterygopalatinus, 30
  sagittalis, 22, 25
  sclerae, 83
  sigmoideus, 20
  transversus, 22, 26
Superciliary ridge (arcus), 25
Suprarenal gland, 416
Sustentaculum tali, 575
Sutura(ae)
  coronalis, 92
  frontalis, 25
  occipitomastoidea, 19
  palatinae, 16
  sagittalis, 91
  sphenofrontalis, 19
  sphenoparietalis, 19
  sphenosquamosa, 19
  zygomaticomaxillaris, 30
Sympathetic nerves, cervical trunk and ganglia, 124
  upper thoracic ganglia, 125
Symphysis ossium pubis, 473, 475

TAENIAE
  coli, 391
  libera, 402
  mesocolica, 391
  omentalis, 402
Talus, 570
Tarsometatarsal articulations, 524
Tarsus of the lids, 82
Tear sac, 77
Teeth, 32
Tegmen tympani, 72
Tela
  subcutanea, 349
  subserosa, 318

Tendo calcaneus (Achillis), 559, 560
Tendon(s), at ankle, 567, 568
    attachments at knee, medial aspect, 537
    of hand, carpal relations, 182
        extensors, 183
        flexor, palmar and medial views, 184
    of plantaris, insertion (variations), 569
    peronaeus longus, plantar course, 575
    plantar, lateral aspect, 573
        medial aspect, 572
    sheaths of hand, 211
Tentorium cerebelli, 85
Testis, 456
Thoracic duct (in thorax), 292
    in abdomen, 426, 427
Thorax (and back), 221–309
    components, 3
    structures adjacent to pleural dome, 117, 118
    wall of, anterior, 246
        internal, 246
Thymus, 258–260
Thyroid cartilage, 131–134
Thyroid gland, 122
Tibia, 520
Tongue. See *Lingua.*
Tonsilla palatina, 50
Topography, general, 5–9
    neck and thorax, anterior, 251–253
Trabeculae carnae, 277, 278
Trachea, 273
    bifurcation, 267
Tractus
    iliotibialis (Maissiati) anterior view, 534
        posterior view, 542
    olfactorius, 95
Tragus, 68
Triangle(s), deltopectoral, 247
    of neck, 99, 100
Trigonum
    urogenitale, 452
    vesicae, 409
Trochanteres, 519
Trochlea
    humeri, 141
    tali, 562
Truncus
    of body, parts of, 3, 4
    sympathicus, pelvic part, 507, 508
        thoracic part, 253
    thyreocervicalis, 119, 283, 284
Tuba
    auditiva, 72, 74
    Eustachii, 72, 74
    uterina, 477, 478
Tuber
    frontale, 25
    ischiadicum, 522
Tuberculum
    articulare, 24
    auriculae, 68
    majus humeri, 141
    mentale, 31
    minus humeri, 141
    of cervical vertebra, 223
    ossis navicularis, 145
    pharyngeum, 22
    posterius atlantis, 224
    pubicum, 522
    supratragicum, 68

Tuberositas
    coracoidea, 139, 140
    costalis, 140
    deltoidea, 141
    infra lenoidalis, 139
    radii, 142
    tibiae, 520
    ulnae, 142
Tuberosity of ischium, 522
Tunica
    albuginea corporum cavernosorum, 457, 458
    dartos, 349, 350
    mucosa
        oesophagi, 134
        recti, 447
        ventriculi, 383
    muscularis
        oesophagi, 133, 134
        recti, 447
    vaginalis propria testis, 456
Tympanic cavity, 69

ULNA, 142
    articulations of, 144–146
Umbilicus, 313
Ureter, origin and terminus, 408, 409
    pelvic course, female, 480, 481
        male, 450
Urethra, female, opening of, 469
        transverse section, 472
    membranous, 409
    penile, 448
    prostatic, 455
Urinary bladder. See *Vesica urinaria.*
Uterus, posterior aspect, attachments, 478, 479
    sectioned, *in situ*, 481, 482
Utriculus (labyrinthi), 73, 74
Uvula
    of palate, 87
    vesicae, 409

VAGINA, sections *in situ*, 482–484
    transverse sections, 469–473
Vagina(ae)
    femoralis, 529, 530
    musculi recti abdominis, 323–326
    nervi optici, 83
    processus styloidei, 24
    tendinum (of the hand), 209–211
Valvula(ae)
    bicuspidalis (mitralis), 277, 278
    coli, 391
    foraminis ovalis, 279
    semilunares, 276
    tricuspidalis, 277, 278
    venae cavae
        inferioris, 279
        Eustachii, 279
Vena(ae). See also *Vessels.*
    anonymae, 121
    axillaris, 189
    azygos, lumbar communications, 422
        terminal part, 256
        unusual course of, 266

Vena(ae) (Continued)
    azygos system, description, 291
        variations, 289, 290
    basilica, 187
    brachiales, 189
    capsulares, of kidneys, 413, 414
    cava
        inferior, 413–416
            abdominal tributaries of, 424
            left (anomalous), 420, 421
        superior, 129
    cephalica, 187
    cerebelli, 93
    cerebri, 93
    ciliares anterior, 84
    circumflexa
        humeri posterior, 193
        ilium profunda, 504
        ilium superficialis, 602–604
        scapulae, 189
    colicae, 365
    conjunctivales posterior, 83
    cordis
        media, 275
        parva, 275
    coronaria ventriculi, 378
    digitales, of the foot, 581, 582
        of the hand, 187
    diploicae, 92, 94
    dorsalis
        penis, 457
        clitoridis, 484
    epigastricae
        inferiores, 351, 352
        superficiales, 603, 604
    faciales, 47, 48
    femoralis, 537, 539
    glutaeae, 505
    haemorrhoidalis superior, 506
    hemiazygos, 283, 284
    hemiazygos accessoria, 284
    hepaticae, 381, 382
    hypogastrica, 503, 504
    ileocolica, 365
    iliaca
        communis, 502–504
        externa, 502–504
    iliolumbalis, 423
    in femoral triangle, 529
    intercostales, 286, 287
    intercostalis suprema, 286, 287
    intestinales, 368
    jugularis
        anterior, 129
        externa, 129
        interna, 129
    lienalis, 378
    lumbales, 423, 424
    lumbalis ascendens, 423
    mammaria interna, 246
    marginales, of foot, 582
    mediana
        antebrachii, 187
        colli (large), 129
    meningeae, 92, 94
    mesentericae, 365, 369
    metacarpeae, 187
    obturatoria, 500
    of head and neck, 51
    of inferior member, superficial, 579–582
    of leg and foot, 581, 582

Vena(ae) (Continued)
of liver, 381
of scalp, diploe and meninges, 92
of superior member, superficial, 187
of trunk, 283, 284
description, 285
ovarica, 487, 488
pelvic, female, 487, 488
perforantes femoris, 539
peronaeae, 591
phrenica inferior, 412–414
poplitea, 590
portae, 381
posterior ventriculi sinistri, 275
pudenda interna, 504
pudendae externae, 601–604
pulmonales, 272–275
renalis, 412–417
sacrales laterales, 504
sacralis media, 506
saphena
accessoria, 602–604
magna, 579, 580
tributaries at terminus, 599
variations, 603
parva, 581
sigmoideae, 369
spermatica interna, 412–417
subclavia, 129
submentalis, 129
suprarenalis, 412, 413
temporales, 48
thoracalis lateralis, 189
thymicae, 259
thyreoideae
inferiores, 259
superiores, 129
tibialis, 591, 592

Vena(ae) (Continued)
transversa
colli, 129
scapulae, 193
uterinae, 487
vertebralis, 420
vorticosae, 81, 83
Ventricles of brain, 88
Ventriculus (stomach), **383**
Ventriculi
cerebri, 88
cordis, 276–278
lateralis, 88
quartus, 88
tertius, 88
Vermiform appendix, 387–389
Vertebrae, 223–225
atypical, 224
description, 225
typical, 223
Vertebral canal, 223
Vertebral column, 226
ligaments, 227
Vertex corneae, 83
Vesica
fellea, 363, 364
urinaria (*in situ*), female, 333
male, 348
sagittal section of, female, 475
male, 448
Vesiculae seminales, 455, 457
Vessels, femoral, at inguinal level, 530
internal thoracic, 246
lumbar, lateral aspect, 503
mesenteric, exposure *in situ*, 360
of abdominal organs (diagrammatic), 365
of buttock and posterior thigh, 589, 590

Vessels, (Continued)
of face, deep, 48
of head, superficial, 47
of leg, 591, 592
of liver, 382
of stomach and liver, 367
of thigh, 583–585
pelvic, relations to nerves, 504
renal, variations, 412–417
uterine, posterior aspect, 480
Vestibulum
labyrinthi, 74, 75
nasi, 69
vaginae, 467
Villi intestinales, 384
Viscera, abdominal, dissections of, 360–364
in situ, anterior, 321
right side, 359
position of, variations, 375
pelvic, female, superior aspect, 333
male, inferior aspect, 454
thoracic, *in situ*, anterior, 251
upper abdominal, undissected, 366
Vomer, 28

WRIST, ligaments, 145, 146
tendons, 176, 178
vessels, 212–215

ZONA ORBICULARIS (of hip joint), 522
Zonula ciliaris (Zinni), 83
Zygomatic bone, 30

To many books of the sixteenth and seventeenth centuries the printers added ornaments to contribute an attractiveness to the letterpress; ofttimes the motivation for selection was moralistic or religious. Flowers and fruits represented the fruition of laudable works. The dove stood for the Holy Spirit, as did also the heart aflame with charity. The serpent was the symbol of healing and immortality. The cock was traditionally the awakener of sleepy minds, whose labors, then, must be neither heedless nor hurried: the palm, slow of growth, in time will bear fruit. The anchor denoted slowness, the dolphin speed; according to Aldus, much could be accomplished by holding fast, and much by pressing on. The same concept is embodied in the companionate emblem of crab and butterfly: temperate haste produces mature works.

On the reader's part, avid search is essential, expressed in the figure of a fox finding honey in a tree, and of a squirrel busied with the task of cracking a nut—there to uncover, and feast upon, the kernel of wisdom. It is the author's hope that his readers will be inspired and guided by such emblematic homilies.

B.J.A.